P9-AQQ-731

Introduction to
OPERATIONS ENGINEERING

IRWIN SERIES IN QUANTITATIVE ANALYSIS FOR BUSINESS

CONSULTING EDITOR   ROBERT B. FETTER   *Yale University*

BERANEK   *Analysis for Financial Decisions*

BIERMAN, BONINI, & HAUSMAN   *Quantitative Analysis for Business Decisions*   3d ed.

BOWEN   *Mathematics: With Applications in Management and Economics*   rev. ed.

BOWMAN & FETTER   *Analysis for Production and Operations Management*   3d ed.

CHANCE   *Statistical Methods for Decision Making*

CLARK & SEXTON   *Marketing and Management Science: A Synergism*

DONNELLY & IVANCEVICH   *Analysis for Marketing Decisions*

ELLIOTT & WASLEY   *Business Information Processing Systems*   3d ed.

FRANK, KUEHN, & MASSY   *Quantitative Techniques in Marketing Analysis: Text and Readings*

FORESTER   *Statistical Selection of Business Strategies*

GIFFIN   *Introduction to Operations Engineering*

GROFF & MUTH (eds.)   *Operations Management: Selected Readings*

HANNA & SABER   *Sets and Logic*

HOWELL & TEICHROEW   *Mathematical Analysis for Business Decisions*

LEVIN & LAMONE   *Linear Programming for Management Decisions*

MCMILLAN & GONZALEZ   *Systems Analysis: A Computer Approach to Decision Models*   rev. ed.

MARTIN   *Electronic Data Processing*   rev. ed.

MASON   *Statistical Techniques in Business and Economics*   rev. ed.

MORRIS   *Analysis for Materials Handling Management*

PETERSON   *A Quantitative Framework for Financial Management*

ROSENTHAL   *Numerical Methods in Computer Programming*

SCHELLENBERGER   *Managerial Analysis*

SCHMIDT & TAYLOR   *Simulation and Analysis of Industrial Systems*

SHOOK & HIGHLAND   *Probability Models: With Business Applications*

THEODORE   *Applied Mathematics: An Introduction: Mathematical Analysis for Management*   rev. ed.

Introduction to OPERATIONS ENGINEERING

WALTER C. GIFFIN
Associate Professor of Industrial Engineering
The Ohio State University

1971

RICHARD D. IRWIN, INC.   HOMEWOOD, ILLINOIS
IRWIN-DORSEY LIMITED, GEORGETOWN, ONTARIO

© RICHARD D. IRWIN, INC., 1971

ALL RIGHTS RESERVED. No part of this publication may be reproduced, stored in a retrieval system, or transmitted, in any form or by any means, electronic, mechanical, photocopying, recording, or otherwise, without the prior written permission of the publisher.

First Printing, February, 1971

Library of Congress Catalog Card No. 71–124168

Printed in the United States of America

T
57
.6
G75

Go 17N71

7E

To
Beverly, Steven, AND *Becky*

Preface

THIS TEXT is concerned with quantitative techniques to assist in management decision making. Many of the models presented are sometimes viewed as being synonymous with the field of operations research. However, the view adopted by this author is that once the basic models have been created, their adaptation to fit particular problem situations is more properly an engineering task than a research task. For that reason the approach of this text could be viewed as management engineering or operations engineering.

The subject matter, as outlined in the Contents, closely parallels the program content of many industrial engineering curricula. This is a natural ordering since modern industrial engineering often assumes the role of the engineering arm of operations research and management science. The goal of the text is to provide an introduction to a set of quantitative techniques found to be useful to industrial engineers and all other engineers of management systems regardless of the particular job title they may hold or aspire to hold.

As with every textbook, this one represents a compromise. There are many books available which cover a comparable spectrum of topics. At one extreme are the survey books which verbally discuss all of the quantitative techniques after assuring the reader that no math beyond high school algebra will be required. At the other extreme are the pure operations research texts geared toward the sometimes elegant mathematical proofs which fill the professional journals. The hope is that this text will fall into the somewhat neglected area between these extremes. Models are presented with sufficient rigor that hopefully the reader will gain an appreciation of both their power and their limitations. At the same time he should develop some facility in adapting the textbook models to fit new problem contexts. To nurture such development, solution of selected problems at the end of each chapter is necessary.

Mathematical background necessary to gain full appreciation of the text should include at least one year of calculus. Readers with additional preparation in probability, statistics, and transform techniques may find that text chapters covering these topics can be deleted with no loss of continuity. The text is written from the mathematical viewpoint of an engineer. This means that a pragmatic approach which implies that "if it works, use it" prevails. Intuitive arguments often replace more formal mathematical proofs.

Chapter 1 is an introduction to the history behind the growth of industrial organizations and their problems. Chapter 2 concerns the origin of the data necessary to make the models work. The balance of the text is a collection of modeling techniques which are useful in the operating environment. Entire texts have been written in each of the areas covered. It is hoped that the reader of this text will gain enough knowledge of these many areas to solve simple problems, make intelligent use of specialists, and provide an entrée into specialized literature in topics of particular interest to him.

Most of the material in this text has been used in courses within the Department of Industrial Engineering at The Ohio State University. With the exception of the material involving Markov processes and transform techniques, all of the topics shown are introduced in a five-hour, one-quarter introductory course for third-year engineers. The basic content of that course has been supplemented by material emanating from advanced undergraduate and graduate courses taught by the author at Ohio State. In its present form selected portions of this text could be used for such an introductory course. The entire text could be used for a three-quarter sequence of three-hour courses designed to introduce undergraduates or nonmajor graduates to the tools of the operations engineer.

Thanks are due to the Department of Industrial Engineering, The Ohio State University, for providing the opportunity to collect the material, the time to write the text, and the secretarial service to reduce it to legible form. My particular thanks go to my department chairman, the late Dr. David F. Baker, who provided the encouragement so necessary to completing the task. My thanks also go to the countless students and colleagues who offered many suggestions and corrections over the years in which this material was incubating in the classroom. Dr. Victor H. Bond is deserving of my special thanks for reading the entire manuscript in its early form and offering many valuable suggestions. Dr. John B. Neuhardt also deserves my special thanks for his assistance on portions of the manuscript. Let me also thank the several publishers and authors who kindly permitted me to reproduce their original material vital to the text. In addition, I want to thank the many reference sources as well as the unnamed authors and teachers who provided the often forgotten genesis for most of my material. Miss Lynn Bowen, Miss Cindy Downs, Mrs. Yvonne Kohli, and Mrs. Margaret Lewis deserve my thanks for their skillful typing. Finally, and most importantly, let me thank my wife Beverly without whose love and encouragement this text would have been impossible.

December, 1970   WALTER C. GIFFIN

Contents

Path Method. PERT. Optimization in Critical Path Planning. Network Cost Control. Job Sequencing at a Single Facility. The General Job Shop Problem.

CHAPTER **1**

Introduction

THE SUBJECT of this book is operations engineering. It is intended to provide an introduction to a variety of tools and techniques found useful by modern industrial engineers, operations researchers, and managers. The orientation is toward the creation and use of mathematical models to assist in the analysis and design of man-machine systems. The implication is that the techniques discussed are useful decision-making aids in management control systems involving men, materials, and equipment as opposed to exclusively hardware oriented engineering techniques.

The Domain of the Operations Engineer

As used in this text, the term operations engineering closely parallels modern industrial engineering. It encompasses many aspects of traditional industrial engineering as well as many of the techniques developed in the field of operations research; hence the term operations engineering.

Our chief topics of discussion will be different mathematical models and modeling techniques. Since many disciplines can legitimately claim to use the language of mathematics and the techniques of science to attack operational problems, it might be well to view one portion of the modeling world in terms of a Venn diagram. Suppose we consider as the total domain, useful quantitative techniques for solving operational problems. Three contributors in this domain have been the fields of pure mathematics, operations research, and industrial engineering. Their relative positions are noted by the Venn diagram of Figure 1–1.

If we consider these disciplines on a scale of relative abstraction we could view pure math as the most general and abstract, industrial engineering as the most specific and concrete, with operations research bridging the gap between.

1

FIGURE 1-1

Discipline Domains

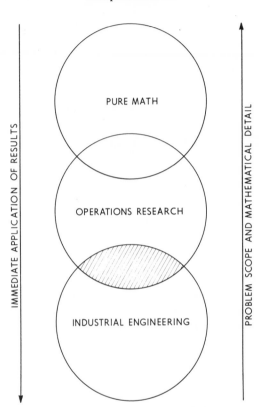

In terms of problem scope and application of results, industrial engineering is most concerned with specific, sometimes narrow, problem solutions and pure math the least. As an example of the relative roles of each of these fields in model development, consider the use of Lagrange multipliers. The theory of Lagrange multipliers and their use in solving constrained maximization problems originated in the field of pure mathematics. Operations research professionals have adapted and extended the theory to include techniques for solving optimization problems for economic systems in which constraints appear in the form of bounds on resources. Industrial engineers have used the Lagrange techniques suggested by operations researchers to assist in the design of inventory control systems for particular companies.

Within each discipline there are also continua of problem scope, mathematical detail, and generality of results. For example, some of the leaders in the field of operations research feel that OR should concentrate on large-scale strategic problems and the development of new and better general solution techniques. At this end of the spectrum the field bears a close resemblance to pure math, as examination of any recent issues of their professional journals will establish. On the other hand, the authors of many textbooks in operations research and many professionals in the field continue to limit the domain of operations research to the application of a common set of tools including mathematical programming, inventory theory, and queueing theory. At this end of the spectrum operations research is indistinguishable from some of the more advanced industrial engineering. Similar comments could be made about the field of industrial engineering. At one end of the scale, some IE departments concentrate on the analysis and design of advanced management control systems employing many of the techniques normally associated with OR. At the other end of the spectrum, some IE departments confine their activities to methods and time study, job evaluation, and other tasks which characterized the entire field prior to 1950.

It is the intersection of the IE and OR sets shown by cross-hatching in Figure 1–1 which is of concern to us in this text. The character of the problems contained in this intersection defines the audience to which this discussion is directed. Although the term operations engineering is certainly not original with this author, it seems to best capture the flavor of the contents of the intersection. Because of the increasingly global nature of the problems addressed, this area of interest is claimed not only by pragmatic operations researchers and mathematically trained industrial engineers but also by an increasing population of quantitatively oriented managers.

The Need for Advanced Management Techniques

The functions of management are often cited as planning, organizing, directing, and controlling. The need for professional groups to execute or assist in executing these functions is of very recent origin as far as recorded history is concerned. Management did not become a speciality until organizations became sufficiently large to tax the ability of one man to control all aspects of their business. The beginning of large-scale organizations and their associated management problems can be traced to the industrial revolution.

Inventions from the Industrial Revolution. The Industrial Revolution started in England in the mid 1700's. Prior to that time nearly all industry was of the cottage variety in which small manufacturing facilities were established in the home. There was no need for management theories and sophisticated analytical techniques when everyone within the organization was in daily face-to-face contact with one another. The origin of management theory depended upon the size of groups organized for economic ends.

The beginning of the Industrial Revolution is associated with the textile industry in England. There were a series of mechanical inventions within this industry which made possible the growth of large organizations. The first of these was the flying shuttle invented by James Kay in 1733. This device removed much of the manual labor from the task of weaving. The result was to permit weavers to weave faster than spinners could make thread.

The imbalance caused by the comparatively high production rates of weavers as opposed to spinners created pressure for the development of improved spinning methods. The response occurred over 30 years later with the advent of the spinning jenny invented in 1764 by James Hargreaves. This invention increased the spinners output and tended to recover the balance with the weavers. Further improvements in spinning followed relatively quickly with the invention of the water frame in 1769 and the mule spinner in 1779. At this point the spinners now had the capability of outrunning the weavers. The next response was the power loom invented by Edmund Cartwright in 1785. This device appeared to swing the balance of work back toward the weavers.

At about the same time as the improved production equipment became available, James Watt developed a satisfactory steam engine to provide more dependable power to run these machines. A short time later, in 1797, Henry Maudslay devised the power-driven lead screw to serve as a tool holder for lathes. This was the big breakthrough for the machine tool industry. It permitted the manufacture of new production tools of many varieties and made possible the production of interchangeable parts.

There are several things to notice about this series of inventions. Of prime importance is the fact that they all concerned the transfer of skill to machines. Secondly, each new invention created the demand for another by means of destroying an existing balance between related portions of a production system. Furthermore, the pressures for new inventions were so great that the elapsed time between significant improvements became smaller and smaller. Finally, the increased production capability by use of less skilled labor created the necessary climate for the growth of increasingly larger industrial organizations.

This technological snowball which began in the 1700's is still picking up momentum. Witness the frequency with which new production processes are being introduced in a great number of contemporary industries. Also note that the transfer of skills to machines has not abated. One of the recent transfers of skill is that of routine decision making being transferred to electronic computers. Decisions which are of a repetitive nature such as how many items to order in an inventory system can often be made once and the resulting policies programmed for the computer. Each time the reorder point is reached, the computer can calculate how many units to purchase. Management is then free to devote its talents to solving the more difficult non-repetitive type decisions.

Organizing Work.   In addition to the developments in new hardware there were accompanying breakthroughs in the ways in which men and equipment were utilized. Adam Smith is credited with being an early contributor to the improvement in the productivity of labor. In his book *The Wealth of Nations*, published in 1776, he argued that improvement in the productivity of labor depends upon its division and its wages.[1] He pointed out that in a manufacturing operation it is possible for a man to specialize in one particular trade. Even though many trades are required to produce a particular product, they are required continuously throughout the year. This is contrasted to agricultural activities in which many skills are required but on a seasonal rather than a continuous basis. The increased quantity of work capability by division of labor in manufacturing was credited by Smith to several factors. He cited the increase of dexterity in every specialized workman, the savings of time normally lost in passing from one task to another, and finally to the invention of machines which enabled one man to do the work of many.

Charles Babbage expressed further thoughts on the division of labor in his book *On the Economy of Machinery and Manufactures* published in 1835.[2] Perhaps the most important observation that he made in extending Smith's thesis was that by dividing the work into different processes, each requiring different skills, a manufacturer could purchase exactly that amount of skill needed to perform each task. In this way a man's time could be devoted entirely to that task for which he was most skilled. It was unnecessary for him to spend a large portion of his working day performing less-skilled tasks which could be easily handled by lower priced workmen. This had distinct cost advantages over total product manufacture in which one man commonly performed all of the tasks necessary to produce one unit of finished product. In that instance the employer must pay for the highest level of skill required by any of the manufacturing tasks even though that skill is only utilized a fraction of the time.

In the United States, the benefits of the Industrial Revolution were realized and extended by men such as Eli Whitney in the early 1800's. Whitney succeeded in making interchangeable parts in his gun shop. This was made possible by improved machining techniques, and it eliminated much of the skilled handwork formerly necessary to assemble a workable firearm. The use of all available mechanization and specialization of labor by manufacturers in the United States in the early 1800's was a natural consequence of the chronic shortage of labor at the time. Furthermore industries were just beginning to develop and were not shackled by the inertia of precedent. There was little resistance to new inventions and procedures because they had no previous ways to be replaced.

Mechanization and specialization of labor naturally led to the development of large organizations. Those organizations with large amounts of capital and large potential markets grew at an increasing rate as high production techniques and equipment became available. As the economic

---

[1] Excerpts from the *Wealth of Nations* as well as many other historically important documents are contained in John A. Ritchey (ed.), *Classics in Industrial Engineering* (Delphi, Ind.: Prairie Publishing Co., 1964), pp. 11–20.

[2] *Ibid.*, pp. 21–27.

organizations devoted to manufacturing grew in size they began to exceed the managerial capacity of their founders. One man could no longer be expert in every one of the many skills required to plan, organize, direct, and control the operation of a now large and complex organization. Evidence that the management functions were becoming specialties in their own right is given by the development of formal training programs at the university level. The Wharton School of Finance in 1881 became the first school to offer a management course.

Frederick W. Taylor.   Management as a profession was popularized by men such as Frederick W. Taylor in the early 1900's. Although many of Taylor's techniques were present earlier, he gave them visibility. He was trained as a mechanical engineer and is credited with a large number of patents for various new processes. He started his experiments in management while serving as a foreman at Midvale Steel. His basic approach was to replace rules of thumb with scientific principles and to separate planning from performance on the part of the worker.

To illustrate the breadth of his activities, some of the major contributions to modern industry attributed to Taylor are:

1. The invention of high-speed steel (together with Munsel White) which served as the source of the Taylor fortune.
2. The discovery and evaluation of variables affecting the cutting of metals.
3. The origination of the functional type of organization which predated our modern line and staff.
4. The development of a philosophy of management which he called scientific management.

Because of his training and the time of his work, most of his efforts centered on organization at the shop level. However, his writings do mark the beginning of what one might call the traditional theory of organizations. Many of his ideas were condensed in the books *Shop Management* and *The Principles of Scientific Management*.[3,4] Excerpts from both books are reproduced by Ritchey.[5]

Taylor considered four major classes of duties as the essential ingredients of scientific management. Roughly stated they are:

1. The development of a science to replace the old rule-of-thumb knowledge of the workmen. This entailed collecting, classifying, and tabulating knowledge possessed by workmen in an organization. Hopefully this would lead to rules, laws, and mathematical formulae which could be used to guide management and workmen to increased output. The

[3] Frederick W. Taylor, *Shop Management* (New York: Harper & Bros., 1911).
[4] Frederick W. Taylor, *The Principles of Scientific Management* (New York: Harper & Bros., 1911).
[5] Ritchey, *op. cit.*, pp. 69–86.

exercise of this duty foreshadowed modern industrial procedures such as written standard practice and methods and time study.

2. The scientific selection and training of workmen. Taylor sought to subject workmen to the same type of studies that had been successfully applied to machines in the past. He wanted to identify the aptitudes of workers and then see that they were trained to make the best use of their talents. These ideas upset many old apprentice concepts and presaged the development of modern personnel practices.

3. The development of a spirit of cooperation between workmen and management to insure that the work will be carried out in accordance with scientifically derived procedures. He sought to inspire the men selected in accordance with principle 2 to adopt the procedures suggested by the studies conducted in accordance with principle 1. The modern counterpart is seen in the operation of departments for industrial relations.

4. The division of work formerly done by workmen into two sections, one of which is handed over to management. This permitted each group to perform the work for which it was best suited rather than the former condition in which most of the work and responsibility fell on the workman. Here Taylor was carrying forth Adam Smith's concept of the division of labor into an area beyond pure manual tasks. Management assumed the tasks of planning and control while leaving the execution of those plans to the workmen. Such a view has far-reaching implications in the modern organization.

Taylor had many followers who greatly influenced the development of modern industrial organizations and procedures. Among some of the more famous were Henry L. Gantt, Harrington Emerson, and Frank and Lillian Gilbreth. Although persons such as these offered positive contributions to the development of modern management techniques, others seriously impeded the field by pushing pieces of Taylor's system without adopting the philosophy of the system as a whole. For instance, wage payment plans and time study techniques advocated by Taylor were modified and applied without regard to the spirit of cooperation considered essential by Taylor. The application and misapplication of Taylor's system caused such a furor that a series of congressional investigations were conducted about the subject. Labor opposition was so strong that time study techniques were banned in all government arsenals and post offices from that time until 1948. Professor Robert Hoxie was called upon to make a special investigation of scientific management in relation to labor in 1914. The conflicts between management and labor goals and the influence of scientific management are summarized by his report, excerpts from which are given by Ritchey.[6]

---

[6] *Ibid.*, pp. 135–50.

Quantitative Techniques and Upper Management

In spite of the criticism leveled against the sometimes pretentious claims of science voiced by Taylor and his followers, they did introduce precision of measurement to management. They attempted to measure things, such as the time to perform a task, which were previously left to subjective evalution. By demonstrating that both human and mechanical factors associated with production were at least crudely quantifiable, they provided the foundation for the increasingly prevalent practice of mathematical modeling of management systems.

Limits to Quantification. We have already mentioned that Taylor was primarily concerned with management problems at the shop level. During the same period of time others such as Henri Fayol were developing principles of management for problems found at higher levels of the organization. However, Fayol's principles centered more on the qualitative aspects of organization structure such as unity of command and the interdependence of responsibility and authority. Quantification did not play a major role.

There are several reasons for the relatively slow adoption of quantitative aids for management at the upper level. Number one is that proper mathematical tools were not available at the time Taylor and Fayol were performing their work. Even at the shop level attacked by Taylor, measurements in production systems commonly exhibit great variation. For example, the output from a job may depend upon the man on the job, job conditions, day of the week, etc. Taylor and his followers attempted to treat such problems by representing the output of man-machine systems by a single number, as they were accustomed to doing in the engineering of hardware systems. Unfortunately very few man-machine systems can be described by a set of deterministic equations in the manner of Newtonian physics where it is axiomatic that $F = ma$. Probability concepts and statistical methods were needed to provide adequate descriptions. Such methods did not become widely available until after World War II.

A second limit to quantification was posed by the magnitude of the problems found in higher management. Not only are stochastic elements the rule rather than the exception but also the number of variables necessary to describe a system often exceed the computational and memory capability of the human analyst. However, modern high-speed digital computers have provided an entree for quantitative analysis of large-scale management systems. This hardware, coupled with recently developed techniques such as mathematical programming and Monte-Carlo simulation, has made operations engineering a reasonable approach to management problems at all levels of the organization.

Finally, one should not underestimate the reluctance of management to subject their problems to quantification as a result of disasters associated with the efficiency experts of the early 1900's. The misapplications of Taylor's techniques had to be lived down.

The Emergence of Operations Research

After the time of Taylor and the proponents of scientific management there were some isolated attempts to apply the methods of science to management problems, such as the celebrated Hawthorne studies at Western Electric. However, it was not until World War II that another scientifically oriented discipline emerged to take the next major step toward quantitative solutions to operational problems. This discipline was operations research.

Operations research is characterized by the scientific approach to decisions. More complete definitions of operations research and arguments of whether or not it is a science fill the early literature in the field. We will not explore the details of such arguments but rather present the definition of one set of spokesmen. Ackoff and Sasieni say that

OR can be considered as being:
  (1)   The application of scientific method
  (2)   by interdisciplinary teams
  (3)   to problems involving the control of organized (man-machine) systems so as to provide solutions which best serve the purposes of the organization as a whole.[7]

The implications of this definition are that operations research employs not only the methods of science but also mathematics, the language of science, in a search for optimal solutions. Quantification is an integral part of nearly all OR studies. Furthermore the systems viewpoint requires that operations research teams be knowledgeable in a variety of subject areas in order to adequately account for tradeoffs among subsystems. The usual argument is that no one man can be expert in all areas which should be considered in problems of the scope ideally considered by OR.

Although not identified as operations research it could be argued that early practitioners such as Taylor were employing the same approach to problems normally credited to OR. In fact mathematical models first suggested by Erlang, a telephone engineer, and Lanchester, an aeronautical pioneer, still form the nucleus for many studies of queues and military engagements found in current OR journals. These men, however, performed their work many years before the term operations research was coined.

The name operations research first appeared during World War II. Study teams consisting of mathematicians and scientists from many different disciplines were created to assist in the analysis of military operations. The research they performed was tagged operations research. They scored notable successes in determining how to organize a radar defense, how many bombers to send on a raid, how to release a bomb load, how to protect a convoy, etc. After World War II industrial groups were formed in both England and the United States to emulate the success of the military OR groups in attacking

---

[7] Russell L. Ackoff and Maurice W. Sasieni, *Fundamentals of Operations Research* (New York: John Wiley & Sons, Inc., 1968), p. 6.

commercial problems. Since that time military, government, and industrial groups have continued to thrive under the title of operations research.

A major key to the development of operations research as a successful approach to management problems was the concurrent emergence of non-deterministic technology. Probability theory and statistics were becoming widely known and accepted at the same time that OR scored its early gains. Both then and now the bulk of the successful models developed employed those tools. A second major boost to the field occurred with the advent of high-speed digital computers. The increased calculation ability accompanying these machines made possible the use of heuristic problem-solving techniques, the solution of large linear programming problems, and a host of specialized simulation tools.

Methods versus Subject.   The successes of operations research are often identified with particular mathematical tools which have evolved in seeking solutions for operational problems. Indeed, most texts on the subject present a topic outline similar to the one used in this book. Some offer chapters on linear programming, queueing theory, and inventory theory as though the tools themselves were the essence of operations research. The same danger is present here that was present for the followers of Taylor. Those who become linear programming experts then dash around in search of problems to fit the technique are not unlike the efficiency experts who wrecked havoc with work measurement in the early 1900's. Ideally, the tools are incidental to the more important philosophy of problem attack.

Norman Barish drew an interesting distinction between the fields of operations research and industrial engineering.[8] He argued that OR is the applied science of managerial systems while IE is the engineering of managerial systems. A parallel is seen in the practice of medicine and medical science. Modern industrial engineering, which by our definition approaches operations engineering, should be concerned with the application and modification of existing techniques to problems of inventory control, scheduling, and the like. Operations research, on the other hand, should seek to discover fundamental relationships and to develop new models, approaches, and techniques. Operations engineering provides the payoff for the scientific research and development of operations research. Obviously there is considerable overlap between the fields as there is, for instance, between physics and mechanical engineering. Many practitioners of both disciplines work in the same areas. This was indicated earlier by our Venn diagram for modeling effort.

Just as mechanical engineers use the mathematical tools of the physicist to analyze and design mechanical systems, so will the operations engineer or industrial engineer use the mathematical tools of the operations researcher to analyze and design management control systems. The purpose of this text is to provide an introduction to the necessary set of tools.

---

[8] N. Barish, "Operations Research and Industrial Engineering," *Operations Research* (Vol. 11, No. 3), 1963.

State of the Art

Qualitative Aspects of Management. Of the four major functions of management (plan, organize, direct, and control), the control function has benefited most from the emergence of quantitative methods. Planning, organizing, and directing have received minimal benefits from mathematical analysis. To some, this represents the frontier of operations research and management science. How can one bring to bear the same quantitative approach to problems in long-range planning, for instance, which has been so successful in areas such as inventory control? Areas of study such as decision theory may well provide inroads into heretofore qualitative areas, but to date they are at the research rather than the engineering level.

Even at the control level, one cannot escape the impact of nonquantitative decisions and constraints which influence systems design. For instance, the design and installation of a new production system must take account of labor relations. If there is a union present, provisions in the union contract may prevent installation of improved methods or even the accurate measurement of tasks involved. In addition to union contracts, system design at the operating level must consider legal constraints imposed by government agencies. State laws limit such things as the number of hours women may work and the weight they may lift. State laws also specify such things as health and safety requirements for all industrial facilities. Federal laws specify the manner in which management must bargain with employees, the minimum wage to be paid, conditions under which strikes are legal, etc. Important legislation such as the Labor Management Relations Act of 1947 (Taft-Hartley Law) should be high on the reading list of operations engineers. In addition, no one should take a job involving the design of production systems without being thoroughly familiar with the union contracts and labor relations history of his potential employer. From the point of view of quantitative analysis and design, a well-conceived system may well be impossible to implement because of both externally and internally imposed policies. Internally imposed policies come from conscious but often subjective decisions by management. Externally imposed policies come from legislation and concessions won by the unions at the bargaining table.

Unfortunately space requirements limit this text to those aspects of management systems analysis and design which will yield to mathematical techniques. This in no way indicates that qualitative techniques and principles of management are less important. The point is that the serious reader should temper his quantitative education with the more subjective expertise available in other areas.

Outlook. The field which we have labeled operations engineering emphasizes the quantitative approach to management problems. It can be characterized by a collection of mathematical tools and the inclination to adapt those tools to a variety of operational problem contexts. Operations engineering offers quantitative assistance for management decision making but in no way disposes of the functions of management. The balance of this text is devoted to a cataloging of useful tools and discussions of their mathematical structure.

The collection of tools we are about to examine find most immediate application in the control function at intermediate to lower levels of management. They are invaluable for establishing optimum inventory levels, production schedules, size of service facilities, and the like. For more global problems, such as determining the products to be manufactured five years in the future and the proper organizational structure for a vertically integrated company, these techniques may offer an initial point of departure. In no way do they solve those which are basically nonquantifiable problems.

Training in operations engineering is valuable, however, for all levels of management. In addition to providing the capability to solve many classes of current control problems, it also provides the mathematical sophistication necessary to comprehend the move toward quantification which will inevitably permeate more global operational problems. More importantly, perhaps, the engineering approach provides a way of looking at the world which extends beyond the development of mathematical models. Pragmatism, an objective viewpoint, well-developed powers of logic, and a belief in the inherent orderliness of nature serve one well regardless of the scope of the problems he faces.

SELECTED BIBLIOGRAPHY

ACKOFF, RUSSELL L., AND SASIENI, MAURICE W. *Fundamentals of Operations Research*. New York: John Wiley & Sons, Inc., 1968.

BUFFA, ELWOOD S. *Modern Production Management. 3rd ed.* New York: John Wiley & Sons, Inc., 1969.

MOORE, FRANKLIN G. *Manufacturing Management. 5th ed.* Homewood, Ill.: Richard D. Irwin, Inc., 1969.

MORRIS, WILLIAM T. *Management Science in Action*. Homewood, Ill.: Richard D. Irwin, Inc., 1963.

NEWMAN, WILLIAM H. AND SUMMER, CHARLES E. *The Process of Management*. Englewood Cliffs, N. J.: Prentice-Hall, Inc., 1961.

RITCHEY, JOHN A. (ed.). *Classics in Industrial Engineering*. Delphi, Ind.: Prairie Publishing Co., 1964.

CHAPTER 2

Models, Man, and Measurement

A MAJOR distinction between operations engineering and conventional business analysis is the tendency of the engineer to formulate all of his problems in quantitative terms. The engineer draws upon a variety of modeling techniques to structure his view of the problem. The techniques may range from simple flow chart analysis through very complex formal mathematical models. Behind each technique, however, lies a belief in the inherent orderliness of nature and a conviction that most operational problems can ultimately be reduced to mathematical terms. The bulk of this text consists of a compendium of mathematical techniques found useful in carrying out the reduction.

Before attempting to construct mathematical models of systems, an analyst should consider several factors:

1. What are the objectives to be achieved by the analysis and how can modeling help further these objectives?
2. What are the potential classes of models available?
3. Where are the major problem areas in the system?
4. How will data required for the model be collected?
5. If humans are involved, what are their strengths and weaknesses as system components?

It is the purpose of this chapter to offer a brief discussion of each of these questions. In so doing, some of the tools available to assist in obtaining answers will be introduced.

13

Models

In general terms, models can be viewed as abstractions of reality used for description, prediction, and control of real world systems. By abstracting only certain portions of reality, the model builder gains benefits of economy at the risk of losing validity. It is possible for a model to be internally consistent in the sense of formal mathematics but bear no relationship to the real world problem it is intended to describe. The belief that a phenomenon is really understood only when expressed in a formal quantitative model must be tempered with an understanding of the limitations of current mathematical know-how.

The Scientific Method. Let us begin by a very simple view of how scientifically trained analysts carry out their work. At the risk of citing the obvious, one might define operations research and engineering as the application of a scientific method to operational problems of management. There are many descriptions of the so-called scientific method but most prescribe the following steps, adapted from Timms.[1]

1. Observe the problem situation.
2. Build a hypothesis to explain the observed relationships.
3. Test and revise the hypothesis.
4. Develop the decision rule.
5. Apply the decision rule.

The only difference between this set of guides and those found in most beginning texts in the physical sciences is the emphasis on decision rules. This then gives us a reason for the existence of operations research and ultimately operations engineering activities. They must provide assistance to management in developing decision rules for improving operations.

Much of the publicity for operations research is derived from steps 2 and 3 of the above scientific method. The tasks of building and testing a hypothesis are the essence of model building. It is the result of this exercise, the model of some particular system, which fills most of the technical literature in the field. The models discussed in this text belong to special classes of models which have been observed to occur frequently in the analysis of operational problems. Evolving from operations research and other fields, these models are the basic tools of the operations engineer who must modify and adapt them to fit similar operational problems as they arise in his work.

Model Types. Used in this context, the term model refers to any abstraction of reality designed to assist in understanding a phenomena. Such abstractions can take many different forms, some of which you know intimately. For example, the written or spoken word can be considered to be a verbal model which abstracts from reality a description of some phenomena.

---

[1] Howard L. Timms, *Introduction to Operations Management* (Homewood, Ill.: Richard D. Irwin, Inc., 1967), p. 71.

Plant layouts and aircraft mock-ups which look like miniature versions of the real thing are physical models of phenomena. The type of model most commonly discussed in the operations research literature is the mathematical model. Mathematical models use symbols to represent the characteristics of the phenomena from which they abstract.

Obviously many other types of models exist and each may perform a useful function in analyzing different aspects of system behavior. Ackoff and Sasieni offer three major classes into which the multitude of models may be grouped.[2] They are iconic, analogue, and symbolic, distinguished by varying levels of abstractness.

Iconic models are those which look like what they represent. Model airplanes used in wind tunnel tests, stick and ball models of the atom, and photographs of a new plant site are all iconic models. They are images of the real world, generally with dimensions scaled up or down. Since they are specific and concrete they are difficult to manipulate for experimental purposes.

Analogue models use one set of properties to represent another set of properties. A commonly encountered analogue model is the graph. A graph uses length and location of lines to represent a wide variety of variables and their interrelations. Other analogues include a host of physical systems in which fluid or electron flows are used as analogues for traffic and economic systems. Such analogue models are more abstract than iconic models of systems in that they bear little physical resemblence to the system being modeled. Although they lose isomorphism with the real system, they gain generality and ease of manipulation.

Symbolic models are the most abstract of the lot. A symbolic model uses letters, numbers, and other symbols to represent relationships among variables. They most often take the form of mathematical relationships that capture the structure of the system being modeled. Since they involve construction by symbols they are the most general and the most easily manipulated of all the model forms.

The biggest weakness of symbolic models is that the analyst employing them may be unaware of the assumptions behind their construction. Unfortunately our mathematical sophistication is relatively small compared with the complexity of the real systems with which an operations engineer must deal. For that reason symbolic models should be used as guides for system analysis and design but not as the panacea for all management ills.

A solution to the set of equations representing a model is just that, a model solution and nothing more. The degree of success in transforming the model solution into system design is a function of the completeness of the model and the awareness of its shortcomings on the part of the analyst. Models do not replace management judgment; they only assist it.

---

[2] Russell L. Ackoff and Maurice W. Sasieni, *Fundamentals of Operations Research* (New York: John Wiley & Sons, Inc., 1968), pp. 60–61.

In many projects all three types of models will be used in sequence. Iconic or analogue models may be used as initial approximations which are later refined into symbolic models. The use of flow process charts by operations engineers is an example of such an initial step. The flow process chart is basically an analogue model of the steps involved in carrying out a particular operation. It can be used to pinpoint unnecessary delays, congestion, excess transportation time, and the like. From this initial analysis, the use of several symbolic models such as queueing and transportation models may be indicated. The total design process then involves using all available tools which may shed light on the system under study. The operations engineer's contribution is to make certain that all quantifiable aspects of the system are properly accounted for. Since symbolic models are easier to maniuplate, often yield more accurate results, and require more specialized training to appreciate, they are the principal subjects of this text.

Reasons for Modeling. Throughout the preceding discussion we have alluded to some of the reasons for the use of models. Let us now be more specific and list the following four basic reasons for constructing models of a system:

1. *Highlight problems of interest.* A model is an abstraction of reality and as such only those characteristics of immediate interest to the decision maker need be included. The problem is not burdened by confusing interactions.

2. *Economical experimentation.* Experimenting with a model is more economical than experimenting with the real system for several reasons. First, there is no risk to current operations by attempting radical departures from past policy. Second, the time scale is compressed in that months of operating experience in the real system can be reproduced by many models in minutes. Third, an experimenter can introduce a variety of competitive environments at will which he could never control in the real world.

3. *Precision of thought.* The very act of understanding a system well enough to capture its salient features by a mathematical representation may lead to the discovery of principles of management for an operation.

4. *Solving operational problems.* The end result of a well-conceived model is of course the guidance offered in answering such questions as how many loading docks do we need to service our shipping department.

Symbolic Model Classification. There are many ways to subdivide the general class of mathematical models. Miller and Starr, for example, list some six different ways of categorizing models.[3] The most common approach within the field of operations research, however, has been to classify models by subject matter and solution technique. Dorfman notes that even though

---

[3] David W. Miller and Martin K. Starr, *Executive Decisions and Operations Research* (Englewood Cliffs, N.J.: Prentice-Hall, Inc., 1960), chaps. vi and vii.

in principle each problem attacked by an OR analyst gets a tailor-made model, in practice essentially similar problems arise from time to time.[4] This leads to a subject classification such as inventory, queues, programming, etc., which serves as the major topic outline for texts in the field.

The word theory is sometimes appended to the major model classes. One hears of work being done in queueing theory or inventory theory. Morris describes this as meaning that some work has been done toward confirmation with promising results and that people are actively engaged in the study of the model.[5] A new model with little results to confirm it is classed as a hypothesis. When workers are no longer actively testing and developing a confirmed model, it is called a law. Most of the models being taught in the classroom hopefully qualify as theory; virtually none in the field of operations research qualify as laws.

Thrall, Coombs, and Davis note that it is important to realize that a model is not itself a theory.[6] It is only a potential theory until a segment of the real world has been mapped into it. A model can be right or wrong on logical grounds, but as a theory we must accept or reject it on the basis of how well it works. The move from hypothesis to theory is a research task. The application of the theory to operational problems is an engineering task.

Within each of the major subject classifications of mathematical models used by the operations engineer, it is helpful to further classify them for reference purposes. The following characteristics are suggested as being most meaningful within the context of this book:

1. Number of variables involved.
2. Predictability of events in the system.
3. Intent of the model.

A subjective measure of the number of variables involved in describing a system is simply few versus many. This limits the size of the system being considered. For example, one might employ very different techniques for studying the manpower necessary to handle a single motive-power unit in a shop as opposed to scheduling work crews for an entire railroad operation.

Predictability of events can be thought of in terms of probabilistic versus deterministic events. A deterministic approach assumes that you know exactly what will happen and when it will happen. For example, a deterministic model of an air-terminal operation might assume that a 5 : 15 flight would arrive at exactly 5 : 15 and would have exactly 120 people on board. A probabilistic approach, on the other hand, assumes that you know the

---

[4] Robert Dorfman, "Operations Research," *American Economic Review*, Vol. L, September, 1960.

[5] William T. Morris, *Management Science in Action* (Homewood, Ill.: Richard D. Irwin Inc., 1963), p. 84.

[6] R. M. Thrall, C. H. Coombs, and R. L. Davis (eds.), *Decision Processes* (New York: John Wiley & Sons, Inc., 1954), chap. ii.

relative frequency of arrival times and load factors but that particular values for these variables are unknown in advance of their occurrence. Obviously the probabilistic viewpoint is closer to reality but more difficult to capture in most models.

The intent of a model can be thought of as descriptive versus prescriptive. A prescriptive model seeks an optimum solution. Management is told exactly what to do to maximize returns. For example, purchase 10 new turret lathes. A descriptive model, on the other hand, seeks to describe the operation of the system under a variety of input assumptions without attempting to tell management what is best. A variety of performance measures which are expected to result from anticipated management actions are presented and management must decide the best course. For example, one might evaluate the effects on work force, costs, schedules, and sales if 10 new turret lathes were purchased versus none purchased. Management can then make the decision unfettered by a single measure of value.

The models which are the primary subjects of this text will cross all of these classifications. To illustrate this point consider some of our major topic headings. We will spend some time discussing the general area of mathematical programming. Most of the models treated in that chapter are deterministic and prescriptive. They employ criterion functions and restraining equations in which all variables are known with certainty. The nonlinear problems contain a small number of variables because of their computational complexity. The linear problems may contain a very large number of variables because of the efficiency of their solution algorithms. In the queueing chapter, all models considered are probabilistic. They reflect stochastic processes in which the major elements of the system are described by time varying random variables. Furthermore, they are basically descriptive in that probability distributions for number in the system and waiting times as functions of system parameters are the output. Optimization is secondary to accurate description. On the other hand, the inventory chapters emphasize optimization. Minimum cost solutions are sought for both deterministic and probabilistic systems. The major elements of uncertainty are daily demand and lead time. These few examples illustrate the diversity in structure and intent of models available to the operations engineer.

The Importance of Computers

Next to the increased utility of probability theory and statistics, the advent of high-speed digital computers has contributed most to the successful use of mathematical models for management systems. The availability of computers has broadened both the feasible solution techniques to be used in system design and the control of solutions once introduced into an operating system. However, it is important that operations engineers and managers learn both the uses and limitations of computer technology.

Evolution. Computers developed so rapidly in the 1950's and 1960's that many engineers and managers found themselves overawed by their computational ability. Most persons in responsible design and decision making positions had no training in the use of these machines. Programming language proliferation only served to deepen the air of mystery surrounding computer operations. Only the chosen few who became programmers were privy to the mechanics of obtaining computer solutions. Because of some early successful applications of computer techniques to management problems, computer output gained a halo of respectability. The attitude on the part of many persons was that if a solution came from a computer it must be right. Unfortunately a number of managers and analysts lost sight of the fact that a computer can do only what it is told. All too often programmers who lacked both technical and managerial know-how were the defacto decision makers in design and control problems. This happened simply because neither analysts nor managers could communicate directly with the computer. The effect was to produce mounds of often meaningless data which management had neither the time nor the capability to understand. Management lost control by not knowing how the computer was working on problems.

Fortunately, today's decision makers have learned how to harness the computational abilities of the computer. This has come about by a combination of education in computer technology and the advent of improved hardware and software. Algebraic languages can be learned by nonprofessional programmers and time-sharing capability permits heuristic problem solutions.

Model Solutions. Many of the techniques treated as routine problem-solving tools today would be little more than academic oddities without the availability of computers. For example, the widespread use of linear programming is directly attributable to the availability of computers. Solution algorithms involve manipulating large arrays of numbers in an iterative fashion until optimality is achieved. When performed by hand, these techniques are tedious for small problems and impossible for most realistic formulations. The same thing is true when solving analytical models encountered in inventory system design. Well-defined models are developed which require numerical techniques to achieve optimal solutions. Such search techniques are easily performed by the computer.

In addition to providing the computational power to solve •analytical models, the computer is responsible for the development of entirely new areas such as simulation and critical path analysis. In simulation studies it is used as an experimental device to evaluate system design changes too difficult to capture with existing analytical models. In critical path analysis it is used to provide an array of alternatives for the preliminary scheduling and ultimate control of large-scale projects. These techniques and many others are made feasible because of the ability of the computer to manipulate large amounts of data at extremely high speeds.

Management Control. In addition to revolutionizing the engineering tools available for designing operations, the widespread use of electronic data processing (EDP) has provided important opportunities for changes in management thinking. As noted by the authors of *Retail Impact*, many of the current generation of high-speed digital computers are capable of simultaneously performing much of a corporations' routine clerical tasks, providing programmed decision making for repetitive operations and serving as experimental tools for testing new management policies.[7] EDP does not replace management skills but rather permits managers to multiply their effectiveness by providing more data, more time, and more alternative courses of action than were possible prior to the advent of the digital computer.

The evolution of computer usage by management in most companies includes several distinct changes. Initially EDP is used to perform routine clerical tasks such as maintaining inventory records and preparing payrolls. In this stage management receives many detailed reports on such things as inventory status and sales trends. However, all of the replenishment decisions are routinely made by the man. The only advantage over manual methods is that more data are available more quickly than before. In the second stage of maturity management begins to program routine decisions for the computer to make. For example, once the operations engineer has established inventory policies relative to when and how much to order, the computer can maintain records, issue shipping notices, and flag exceptional cases for management attention. The final stage of maturity involves using the computer as an experimental tool to test the effects of new management policies on system performance. At this point the roles of the operations engineer and manager merge. For example, a particular item may currently be stocked on the basis of four weeks' average sales. The effects of changing this policy to six weeks' average sales can be easily evaluated by a simulation run in parallel with the real inventory system without disturbing current operations. The fully mature system then functions in all three areas of routine data processing, control, and experimentation.

It should be emphasized that the computer often provides better control than could be obtained by delegating similar responsibilities to clerical persons through its extremely large data storage capacity and high-speed processing. In addition to providing cleaner data in the sense of fewer clerical errors, the computer can give more rapid response and better forecasts than manual means.

In the area of inventory control, for example, a rapid response is desirable not only from the point of view of customer satisfaction but also providing a more stable control system. It can be shown that in a multiechelon inventory system, time lags in receiving and processing information may cause stock level perturbations which could easily be misinterpreted as seasonal demand patterns. Only the electronic computer has the capability of handling of all the data needed in a properly designed integrated data processing system.

---

[7] IBM Application Program, *Retail Impact* (White Plains, N.Y., 1965).

Meaningful forecasts of future demands and deliveries depend upon large volumes of data which can be analyzed rapidly on a routine basis. The number of stock items involved and the necessary history of each item preclude manual computation with the same speed and accuracy obtained by EDP. The lack of this capability would reduce many analytical models from the role of dynamic decision aids to sterile approximations.

Schematic Models

The initial step in any model building exercise is to organize the elements of the system under study in some systematic fashion. Schematic models provide a systematic means of visualizing system structure and operation without jumping immediately to an often obscure mathematical representation of the system. They are easily constructed and appear to require little training beyond an appreciation for minute detail. However, one should not underestimate their power. Schematic representations of operations often reveal redundancies and system weaknesses which can be corrected without extensive formal analysis. Indeed, understanding a system well enough to construct a schematic model of its operation may be the most important benefit of an operations engineering study.

There are many kinds of schematic models which may be of use to the operations engineer. Although we will speak of several types as though they are standardized tools for analysis, every practicing engineer soon learns to improvise and adapt other graphical structures to fit particular problems of interest to him. There is no such thing as a standard charting technique for every system study. All such charts are merely attempts to organized knowledge in a logical fashion such that time, space, and structural relationships are easily understood. For purposes of our discussion we will divide charting techniques into organizational charts, process charts, activity charts, and logic flow charts.

Organization Charts.   Nearly all activities require some form of organization. The usual concept of an organization chart is that of a series of blocks and lines showing the manner in which individuals and functions are related to each other. They depict functional responsibility and chain of command.

Organization charts provide snapshots of a company's structure at one particular point in time. They are essentially a static display of relationships. For that reason, some companies prefer not to make use of organization charts. They fear that rigidly defined lines of responsibility may stifle more energetic executives from profitable expansion of their activities. Nonetheless most companies of appreciable size maintain organization charts to map responsibility for major corporate functions. Figure 2–1 gives an example of a simple functional organization.

An alternative to the functional type of organization is one which is product oriented. In those cases each product line leads to a separate structure similar to the one depicted in Figure 2–1. A quick glance at such charts

FIGURE 2–1

A Simple Functional Organization

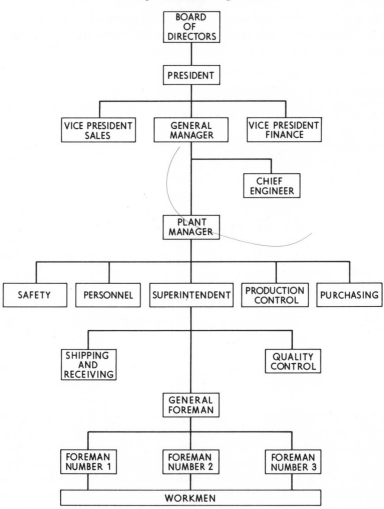

establishes at least formally the complete chain of command. Figure 2–1 for instance shows a line and staff type of breakdown with line responsibility running from the president through the general manager and on down through the workmen. Staff functions which provide auxilliary services or advice are shown as branches off the main line of authority.

Unfortunately there is often considerable difference between what many existing organization charts say about corporate responsibility and authority and what actually occurs in daily operations. For that reason an analyst who is concerned with organizational problems would do well to construct his own diagram depicting how decisions are really made by the informal organization on the basis of his personal observation.

In spite of its shortcomings the organization chart can be a valuable tool for both operations managers and engineers. Some specific uses listed by Amrine *et al.* are:[8]

1. To show lines of direct authority and thereby serve as a quick check on who is responsible for the various functions.
2. To illuminate organizational weaknesses such as more than one person being assigned the same work or certain work being assigned to no one.
3. To serve as a training device and guide in planning for expansion.
4. To alert the public about work relationships within the company.
5. To remind employees about who supervises whom.

Process Charts. Process charts provide a graphical representation of movement through a process. They are most commonly used to chart the movement of material through a manufacturing process but can be easily adapted to chart the activities of a human operator or the flow of information in a system. It is considered sound practice, however, to limit each chart to one class of movement, e.g., do not mix materials and men on the same chart. There has been some attempt to standardize the symbols used in certain classes of process charts. One commonly used set is that developed by the ASME for use on operation process and flow process charts.[9]

Operation Process Charts. An operation process chart gives production detail. When used in a manufacturing system it portrays all operations, inspections, time allowances, and material used in the manufacturing process. It is especially valuable for showing the introduction of a variety of material into the process. An operation process chart is constructed from two basic symbols connected by horizontal and vertical lines. A circle is used to denote an operation and a square to denote an inspection. Vertical lines represent the flow of the process with horizontal lines denoting the flow of material being introduced into the process. Material specifications are normally written above each horizontal line. Time required and a description of each operation are written to the left and right of the symbol to complete the chart detail. Figure 2–2 is an example of a simple operation process chart.

As discussed by Niebel,[10] an operation process chart can be used to:

1. Visualize the present method so new and better procedures can be devised.
2. Show the effect a change on a given operation will have on preceding and subsequent operations.

---

[8] Harold T. Amrine, John A. Ritchey, and Oliver S. Hulley, *Manufacturing Organization and Management* (2d ed.; Englewood Cliffs, N.J.: Prentice-Hall, Inc., 1966), p. 29.

[9] ASME, Operation and Flow Process Chart Standard, 1947.

[10] Benjamin W. Niebel, *Motion and Time Study*, (4th ed., Homewood, Ill.: Richard D. Irwin, Inc., 1967), p. 27.

FIGURE 2–2

Operation Process Chart Illustrating Manufacture of Telephone Stands

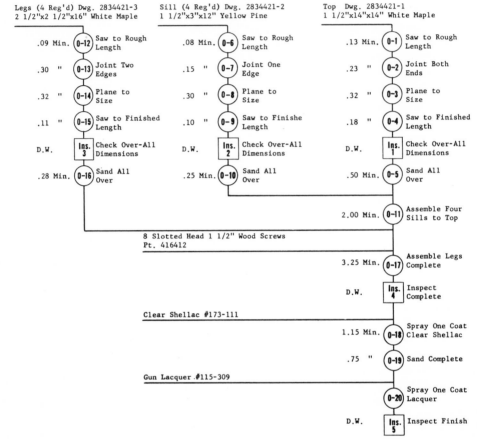

OPERATION PROCESS CHART

Manufacturing Type 2834421 Telephone Stands--Present Method
Part 2834421   Dwg. No. SK2834421
Charted By B.W.N. 4-12-

SUMMARY:

Event	Number	Time
Operations	20	16.43 minutes
Inspections	5	Day work

Reprinted with permission from Benjamin W. Niebel, *Motion and Time Study* (4th ed., Homewood, Ill.: Richard D. Irwin, Inc.: 1967), p. 24.

3. Indicate plant layout.
4. Promote and explain proposed methods.

An operation process chart gives a bird's-eye view of everything which must be done to a product. In a sense it can be viewed as the ideal plant layout for that single product.

The success of the operation process chart depends upon the level of detail considered in its construction. Every distinguishable task should be given its own block on the diagram. Once constructed, a series of common-sense questions concerning the purpose of each operation, the design of parts, materials, layout, etc., can be raised for each block on the diagram. Only after all redundant operations have been eliminated and all necessary ones streamlined by improving materials, working conditions, etc., should the analyst turn to more abstract mathematical analyses of the system.

To illustrate how this simple charting technique can highlight potential areas for improvement, consider a trivial example from your personal daily life. Suppose that the process to be analyzed is that of smoking a cigarette. The materials to be used are filter-tip cigarettes and matches carried in the smoker's pocket. An uncritical view of this process might indicate two operations, lightup and smoke. However, a closer look at the process might yield a chart such as Figure 2–3.

Suppose now that for a student who chain smokes while studying for exams, we have the task of making this process more efficient in the sense of requiring less time. We might consider such things as replacing the filter-tip cigarettes in a pack with regular cigarettes in an open dish. This would eliminate inspection I–1, I–2, and I–3 and operations O–1, O–4. Furthermore we might place a lighted candle on the desk to provide ignition. This would eliminate inspections I–4 and I–7 and operations O–5, O–6, O–7, O–8, O–9, O–12, O–13, and O–14. The resulting operation process chart would appear as in Figure 2–4. Note that we have cut the number of inspections from 7 to 2 and the number of operations from 15 to 4.

Obviously this is a trivial example with fictitious times which might not fit any particular smoker. Furthermore smoking is rarely a high-production process which would require squeezing out the last few seconds of unnecessary time. However, the point is that even on a simple daily task familiar to most persons, there are considerable savings available if the task is closely examined. If we consider much more complex processes in an industrial setting, the same attention to detail and careful recording of relationships may reveal a similar magnitude of savings.

Flow Process Charts.   A flow process chart adds one more level of detail beyond the operation process chart. Since it shows operations and inspections plus delays and storages, the flow process chart tends to highlight hidden costs associated with excessive distances traveled, unproductive delays, and

FIGURE 2–3

Normal Smoking Process

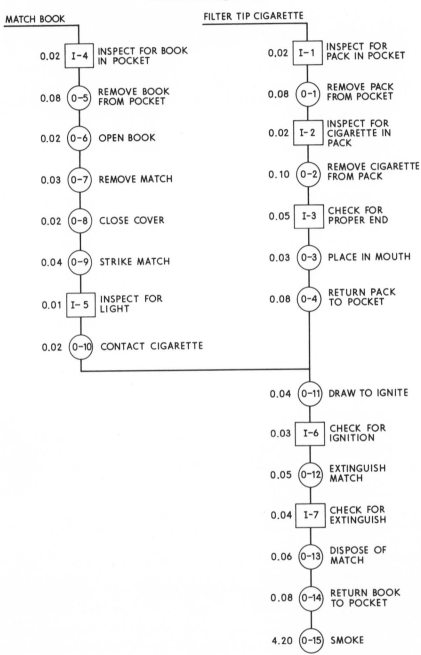

FIGURE 2–4

Improved Smoking Process

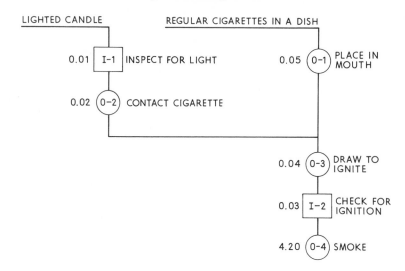

unwarranted storages. One commonly used set of symbols for flow process charts is as follows:

◯ Operation such as turning a shaft or driving a nail.

▢ Inspection such as reading a gage or examining for quality.

▽ Storage such as in a bin or file drawer.

⇨ Transportation such as moving material from work station to work station.

D Delay of shorter duration than storage such as material waiting for processing or persons in line.

Because of its additional detail, the flow process chart is normally limited to a single item rather than showing the assembly details common on operation process charts. Figure 2–5 illustrates a flow process chart for a laundry operation developed on a preprinted form. Such preprinted forms simplify the construction of the chart and provide a natural check list for potential improvements.

Flow Diagrams. The term flow diagram is used to represent two different concepts in present-day operations engineering. In classical parlance the simplest form of the flow diagram is a pictorial plan of the flow of the work.

FIGURE 2–5

Flow Process Chart for Flat Laundry

PROCESS ANALYSIS

Present ☒   Proposed ☐

page
IE 663
FILE NUMBER

SUMMARY		Number	Time ( )		
OPERATIONS	○	10		PRODUCT : FLAT LAUNDRY	
INSPECTIONS	☐	3		CHART BEGINS WITH OPERATION: RECEIPT OF DIRTY LAUNDRY	
TRANSPORTATIONS	⇨	8		DEPARTMENT : RECEIVING	
DELAYS	D	2		CHART ENDS WITH OPERATION: SHIPMENT OF CLEAN LAUNDRY	
STORAGES	▽	2		DEPARTMENT : SHIPPING	
UNITS PRODUCED			TOTAL	ANALYST : WCG	
TOTAL DISTANCE		325'		DATE : 10-15-	

Description Notes	Classification	Dist.	EQUIP	Analysis Notes
1. REMOVE FROM TRUCK	●⇨■D▽		HAND	CHECK CONTENT UPON RECEIPT
2. TRANSPORT TO STORAGE	○⬛☐D▽	30'	BASKETS	
3. STORE UNTIL SCHEDULED	○⇨☐D▼		BASKETS	STORAGE AREA CONGESTED
4. PUSH BASKETS TO WASHERS	○⬛☐D▽	112'	BASKETS	
5. WASH	●⇨☐D▽		WASHER	LOAD AND UNLOAD BY HOIST
6. TRANSFER TO EXTRACTOR	○⬛☐D▽	70'	HOIST	REMOVEABLE EXTRACTOR CONTAINER
7. EXTRACT	●⇨☐D▽		EXTRACTOR	REMOVE WATER BY CENTRIFUGAL FORCE
8. TRANSFER TO SHAKE-OUT	○⬛☐D▽	25'	HOIST	
9. QUEUE FOR SHAKE-OUT	○⇨☐◼▽		HOIST	WAIT TURN AT SHAKE-OUT
10. LOAD SHAKE-OUT CONVEYOR	●⇨☐D▽		HOIST	
11. TRANSFER TO SHAKE-OUT	○⬛☐D▽	3'	CONVEYOR	
12. SHAKE-OUT	●⇨☐D▽		SHAKE-OUT	UNTANGLE LAUNDRY- DUMP ON TABLE
13. SORT	●⇨■D▽		TABLE	HAND SORT AND INSPECT
14. TRANSFER TO IRON	○⬛☐D▽	40'	BASKET	
15. QUEUE FOR IRON	○⇨☐◼▽		BASKET	
16. IRON	●⇨☐D▽		IRON	
17. FOLD	●⇨■D▽		HAND	
18. WEIGH	●⇨☐D▽		SCALES	
19. MOVE TO BASKETS	○⬛☐D▽	15'	HAND	HAND OPERATION- WASTED MOVES
20. STORE FOR SHIPMENT	○⇨☐D▼		BASKETS	
21. MOVE TO TRUCK	○⬛☐D▽	30'	BASKETS	PUSH BASKETS
22. LOAD TRUCK	●⇨☐D▽			
	○⇨☐D▽			

Such a pictorial plan gives the layout of work areas, machines, desks, etc., with connecting arrows and lines to indicate the route of travel. Figure 2–6 depicts a flow diagram for the previously discussed laundry operation.

It is possible to show the simultaneous flow of several materials on the same diagram by superimposing multiple flow paths. The flow diagram used in this sense highlights backtracking, areas of traffic congestion, and weaknesses in layout. It is often used to supplement the flow process chart.

Since the advent of digital computers the term flow diagram has also been used to denote a chart of the logic steps contained in computer programs.

FIGURE 2–6

Flow Diagram of Laundry Processing

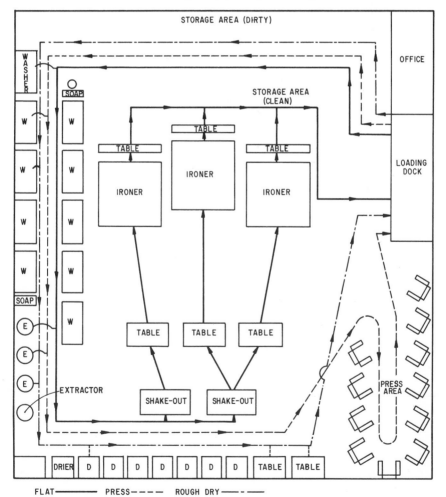

FIGURE 2-7

Flow Diagram for Calculating Mean

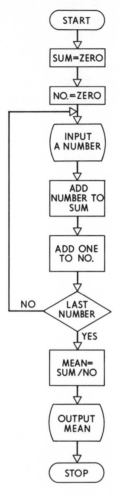

Figure 2-7 illustrates a simple flow diagram one might prepare prior to writing a program to calculate the mean of a sequence of numbers. The ability to structure a problem in logical flow diagram form is valuable for all manner of systems analysis and is not limited to programming applications. Indeed, some analysts have found that by attempting to flow chart the sequence of operations performed in many real systems, preparatory to simulating that operation, they gain sufficient knowledge of how the system works to negate the need for the simulation study. Again it is the attention to minute detail which assures successful application of this tool.

Multiple Activity Charts. Multiple activity charts are used to present the method of repetitive work performed by a man when his work is co-ordinated with one or more men or machines which control the cycle time. Such charts are useful to determine the number of machines to assign to a production worker, the number of helpers to provide for complex processes, and the potential for secondary tasks during idle time. Since no allowances are made for random variation in performance times, this tool is limited to constant time operations and those which are essentially machine con trolled. When performance variation becomes important, more sophisticated analyses such as queueing theory are required.

Figure 2–8 illustrates a multiple activity chart for a task involving one operator and three machines. One can tell at a glance that the machines have a considerable amount of idle time when the system operates in this fashion. Since one press is idle at all times, it is obvious that this system was not designed for the task being analyzed. An improved method for the same operation might consider using two operators and all three presses. For a continuous process such as this one, the savings are sizable. As with the other charting techniques, multiple activity charts require careful attention to detail and examination of single components of the system at a time.

Therblig and Simo Charts. The same approach used to construct multiple activity charts may be applied to charting the simultaneous motions of different body members for a human operator. Although some charts go so far as to identify the movements of each finger separately, the most common version treats the simultaneous movements of the left and right hands. For obvious reasons these are often referred to as left-hand, right-hand charts.

These charts represent the smallest practical breakdown of a task for most analyses. Since they are so detailed they require considerable time and expense to construct. For that reason they are only used for high-production systems in which particular operations by human operators require improv-ment beyond that attainable by analyzing operation process charts.

In his early work in motion study, Frank B. Gilbreth developed a list of certain events which he thought were common to all kinds of manual work. Seventeen of these subdivisions of work, which he called therbligs (Gilbreth spelled backwards), survive in present-day motion study. As presented by Barnes,[11] these include:

1. Search (Sh)—the time during which one is groping for the object.
2. Select (St)—choosing one object from among several.
3. Grasp (G)—taking hold of an object.
4. Transport Empty (TE)—moving the empty hand.
5. Transport Loaded (TL)—moving an object from place to place.
6. Hold (H)—retaining an object after it has been grasped. No movement.

---

[11] Ralph M. Barnes, *Motion and Time Study* (5th ed.; New York: John Wiley & Sons, Inc., 1963), pp. 136–43.

FIGURE 2-8

Multiple Activity Chart

	OPERATOR	TIME (SEC.)	MACHINE (LEFT)	TIME (SEC.)	MACHINE (CENTER)	TIME (SEC.)	MACHINE (RIGHT)	TIME (SEC.)
	OPERATION: REMOVE WRINKLES (IRON)							
	PART NAME: DRESS (SKIRT ONLY)							
	MACHINE NAME: PRESSES							
5	LOAD LEFT	10	IDLE	10				
10								
15								
20	LOAD RIGHT & SPRINKLE	30	PRESS	30			IDLE	40
25								
30								
35								
40								
45	TURN LEFT	10	IDLE	10			PRESS	10
50								
55	TURN RIGHT	10	PRESS	10			IDLE	10
60								
65	TURN LEFT	10	IDLE	10	IDLE	142	PRESS	10
70								
75								
80	TURN RIGHT	20	PRESS	20			IDLE	20
85								
90								
95	TURN LEFT	5	IDLE	5			PRESS	5
100	TURN RIGHT	10	PRESS	10			IDLE	10
105								
110	TURN LEFT	7	IDLE	7			PRESS	7
115								
120	TURN RIGHT	10	PRESS	10			IDLE	10
125								
130	UNLOAD LEFT	10	IDLE	20			PRESS	10
135								
142	UNLOAD RIGHT	10					IDLE	10

(TIME IN SECONDS)

SUMMARY				
	OPERATOR	LEFT	CENTER	RIGHT
IDLE TIME	0 SEC.	62 SEC.	142 SEC.	100 SEC.
WORKING TIME	142 SEC.	80 SEC.	0 SEC.	42 SEC.
CYCLE TIME	142 SEC.	142 SEC.	142 SEC.	142 SEC.
% UTILIZATION	$142/142 = 100\%$	$80/142 = 56.3\%$	$0/142 = 0\%$	$42/142 = 29.5\%$

7. Release Load (RL)—letting go of an object.
8. Position (P)—orienting an object into its intended location.
9. Pre-position (PP)—orienting object into correct position for some subsequent motion.
10. Inspect (I)—examining an object.
11. Assemble (A)—placing one object into or on another to form an integral part.
12. Disassemble (DA)—separating one object from another.
13. Use (U)—manipulating a tool, such as a wrench, for the purpose intended.
14. Unavoidable Delay (UD)—delay beyond operator control.
15. Avoidable Delay (AD)—delay over which operator has control.
16. Plan (Pn)—mental reaction preceding physical movement.
17. Rest for Overcoming Fatigue (R)—delay factor for overcoming fatigue.

When used without a time scale, a chart employing these symbols is called a therblig chart. Therblig charts form a basic tool for visual motion study. When presented with a time scale, in the manner of our multiple activity charts, they form a simo (simultaneous motion) chart. Figure 2–9 illustrates such a chart.

Since the breakdown of motion is so fine, when the time to perform each therblig is required, it is normally obtained by a motion-picture technique known as micromotion study. Films of a manual task are taken at say 1,000 frames per minute then analyzed frame at a time to identify the appropriate therbligs. Time is determined by counting frames or by reading a special clock, called a microchronometer, often placed in the field of view of the camera. The microchronometer, also designed by Gilbreth, is a fast-moving clock which measures time in units of 0.0005 minutes. This time unit is called one wink.

Information gathered on such charts is used together with an extensive list of "principles of motion economy" to design better methods for human operators. Such principles are distillations of commonsense rules practiced by classical industrial engineers. The interested reader may consult any text on motion study for a detailed discussion.

Schematic Model Summary.   Recall that the purpose of this section was to introduce several means of organizing the elements of systems under study in a systematic fashion. A variety of special-purpose charting techniques have been discussed to illustrate the range of subject matter and detail which can be treated. They ran all the way from the very gross representations of organizations by organization charts through the movement of an operators hands as recorded by simo charts. Each of these charts can be used as a tool for analysis in its own right. However, for the balance of this text they will be treated primarily as devices for organizing knowledge about how a system is structured. More quantitatively oriented graphs such as signal flow graphs

FIGURE 2–9

Simo Chart

PART: DRAWER PULL ASSEMBLY

OPERATOR: JSM

METHOD: 461

DATE: 10-22-

ANALYST: WCG

LEFT HAND	SYMBOL		2000ths OF A MINUTE		SYMBOL	RIGHT HAND
ASSEMBLY TO BIN	TL	82		85	UD	HAND AT REST
RELEASE ASSEMBLY	RL	18	90	15	TE	REACH FOR HEAD
REACH FOR PIN	TE	03		03	SE	SELECT HEAD
SELECT PIN	SE	13				
GRASP PIN	G	19	120	22	G	GRASP HEAD
MOVE TOWARD HEAD	TL	02		16	TL	MOVE TOWARD LH
POSITION PIN	P	03		06	P	POSITION HEAD
ASSEMBLE PIN	A	02	150			
HOLD PIN	H	49	180	38	A	ASSEMBLE HEAD
				06	H	HOLD HEAD
RELEASE PIN	RL	08		07	RL	RELEASE HEAD
REACH FOR HEAD	TE	03		17	TE	REACH FOR BODY
GRASP HEAD	G	04	210			
HOLD HEAD	H	22		03	SE	SELECT BODY
				09	G	GRASP BODY
MOVE TOWARD BODY	TL	10		08	TL	MOVE TOWARD PIECE
			240	01	P	POSITION BODY
			270			
			300			
				165	A	ASSEMBLE BODY
			330			
			360			
HOLD PIECE WHILE BEING ASSEMBLED	H		390			
				14	TE	REACH FOR COLLAR
				03	SE	SELECT COLLAR
		532	420	02	G	GRASP COLLAR
				09	TL	MOVE TOWARD PIECE
				07	P	POSITION COLLAR
				02	A	ASSEMBLE COLLAR
				09	RL	RELEASE COLLAR
			450	10	TE	REACH FOR WASHER
				03	SE	SELECT WASHER
				15	G	GRASP WASHER
			480	13	TL	MOVE TOWARD PIECE
				03	P	POSITION WASHER
				12	A	ASSEMBLE WASHER
			510	08	RL	RELEASE WASHER
				10	TE	REACH FOR NUT
				04	SE	SELECT NUT
				13	G	GRASP NUT
			540	19	TL	MOVE TOWARD PIECE
			570	04	P	POSITION NUT
			600			
				122	A	ASSEMBLE NUT
			630			
			660			
MOVE TOWARD BIN	TL	15				MOVE TOWARD HEAD
RELEASE IN BIN			690			
			720			
			750			

and project network diagrams will be introduced in later chapters. The quantitatively oriented graphs often serve as initial models for more mathematical treatments of system problems.

Work Measurement

To some persons engaged in operations engineering, work measurement connotes a stopwatch and clipboard task which they consider beneath their dignity to perform. However, it is important to note that regardless of the complexity of the mathematical models used to analyze system performance, data is required which at times may only be obtainable by such pedestrian acts as time study. For that reason every operations engineer should be familiar with the techniques used to determine the time required to perform a task when human operators are involved. This does not mean that he must be an expert in time study but it does mean that he should appreciate the strengths and weaknesses of the data base upon which his models must often be constructed.

Time Study Data.   To the typical production worker the term time study connotes techniques used to set production standards by which his performance will be judged. Historically, the close association of time study with wage payment plans has colored the views of operating employees and made it difficult to achieve their cooperation in measuring performance. Unfortunately the point overlooked by many operators, managers, and analysts is that time study can have many important uses beyond setting of production standards for wages. From management's viewpoint production standards are necessary to determine schedules, plan work, assign machines, etc., all of which have nothing directly to do with wages.

Another obvious requirement for time study is to establish an estimate of cost incurred in producing a product. Particularly in plants where a variety of products are manufactured, good cost control requires that the cost of operating each stage of manufacture for each item be accurately known. It is not sufficient merely to allocate total labor costs over all items in some arbitrary fashion such as total number produced. Such policies may conceal the fact that a few items are extremely profitable while others are actually losing money for the corporation. This cost information when human operators are involved is most accurately obtained from basic time study data.

In addition to establishing costs, time study data is needed to provide basic time input for a host of sophisticated mathematical models treated in this text and elsewhere. For example, all of the line balancing and scheduling techniques require time estimates for each element of the production process. Queueing models require probability distributions for service times and inter-arrival times which can be developed from basic stopwatch data. Linear programming techniques involving allocation of limited processing times among competing products require time study data. The list is endless. Any model which requires a time estimate and which treats a process with a human operator will of necessity use time study data.

Stopwatch Techniques. The most common means of measuring performance of the human operator is to time his performance with a stopwatch. Although it sounds simple enough, this task can become a very delicate exercise in human relations, requires considerable subjective judgment on the part of the time study man, and demands the same careful attention to detail exercised in methods study. Most of these demands arise from the necessity of using the data developed from a time study to represent the performance of qualified and well-trained persons working at a normal pace. Unfortunately there is a wide variance among different operators with respect to capabilities and desire as well as variation from time to time with the same operator. Such variations coupled with a lack of firm bench marks for "normal" performance make time study data totally suspect for many persons. The only counter is that no better means of measuring are yet available.

Once it has been decided that a time study must be conducted for a particular job, several identifiable steps are undertaken by the analyst. A rough listing of these steps is as follows:

1. Select the operator to be studied.
2. Inform all interested parties about the purpose of the study.
3. Collect complete information about the materials and methods employed on the job.
4. Design the study.
5. Record the observed times.
6. Determine a rating factor.
7. Establish allowances.
8. Calculate the standard time.

The selection of the operator to be timed follows commonsense rules. The operator should be one of average ability in order to simplify the rating task. He should be well trained in the method being used so that the observations taken will be representative of a steady-state condition rather than a slice from a transient learning process. In the event that the job to be timed is a new one, the operator should be given some practice with the suggested method before timing takes place.

The task of properly informing the operator, his foreman, the union, and any others directly affected may be necessary from both a human relations and a legal point of view. If the timing is used to set standards for wage payment, the delicacy of the operation is obvious. Even if it is to be used to provide raw data for modeling, the occurrence and purpose of the study should be carefully explained. This will give some assurance that the performance to be observed is a typical one and not one staged for the benefit of the analyst. Early efficiency experts rightfully earned the wrath of the working man by performing time studies on the sly which were later used to establish standards and ultimately pay for the job.

A careful record of the materials and methods employed on the job is necessary for several reasons. First, the analyst cannot design a proper time study unless he is thoroughly familar with the task he is to time. He must know what events will occur every cycle and what events occur once every several cycles. This permits him to establish a proper element breakdown and prevents the exclusion of events which are properly a part of the time required to perform a task. In addition to the education of the analyst, records are necessary in order to establish a bench mark for retiming. Any change in materials or method used in a job may necessitate a new time study. However, the need for the new study may be overlooked if no records are available to describe conditions present at the time of the original study.

The design of the study consists of specifying the conditions under which the study will be performed, the length of the study, and the element breakdown. Conditions under which the study is to be performed include the days to be covered, the time of day, where the analyst will be positioned, etc. The length of the study specifies the number of observations to be taken. There are statistical techniques, introduced in later chapters, which can be used to establish the necessary sample size to have a quantifiable level of assurance of achieving any desired accuracy.

The element breakdown consists of identifying subportions of the total task each of which will be individually timed. According to Barnes, this is preferable to timing an entire operation as one element for several reasons:[12]

1. An operation is best described by breaking it down into definite and measurable elements.
2. Standard time values may be determined for elements of a job thus permitting synthetic evaluation of portions of the total, i.e., timing of those elements with standard values may be unnecessary. The standard values provide a synthetic evaluation.
3. Time study may show that certain elements require excessive time while others receive too little time. It may also reveal variations in method not easily detected from an overall study.
4. An operator may change tempo throughout the cycle. Time study permits separate performance ratings for each element of the job.

There have been many rules devised for identifying time study elements. However, most can be reduced to four major suggestions:

1. Select elements with easily identified breakpoints such as characteristic sounds.
2. Select elements as short in duration as can be accurately timed with the device to be used.

---

[12] *Ibid.*, p. 359–60.

3. Separate manual from machine controlled time.
4. Separate constant from variable elements. Here the term constant refers
    to those tasks that are the same from job to job independent of the size,
    weight, or shape of the object being handled. For instance, lowering a
    drill to the workpiece might be a constant element while inserting a part
    in a jig might be variable.

Methods for recording the observed time vary among the devices used
to measure time. The most common measuring device of course is the stopwatch which can be used in two modes. The modes of operation are referred
to as continuous and snapback timing. Continuous timing permits the watch
to run continuously with total elapsed time being recorded by the analyst
at the end of each element. Element times are then obtained by subtracting
successive readings. Snapback timing, on the other hand, requires that the
analyst snap the watch back to zero at the end of every element after recording the elemental time. Other means of measurement such as motion-picture
analysis and marstochron are less commonly used and require their own
form of recording. Figure 2–10 illustrates a typical data sheet used to record
stopwatch data. Note that there is considerable variation among observations
of the same element. This inherent variation of the human operator
makes it necessary to take a large number of observations before one can be
reasonably certain that the mean observed time is representative of actual
process time.

Up to the point of recording the observed time to perform a task, the usual
time study procedure is reasonably free of analyst bias. For purposes of many
of the models used by the operations engineer, this may be as far as he needs
to consider the topic if he is the one collecting the data. However, the classical
purpose of time study is to determine how long a task should take as opposed
to how long it was observed to take at the time of the study. Therefore, most
data from existing files will include rating factors and allowances, which in
the time study man's eyes are reasonable modifications to observed time to
reflect the time that a job should take.

The determination of a rating factor is the most controversial aspect
of the whole time study procedure. The rating factor relates the pace exhibited
by the operator being observed to the analyst's concept of a normal pace.
For instance, a rating factor of 125 percent indicates that the analyst feels
that a normal operator should take 1.25 times as long to perform the task
under study as did the observed operator. Rating factors are sometimes
applied to each element separately or may be applied to the job as a whole.
In addition, some special schemes exist where an operator is rated by separate
factors such as skill, effort, consistency, etc., in an attempt to establish a more
accurate overall rating.

The difficulty with all such schemes is in providing meaningful benchmarks
for what constitutes a normal pace. Training films exist which attempt to

FIGURE 2–10

Time Study Observations for a Valve Assembly, Continuous Timing

TIME STUDY OBSERVATION

DATE 10-22
TIME START 9:28 P.M.
TIME STOP 9:43 P.M.
ELAPSED TIME 15 MIN.
NUMB. PIECES 16

ELEMENTS: LOAD, FACE, TURN O.D., FILE, REMOVE, INSPECT

SHEET NO. 1
NO. SHEETS 1
FOREIGN ELEMENTS

Line	LOAD T	R	FACE T	R	TURN O.D. T	R	FILE T	R	REMOVE T	R	INSPECT T	R	SYM	R	T	DESCRIPTION
1	06	06	18	24	37	61	06	67	05	72			A	696/710	14	INSPECT
2	06	78	17	95	37	132	08	140	04	144			B	1063/1134	71	DRINK OF WATER
3	06	150	15	165	37	202	08	210	04	214			C			
4	06	220	17	237	36	273	06	279	05	284			D			
5	06	290	15	305	38	343	06	349	04	353			E			
6	04	357	14	371	37	408	07	415	03	418			F			
7	06	424	18	442	35	477	06	413	04	487			G			
8	05	492	16	508	39	547	06	553	04	557			H			
9	06	563	18	581	37	618	07	625	03	628			I			
10	06	634	17	651	37	688	06	694	05	713 (a)	14					
11	05	718	19	737	35	772	06	778	04	782						
12	05	787	18	805	37	842	06	848	04	852						
13	06	858	18	876	35	911	07	918	03	921						
14	06	927	18	945	36	981	06	987	04	991						
15	05	996	18	1014	36	1050	06	1056	05	1061 (b)						
16	05	1137	18	1155	37	1192	05	1197	03	1200						

Av. Cycle Time 0.706
Cycle Rating Factor 110
Normal Cycle Time 0.713

Percent Allowances

Pers.	Fat.	Delay	Total
4.17		3.33	7.50

Std. Time Per Unit 0.713
Pieces Per Hour 76.6
Std. Hours Per 100 1.305

Allowances in Minutes

Pers.	Fat.	Delay	Total
20		16	36

Avail. Prod. Min. Per Hr. ____
Pieces Per Hour ____
Std. Hrs. Per 100 ____

SUMMARY

	LOAD	FACE	TURN O.D.	FILE	REMOVE	INSPECT
Total Time	0.89	2.74	5.86	1.02	0.64	0.14
No. of Readings	16	16	16	16	16	1
Av. of Readings	.056	.171	.366	.064	.04	.14
Frequency	1	1	1	1	1	1/16
Average Time	.056	.171	.366	.064	.04	.009
E.I. Rating Factor	110	110	100	90	105	100
E.I. Normal Time	.0616	.188	.366	.058	.042	.009

train time study personnel to recognize a normal pace by establishing benchmarks for the time necessary to deal 52 cards or the speed with which a man walks across level ground. To the skeptical observer it remains unclear how concepts of pace learned by observing such simple tasks on film can be transferred into the work environment and applied to very complex physical skills.

The final measurement which must be made before the time study is complete is to determine the allowances to be added to an uninterrupted normal time. Allowances account for those variations not accounted for during the rating portion of the study. These include factors such as fatigue, personal needs, and unavoidable delays. Ideally the time for these factors should also be established through sound time study data. Practically this is very difficult to achieve, particularly for such ill-defined factors as fatigue. The unions recognize this and at times have bargained for allowances as though they are fringe benefits. Usually this becomes a fixed factor based upon the analyst's experience and past shop practice which is added to the normal time to perform a task.

After all these data are collected the standard time can be established. The observed data are used to establish a selected cycle time by adding the mean observed times for those elements occurring every cycle and an appropriate fraction of those elements occurring less frequently. For example, if an element occurs only once in three cycles, one third of its mean observed time would be included in the selected cycle time. The selected cycle time is then multiplied by the rating factor to get the normal time for the job. Finally allowances are added to achieve standard time. In equation form this is most easily expressed as:

$$\text{Standard} = (\text{Selected Cycle Time}) \times (\text{Rating Factor}) + \text{Allowances} \qquad (2\text{--}1)$$

Another commonly used calculation when all times are expressed in minutes is:

$$\text{Standard} = \frac{\text{Minutes per Day} - \text{Allowances per Day}}{\text{Normal Time per Piece}} = \frac{\text{Pieces}}{\text{Day}} \qquad (2\text{--}2)$$

Such are the sources of data the operations engineer is often forced to employ when he must establish the time and/or cost to perform a task involving human operators. They should be handled with due respect, especially when making claims for the accuracy of calculations involving sophisticated models when some of the inputs are standard times.

Standard Data Systems. One commonly used alternative to executing a stopwatch time study is to synthesize the time from tables of data for elemental times. For the most part such elemental time standards are taken from time studies in the past which have proven to be satisfactory. Unique standard data systems are often established by frequent users of time study for use within their own organization. Standard data systems have the advantage of consistency in that several analysts should get the same times by this procedure, something which may not occur with stopwatch studies. In addition, times can be established much more rapidly since the time study procedure is essentially complete once the elements of a job have been established. No extensive observations are required. Of course their use is subject to the criticism that conditions continually change and that standards established for elements from job A may be completely wrong for what appear to be similar elements from job B.

When the idea of a standard data system is extended to more fundamental motions and groups of motions one refers to synthetic basic motion times. In this type of analysis a task is broken up into extremely small elements approaching therbligs by micromotion techniques. Times for each of these basic motions are then summed to obtain an estimate for overall time to perform a task.

Several systems of basic motion times data are available from commercial sources. One of the more widely used of these is the Methods Time Measurement (MTM) system. An abbreviated version of these tables is contained in Table 2–1. The time unit used is one TMU which equals .00001

TABLE 2–1

MTM Standard Data

TABLE I—REACH—R

Distance Moved Inches	Time TMU				Hand In Motion		CASE AND DESCRIPTION
	A	B	C or D	E	A	B	
¾ or less	2.0	2.0	2.0	2.0	1.6	1.6	**A** Reach to object in fixed location, or to object in other hand or on which other hand rests.
1	2.5	2.5	3.6	2.4	2.3	2.3	
2	4.0	4.0	5.9	3.8	3.5	2.7	
3	5.3	5.3	7.3	5.3	4.5	3.6	
4	6.1	6.4	8.4	6.8	4.9	4.3	**B** Reach to single object in location which may vary slightly from cycle to cycle.
5	6.5	7.8	9.4	7.4	5.3	5.0	
6	7.0	8.6	10.1	8.0	5.7	5.7	
7	7.4	9.3	10.8	8.7	6.1	6.5	
8	7.9	10.1	11.5	9.3	6.5	7.2	**C** Reach to object jumbled with other objects in a group so that search and select occur.
9	8.3	10.8	12.2	9.9	6.9	7.9	
10	8.7	11.5	12.9	10.5	7.3	8.6	
12	9.6	12.9	14.2	11.8	8.1	10.1	
14	10.5	14.4	15.6	13.0	8.9	11.5	**D** Reach to a very small object or where accurate grasp is required.
16	11.4	15.8	17.0	14.2	9.7	12.9	
18	12.3	17.2	18.4	15.5	10.5	14.4	
20	13.1	18.6	19.8	16.7	11.3	15.8	
22	14.0	20.1	21.2	18.0	12.1	17.3	**E** Reach to indefinite location to get hand in position for body balance or next motion or out of way.
24	14.9	21.5	22.5	19.2	12.9	18.8	
26	15.8	22.9	23.9	20.4	13.7	20.2	
28	16.7	24.4	25.3	21.7	14.5	21.7	
30	17.5	25.8	26.7	22.9	15.3	23.2	

TABLE II—MOVE—M

Distance Moved Inches	Time TMU			Hand In Motion B	Wt. Allowance			CASE AND DESCRIPTION
	A	B	C		Wt. (lb.) Up to	Factor	Constant TMU	
¾ or less	2.0	2.0	2.0	1.7	2.5	1.00	0	
1	2.5	2.9	3.4	2.3				
2	3.6	4.6	5.2	2.9	7.5	1.06	2.2	**A** Move object to other hand or against stop.
3	4.9	5.7	6.7	3.6				
4	6.1	6.9	8.0	4.3				
5	7.3	8.0	9.2	5.0	12.5	1.11	3.9	
6	8.1	8.9	10.3	5.7				
7	8.9	9.7	11.1	6.5	17.5	1.17	5.6	
8	9.7	10.6	11.8	7.2				
9	10.5	11.5	12.7	7.9	22.5	1.22	7.4	**B** Move object to approximate or indefinite location.
10	11.3	12.2	13.5	8.6				
12	12.9	13.4	15.2	10.0	27.5	1.28	9.1	
14	14.4	14.6	16.9	11.4				
16	16.0	15.8	18.7	12.8	32.5	1.33	10.8	
18	17.6	17.0	20.4	14.2				
20	19.2	18.2	22.1	15.6				
22	20.8	19.4	23.8	17.0	37.5	1.39	12.5	
24	22.4	20.6	25.5	18.4				**C** Move object to exact location.
26	24.0	21.8	27.3	19.8	42.5	1.44	14.3	
28	25.5	23.1	29.0	21.2				
30	27.1	24.3	30.7	22.7	47.5	1.50	16.0	

TABLE III—TURN AND APPLY PRESSURE—T AND AP

Weight	Time TMU for Degrees Turned											
	30°	45°	60°	75°	90°	105°	120°	135°	150°	165°	180°
Small— 0 to 2 Pounds	2.8	3.5	4.1	4.8	5.4	6.1	6.8	7.4	8.1	8.7	9.4
Medium—2.1 to 10 Pounds	4.4	5.5	6.5	7.5	8.5	9.6	10.6	11.6	12.7	13.7	14.8
Large— 10.1 to 35 Pounds	8.4	10.5	12.3	14.4	16.2	18.3	20.4	22.2	24.3	26.1	28.2

APPLY PRESSURE CASE 1—16.2 TMU.   APPLY PRESSURE CASE 2—10.6 TMU

TABLE 2-1 *(Continued)*

TABLE IV—GRASP—G

Case	Time TMU	DESCRIPTION
1A	2.0	**Pick Up Grasp**—Small, medium or large object by itself, easily grasped.
1B	3.5	Very small object or object lying close against a flat surface.
1C1	7.3	Interference with grasp on bottom and one side of nearly cylindrical object. Diameter larger than $\frac{1}{2}''$.
1C2	8.7	Interference with grasp on bottom and one side of nearly cylindrical object. Diameter $\frac{1}{4}''$ to $\frac{1}{2}''$.
1C3	10.8	Interference with grasp on bottom and one side of nearly cylindrical object. Diameter less than $\frac{1}{4}''$.
2	5.6	Regrasp.
3	5.6	**Transfer Grasp.**
4A	7.3	Object jumbled with other objects so search and select occur. Larger than $1'' \times 1'' \times 1''$.
4B	9.1	Object jumbled with other objects so search and select occur. $\frac{1}{4}'' \times \frac{1}{4}'' \times \frac{1}{8}''$ to $1'' \times 1'' \times 1''$.
4C	12.9	Object jumbled with other objects so search and select occur. Smaller than $\frac{1}{4}'' \times \frac{1}{4}'' \times \frac{1}{8}''$.
5	0	Contact, sliding or hook grasp.

TABLE V—POSITION*—P

CLASS OF FIT		Symmetry	Easy To Handle	Difficult To Handle
1—Loose	No pressure required	S	5.6	11.2
		SS	9.1	14.7
		NS	10.4	16.0
2—Close	Light pressure required	S	16.2	21.8
		SS	19.7	25.3
		NS	21.0	26.6
3—Exact	Heavy pressure required.	S	43.0	48.6
		SS	46.5	52.1
		NS	47.8	53.4

*Distance moved to engage—1″ or less.

TABLE VI—RELEASE—RL

Case	Time TMU	DESCRIPTION
1	2.0	Normal release performed by opening fingers as independent motion.
2	0	Contact Release.

TABLE VII—DISENGAGE—D

CLASS OF FIT	Easy to Handle	Difficult to Handle
1—Loose—Very slight effort, blends with subsequent move.	4.0	5.7
2—Close — Normal effort, slight recoil.	7.5	11.8
3—Tight — Considerable effort, hand recoils markedly.	22.9	34.7

TABLE VIII—EYE TRAVEL TIME AND EYE FOCUS—ET AND EF

Eye Travel Time $= 15.2 \times \dfrac{T}{D}$ TMU, with a maximum value of 20 TMU.

where T = the distance between points from and to which the eye travels.
D = the perpendicular distance from the eye to the line of travel T.

Eye Focus Time = 7.3 TMU.

TABLE 2–1 *(Concluded)*

TABLE IX—BODY, LEG AND FOOT MOTIONS

DESCRIPTION	SYMBOL	DISTANCE	TIME TMU
Foot Motion—Hinged at Ankle.	FM	Up to 4″	8.5
With heavy pressure.	FMP		19.1
Leg or Foreleg Motion.	LM —	Up to 6″	7.1
		Each add'l. inch	1.2
Sidestep—Case 1—Complete when leading leg contacts floor.	SS-C1	Less than 12″	Use REACH or MOVE Time
		12″	17.0
		Each add'l. inch	.6
Case 2—Lagging leg must contact floor before next motion can be made.	SS-C2	12″	34.1
		Each add'l. inch	1.1
Bend, Stoop, or Kneel on One Knee.	B,S,KOK		29.0
Arise.	AB,AS,AKOK		31.9
Kneel on Floor—Both Knees.	KBK		69.4
Arise.	AKBK		76.7
Sit.	SIT		34.7
Stand from Sitting Position.	STD		43.4
Turn Body 45 to 90 degrees—			
Case 1—Complete when leading leg contacts floor.	TBC1		18.6
Case 2—Lagging leg must contact floor before next motion can be made.	TBC2		37.2
Walk.	W-FT.	Per Foot	5.3
Walk.	W-P	Per Pace	15.0

TABLE X—SIMULTANEOUS MOTIONS

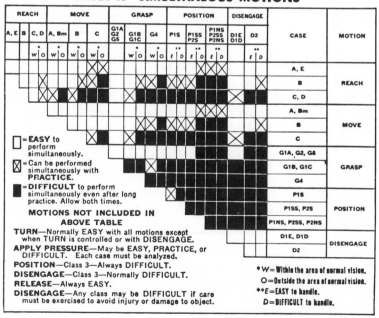

□ = EASY to perform simultaneously.

⊠ = Can be performed simultaneously with PRACTICE.

■ = DIFFICULT to perform simultaneously even after long practice. Allow both times.

MOTIONS NOT INCLUDED IN ABOVE TABLE

TURN—Normally EASY with all motions except when TURN is controlled or with DISENGAGE.

APPLY PRESSURE—May be EASY, PRACTICE, or DIFFICULT. Each case must be analyzed.

POSITION—Class 3—Always DIFFICULT.

DISENGAGE—Class 3—Normally DIFFICULT.

RELEASE—Always EASY.

DISENGAGE—Any class may be DIFFICULT if care must be exercised to avoid injury or damage to object.

*W = Within the area of normal vision.

O = Outside the area of normal vision.

**E = EASY to handle.

D = DIFFICULT to handle.

Copyright 1965 by the MTM Association for Standards and Research. Reproduced by permission of the MTM Association. No reprint permission is granted without express written consent of the MTM Association, 9–10 Saddle River Road, Fair Lawn, New Jersey 07410.

Note: 1TMU = .001 hr.; .006 min.; and .036 sec.

hour. The MTM data were obtained by a frame-by-frame analysis of motion-picture films involving a variety of work. The raw film data have been rated in much the same manner as a time study man rates during a stopwatch study.

With all of the synthetic systems, the problems associated with reducing observed times to the time it should take to perform a task have not been eliminated. They have only been moved back to the original analyst who established the tables. Their principal advantage beyond speed of application is that they place total responsibility for rating on the original data analyst rather than permitting the multitude of opinions of what constitutes normal performance among a group of company analysts.

Work Sampling.   Before leaving the area of work measurement, one other technique for obtaining time estimates should be mentioned. That is the work sampling technique.

Work sampling is a statistical procedure for allocating time over activities. The idea behind it is that the relative frequency with which an operator is observed to be engaged with a particular element over a large number of observations is indicative of the way his total workday is expended. Data are collected by observing the operator at random times over an extended period and recording which element he was performing at the instant of observation. Such a procedure has the advantages of not requiring continuous attention on the part of the analyst, capturing the worker in more normal working conditions, and minimal training for the observer. Once the elements of the job have been identified and the observation schedule established, anyone can provide the check mark beside the observed elements at each occasion of observation. To eliminate the tendency of an observer to record immediately past events or to anticipate what will be done next, a camera set to shoot a short burst of films at random intervals is often used. This guarantees that only the snapshot desired will be recorded.

From the frequency data, relative frequencies for each element are calculated by dividing the number of observations recorded for that element by the total number of observations made in that sample. This technique is especially valuable for establishing such things as the percent of idle time among a group of machines which may require service at random intervals. As with the more normal stopwatch techniques, the number of observations necessary to give the desired level of precision and confidence can be established by simple probability arguments. The development of these equations will be deferred until the next chapter.

The Human Variable

Because of the nature of the systems he is called upon to design, the operations engineer is more concerned than most engineers with the vagaries of human behavior. At the operating level care must be taken to insure that the man portions of our man-machine systems are properly cared for in both a mechanical and a psychological sense. This means that job designers must know the physical dimensions, strengths, endurance, and variations in operator performance. In addition, they must be sensitive to psychological factors which control human behavior. Questions of the influence of factors ranging from working environment to incentive plans on worker morale, and ultimately productivity, must be considered.

The human element also plays an important role at the decision-making level. The systems designer must be able to communicate with managers charged with implementing new designs. This means that the analyst often must be able to present the intricate details of his work to nontechnically trained persons with sufficient clarity and enthusiasm to guarantee its adoption. In addition to selling the results of his analysis, the operations engineer must have an understanding of how management decisions are made and a sensitivity for the organizational structure.

In consumer-oriented industries a concern for the psychological and physiological make-up of individuals spills over into product design and marketing strategy. The consumer is recognized as a complex being to whom a product must be fitted and with whom communication must be established.

The study of human behavior is a very large and complex undertaking. We will make no attempt to be exhaustive in our introduction to the topic. We will be concerned only with those aspects of human behavior which play a direct role in the collection and evaluation of data used in our model construction. We have already considered some of the routine problems of measuring human performance. We will now consider some of the limitations of the human as a system component. Space limitations preclude more extensive discussions of human factors engineering and worker motivation. Our emphasis is on the analysis and design of those systems which will yield to quantitative techniques as opposed to the management functions of staffing and directing.

Man as a System Component. In our early discussion of the industrial revolution we noted that technology made possible our industrial complex by diverting to machines many of the functions formerly carried out by men. We also noted that this diversion of skills was still going on in that many of the decision-making functions, formerly considered the sole province of man, are now being automated. One important result of this swing to automation is that man must now take on the role of monitor and backup controller for extremely complex, high-speed systems. His role as monitor and controller is illustrated on the industrial scene by operations ranging from grinding bearing cones to running a high-speed strip mill. In transportation and space activities he must monitor and control high-speed vehicles with many automated functions. It is the purpose of this section to examine briefly man's strengths and weaknesses in the role of monitor and controller.

The position held by this author is that automated control comes about slowly with various functions once performed by human operators being automated only as changing technology makes it impossible for direct human monitoring and control. The human operator often continues to remain on board if only to serve as the ultimate judge on which automatic subsystem to engage in times of prime system failure. Intelligent use of the human monitor and replacement of his functions by automatic devices both require an understanding of the limiting potentialities of man. One must answer such problems as: How many signals can a man perceive simultaneously? How fast and in what form can he perform the decoding operation? What is the speed of conversion of his reactions?

If one operates under the premise that the best control system is one that utilizes both man and machine to their fullest extent, a comparative evaluation in functions they fulfill in processing information is in order. Most human factors texts contain lists similar to the following adapted from Lomov.[13]

1. Receipt of information—man excels because he is not limited to one means of transmission of signals. (In railroad signaling for example, a failure of mechanical or electrical systems could be overcome by hand signals at track side.)
2. Plasticity of sensory input—man can interpret a broader range of signals, e.g., read handwriting, printing, type, etc.
3. Man is not limited to a circuit signal, e.g., in the event of undercarriage failure he might feel vibrations before any indication is shown on gages.
4. Man is able to grasp "improbable events." A machine must be pre-programmed for each event or it cannot handle it.
5. A machine is able to handle a larger volume of information per unit time. This is especially critical at very high speeds. Lomov comments that at Mach 3 a pilot experiences illusions in that objects 100 meters behind the aircraft are seen on an equal level with the aircraft rendering visual flight impossible.
6. Machines are better at precision tasks.
7. Machines excel in speed.
8. Man is adaptable but lags machines in the time during which he can work on a given problem with no breaks.

From the point of view of human control of a high-speed system a critical parameter is the time necessary to respond to a previously known but suddenly appearing signal. Different authors give average values of 120 to 180 msec. for aural signals and 150 to 200 msec. for visual signals. This latent period of reaction is also a function of the intensity of the signal stimulus and its dimensions relative to the surrounding background. Greater contrast between stimulus and background implies a decreased reaction time. The latent period increases in proportion to the number of signals from which a selection must

[13] B. F. Lomov, *Man and Technology* (Washington, D.C.: USSR, U.S. Department of Commerce, Joint Publications Research Service, 1963).

be made. Other miscellaneous observations about reaction times include the fact that reaction to the disappearance of a light is 8 to 13.5 percent shorter than to the appearance of a light and that the size of the visual field is more important for precision of reaction than is the speed of the object. In addition there appears to be an optimum tempo of work which ensures maximum precision. Exceeding or falling below this rate leads to an increase in the number of errors.

A major problem faced by operators in complex man-machine systems is that of maintaining vigilance over long periods of time to watch or listen for signals of varying intensity that occur irregularly or at unpredictable intervals. In addition to designing for the sensory threshold data previously discussed for such detection, one must account for a potential loss of efficiency due to fatigue or boredom as duty time increases. Mackworth describes a series of experiments with radar operators in which a regular and significant fall of efficiency in terms of missed stimuli occurs towards the end of the first 30 minutes of work.[14] This sharp limit of tolerance has been repeatedly confirmed under operational conditions.

According to Mackworth this sharp decrease in efficiency seems to be due to a change in the central nervous or mental control of the whole sequence of performance. Apparently the operator does not lose any actual ability to distinguish signals if they are presented outside the normal sequence but does have difficulty if they occur in the setting of a continuous task. The recommended procedure for countering this fall of efficiency is to arrange shorter tours of duty or if that is impossible to give the operator exact information on the progress he is making.

Studying the sensitivity of various human analyzers is only one aspect of conveying information. A second aspect is the quantity of information transmitted to a person by means of a particular signal. A large number of empirical studies have appeared in the literature attempting to establish the basic channel capacities of the eye and the ear. Mowbray and Gebhard cite estimates derived from communications theory concepts.[15] They point out that in theory the ear is capable of transmitting about 0.3 bit per second per nerve fiber whereas the eye is capable of transmitting 5 bits per second per nerve fiber.[16] These figures are of little practical value since useful information rates are much lower. They cite practical figures of 2 to 25 bits per second for the entire sense channel depending upon the method of encoding used. This agrees with Lomov's remark that the maximum potentiality of

[14] N. H. Mackworth, "Researches on the Measurement of Human Performance," appearing in H. W. Sinaiko (ed.), *Selected Papers on Human Factors in the Design and Use of Control Systems* (New York: Dover publications, 1961).

[15] G. H. Mowbray and J. W. Gebhard, "Man's Senses as Informational Channels," appearing in Sinaiko, *op. cit.*

[16] A "bit" is the unit for measurement of information. One bit is defined as the information contained in an experiment with two equally likely outcomes. The information contained in an experiment with n equally likely outcomes is $\log_2 n$ bits.

information transmission in the identification of unidimensional stimuli averages 2.6 bits per second.

Other studies such as that by Nicholson provide empirical curves to illustrate the relationship between rate of information presentation and correct responses.[17] In this study subjects gave verbal responses to signals from a light panel flashing different colored lights in different locations for different durations. Curves are drawn which show that as the rate of information presentation increases, the correct responses decrease. The ultimate goal is to establish maximum information handling rates.

Lomov presents a list of events that may occur when the speed of input information exceeds a persons capacity.[18] They include:

1. Omission of signals.
2. Garbling of particular signals (erroneous identification).
3. Delay in transmitting certain signals.
4. Filtering of the flow of information.
5. Reduction in the completeness of discrimination and identification of a signal.
6. Parallel switching to additional channels.
7. Cessation of activity if overload is too great.

In his view the basic index of decline in efficiency in event of overloading is not an increase in errors but an increase in the loss of input information.

An interesting paradox exists in that efficiency of a person's activity is lowered not only by overloading but also in the event of information shortage. This implies that in designing signaling facilities one must aim at a rate of information supply which is less than capacity but sufficiently high to maintain activity.

Potential Study Techniques. Most of the previous discussion has revolved about empirical studies of the limiting potentials of the human operator in signal detection. An obvious next step is to investigate theoretical frameworks in which these empirical data may be explained and ultimately used to improve overall system design. Two bodies of knowledge seeming to offer potential assistance in studying man-machine control problems for high-speed systems are control theory and information theory.

There exists a large number of articles that attempt to treat the human operator of a control system in mathematical terms much the same as they would any servomechanism. The goal of these studies is to derive a "human transfer function" which can then be treated mathematically on the same terms as the electromechanical components of the system. The characteristics of the human operator which influence the form of this transfer function are

---

[17] R. M. Nicholson, "Maximum Information Handling Rates for Sequentially Presented Visual Stimuli," *Human Factors Journal*, Vol. 4, No. 6 (December, 1962), pp. 367–73.
[18] *Ibid.*

derived from human engineering data of the type previously discussed. Transfer functions for a component are based upon the ratio of transforms of an observed output signal to its associated input. Transfer functions are discussed in Chapter 6.

The study by Higgins and Holland illustrates one approach to developing an expression for the human transfer function.[19] They argue that their study is unique in that it considers a vital feedback path internal to the human element which renders it a closed loop control system and that the input to this system is treated as a single sequence operation. They consider the human operator as having the ability to focus on the input stimulus or the feedback monitor but not both simultaneously. The sampling cycle for the human control system is described in terms of the times necessary to analyze a signal, send it to the motor element, analyze the motor response, and switch back to the act of recognizing new stimuli. Laplace transforms for the sum of repeated monitoring pulses such as these are developed and treated as actuating signals to the human operator's closed-shop control system. This, multiplied by a transfer function encompassing neuromuscular lag plus limb and load inertia leads to the operator's response function. A block diagram for the human control system with feedback is then formed and the "human transfer function" is presented in the usual terms of the ratio of output transform over input transform.

The stability of the resulting system is analyzed as a function of the various time delays, such as reaction time, inherent in human activity. Observations made by human factors researchers concerning the failure of human operators to maintain 1 : 1 correspondence between input and output at extremely high and extremely low frequencies are explained in terms of the lack of feedback time or inadequate feedback data by means of this model. The design considerations evolving from this study include such things as keeping the task as simple as possible such that reaction time is small and keeping the neuromuscular lag time low by requiring that the operator use only small movements and small loads. In addition it is suggested that the human operator should not be expected to respond accurately to stimuli spaced less than one second apart and that if compensation is required he must have ample opportunity to develop strong feedback signals within his own closed-loop control system.

One major criticism of models such as these is that they assume that the operator functions as a linear system when there is considerable evidence that that is not true. Birmingham and Taylor suggest that in addition to the obvious approximations implied by using linear differential equations, a more fundamental problem is that man appears to have many transfer

[19] T. J. Higgins and P. B. Holland, "The Human Being as a Link in an Automatic Control System," *I.R.E. Transactions on Medical Electronics*, Vol. ME-6, No. 3 (September, 1959), pp. 125–33.

functions.[20] They suggest that through learning man modifies his transfer function and alters his gains to suit the control task with which he is confronted. This adaptability is a great boon for the control designer since he can rely on the human to make good use of even an inadequate control system. However, this adaptability makes any specific mathematical expression describing human behavior in a particular control loop invalid for another man-machine arrangement. They imply that searching for "the human transfer function" is a fruitless quest. They suggest that control systems be designed such that the transfer function required of the man be mathematically as simple as possible, preferably no more complex than that of a simple amplifier.

Licklider suggests that the way to get around the variability of the human operator particularly in manual tracking tasks is to employ "quasi-linear" models.[21] He defines quasi-linear models as linear models which change when the system parameters are altered. In effect he is assuming that time variation of parameters is slow enough to use a linear model as a good approximation for a short time interval. He changes to a new linear model for later intervals as the parameters of the system drift.

Along with attempts to develop a transfer function for the human operator in control systems, psychologists have attempted to apply information theory to ascertain the amount of information per unit time (bits per second) a human subject can transmit as some independent variable is manipulated. Luce reports on a large number of older empirical studies in psychology which have attempted to establish channel capacities for the human being.[22]

There seems to be some confusion among the studies cited concerning just how one establishes a reasonable channel capacity. Luce points out that there is considerable debate among the psychologists on whether it is even useful to treat men as channels unless one includes "an operational definition of the experimental context." Lomov voices the same thoughts in terms of the difficulties of defining the "alphabet" in each case in which information theory is employed to study the nervous system.[23] He points out that the amount of information in any state of a signal is a relative quantity depending upon its total number of possible states. The longer the "alphabet" the greater the average information per symbol. In his view, the hardest question for psychological research is how to determine the alphabet in each concrete case. In computing information the experimenter usually proceeds on the assumption that the system which receives and digests it makes a series of choices from a known set, i.e., all possible choices are known to the system.

---

[20] H. P. Birmingham, and F. V. Taylor, "A Design Philosophy for Man-Machine Control Systems," appearing in Sinakio, *op. cit.*, p. 74.

[21] J. C. R. Licklider, "Quasi-Linear Operator Models in the Study of Manual Tracking," appearing in R. D. Luce (ed.,), *Developments in Mathematical Psychology* (Glencoe, Ill.: Free Press, 1960).

[22] *Ibid.*

[23] *Ibid.*, p. 132.

This means that the alphabet must be established beforehand in the system. In Lomov's opinion there is some question whether or not one can regard perception, recognition, and memorization as simple acts of choosing.

Lomov continues his remarks on the shortcomings of information theory study of man's activities by listing a series of problems which must be solved before it can be used for computations of man-machine systems. They include:

1. The establishment of the maximum permissable and optimum length of alphabet with which man can work. It is not known how an operational "working alphabet" is formed or what it is.
2. The change in capacity of a man's analyzers in the course of activity. The maximum rate of processing, reception, and transmission of information changes in the course of a working day.
3. The rate of transmission from stimulus to response. The capacity is 10 to 20 times less for response than for pure reception. This appears to be a function of the response reaction and the compatability of stimulus and reaction.
4. The "significance" of a message. Information theory does not consider the value of a message for its recipient. Transmission rate is a function of the significance of a signal.

He uses these remarks to attest to the limited nature of a formal approach to the study of the speed of information reception and transmission by man.

Summary. The purpose of this chapter has been to raise questions relative to models, measurement, and man prior to our becoming immersed in the mathematical detail of the balance of the text. To that end we have discussed the general classes of models available to the operations engineer and illustrated some particular graphic techniques. We have also examined some of the characteristics of the data the operations engineer will be called upon to use in later models. In particular we looked in some detail at time study data. Finally we have taken a brief look at some of the questions to be considered when attempting to design man-machine systems. Since the balance of this text emphasizes models for management decisions, we limited our discussion here to the operating level and man as a monitor/controller.

SELECTED BIBLIOGRAPHY

ACKOFF, RUSSELL L., AND SASIENI, MAURICE W. *Fundamentals of Operations Research.* New York: John Wiley & Sons, Inc., 1968.

AMRINE, HAROLD T.; RITCHEY, JOHN A.; AND HULLEY, OLIVER S. *Manufacturing Organization and Management.* 2d ed. Englewood Cliffs, N. J.: Prentice-Hall, Inc., 1966

BARNES, RALPH M. *Motion and Time Study.* 5th ed. New York: John Wiley & Sons, Inc., 1963.

DORFMAN, ROBERT. "Operations Research," *American Economic Review*, Vol. 50. (September 1960).

HIGGINS, T. J., AND HOLLAND, D. B. "The Human Being as a Link in an Automatic Control System," *I.R.E. Trans. on Medical Electronics*, Vol. ME-6, No.3. (September, 1959), pp. 125–33.

LOMOV, B. F. *Man and Technology.* Washington, D.C.: USSR, U.S. Department of Commerce, Joint Publications Research Service, 1963.

LUCE, R. D. (ed.). *Developments in Mathematical Psychology.* Glencoe, Ill.: Free Press, 1960.

MILLER, DAVID W., AND STARR, MARTIN K. *Executive Decisions and Operations Research.* Englewood Cliffs, N. J.: Prentice-Hall, Inc., 1960.

MORRIS, WILLIAM T., *Management Science in Action.* Homewood, Ill.: Richard D. Irwin, Inc., 1963.

NIEBEL, BENJAMIN W. *Motion and Time Study.* 4th ed. Homewood, Ill.: Richard D. Irwin, Inc., 1962.

SINAIKO, H. W. (ed.). *Selected Papers on Human Factors in the Design and Use of Control Systems.* New York: Dover Publications, 1961.

SWETS, J. A. (ed.). *Signal Detection and Recognition by Human Observers.* New York: John Wiley & Sons, Inc., 1964.

TIMMS, HOWARD L. *Introduction to Operations Management.* Homewood, Ill.: Richard D. Irwin, Inc., 1967.

PROBLEMS

2–1 Construct an organization chart for your college beginning with the dean and extending through the level of student assistant. Compare the ways in which you have observed the system work with the way it appears on a formal organization chart.

2–2 Models of systems are often classified as iconic, analogue, or symbolic. Consider the operation of an airline ticket counter with three clerks. Discuss how a model of each class can be constructed for this operation. Justify the data required and explain how you would collect it. What purposes would each model serve?

2–3 Construct an operation process chart of the current way you brush your teeth. Suggest methods improvements and chart the revised prodecure.

2–4 Using the standard symbols, construct a flow process chart for the processing of university student registrations. Suggest an improved procedure.

2–5 Disassemble a ballpoint pen and place the pieces in a pile in front of you. Construct a simo chart for the act of reassembling the pen. Determine a standard time for one pen assembly by making use of the MTM data in Table 2–1. Do the same thing for an improved method of your own design.

2–6 Being an antiquated shop, the BVD company has a variety of machines that all perform the same task at varying speeds. You as a neophyte methods expert are asked to evaluate a proposed addition to the beanie-making activity based on the following data:

One man currently operates two machines:

Time to service machine No. 1 = 1.0 minute
Time to service machine No. 2 = 2.0 minutes
Operating time machine No. 1 = 2.0 minutes
Operating time machine No. 2 = 4.0 minutes

Both No. 1 and No. 2 produce one beanie per operation.

A third machine can be purchased which will produce three beanies per cycle with—

Operating time = 4 minutes
Service time   = 3 minutes

Costs are as follows:

Man   = $2.40 per hour
Machine No. 1 = $3.00 per hour operating; $1.80 per hour idle.
Machine No. 2 = $1.20 per hour operating; $0.60 per hour idle.
Machine No. 3 = $6.00 per hour operating or idle.

Assume that the alternatives are to operate in the current manner or to give the man the added machine. For costing, consider machine service times as idle time. Assume that walking time is negligible.

a) Construct a man-machine *chart* for each case.

b) What is the expected cost per beanie under each setup? Show all calculations.

2–7   The martini production line of a large metropolitian spa contains an old and a number of new olive pitters. One man currently operates the old one and another the new pitters. Based upon data given below, determine the optimum number of new pitters to assign the old operator in addition to his regular duties. Draw a man-machine chart for the optimum setup. Assume that the old pitter must be kept.

Old Pitter	*New Pitter (Each Machine)*
Unload, load, and start = 0.5 minute	Unload, load, and start = 0.7 minute
Pit (automatic) = 1.5 minutes	Pit (automatic) = 1.3 minutes

Operator walk time between machines = 0.1 minute
Operator wage = $3.00 per hour
Old pitter cost = $3.60 per hour
New pitter cost = $2.40 per hour running; $1.80 per hour idle

2–8   The following data are available for a man-machine operation.

Load, unload, and start = 0.8 minute per machine
Machine operation (automatic) = 3.3 minutes per machine per cycle
Walk to adjacent machine = 0.2 minute
K_1 = $2 per hour for man
K_2 = $6 per hour for machine running
K_3 = $3 per hour for machine idle
X = 6 pieces per cycle per machine

One operator is available and no more than three machines can be found.

How many machines should the operator be given for a minimum cost configuration? Show all calculations.

2–9   The Indian Maid Bead Company employs a young brave for a bead polishing operation. He currently operates one semiautomatic polisher which requires operator attention for 1.2 minutes each cycle. Each cycle provides the company with two finished beads. An observant methods man notes that more machines could be installed in a circular layout such that walking time between adjacent machines will be 0.3 minute. Assume that the brave operator is paid $2.40 per hour, machines running cost $6 per hour, and machines idle cost $3 per hour. If all machines to be installed are identical to the original, calculate the optimum number of machines for this work station based on a minimum expected cost per bead. Construct a man-machine chart for the operation configuration.

Machine running time = 3.5 minutes per cycle.

2–10   The Five Gallon Hat Company is considering the problem of updating their freshman beanie operation. The operator on this task currently tends one semiautomatic machine which requires his attention 1.2 minutes each cycle. Half of this time is needed to start the cycle and half is needed midway during the cycle. The machine time is 4.8 minutes per cycle, and two beanies are produced. Operating costs on the old machine are $6 per hour for both running and idle times. The operator's wage is $3 per hour. Joe I. E. has found that additional new machines requiring 2.3 minutes run time and 0.6 minute operator attention each cycle are available. These machines produce one beanie per cycle and cost $9/hour while running and $7.20/hour when idle. Assume that a circular layout is possible with walk time between machines being negligible. Under the assumption that the old machine must be retained:

a) Calculate the number of new machines the operator may be given such that the old machine is idle only while being serviced.
b) Calculate the average cost per beanie under the new setup.
c) Draw a man-machine chart for the new operation.

2–11   The tail twisting operation in a local plant has been timed at an average of 2.0 minutes per tail. Of that two minutes, 0.5 minute is performed by an automatic jerker. Tables of standard data reveal that the element grab, which appears as 0.8 minute in the observed cycle, should be performed in 1.0 minutes Thirty minutes per day are given for allowances. Company policy is to rate all machine controlled operations at 100 percent. Calculate the standard in terms of tails per day.

2–12   A time study analyst has established that the cycle time for producing a single piece should be 5.0 minutes by referring to a table of synthetic times (MTM tables) and the machinists' handbook. Eighty percent of the cycle is machine controlled, and 20 percent is man controlled. The operator who normally performs this task has been previously rated at 120 percent. Work sampling data indicate that over a one-week period the operator was away from his machine 10 times on legitimate errands and 90 times he was performing useful work.

a) What is the normal time per piece?

b) What is the standard in terms of pieces per hour?

c) If the operator is paid on a piece rate basis for all units above standard and usually grosses $160 per week, what is the guaranteed base rate?

2–13 Outline the characteristics of the MTM system with respect to

a) Fundamental motions considered.

b) The original source of data.

c) Factors other than distance considered in the fundamental motion "Reach."

2–14 Given the following time study sheet and facts, answer the questions below.

		Cycle					Standard Data Time
Element		1	2	3	4	5	
1.	Man	0.16	0.10	0.13	0.15	0.11	0.10
2.	Machine	0.17	0.13	0.15	0.16	0.14	0.15
3.	Man	0.12	0.15	0.09	0.10	0.14	0.10
4.	Man	0.16	0.20	0.17	0.19	0.18	
5.	Machine	0.23	0.24	0.25	0.27	0.21	0.24
6.	Man	0.18	0.15	0.16	0.17	0.19	

Company practice is to rate machine elements at 133 percent. A work sampling study indicated 60 allowable instances of personal time, unavoidable delays, etc., and 540 instances of productive work during the observations. Employees are given a 30-minute lunch period during their 8 hours in the plant which is *not* accounted for in the above work sampling study.

a) What are the mean elemental times?

b) What is the rating factor for the man elements?

c) What is the normal cycle time?

d) What is the standard in pieces per hour?

2–15 Given the following mean observed times from a time study sheet and the following facts, answer questions below.

	Element	Mean Time	Standard Data Time
1.	Man	0.13 min.	0.10
2.	Machine	0.15	0.15
3.	Man	0.12	0.10
4.	Man	0.18	
5.	Machine	0.24	0.24
6.	Man	0.17	

Company practice is to rate machine elements at 133 percent. A work sampling study indicated that there were 60 allowable instances of personal time, unavoidable delays, etc., and 540 instances of productive work during the observations. Employees are given a 30-minute lunch period during the 8-hour shift. (This time is *not* accounted for the in above work sampling study).

a) What is the rating factor for the man elements?
b) What is the normal cycle time?
c) What is the standard in pieces per hour?

2–16   Given the following information:

Mean observed cycle time = 3.0 min.
Speed rating factor   = 150 percent
Allowances = 30 minutes per 8 hour shift

Calculate:
a) Normal cycle time.
b) Standard in pieces per eight-hour shift.

2–17   Given the following:

| | *Time (in minutes)* | | |
Element Number and Type	Mean Observed	Standard Data	Allowances
1. Man	0.10		Personal 10%,
2. Man	0.15		other 24 min.
3. Machine	0.15	0.15	Machine rated at
4. Man	0.24	0.36	125%
5. Machine	0.60		
6. Man	0.16	0.20	
7. Man	0.06		

Solve for the standard time in minutes per piece.

2–18   You have been asked by a local management club to present a paper on "The Techniques of Establishing Standard Times." List and briefly describe the points your talk will cover. (Consider the methods of obtaining times for a job, rating techniques, and methods of establishing allowances.)

2–19   You are going to give a talk to an AFL–CIO local on "The Techniques of Establishing Standard Times." List and briefly describe the points your talk will cover. (Consider the methods of obtaining times for a job, rating techniques, and allowances.)

2–20   Techniques of time study were presented in the text. Under the assumption that a stopwatch will be used for obtaining data, *outline* the *full procedure* you would use to establish standards on a new job in the shop.

CHAPTER 3

Elements of
Probability Theory

MANY OF THE remaining chapters of this book require some familiarity with the basic notions of probability. The mathematical models which serve as aids for management decisions all require numbers as input and provide numbers as output. Whenever there is some doubt about the exact value of such numbers, the theory of probability can be used to express the level of doubt in mathematical terms.

It is the purpose of this chapter to present the background material from the theory of probability which will be needed in future chapters. A rigorous development of probability theory involves high-order mathematical difficulties and will not be attempted here. Our approach will be to provide working definitions of the major concepts to serve as a brief review for those with previous background and as a minimum primer and guide for further study for those less well prepared.

Foundations of Probability

The foundations of probability can be developed from several points of view. The usual intuitive concept centers around the notion of "equal likelihood." In this view one considers an experiment possessing n different possible outcomes which are assumed to have equal chances of occurring. Let m of these outcomes be distinguished and let the event E be said to have occurred if the outcome of the experiment is one of these. Then the probability of the event E, written $P(E)$, is defined as the ratio m/n. For example, suppose that there are 4 defective parts in a batch of 10. The probability of obtaining a defective part if one is drawn at random from the batch is then $4/10$.

The relative *frequency* or *statistical* view of probability requires neither a finite number of possible occurrences nor the notion of equal likelihood. Roughly speaking, one considers a situation in which an experiment has been performed a large number of times and the results noted. The ratio of the number of occurrences of the event E to the number of experiments is then considered to be an estimate of the probability that E will occur on the next trial. For example, if it has been observed that of a representative group of 1,000 transistors produced, 50 have been defective, it would be estimated that the probability of a transistor being defective is 50/1,000. Probabilities obtained in this fashion might be called empirical probabilities.

The modern mathematical theory of probability is based on a set of axioms. In the *axiomatic approach* one specifies a set of rules for a basic calculus of probability without concerning himself with how the probability of a given event may be determined. The object is to start with a set of definitions and axioms which are consistent with the intuitive notions of probability and from these to mathematically deduce the various consequences of the theory.

We shall not be directly concerned with any one of the above points of view. For our purposes, we will assume that a decision maker must be able to assign nonnegative numerical weights to each possible event such that if an event is certain, its associated weight equals one. In a sense, probability assessments reflect the analyst's or decision maker's state of mind. A number becomes a probability because some person says it is so. Historical data have decision-making relevance only if they reflect the decision makers' judgment about future conditions. Probability distributions in this context are obtained by some combination of historical data, approximations, axioms, and introspection. We will now set down some basic rules for operating with such probability weights and explain their operational meanings.

Sets and Set Operations.   In order to discuss the basic rules of probability we need some definitions and elementary facts concerning sets. In this context we will regard the term set as synonymous with collection. A set is a collection of certain elements possessing a common property. This common property permits one to determine whether an arbitrary entity is or is not a member of the set in question. For example, suppose that the set of interest consists of all pistons whose diameters fall between 2.000 and 2.010 inches. A piston which measures 2.004 inches is a member of the set while one which measures 2.015 inches is not.

A set may contain a finite or an infinite number of elements. If the elements of an infinite set can be placed in one-to-one correspondence with the infinite set of positive integers, we say that the set is countable. An example of a countable set is the set of all prime integers. An example of a noncountable set is the set of all points on a line segment. Everything which follows in this section can be applied without distinction to both finite and infinite sets.

The *sum* or *union* of two sets A and B is defined to be the set of all elements contained in either A or B or both. We shall use the notation $A \cup B$ to denote the union of A and B. The *product* or *intersection* of sets A and B, written $A \cap B$, is defined as the set of all elements contained in both A and B. A set A is said to be a subset of B if every element of A is also an element of B. This is written as $A \subset B$. The complement $\bar{A}$ of a set A, with respect to some reference set S which contains A, is defined as all elements not in A. That is $\bar{A} = S - A$. This relationship defines the "minus" operator in set theory. The *empty set* or *null set*, denoted by $\varnothing$, is the set which contains no elements.

The above definitions relative to sets can best be illustrated by means of a Venn diagram. Suppose that our *universe* (U) is the set of all pistons manufactured in a particular plant. Let us define the following subsets:

$A =$ the set of all pistons whose diameters fall between 2.000 and 2.010 inches

$B =$ the set of all pistons whose diameters fall between 2.005 and 2.015 inches

$C =$ the set of all pistons whose diameters fall between 1.995 and 2.006 inches.

A Venn diagram depicting these sets is shown in Figure 3–1. The intersection of the three sets $(A \cap B \cap C)$ is shown by the crosshatched area ABC. This set (ABC) contains all pistons whose diameters fall between 2.005 and 2.006 inches. Any pistons in this range are members of each of the sets A, B,

FIGURE 3–1

Venn Diagram

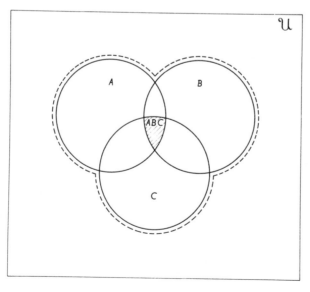

and C. The union of the three sets $(A \cup B \cup C)$ is contained within the dotted line. All elements inside this line are members of one or more of the sets A, B, and C. The pistons whose diameters fall in the range 1.995 to 2.015 are members of the union $A \cup B \cup C$. The complement of the union $A \cup B \cup C$ is represented by all of the elements falling within U but outside of the dotted line. All pistons with diameters less than 1.995 or greater than 2.015 are members of $\overline{A \cup B \cup C}$.

Set theory plays an important role in probability as can be easily seen when we consider the outcome of an experiment depending upon chance. The fundamental set of elements which constitutes all possible outcomes of an experiment is called the *sample space* for the experiment. Here the term sample space is used as a synonym for the word set. Suppose we let U represent the sample space of all possible outcomes of an experiment and A be a subset of this sample space. Further suppose that the event E_1 occurs whenever the outcome of the experiment yields a member of the set A. If this experiment is performed a large number of times N with n observations of E_1 then the relative frequency p of observing E_1 is

$$p_{E_1} = \frac{n}{N}$$

Since $0 \leq n \leq N$, it is obvious that $0 \leq p_{E_1} \leq 1$. Furthermore suppose that p_{E_1} tends to a limit as N becomes infinite, then this limit

$$P(E_1) = \lim_{N \to \infty} \frac{n}{N}$$

is a nonnegative real number and is defined for all sets of the sample space U. The function $P(E)$ is called a probability function.

Basic Axioms of Probability. Consider an experiment whose outcomes can be one or more of the finite number of events $E_1, E_2, \ldots, E_n$. Furthermore suppose that these events can only be described probabilistically. The three basic axioms of probability are:

1. $\qquad 0 \leq P(E_i) \leq 1 ; i = 1, 2, \ldots, n$ (3–1)

2. $\qquad P(E_i \cup E_j) = P(E_i) + P(E_j) - P(E_i \cap E_j), i \neq j$ (3–2)

3. $\qquad P(E_i \cap E_j) = P(E_i | E_j)P(E_j) = P(E_j | E_i)P(E_i), i \neq j$ (3–3)

and $P(E_i)$, $P(E_j) \neq 0$.

The intuitive meaning of $P(E_i | E_j)$ is the probability that the event E_i will occur if we know that the event E_j has occurred. $P(E_i | E_j)$ is defined as the conditional probability of E_i given E_j.

To illustrate these properties let us revert to a sampling experiment in which the number of elements in our sample space is finite. Specifically, suppose that we are training inspectors by having them look for defects in a lot of 100 TV cabinets. It is known beforehand that 60 of the cabinets have no defects, 20 are only scratched, 15 are only out of plumb, and 5 are both scratched and out of plumb. Define the sets A, B, and C as

$$A = \text{all cabinets with no defects, } n_A = 60$$
$$B = \text{all cabinets with scratches, } n_B = 25$$
$$C = \text{all cabinets out of plumb, } n_C = 20$$

The inspector trainee is to draw a cabinet at random from the total set of 100 and inspect it for defects.

If we say that the event E_A occurs whenever our trainee pulls an undamaged cabinet, then there are 60 opportunities for this event to occur in our sample space of 100. Assuming that all cabinets are equally likely to be selected at the time of a draw, the probability of selecting an undamaged cabinet can be related to the relative frequency with which such cabinets appear in the total population. That is,

$$P(E_A) = \frac{n_A}{N} = \frac{60}{100} = 0.60$$

In similar fashion

$$P(E_B) = \frac{n_B}{N} = 0.25$$

and

$$P(E_C) = \frac{n_C}{N} = 0.20$$

Obviously these three probabilities satisfy our first basic rule (Equation 3–1) in that all fall in the interval zero to one. The astute reader may be disturbed, however, when he notes that the sum of probabilities for these three events exceeds one. Since probability has a relative frequency connotation, the sum of all relative frequencies for events should not exceed one. The key of course is that there is an overlap between the sets B and C. Any cabinet which simultaneously possesses a scratch and is out of plumb is a member of both sets B and C.

This brings us to a demonstration of our second rule of probability (Equation 3–2). The intersection of the events E_B and E_C occurs whenever a cabinet is selected which is a member of both sets. From the data we know that five such cabinets exist. This implies that

$$P(E_B \cap E_C) = \frac{n_{B \cap C}}{N} = \frac{5}{100} = 0.05$$

Since cabinets are defective if they are either scratched or out of plumb, we might be tempted to identify the number of elements in the defective set as the sum of the number scratched and the number out of plumb. However, the 25 scratched cabinets include 5 which are both scratched and out of plumb. Similarly the 20 out-of-plumb cabinets also includes the 5 doubly defective ones. If we simply add the number in B and the number in C we have counted the five doubly defective ones twice. Therefore the total number of defective cabinets is

$$n = n_B + n_C - n_{B \cap C} = 25 + 20 - 5 = 40$$

Dividing this equation through by the number of cabinets in our sample space gives the probability of selecting a defective cabinet. That is,

$$P(\text{defective}) = \frac{n}{100} = \frac{n_B}{100} + \frac{n_C}{100} - \frac{n_{B \cap C}}{100}$$

$$= 0.25 + 0.20 - 0.05 = 0.40$$

This result verifies our second rule, namely,

$$P(\text{defective}) = P(E_B \cup E_C) = P(E_B) + P(E_C) - P(E_B \cap E_C)$$

It also establishes that the total probability associated with our sample space, being the sum of $P(E_A)$ and $P(E_B \cup E_C)$, is unity as desired.

Two events are said to be mutually exclusive if the simultaneous occurrence of both cannot occur. In our example, the event of selecting a cabinet from set A (not defective) and the event of selecting it from set B (scratched) are mutually exclusive. In set notation this means that the intersection of the sets A and B is the null set. When the events are mutually exclusive our second law reduces to

$$P(E_A \cup E_B) = P(E_A) + P(E_B)$$

Verbally this says that the probability of selecting a cabinet which is either nondefective or scratched is equal to the sum of the probabilities of the separate events. The extension to larger numbers of events is straightforward. If they are mutually exclusive, the probability of their union occurring is simply the sum of each of the separate event probabilities. If they are not mutually exclusive, appropriate terms must be subtracted to eliminate multiple counts of the same elements.

The reader is urged to draw a Venn diagram of these sets and identify the appropriate intersections, unions, number of elements, and relative frequencies to illustrate these concepts.

Our third basic rule of probability involves conditional probabilities. In the example problem consider the information conveyed by knowing that the cabinet selected has a scratch. Perhaps our trainee has discovered the scratch and now wishes to determine the probability that this cabinet also is out of plumb. Knowing that the selected cabinet is scratched has the effect of reducing our sample space from the original set of 100 cabinets to the subset of 25 known to contain scratches. With this information the probability of the cabinet also being out of plumb can be determined from the ratio of the number of cabinets known to have both defects and the number known to be scratched. That is,

$$P(E_C \mid E_B) = \frac{n_{B \cap C}}{n_B} = \frac{5}{25} = 0.20$$

If we divide the numerator and denominator on the right by the total number of cabinets in our original population we have

$$P(E_C \mid E_B) = \frac{n_{B \cap C}/100}{n_B/100} = \frac{P(E_B \cap E_C)}{P(E_B)}$$

provided, of course, that $P(E_B)$ is not zero. Cross-multiplying leads to verification of our third rule of probability, namely,

$$P(E_B \cap E_C) = P(E_C \mid E_B)\, P(E_B)$$

If the conditional probability of an event may be written as

$$P(E_i \mid E_j) = P(E_i) \tag{3-4}$$

so that $P(E_i \mid E_j)$ does not depend on E_j, then the events E_i and E_j are said to be *independent*. In that case our third basic rule reduces to

$$P(E_i \cap E_j) = P(E_i)\, P(E_j) \tag{3-5}$$

Equation 3-5 is the definition of independence relative to any two events. Two events are independent if and only if they satisfy this relationship.

To illustrate the concept of independence between events, suppose that an inspector trainee must select two cabinets from the test lot of 100 for inspection. Let E_{A1} be the event that the first cabinet selected belongs to set A (no defects) and E_{A2} be the event that the second cabinet selected belongs to set A. If the first cabinet inspected is returned to the lot before the second is selected, then the events E_{A1} and E_{A2} are independent. That is,

$$P(E_{A1} \cap E_{A2}) = P(E_{A1} \mid E_{A2})\, P(E_{A2}) = P(E_{A1})\, P(E_{A2})$$

Since

$$P(E_{A1}) = P(E_{A2}) = 0.60$$

the probability of the joint occurrence of these two events is

$$P(E_{A1} \cap E_{A2}) = P(E_{A1})\, P(E_{A2}) = 0.36$$

If, however, the first cabinet is not returned to the lot but rather set aside, then the events E_{A1} and E_{A2} are dependent. Knowing that the first cabinet is nondefective reduces the population from which the second cabinet is drawn. The relative frequency for a nondefective cabinet at the time of the second draw is the ratio of total remaining good cabinets and total remaining cabinets. That is,

$$P(E_{A_2} | E_{A_1}) = \frac{59}{99}$$

and

$$P(E_{A_1} \cap E_{A_2}) = P(E_{A_2} | E_{A_1})\, P(E_{A_1})$$

$$= \frac{59}{99}(0.60)$$

Random Variables. A random variable is a numerically valued function defined over a sample space. Here the term function denotes a rule which assigns a number to each value in the domain of definition. A random variable then is nothing more than a real number whose value is determined by the outcome of a random experiment.

Unfortunately the concepts of "random variable" and "sample point" often tend to fuse together. In experiments such as our example involving cabinet inspection, this confusion is less apt to occur than it would be in an experiment involving measurements of piston diameters. In the cabinet inspection example we never bothered to assign real numbers to the possible events or outcomes of the experiments. Our sample space consisted of the events nondefective, scratched, and out of plumb. Consider an experiment in which cabinets are classed as either defective or nondefective. If we assign a number to each event say zero for nondefective and one for defective, we could describe the results of an experiment by simply saying that the outcome is zero or one. If we further introduce a variable r and define its values to be zero or one, depending upon the two mutually exclusive outcomes of our experiment, the quantity r is called a random variable.

Contrasting this experiment with one involving the measurement of piston diameters, we see that the possible outcomes of a piston experiment are already identified by real numbers. The sample space itself is a set of real numbers (x) which can be taken as the values of a random variable to be associated with the experiment. One tends to think in terms of diameter as *the* random variable. That need not be the case, however. We could just as easily assign a new set of numbers, say dollars, for different subsets of events within the sample space. For example we might say that y is a random variable representing cost where

$$y = \begin{cases} 5 \text{ if } 1.995 \le x < 2.000 \\ 7 \text{ if } 2.000 \le x < 2.005 \\ 9 \text{ if } 2.005 \le x \le 2.015 \end{cases}$$

We have defined a numerically valued function (y) over the sample space consisting of events (x) which happen also to be associated with real numbers.

If we elect to identify diameter (x) as a random variable, then any function of x is also a random variable. By this definition $5x$, $3x^2 - e^x$ and $\log x$ are all random variables. All of these functions assign real numbers to each element in the sample space. At this point it should be obvious that there is a multitude of random variables associated with each experiment.

Random variables are often classed as being either continuous or discrete. A continuous random variable is one which is not restricted to have only isolated values. A continuous random variable may have any value in a certain interval or collection of intervals. Ignoring the restrictions on the accuracy of our measuring instruments, piston diameter can be viewed as a continuous random variable. It can take on any value in the interval zero to infinity. On the other hand, the random variable r, which we associated with cabinet inspection, is discrete. Its only possible values are the integers zero and one. Any random variables which take on only isolated values are discrete random variables.

Properties of Probability Distributions. Having introduced the idea of a random variable, we are now interested in the relationship of events in the sample space to probabilities associated with random variables. Suppose that x is a random variable which assumes values in a set S of real numbers. Associated with this random variable is a cumulative distribution function $F(x)$. By definition

$$F(x_1) = P(x \leq x_1) \tag{3-6}$$

This function can be used to determine the probability that x will assume a value lying in any subset of S defined by the real numbers a and b where $a < b$. If x is to assume a value less than or equal to b, then it must either be less than a or lie somewhere between a and b. Since these events are mutually exclusive, we can apply the modified version of our second basic rule of probability. That is,

$$P(x \leq b) = P(E_1 \cup E_2) = P(E_1) + P(E_2)$$
$$= P(x \leq a) + P(a < x \leq b)$$

from which

$$P(a < x \leq b) = P(x \leq b) - P(x \leq a)$$
$$= F(b) - F(a) \tag{3-7}$$

Recall also that the probability of any event falls between zero and one. This fact together with Equation 3–7 assures us that $F(x)$ is a monotonic nondecreasing function of x. That is,

$$F(x_1) \leq F(x_2) \qquad \text{whenever } x_1 \leq x_2 \tag{3-8}$$

Furthermore it is always true that

$$\lim_{x \to -\infty} F(x) = 0 \quad \text{and} \quad \lim_{x \to \infty} F(x) = 1 \tag{3-9}$$

Hence the cumulative distribution $F(x)$ is positive and assumes values between zero and one.

Closely associated with the cumulative distribution function is the probability distribution or density function. The probability distribution function serves as a model of the population from which random experiments are drawn. If the events defined over the sample space are discrete, the probability distribution function $f(x)$ defines the relative frequency with which the random variable x takes on particular values. That is,

$$f(x_1) = P(x = x_1) \qquad \text{for } x \text{ discrete} \qquad (3\text{--}10)$$

The relationship between the distribution function and the cumulative distribution function for discrete random variables is obviously

$$F(x_1) = \sum_{x = -\infty}^{x_1} f(x) \qquad (3\text{--}11)$$

Furthermore since $f(x)$ represents the relative frequency with which x can assume each of its denumerable values, it must be true that

$$\sum_{x = -\infty}^{\infty} f(x) = 1 \qquad (3\text{--}12)$$

Thus we see that any function, which we wish to submit as a candidate for modeling a population from which a random variable is drawn, must satisfy two conditions:

1. $f(x) \geq 0$ for all x and

2. The sum of $f(x)$ over all x must equal one.

If one possesses information about the cumulative distribution function for a discrete random variable, the distribution function can be obtained by taking differences. Let us define the difference of a function $h(x)$ as

$$\Delta h(x) = h(x + 1) - h(x) \qquad (3\text{--}13)$$

where the Greek letter delta is considered to be the difference operator applied to the function $h(x)$.
It then follows that

$$\begin{aligned} \Delta F(x) &= F(x + 1) - F(x) \\ &= \sum_{j = -\infty}^{x+1} f(j) - \sum_{j = -\infty}^{x} f(j) \\ &= f(x + 1) \end{aligned} \qquad (3\text{--}14)$$

In this fashion standard techniques from the calculus of finite differences can be used to move from cumulative to distribution functions and vice versa.

If the random variable under consideration is continuous rather than discrete, the interpretation of the probability distribution function must be altered slightly. If we were to interpret $f(x)$ as the probability that the random variable assumes the value x, where x has an infinite number of possible values between any two real numbers, then the sum of $f(x)$ would surely exceed one. For that reason it is often said that the probability of a continuously distributed random variable achieving any particular value is zero. The only meaningful statement is that the probability of the random variable falling in a particular interval is known. We might then interpret the product $f(x)\,dx$ as the probability that the random variable falls in the interval bounded by x and $x + dx$. For continuous random variables the function $f(x)$ is referred to as the probability density function.

We will often use a continuous function to represent the probability distribution of measurable quantities such as the diameter of pistons. At this point the reader might object and say that it is possible to find a particular value of piston diameter in a production lot. For that reason a continuous density function may appear to be a poor model for the population. The discrepancy can be associated with the accuracy of our measuring instruments. Suppose we have micrometers which are read to the nearest ten thousandth of an inch. When we measure a piston diameter of 2.0005 inches, all we really know is that this piston falls somewhere between 2.00045 and 2.00055 inches. This is an interval we can associate with the cumulative distribution such that

$$P(2.00045 < x \le 2.00055) = F(2.00055) - F(2.00045)$$

It does make sense then to speak in a relative frequency sense of the probability of finding a piston diameter of 2.0005 inches. In effect we have defined a new event, the event of finding piston diameters in the specified interval. Even though defined over a continuous sample space, this event is discrete and does have a definite nonzero probability associated with its occurrence.

When x is a continuously distributed random variable, the relationships between the cumulative distribution and density functions are expressed in derivatives and integrals. They have the following properties:

1.
$$F(x) = \int_{-\infty}^{x} f(u)\,du \tag{3-15}$$

2.
$$f(x) = \frac{d\,F(x)}{dx} \tag{3-16}$$

3.
$$P(a < x < b) = \int_{a}^{b} f(x)\,dx \tag{3-17}$$

4.
$$\int_{-\infty}^{\infty} f(x)\,dx = 1 \tag{3-18}$$

For continuously distributed random variables, $P(a \le x \le b)$ is indistinguishable from $P(a < x < b)$ because of continuity.

If we were to graph a probability distribution function for a discrete random variable, the graph would be a series of spikes whose magnitudes would sum to one. The cumulative distribution for such a variable would appear as a stairstep function with an upper limit of one. For a continuously distributed random variable, the density function would commonly appear as a smooth curve over the range of the variable and would enclose an area equal to one. The cumulative distribution for most such variables would appear as a monotonically increasing function of x which is asymptotic to one. Graphs for each of these cases are shown in Figure 3–2.

FIGURE 3–2

Probability Distribution Functions and Cumulative Distributions

(*a*) Probability Distribution Function for Discrete Random Variable

(*b*) Cumulative Distribution for Discrete Random Variable

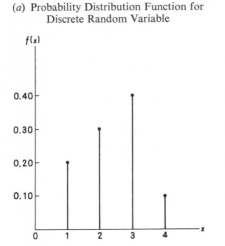

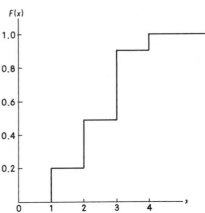

(c) Probability Distribution Function for a Continuous Random Variable

(*d*) Cumulative Distribution for Continuous Random Variable

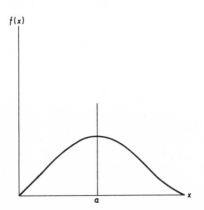

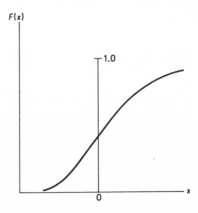

Sample and Population Models. A sample can be viewed as a set of observations taken from a larger set representing the totality of all conceivable observations. Corresponding to the universal set of our earlier discussions on set theory, the larger group is called a population. When summary measures such as the arithmetic mean are developed from sample data they are called sample statistics. When these same measures refer to a population they are called population parameters.

The kinds of populations usually treated in our model development are hypothetical as opposed to real populations. Although it is hoped that any models we construct of our hypothetical populations will lead to an understanding of real populations, they exist only in theory. We employ such techniques because most real populations are at least partially inaccessible. In effect we attempt to estimate the character of the underlying theoretical distributions on the basis of sampling information gleaned from experiments.

Since population parameters are estimated from sample data, it is common practice to distinguish the parameter from its estimate by using two different symbols to represent the same thing. English letters are normally used for sample statistics and Greek letters for their corresponding population parameters. For instance μ (the Greek letter " mu ") is the symbol for population mean while $\bar{x}$ is the standard symbol for sample mean. Similarly σ (lowercase Greek sigma) is the symbol for population standard deviation while s is commonly used for sample standard deviation. These statistics will be discussed in detail in later sections.

One often uses empirical data to construct frequency functions. These functions may be used to develop probability statements in their own right or to suggest the general form of underlying probability distribution functions. For example, suppose that we have collected data on the number of paint defects found on automobile hoods produced in a particular plant. In the process of inspecting 100 hoods the following number of defects have been discovered:

Number of Defects (x)	Number of Hoods Containing x Defects
0	16
1	26
2	26
3	20
4	8
5	4
Total	100

The frequencies of each of the events E_x, representing the occurrence of x defects on a hood, are represented by the bar graph of Figure 3–3.

If we divide the frequency with which each value of the variable x occurred by the total number of observations (100), we obtain the relative frequency of occurrence for each value. When this information is displayed graphically as in Figure 3–4, it is sometimes referred to as a histogram.

FIGURE 3–3

Frequency of Hood Defects in a Sample of 100

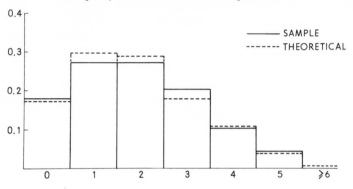

The histogram itself may provide sufficient information about the process to satisfy many needs. An analyst may decide that the sample of 100 is sufficiently representative of the infinite population of hoods that may be produced to permit the histogram information to be used as a probability distribution function for the entire population. The danger here of course is that the particular events and frequencies observed may be mere freaks of the sample selected. Future samples of 100 might yield a much different picture. For that reason the analyst may be more comfortable with his predictions of future occurrences of paint defects if he can associate a theoretical distribution with the process. Such a theoretical distribution must be consistent with his experimental observations but may admit the possibility of a much larger number of events than those observed to date.

FIGURE 3–4

Relative Frequency of Hood Defects in a Sample of 100

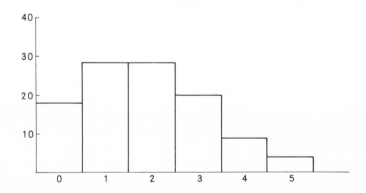

To an experienced analyst, the general shape of the histogram and knowledge of the production process might suggest the Poisson distribution as a reasonable model for the statistical population. The model in this case is merely an equation for a curve expressed as a function of parameters which determine its shape. The Poisson is a single parameter discrete distribution, that parameter being the mean of the distribution. To be consistent with our observations, the estimate of the value of the mean or average number of defects per hood should be taken from our sample data. In the sample we observed 26 hoods with one defect, 26 with two, etc. The average number of defects per hood is then equal to the total number of defects divided by 100 or

$$\bar{x} = \frac{(26)(1) + (26)(2) + (20)(3) + (8)(4) + (4)(5)}{100} = 1.9$$

From the tables for the Poisson distribution with $\mu = 1.9$ contained in the Appendix, we can see that the theoretical frequencies for defects per hood are

x	$f(x)$
0	0.1496
1	0.2842
2	0.2700
3	0.1710
4	0.0812
5	0.0309
≥ 6	0.0131

Figure 3–4 shows both the theoretical and empirical distributions. Note that there is close agreement between the two, although they are not exactly equivalent. There are standard statistical tests, such as the chi-square goodness-of-fit test, which can be used to quantify the degree of agreement between them. This technique is discussed in Chapter 4. By using the theoretical model for the infinite and unobservable population, one should now be able to make accurate predictions about any number of defects to be found on hoods produced in the future.

By this time the reader should begin to have some feel for the interaction between sample data and theoretical models of statistical populations. We must hasten to point out, however, that not all estimation problems are as easy to solve as our simple example. Since a statistical population is a mathematical relationship, there could be any number of mathematical expressions which *might* be potential candidates for description. Unfortunately the mathematical relationships having the desirable properties of many populations often appear rather foreboding. Even the Poisson, which we so glibly acquired from the tables, is not an expression one can manipulate with ease. The invention of new and useful population models and the derivation of their properties is left to the field of mathematical statistics. We as operations engineers will attempt to employ existing models to fit statistical populations encountered in our work.

Common Probability Distributions

A probability distribution or density function is nothing more than a mathematical model of a statistical population. For our purposes we will be mainly concerned with populations involving single random variables. If we evaluate a probability distribution function for various admissible values of the random variable, we obtain a graph similar to the histograms introduced in the last section. For purposes of manipulation, any of the sometimes complex expressions we use for probability distributions can be viewed as equations for curves. Measures from the population, such as probability of an event, mean, variance, etc., are obtained by appropriate sums or integrals involving those curves.

For purposes of enumeration we can divide population models into discrete and continuous distributions. A discrete distribution is associated with a random variable which can assume only integral values. A continuous distribution is associated with a random variable which can assume any value over a prescribed interval.

The Normal Distribution. The most important distribution in the study of probability and statistics is the normal distribution. This is the well-known bell-shaped curve used to describe the probability of occurrence of many physical phenomena. It is a continuous distribution described by the formula

$$f(x) = (2\sigma^2\pi)^{-1/2} e^{-(x-\mu)^2/2\sigma^2} \tag{3-19}$$

where

$$\mu = \text{population mean}$$

and

$$\sigma^2 = \text{population variance}$$

are the parameters of the distribution. The symbol $N(\mu, \sigma)$ will be used as shorthand notation for this density. The meaning of "population variance" will be discussed in detail in later sections. For now let us treat it as a parameter of the population.

The normal distribution was originally based upon the effect of a large number of mutually independent "errors." It measured the spread of readings obtained from a process which was subject to many random effects. Scientists often found that repeated measurements of the same quantity seemed to follow this well-defined curve. Later it was observed that many human mental and physical characteristics followed the same error curve as did physical measurements. From that point on the normal curve was applied to a wide variety of social, biological, and economic problems. Finally, with the advent of modern statistical theory, the normal curve has been found to play a central role in theorems for sample statistics. The central limit theorem discussed later in this chapter, for example, shows that the distribution for many combinations of random variables will approach normality. Certainly not all random variables are normally distributed, but enough are to make this the single most important population model at our disposal.

A typical graph obtained from Equation 3–19 is shown in Figure 3–5. The normal distribution is a smooth curve, symmetric about the mean μ. To determine values for $f(x)$ and the cumulative $F(x)$ is not a simple matter due to the complicated nature of the formula. For that reason we will resort to tables given in the Appendix whenever we are required to evaluate probabilities associated with a normally distributed random variable.

The tables for the normal distribution have been developed for the special case of a random variable which has mean zero and variance one. We will refer to this as z, the standard normal deviate. Fortunately there is a transformation which will permit us to determine values for $f(x)$ and $F(x)$ for any normally distributed random variable x from tabulations in z. The transformation is

$$z = \frac{x - \mu}{\sigma} \tag{3–20}$$

where μ and σ are the mean and standard deviation of x. (Standard deviation is a term used for the square root of the variance.) Intuitively, z measures the number of standard deviation units that x lies to the left ($z < 0$) or to the right ($z > 0$) of the mean. Knowing the number of standard deviation units between x and the mean, we can determine $F(x)$.

It may be shown that any transformation on x resulting in the random variable $ax + b$ (for constants a, b) yields a normally distributed random variable. For $a = 1/\sigma$, $b = -\mu/\sigma$, $ax + b = z$ and so is also normally distributed. Probability statements about x can then be converted into probability

FIGURE 3–5

A Normal Distribution

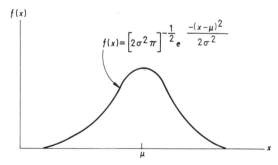

$$f(x) = \left[2\sigma^2 \pi \right]^{-\frac{1}{2}} e^{\frac{-(x-\mu)^2}{2\sigma^2}}$$

statements about z which in turn can be evaluated by using the normal tables. That is,

$$P(a \leq x \leq b) = P\left(\frac{a - \mu}{\sigma} \leq \frac{x - \mu}{\sigma} \leq \frac{b - \mu}{\sigma}\right)$$

$$= P\left(\frac{a - \mu}{\sigma} \leq z \leq \frac{b - \mu}{\sigma}\right) \qquad (3\text{--}21)$$

where z is normally distributed with mean zero and variance one.

Since the normal distribution is symmetric, it is common practice to tabulate $f(z)$ and $F(z)$ for only one half of the curve, i.e., $0 \leq z \leq \infty$. Because of symmetry

$$f(z) = f(-z) \qquad (3\text{--}22)$$

and

$$F(-z) = 1 - F(z) \qquad (3\text{--}23)$$

The first entry in the $F(z)$ table is 0.5000. This represents the area under the $f(z)$ curve from minus infinity to zero. That is,

$$F(0) = \int_{-\infty}^{0} (2\pi)^{-1/2} e^{-z^2/2} \, dz = 0.5000$$

Similarly, we can obtain the probability that the standard normal deviate z is less than -1.0 by finding

$$F(-1) = \int_{-\infty}^{-1} (2\pi)^{-1/2} e^{-z^2/2} \, dz$$

$$= 1 - F(1) = 1 - 0.8413 = 0.1587$$

The visual impact of these calculations is shown in Figure 3–6. The value

FIGURE 3–6

Calculations with the Standard Normal Deviate

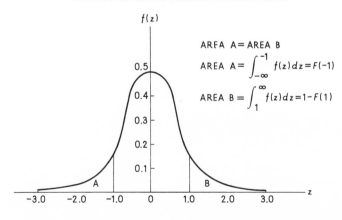

of $F(-1)$ is represented by the area A under the standard normal curve from minus infinity to minus one. Because of the symmetry of the distribution, this area is equal to area B under the curve from one to infinity. Although we cannot read the value of area B directly from the tables, it is easy to obtain by recognizing that the total area under the curve from minus infinity to plus infinity must be equal to one. Therefore

$$\text{Area } A = \text{Area } B = 1 - F(1)$$

Area C appearing to the right of any point x is called the complementary cumulative distribution. The complementary cumulative distribution is given by

$$\hat{F}(x) = 1 - F(x) \tag{3-24}$$

regardless of the particular distribution in use.

To illustrate the use of the normal tables, consider a quality control system in which the mean weight of a random sample of 10 cereal boxes is measured from each hour's production. From statistical theory it has been decided that the model to use for the distribution of these mean values is the normal distribution with a mean of 14 ounces and a variance of 0.25. (Note that weighing each sample of 10 boxes yields a single value $\bar{x}$ which we believe is normally distributed.) Control limits of 13 and 15 ounces have been established for sample means. As long as sample means fall within these limits, the process is assumed to be in control. When a mean value falls outside the specified limits, a search for cause will be initiated.

The probability that a sample chosen at random will yield a mean which is less than 15 ounces is

$$P(\bar{x} < 15) = \int_{-\infty}^{15} f(\bar{x}) \, d\bar{x}$$

where $f(\bar{x})$ is

$$N(\mu = 14, \sigma = 0.5).$$

Converting to the standard normal deviate

$$P(\bar{x} < 15) = P\left(z < \frac{15 - 14}{0.5}\right) = F(2.0)$$

From the tables,

$$F(2.0) = 0.9772$$

Therefore, nearly 98 percent of the time we would expect to observe a sample mean which is less than 15 ounces, provided that the underlying process generating our population statistics remains unchanged. The frequency with which sample means will fall outside the established limits is obtained from the sum of the probability of falling above the upper limit and the probability of falling below the lower limit. That is,

$$P(\text{out of limits}) = P(\bar{x} < 13) + P(\bar{x} > 15)$$

which reduces to

$$P\left(z < \frac{13 - 14}{0.5}\right) + P\left(z > \frac{15 - 14}{0.5}\right) = F(-2.0) + \hat{F}(2.0)$$

But due to symmetry

$$F(-2.0) = 1 - F(2.0)$$

and due to total probability summing to one,

$$\hat{F}(2.0) = 1 - F(2.0)$$

Therefore, from the tables,

$$P(\text{out of limits}) = 0.0228 + 0.0228 = 0.0456$$

We will make extensive use of the normal distribution for the balance of this text. The important fact to remember is that the formula is simply an equation for a curve which has been tabulated for our own convenience. The complexity of the expression need not concern us.

Binomial and Poisson Distributions. When the system under study contains random variables which can assume only integer values, we require discrete distributions for our population models. The two most popular models for discrete populations are the binomial and Poisson distributions. Before examining the formulas for these distributions, we must consider some notation associated with counting processes.

Suppose that we have three different objects *a*, *b*, *c* which we wish to arrange in distinct order. Consider these objects to occupy three positions which we will fill in sequence. There are three ways to fill the first position. We can select *a* or *b* or *c* for that slot. Having selected one object for the first position, we have two candidates left for position two. After selecting one of the remaining two for the second slot, we have no choice but to place the last one remaining in the third slot. The total number of ways to arrange *a*, *b*, and *c* is then (3)(2)(1) = 6. These six unique arrangements in which order is important are

$$\begin{array}{ll} abc & bac \\ acb & cba \\ bca & cab \end{array}$$

Such arrangements are called *permutations*. If we had *n* objects there would be a total of $(n)(n-1)(n-2) \cdots (2)(1)$ arrangements to tabulate. This number is expressed mathematically as

$$n! = n(n-1)(n-2) \cdots (2)(1) \tag{3-25}$$

where it is common to define $0! = 1$.

Now suppose that we have *n* objects but that only *r* of these objects are to be used in any given permutation. Arguing as before, we have r positions to be filled. The first can be filled n ways, the second $n - 1$ ways, etc., until all r positions are occupied. Mathematically, the number of permutations of n objects taken r at a time can be written as

$$P^n_r = n^{(r)} = \frac{n!}{(n - r)!} = n(n - 1) \ldots (n - r + 1) \qquad (3\text{-}26)$$

The symbol $n^{(r)}$, which is read n, r-factorial, frequently appears in the calculus of finite differences. It is a more general case than the $n!$ notation previously introduced since $n^{(n)} = n!$.

We can use the information contained in Equation 3-26 to solve the following problem: In how many different ways can r objects be selected from n objects? This is referred to as the number of *combinations* of n objects taken r at a time. The arrangements abc and bac are different permutations of the same combination of the three letters a, b, and c. Two combinations are different only if they contain different sets of objects. Thus abc and abd are different three-letter combinations. It is obvious that each combination contains $r!$ arrangements, since the r objects in a given combination can be permuted in that many ways. If we let the symbol C^n_r denote the number of different combinations, then

$$P^n_r = C^n_r(r!) \qquad (3\text{-}27)$$

Solving for C^n_r we have

$$C^n_r = \binom{n}{r} = \frac{P^n_r}{r!} = \frac{n!}{r!(n - r)!} \qquad (3\text{-}28)$$

To illustrate these concepts, suppose that we wish to form a three-man fact-finding committee from the five leading executives in the company. If the committee positions are distinguishable, e.g., chairman, vice-chairman, and secretary, the total number of possible committee structures is

$$P^5_3 = \frac{5!}{2!} = \frac{(5)(4)(3)(2)(1)}{(2)(1)} = 60$$

If, however, the three positions are indistinguishable from one another, the total number of potential committee structures is

$$C^5_3 = \frac{5!}{3!\,2!} = 10$$

Now let us go one step further and propose that the size of our fact-finding committee be a random variable. There may be any number from zero through five on the committee, depending upon how many of our five top executives can qualify for membership. Suppose that any executive can qualify 40 percent of the time. In examining a potential member we might then expect the probability of success to be 0.4. If five executives are examined, say in order E_1, E_2, E_3, E_4, E_5, the probability of the first three passing and the last two failing would be

$$(0.4)(0.4)(0.4)(0.6)(0.6) = (0.4)^3(0.6)^2$$

However, we are not concerned with the order of selection but rather with the number of successes in five tries. Any arrangement of three successes in the five trials has the same probability, namely $(0.4)^3(0.6)^2$. The number of such arrangements is C_3^5. The total probability of obtaining a three-man committee must then be

$$P(x = 3) = C_3^5(0.4)^3(0.6)^2 = 0.2304$$

If x is the random variable representing committee size, the general term for the probability distribution $f(x)$ is

$$f(x) = C_x^5(0.4)^x(0.6)^{5-x} \qquad (3\text{--}29)$$

The above model is a special case of the binomial distribution. The binomial is a two parameter distribution in which n may represent the number of trials to be run in an experiment and p may represent the probability of success on a single trial. The distribution for number of successes is then

$$f(x) = C_x^n(p)^x(1 - p)^{n-x} \qquad 0 \le x \le n \qquad (3\text{--}30)$$

This distribution arises quite naturally in a wide variety of physical contexts. Its mean and variance are $\mu = np$ and $\sigma^2 = np(1 - p)$.

The Poisson distribution is closely related to the binomial. For that reason it is often used as a convenient approximation to the binomial, as well as a population model of considerable importance in its own right. The probability distribution for the Poisson is represented by the discrete function

$$f(x) = \frac{e^{-\mu}(\mu)^x}{x!} \qquad x = 0, 1, 2, \ldots, \infty \qquad (3\text{--}31)$$

where μ is the mean value of the distribution. For this distribution, the variance is also μ.

The Poisson distribution is most often used when success can be associated with small increments of time or area. For example, when examining an automobile hood for defects, the probability of finding a defect (success) in an infinitesimally small area "a" might be λa. (The proportionality constant lambda can be interpreted as a rate of defects.) The total number of defects in a hood with total area "A" could range from zero to infinity with a mean value of λA. The distribution of these defects is Poisson with $\mu = \lambda A$. This is not unlike the binomial argument in which n possible cases are examined for success, only now n is infinitely large. The Poisson also arises in counting processes where we are concerned with such things as the number of customer arrivals, machine breakdowns, insurance claims, etc., which may occur over a specified time interval. Tables exist for both the binomial and Poisson distributions for limited values of the parameters. Most binomial tables stop at $n = 20$. The reason for this is that for larger values of n the Poisson distribution provides a very close approximation to the binomial. An additional rule-of-thumb restriction is usually imposed by saying that the Poisson approximation to the binomial can be used whenever $np < 5$ and $n > 20$. The Poisson approximation employs a mean of $\mu = np$.

The Poisson distribution itself is not usually tabulated beyond $\mu = 20$ because for larger mean values the normal distribution provides a suitable approximation. The normal approximation for the Poisson of course retains the same mean and variance, μ. Since the Poisson is a discrete distribution and the normal is continuous, the accuracy of the approximation is improved by moving one-half unit away from the value of the Poisson variable when reading the normal tables. For example, if x is Poisson distributed with a mean of 36, the probability that x lies between 30 and 40 is

$$P(30 \leq x \leq 40) = \sum_{x=0}^{40} \frac{e^{-36}(36)^x}{x!} - \sum_{x=0}^{29} \frac{e^{-36}(36)^x}{x!}$$

$$\approx F(40.5) - F(29.5)$$

where $F(x)$ is normal with mean 36 and standard deviation 6.

The normal distribution can also be used as a good approximation to the binomial whenever $np \geq 5$ regardless of the value of n. Here the normal density assumes a mean np and standard deviation $[np(1 - p)]^{1/2}$. The previous comments concerning the increased accuracy of the approximation apply equally well for the binomial. The fact that both the binomial and Poisson tend toward normality is illustrated by Figures 3–7 and 3–8.

Other Important Distributions. So far we have discussed only three of the commonly used statistical population models. Many more are available for our use. Although any one of them can be used to describe a system, there are usually good reasons for suspecting that certain ones may be the best candidates without trying them all on for size. A few of these distributions and their major characteristics are listed in Table 3–1. This comprises our grab bag of prototype models to be used whenever system performance must be described in terms of random variables.

The contexts in which each of the tabled distributions may arise are briefly discussed below. A more detailed discussion of these characteristics may be found in Springer et al.[1]

---

[1] Clifford H. Springer, Robert E. Herlihy, Robert T. Mall, and Robert I. Beggs, *Statistical Inference* (Homewood, Ill.: Richard D. Irwin, Inc., 1966), pp. 156–59.

FIGURE 3–7

Binomial Distribution and the Tendency toward Normal

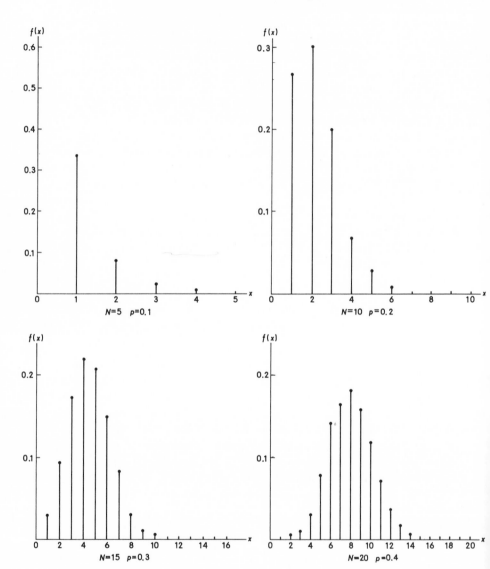

FIGURE 3–8

Poisson Distribution and the Tendency toward Normal

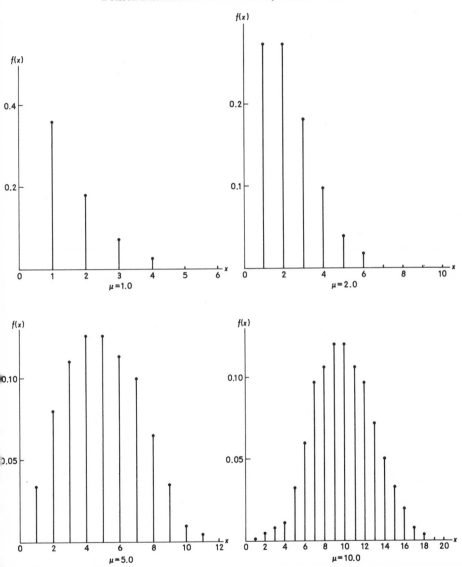

TABLE 3-1
Common Probability Distributions

Distribution of Random Variable x	Formula	Range of x	Parameters	Mean	Variance
Discrete:					
1. Binomial	$f(x) = C_x^n p^x (1-p)^{n-x}$	$x = 0, 1, 2, \ldots, n$	n, p	np	$np(1-p)$
2. Poisson	$f(x) = \dfrac{e^{-\mu}\mu^x}{x!}$	$x = 0, 1, 2, \ldots, \infty$	μ	μ	μ
3. Geometric	$f(x) = p(1-p)^x$	$x = 0, 1, \ldots, \infty$	p	$\dfrac{1-p}{p}$	$\dfrac{1-p}{p^2}$
4. Uniform	$f(x) = \dfrac{1}{n}$	$x = 1, \ldots, n$	n	$\dfrac{n+1}{2}$	$\dfrac{n^2-1}{12}$
Continuous:					
5. Normal	$f(x) = (2\sigma^2\pi)^{-1/2}e^{-(x-\mu)2/2\sigma^2}$	$-\infty \le x \le \infty$	μ, σ	μ	σ^2
6. Beta	$f(x) = \dfrac{\Gamma(a+b)}{\Gamma(a)\Gamma(b)}x^{(a-1)}(1-x)^{(b-1)}$	$0 \le x \le 1$	a, b	$\dfrac{a}{a+b}$	$\dfrac{ab}{(a+b)^2(a+b+1)}$
7. Gamma	$f(x) = \dfrac{x^{(a-1)}e^{-x/b}}{\Gamma(a)b^a}$	$0 \le x \le \infty$	a, b	ab	ab^2
8. Exponential	$f(x) = a^{-1}e^{-x/a}$	$0 \le x \le \infty$	a	a	a^2
9. Rectangular	$f(x) = (b-a)^{-1}$	$a \le x \le b$	a, b	$\dfrac{b+a}{2}$	$\dfrac{(b-a)^2}{12}$
10. Chi-square	$f(x) = \dfrac{x^{(a-2)/2}e^{-x/2}}{2^{a/2}\,\Gamma(a/2)}$	$0 \le x \le \infty$	a	a	$2a$

A. Discrete Distributions
1. *Binomial*—gives the probability of obtaining exactly x successes in a sample of n independent trials, where the single-trial success probability is known.
2. *Poisson*—gives the probability of the occurrence of exactly x events in a given interval when the probability of a single event in a very short interval is proportional to the length of the interval. This distribution arises in quality control, queueing theory, reliability theory, and many other industrial processes.
3. *Geometric*—gives the probability distribution for the number of successes before the first failure is observed where the single-trial success probability is known.
4. *Uniform*—gives the probability distribution for a number of equally likely events.

B. Continuous Distributions
1. *Normal*—a fundamental distribution which describes many physical phenomena and plays an important role in mathematical statistics.
2. *Beta*—a general distribution which can acquire a wide variety of shapes between any two finite values the analyst cares to choose. This flexibility of form makes the beta a useful distribution to fit to empirical data when no theoretical justification for another distribution can be found.
3. *Gamma*—a general distribution which can acquire a wide variety of shapes between a finite lower bound and infinity. The gamma is a good model for many physical phenomena, in addition to its potential as a fitted curve for empirical data with no known theoretical distribution.
4. *Exponential*—a special case of the gamma distribution which frequently arises in reliability and waiting line calculations. This distribution exhibits the property of "forgetfullness" when used in service time calculations, i.e., the distribution for time to complete service is independent of the length of time an element may already have been at the service facility.
5. *Rectangular*—gives the probability that a sample value will fall within a given interval when probability is directly proportional to the length of the interval. This distribution is also referred to as the uniform distribution in the continuous case.
6. *Chi-square*—a special case of the gamma distribution. It is especially valuable for making goodness-of-fit tests and deriving confidence limits in estimation problems.

This list is in no way exhaustive. The only criterion for selecting the 10 distributions shown is that these appear quite often in system models of interest to the operations engineer. Other distributions used in statistical inference will be introduced in the next chapter.

The gamma function $\Gamma(\cdot)$, which appears in the expression for several of these distributions, is defined by

$$\Gamma(a) = \int_0^\infty s^{a-1} e^{-s} ds \qquad \text{for all } a > 0 \qquad (3\text{-}32)$$

If a is an integer, the value of the integral reduces to

$$\Gamma(a) = (a-1)! = (a-1)(a-2) \cdots (3)(2)(1) \qquad (3\text{-}33)$$

Compound Events

So far our discussion about probability distributions has been limited to distributions of a single random variable x. However, we recognize from our earlier discussion, concerning the relative frequency with which events occur, that we may have occasion to develop statements concerning the intersection of sets of potential events. Let us now turn our attention to the probability distributions involved in such calculations.

Multivariate Distributions. Consider an experiment which measures the output from an injection molding machine. Here we might be interested in the vector random variable, (x_1, x_2), representing output during the first and second hours of operation after changing dies. We now have two random variables x_1 and x_2 which always appear together. Suppose for the moment that x_1 and x_2 are discrete. The function $f(x_1, x_2)$ can be introduced for each set of values x_1, x_2, which gives the probability of the event $x_1 \cap x_2$. The function $f(x_1, x_2)$ is called the joint distribution function for the random variables x_1, x_2. As in the case of one variable, we require that

$$f(x_1, x_2) \geq 0$$

and

$$\sum_{x_1} \sum_{x_2} f(x_1, x_2) = 1 \qquad (3\text{-}34)$$

If the random variables are continuous, the joint density function must satisfy

$$f(x_1, x_2) \geq 0$$

and

$$\int_{-\infty}^\infty \int_{-\infty}^\infty f(x_1, x_2)\, dx_1\, dx_2 = 1 \qquad (3\text{-}35)$$

We can now define the event

$$E_{b_1, b_2} = \{x_1 \leq b_1, x_2 \leq b_2\}$$

as the set of outcomes in the sample space such that x_1 takes on a value less than or equal to b_1 and x_2 takes on a value less than or equal to b_2. The probability of this event can be written as

$$P(x_1 \leq b_1, x_2 \leq b_2) = \int_{-\infty}^{b_2} \int_{-\infty}^{b_1} f(x_1, x_2)\,dx_1\,dx_2 \qquad (3\text{--}36)$$

for continuous random variables or

$$P(x_1 \leq b_1, x_2 \leq b_2) = \sum_{x_2=-\infty}^{b_2} \sum_{x_1=-\infty}^{b_1} f(x_1, x_2) \qquad (3\text{--}37)$$

for discrete random variables. It is even possible to mix continuous and discrete random variables. For example, suppose that the length of a production run (x_1) is continuously distributed while the number of units produced (x_2) is a discrete random variable. The probability of finding a production run of less than a_1 hours in which the number of units produced is less than or equal to b_2 units is then

$$P(x_1 \leq a_1, x_2 \leq b_2) = \int_0^{a_1} \sum_{x_2=0}^{b_2} f(x_1, x_2)\,dx_1 \qquad (3\text{--}38)$$

where $f(x_1, x_2)$ is the joint density for x_1 and x_2.

The extension of these ideas to systems involving more than two random variables is obvious. Any function $f(x_1, x_2, \ldots, x_k)$ may be regarded as a distribution function of k random variables provided that

$$f(x_1, x_2, \ldots, x_k) \geq 0$$

and

$$\int_{-\infty}^{\infty} \int_{-\infty}^{\infty} \cdots \int_{-\infty}^{\infty} f(x_1, x_2, \ldots, x_k)\,dx_1\,dx_2 \ldots dx_k = 1 \qquad (3\text{--}39)$$

Marginal Distributions. Let us now ask the question, "What is the distribution of x_1 without regard to the values that the other random variables may take on?" This distribution, denoted by $f(x_1)$, is called the marginal distribution of x_1. Obviously there are several marginal distributions associated with any distribution of more than one variable. If the variables x_1 and x_2 are discrete, we can, for example, obtain the probability that x_1 will be equal to c by summing over all possible values of x_2. That is,

$$f(x_1 = c) = \sum_{x_2} f(x_1 = c, x_2) \qquad (3\text{--}40)$$

since the events $(x_1 = c, x_2 = i)$ for every i are mutually exclusive and the joint occurrence $\sum_i (x_1 = c, x_2 = i)$ is by definition $(x_1 = c)$. If the variables are continuous, we can obtain the marginal density of x_1 by integrating over x_2.

$$f(x_1) = \int_{-\infty}^{\infty} f(x_1, x_2)\,dx_2 \qquad (3\text{--}41)$$

If, for example, the joint distribution of inquiries and sales over a one-year period is known, integrating over inquiries would give the annual sales distribution.

In a more general sense we can obtain the marginal density of x_1, x_2, and x_4, for example, by integrating over all other variables in the multivariate distribution. The result is a joint density relative to x_1, x_2, and x_4 but a marginal density relative to the original function.

$$f(x_1, x_2, x_4) = \int_{-\infty}^{\infty} \int_{-\infty}^{\infty} \cdots \int_{-\infty}^{\infty} f(x_1, x_2, \ldots, x_k) \, dx_3 \, dx_5 \, dx_6 \ldots dx_k \quad (3\text{-}42)$$

Marginal densities satisfy the requirements of all probability functions, namely,

$$f(x_i) \geq 0$$

and

$$\int_{-\infty}^{\infty} f(x_i) \, dx_i = 1$$

Conditional Distributions. Consider first a bivariate density, say $f(x_1, x_2)$, which might be represented as a surface in three-dimensional space. Suppose a point (x_1, x_2) is drawn and suppose that the second variate x_2 is observed but not the first. We would like to define a function $f(x_1 \,|\, x_2)$ which will give the density of x_1 when x_2 is known. If we develop such a relationship in terms of probabilities, we can use the conditional probability statement given in Equation 3-3. That is,

$$P(a \leq x_1 \leq b \,|\, c \leq x_2 \leq d) = \frac{P[(a \leq x_1 \leq b) \cap (c \leq x_2 \leq d)]}{P(c \leq x_2 \leq d)} =$$

$$\frac{\int_a^b \int_c^d f(x_1, x_2) \, dx_1 \, dx_2}{\int_c^d \int_{-\infty}^{\infty} f(x_1, x_2) \, dx_1 \, dx_2} = \frac{\int_a^b \int_c^d f(x_1, x_2) \, dx_1 \, dx_2}{\int_c^d f(x_2) \, dx_2} \quad (3\text{-}43)$$

Since this relation holds true for any a, b, c, and d it follows that the density can be written as

$$f(x_1 \,|\, x_2) = \frac{f(x_1, x_2)}{f(x_2)} \quad (3\text{-}44)$$

By similar reasoning

$$f(x_2 \,|\, x_1) = \frac{f(x_1, x_2)}{f(x_1)} \quad (3\text{-}45)$$

This relationship among joint, marginal, and conditional distributions holds equally well for both continuous and discrete distributions.

The function $f(x_1 \mid x_2)$ is a function of the single variable x_1. The variable x_2 is simply a parameter which will assume some numerical value in any particular conditional distribution. This implies that $f(x_2)$ is to be regarded as a constant. The conditional distribution behaves exactly like any other probability distribution. Its value is always greater than or equal to zero and it sums to one.

Conditional distributions are defined in similar fashion for higher order multivariate distributions. Therefore, if we have a density $f(x_1, x_2, x_3, x_4, x_5)$ for five random variables, then the conditional distribution of $x_1, x_2, x_3,$ given specific values of $x_4 = X_4$ and $x_5 = X_5$ is

$$f(x_1, x_2, x_3 \mid X_4, X_5) = \frac{f(x_1, x_2, x_3, x_4, x_5)}{f(X_4, X_5)} \qquad (3\text{-}46)$$

where $f(X_4, X_5)$ is the value of the distribution at X_4, X_5.

If two random variables are independent in a probability sense, then their joint distribution is equal to the product of their marginal distributions. Equivalently, the conditional and marginal distributions are equal. It follows that if x_1 and x_2 are independent, then

$$f(x_1, x_2) = f(x_1)f(x_2) \qquad (3\text{-}47)$$

Examples. The concepts of joint, marginal, and conditional distributions are best illustrated by numerical examples. Suppose that we have developed relative frequency information about production on an injection molding machine for the first two hours after the dies have been changed. The random vector (x_1, x_2) has the following empirical distribution:

(x_1, x_2)	$f(x_1, x_2)$
(0, 1)	0.05
(0, 2)	0.10
(0, 3)	0.15
(1, 1)	0.10
(1, 2)	0.04
(1, 3)	0.16
(2, 2)	0.20
(2, 3)	0.12
(2, 4)	0.08

From the table we can see that first hour's production (x_1) ranges from zero to two units, second hour's production ranges from one to four units, and that

$$\sum_{x_1, x_2} f(x_1, x_2) = 1$$

The marginal distribution for x_1 can be developed from the joint by fixing x_1 and summing over x_2, i.e.,

x_1	$f(x_1) = \sum_{x_2} f(x_1, x_2)$
0	$f(0, 1) + f(0, 2) + f(0, 3) = 0.30$
1	$f(1, 1) + f(1, 2) + f(1, 3) = 0.30$
2	$f(2, 2) + f(2, 3) + f(2, 4) = 0.40$

This distribution tells us that 40 percent of the time we can expect to produce two units during the first hour.

Suppose now that we know that the first hour's production was two units and we want to develop a conditional distribution for the second hour's production which accounts for this fact. The conditional distribution is

x_2	$f(x_2 \mid x_1 = 2) = \dfrac{f(x_2, x_1)}{f(x_1)}$
2	$\dfrac{f(2,2)}{f(2)} = \dfrac{0.2}{0.4} = 0.5$
3	$\dfrac{f(3,2)}{f(2)} = \dfrac{0.12}{0.4} = 0.3$
4	$\dfrac{f(4,2)}{f(2)} = \dfrac{0.08}{0.4} = 0.2$

Let us now move up one level in abstraction and hypothesize that the number of units (x) produced by this machine in any given time period (t) after warm-up is Poisson distributed with mean $3t$. Furthermore we have data which indicate that the length of time that the machine can run without changing dies is exponentially distributed with a mean of two hours. What is needed is the distribution for number of units produced between die changes.

Using formulas 2 and 8 from Table 3–1 we have

$$f(x \mid t) = \frac{e^{-3t}(3t)^x}{x!}$$

and

$$f(t) = \tfrac{1}{2}e^{-t/2}$$

In this case we have $f(x \mid t)$ as a discrete distribution and $f(t)$ as a continuous distribution. Applying our basic rules, the joint distribution for x and t can be obtained from

$$f(x,t) = f(x \mid t) f(t) = \frac{e^{-3t}(3t)^x}{x!} \tfrac{1}{2} e^{-t/2}$$

The distribution we really need is the marginal distribution $f(x)$. This can be obtained from the joint by integrating over all values of the continuous variable t as

$$f(x) = \frac{1}{2(x!)} \int_0^\infty e^{-3.5t}(3t)^x \, dt$$

Mathematical Expectation

The expected value of any random variable is simply the weighted average of all the values the variable may assume. The weights are obtained from the probability distribution of the random variable. The expected value, or mean value, of a random variable x is a theoretical number which might never be achieved in a practical experiment. We do not anticipate that x will take on its expected value in any given trial of an experiment. In some cases it might even be impossible for x to take on its expected value. However, what we do anticipate is that the average value of the random variable x in a great number of trials will be somewhere near the expected value of x. The expected value concept is widely employed in system models in which one wants a single value to characterize the random variable and its probability distribution. We will, for example, require the expected value for demand over lead time in our inventory models and the expected time between customer arrivals in our queueing models.

The general definition for the expected value of a discrete variate is

$$E(x) = \sum_x x f(x) \tag{3-48}$$

where $f(x)$ is the distribution of x and the sum is taken over all values of x. The symbol $E(x)$ is standard notation for the expectation operation. If x is a continuous random variable, the expected value of x is written as

$$E(x) = \int_x x f(x) \, dx \tag{3-49}$$

where the integration is carried out over the entire range of x.

To illustrate this calculation, suppose that we have developed the distribution for number of customers (n) in a service system as the geometric distribution

$$f(n) = p^n(1-p), \, n = 0, 1, 2, \ldots, 0 < p < 1$$

The expected number in the system is given by the infinite sum

$$E(n) = \sum_{n=0}^{\infty} np^n(1 - p) = (1 - p) \sum_{n=0}^{\infty} np^n$$

The infinite sum can be evaluated by reference to an appropriate handbook on sum calculus or by conversion into a better known expression. One such conversion can be obtained by recognizing that

$$\frac{d}{dp}(p^n) = np^{n-1}$$

The expression for $E(n)$ can then be rewritten as

$$E(n) = (1 - p)p \sum_{n=0}^{\infty} np^{n-1} = (1 - p)p \sum_{n=0}^{\infty} \frac{d}{dp}(p^n)$$

$$= (1 - p)p \frac{d}{dp}\left(\sum_{n=0}^{\infty} p^n\right)$$

But the sum in brackets is a geometric series which closes to the well-known expression

$$\sum_{n=0}^{\infty} r^n = \frac{1}{1 - r} \tag{3-50}$$

when $r < 1$. Therefore

$$E(n) = (1 - p)p \frac{d}{dp}\left(\frac{1}{1 - p}\right)$$

which, after differentiating becomes

$$E(n) = (1 - p)p\left(\frac{1}{(1 - p)^2}\right)$$

$$= \frac{p}{1 - p} \tag{3-51}$$

Functions of Random Variables. The concept of expectation can be easily extended to functions of a random variable. If y is some function of the random variable x, say $y = g(x)$, then $g(x)$ is itself a random variable. If we assume that g is a single valued function of a discrete variable x, then the frequency with which this numerically valued function can take on a value $g(x)$ is simply $f(x)$. The weighted average of $g(x)$ is, therefore,

$$E[g(x)] = \begin{cases} \sum_{x} g(x)f(x) & x \text{ discrete} \\ \int_{x} g(x)f(x)\,dx & x \text{ continuous} \end{cases} \tag{3-52}$$

The same concepts can be extended to functions of several random variables when their joint density is known. For example, if $h(x_1, x_2, \ldots, x_n)$ is a function of the random variables x_1 through x_n, then

$E[h(x_1, x_2, \ldots, x_n)]$

$$= \int_{-\infty}^{\infty} \int_{-\infty}^{\infty} \cdots \int_{-\infty}^{\infty} h(x_1, x_2, \ldots, x_n) f(x_1, x_2, \ldots, x_n) \, dx_1 \ldots dx_n \quad (3\text{--}53)$$

where f is the joint density of the random variables.

Two simple properties of the expectation operator which are particular applications of the definition of the expected value of a function are

$$E[cg(x)] = cE[g(x)] \quad (3\text{--}54)$$

$$E[g(x) + h(x)] = E[g(x)] + E[h(x)] \quad (3\text{--}55)$$

Here it is assumed that x is distributed by $f(x)$, c is any constant, and g and h are functions of x. These two relations follow directly from the corresponding relations for integrals and sums:

$$\int_{-\infty}^{\infty} c\, g(x) f(x) \, dx = c \int_{-\infty}^{\infty} g(x) f(x) \, dx$$

$$\int_{-\infty}^{\infty} [g(x) + h(x)] f(x) \, dx = \int_{-\infty}^{\infty} g(x) f(x) \, dx + \int_{-\infty}^{\infty} h(x) f(x) \, dx$$

To illustrate these concepts, suppose that the cost incurred by holding n units in our service system example is

$$g(n) = 5n^2 + n$$

From Equations 3–54 and 3–55 the expected cost is then,

$$E[g(n)] = \sum_{n=0}^{\infty} g(n) f(n)$$

$$= \sum_{n=0}^{\infty} (5n^2 + n) f(n)$$

$$= 5E(n^2) + E(n)$$

The term $E(n)$ was evaluated in Equation 3–51. The function $h(n) = n^2$ has the expected value

$$E(n^2) = \sum_{n=0}^{\infty} n^2 p^n (1 - p)$$

$$= (1 - p)\left[p^2 \frac{d^2}{dp^2} \left(\sum_{n=0}^{\infty} p^n \right) + \sum_{n=0}^{\infty} np^n \right]$$

$$= (1 - p)\left[p^2 \frac{d^2}{dp^2} \left(\frac{1}{1 - p} \right) + \frac{p}{(1 - p)^2} \right]$$

$$= (1 - p)\left[p^2 \left(\frac{2}{(1 - p)^3} \right) + \frac{p}{(1 - p)^2} \right]$$

$$= 2\left(\frac{p}{1 - p} \right)^2 + \frac{p}{1 - p} = \frac{p}{1 - p}\left[\frac{2p}{1 - p} + 1 \right] \quad (3\text{--}56)$$

It follows, then, that

$$E[g(n)] = \frac{5p}{1-p}\left(\frac{2p}{1-p}+1\right)+\frac{p}{1-p}$$

is the expected cost incurred by operating the specified service system.

Moments.   The moments of a distribution are the expected values of the powers of the random variable which has that distribution. The physical analog of the moments of a distribution can be found in the simple beam loading problems encountered in physics and engineering mechanics.

Consider a beam attached at the point $x = 0$ and subjected to a series of forces $f(x_i)$ as indicated in Figure 3–9. The torque about the point $x = 0$, produced by a force $f(x_i)$ being applied at $x = x_i$, is the product of the magnitude of the force by the lever arm of the force. This product, or torque resulting from the force, is called the first moment of the force. If we have a series of such forces acting at various distances from the origin, the total first moment is simply the sum of moments induced by each of the individual forces. The centroid, or center of gravity, for this simple loading is the distance from the origin at which the application of a single force equal in magnitude to the sum of all the applied forces would produce the same moment. It can

FIGURE 3–9

The First Moment for a Loaded Beam

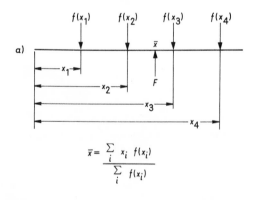

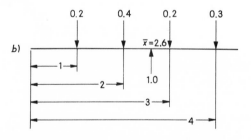

be viewed as the balance point for the given forces. If the beam is supported at the centroid, no rotation will occur.

In general, the total first moment can be written as

$$M = \sum_i x_i f(x_i) \tag{3-57}$$

The centroid is then

$$\bar{x} = M/F = \frac{\sum_i x_i f(x_i)}{\sum_i f(x_i)}$$

If we look carefully at the particular example shown in Figure 3–9, we note that the total forces or weights acting on the beam sum to one. In this case it is not unreasonable to view $[f(x_i)]$ as a set of probability weights, since it satisfies all of the requirements for a probability distribution. The first moment of this distribution is

$$M = \sum_i x_i f(x_i) = 1(0.2) + 2(0.3) + 3(0.2) + 4(0.3) = 2.6$$

Furthermore, since the total probability weight is one, the centroid must be

$$\bar{x} = \frac{\sum_i x_i f(x_i)}{\sum_i f(x_i)} = \frac{2.6}{1.0} = 2.6$$

It is obvious that the first moment of a probability distribution is equivalent to the expected value of x. It is also apparent that the first moment and the centroid of a probability distribution have the same numerical values. This permits $E(x)$ to be viewed as a balance point for the distribution. The expected value of x then takes on three interpretations: the first moment, the centroid, and the mean value of the random variable.

The higher moments of a distribution can be viewed in similar fashion. The second moment about the origin is the squared length of the moment arm times the magnitude of the force, the third moment is the cubed distance times force, etc. In general the rth moment about the origin is

$$\mu_r = E(x^r) = \begin{cases} \sum_x x^r f(x) & \text{for } x \text{ discrete} \\ \int_x x^r f(x)\, dx & \text{for } x \text{ continuous} \end{cases} \tag{3-58}$$

The Greek letter μ (mu) without a subscript will be understood to represent μ_1 in future sections.

The first moment or mean of a distribution is an important parameter which appears explicitly in the formulas of many distributions such as the normal and Poisson. Furthermore, this single number is often used to characterize a random variable and its probability distribution in model construction. However, another moment rivals the mean in importance when more detailed knowledge about the distribution is desired. That moment is the second moment about the mean.

Again, the physical analog illustrated by a beam loading problem is significant. The rth moment of a force about any point "a" is the distance from "a" to the application point of the force raised to the rth power, then multiplied by the magnitude of the force. When the reference point is $\bar{x}$, the centroid of a particular force configuration, the second moment about $\bar{x}$ is called the moment of inertia. The probability analog is called the variance of the distribution. The variance, σ^2, is the second moment about the mean or

$$\sigma^2 = E[(x - \mu)^2] = \begin{cases} \sum_x (x - \mu)^2 f(x) & x \text{ discrete} \\ \int_x (x - \mu)^2 f(x)\,dx & x \text{ continuous} \end{cases} \quad (3\text{--}59)$$

The term standard deviation is used to refer to the square root of the variance, i.e.,

$$\sigma = [E((x - \mu)^2)]^{1/2} \quad (3\text{--}60)$$

The standard deviation appears explicitly in the formula for the normal distribution and will play an important role in later discussions about hypothesis testing.

In order to facilitate calculations, it is often convenient to use a computational form of the variance. Employing properties 3–54 and 3–55 of expected values one can obtain

$$\sigma^2 = E[(x - \mu)^2] = E(x^2 - 2\mu x + \mu^2)$$
$$= E(x^2) - 2\mu E(x) + \mu^2 \quad (3\text{--}61)$$
$$= E(x^2) - [E(x)]^2$$

For example, suppose that the length of scrap remaining from a bar-stock cutting operation is uniformly distributed in the interval of one to five inches. The mean length for scrap is

$$E(x) = \int_a^b x f(x)\,dx = \int_a^b x\left(\frac{1}{b - a}\right) dx$$
$$= \int_1^5 \frac{x}{4}\,dx = 3$$

The variance for scrap length is

$$\sigma^2 = E(x^2) - [E(x)]^2 = \int_a^b x^2 f(x)\,dx - \left[\int_a^b x f(x)\,dx\right]^2$$
$$= \int_1^5 \frac{x}{4}\,dx - (3)^2 = 1.333$$

A few facts about the interpretation of the moments as statistical parameters of a distribution should be noted. First, the first moment or mean of a distribution is a measure of central tendency. It tells one where the center of the distribution (in a center-of-gravity sense) lies on the x axis. Second, if $f(x)$ is symmetric about any value $x = x_0$, then the mean will be $\mu = x_0$ and all odd numbered moments about the mean will be zero. That is,

$$\int_{-\infty}^{\infty} (x - \mu)^n f(x)\,dx \qquad \text{for } n \text{ odd}$$

will be zero. Third, the variance of a distribution, which is always positive, is a measure of its spread or dispersion. If $f(x)$ is a curve which is sharply peaked at μ, the variance will be smaller than if the curve is flattened out. The variance vanishes only when the distribution is discrete with a single possible value for the random variable. Finally, while any particular moment gives little information about a distribution, the whole set of moments will ordinarily determine the distribution exactly. More will be said about this topic when we discuss moment generating functions in Chapter 6. However, at the level of operations engineering, most work in applied statistics employs only the first two moments of a distribution.

Conditional Expectations. The conditional expectation of a random variable $g(x)$, subject to hypothesis A, is given by

$$E[g(x)\,|\,A] = \int_{-\infty}^{\infty} g(x) f(x\,|\,A)\,dx \tag{3-62}$$

where $f(x\,|\,A)$ is the related conditional density for x.

The quantity $E[g(x)\,|\,A]$ can often be calculated directly from the density $f(x)$ without developing an explicit expression for $f(x\,|\,A)$. For example, consider that the event A occurs whenever $(a \leq x \leq b)$. This means that we have reduced our total sample space from all possible x to only those x falling in the prescribed interval. In order to maintain a probability density which sums to one, it is necessary to scale our original function $f(x)$ by an appropriate factor which reflects the reduced sample space. The result is that

$$f(x\,|\,a \leq x \leq b) = \frac{f(x)}{\displaystyle\int_a^b f(x)\,dx} \tag{3-63}$$

Therefore, our expectation can be written as

$$E[g(x)\,|\,a \leq x \leq b] = \frac{\displaystyle\int_a^b g(x) f(x)\,dx}{\displaystyle\int_a^b f(x)\,dx} \tag{3-64}$$

This relation is quite handy for manipulating so-called truncated distributions in which one of the tails of a standard distribution may be cut off, i.e., some portion of the original set of feasible values for the random variable is no longer admissible.

There is one other useful relation involving conditional expectation. If the set $\{A_i\}$ is a set of mutually exclusive and collectively exhaustive events and $g(x)$ is any random variable defined over the sample space, then

$$E[g(x)] = \sum_{A_i} P(A_i) E[g(x)|A_i] \tag{3-65}$$

This relation permits us to manipulate conditional and unconditional expectations in the same manner that we have manipulated joint, marginal, and conditional probabilities.

To illustrate the use of conditional expectations, suppose that we are sorting the output from a rough finishing lumber mill into two grades. Grade A boards are those which are longer than eight feet. Any boards which are less than or equal to eight feet are classed as grade B. Past performance indicates that the length of logs received at the mill is approximately uniformly distributed in the interval (7, 13). The task is to estimate the average length of grade A boards.

$$E(x \,|\, A) = \frac{\displaystyle\int_8^{13} \frac{x}{6}\,dx}{\displaystyle\int_8^{13} \frac{1}{6}\,dx} = 10.5$$

The average length of grade B boards can be shown in similar fashion to be

$$E(x \,|\, B) = \frac{\displaystyle\int_7^{8} \frac{x}{6}\,dx}{\displaystyle\int_7^{8} \frac{1}{6}\,dx} = 7.5$$

Let us now suppose that we have measured the boards in grades A and B with the indicated results. We further recognize that $\frac{1}{6}$ of all boards are grade B and $\frac{5}{6}$ are grade A. Without regard to grade, the expected length of all boards is by application of Equation 3–65,

$$E(x) = P(A)\,E(x \,|\, A) + P(B)\,E(x \,|\, B)$$
$$= (\tfrac{5}{6})(10.5) + (\tfrac{1}{6})(7.5) = 10$$

This is the value we would obtain by taking the expected value of the original uniform distribution.

Combinations of Random Variables

In constructing system models it is often necessary to combine several random variables. Combinations occur in the form of sums, differences, products, and quotients. The mathematical problem to be solved is that of characterizing the probability distribution of such combinations. When the random variables involved are statistically independent, there are means of developing exact expressions for the distribution of simple sums from a knowledge of the component distributions. However, exact expressions for distributions of products and quotients of independent random variables are not easily developed. Nor are the distributions for any combinations of dependent random variables easy to come by. In most cases we must be satisfied with the mean and variance to characterize the distributions. The bulk of this section is devoted to the development of estimates for those parameters.

Covariance and the Correlation Coefficient. Recall that when two random variables are independent, their joint distribution is equal to the product of their marginal distributions. An equivalent way of expressing independence is that their marginal and conditional distributions are equal. When two random variables are not independent, we need some measure of their dependence on each other. The parameter which tells the degree to which two variables (x_1, x_2) are related is the correlation coefficient $r_{x_1 x_2}$. By definition,

$$r_{x_1 x_2} = \frac{\sigma_{x_1 x_2}}{\sigma_{x_1} \sigma_{x_2}}$$
(3–66)

where

$\sigma_{x_1 x_2}$ = covariance of (x_1, x_2) as defined in Equation 3–67,

and

σ_{x_i} = standard deviation of x_i.

The correlation coefficient ranges in value over $-1 \le r \le 1$. If $r = 1$, the variables are perfectly correlated and directly related in that increasing values of one variable are associated with increasing values of the second variable. If $r = -1$, the variables are perfectly correlated and inversely related in that increasing values of one variable are associated with decreasing values of the second variable. If $r = 0$, no linear relation exists between the variables.

The covariance is defined as

$$\sigma_{x_1 x_2} = E[(x_1 - E(x_1))(x_2 - E(x_2))]$$
(3–67)

Note that covariance has the same basic dimensions as the variance of a single random variable. In fact, if x_1 and x_2 are the same random variable it reduces to the variance. A computational form of the covariance is easily developed from the expectation operation as

$$\sigma_{x_1 x_2} = E[(x_1 - E(x_1))(x_2 - E(x_2))] = E(x_1 x_2) - E(x_1) E(x_2)$$
(3–68)

These parameters will be used to define means and variances for combinations of dependent random variables.

Multiplication by a Constant. One of the most common operations performed on random variables is to multiply them by constants. For example, each unit of demand generates C dollars of profit. Profit is a random variable with mean and variance of

$$\mu_p = E(Cx) = \int_x Cx f(x)\, dx = C\,E(x) \tag{3-69}$$

$$\sigma_p^2 = E[(Cx - \mu_p)^2] = C^2 E[(x - \mu_x)^2] = C^2 \sigma_x^2 \tag{3-70}$$

The important fact to remember is that multiplying a random variable by a constant simply multiples the mean by the same constant but multiplies the variance by the square of that constant.

Coefficient of variation is defined as the ratio of standard deviation to mean.

$$v = \frac{\sigma}{\mu}$$

This is a common measure of relative dispersion of a random variable around its mean. If we apply this measure to the random variable Cx we note that

$$v = \frac{C\sigma_x}{C\mu_x} = \frac{\sigma_x}{\mu_x}$$

so that the coefficient of variation for the new distribution remains unchanged.

Sums of Random Variables. To evaluate the mean and variance of a sum of random variables, let us suppose that their joint density is known. The random variable $y = x_1 + x_2$ has a mean of

$$\mu_y = E(x_1 + x_2) = \int_{x_1} \int_{x_2} (x_1 + x_2) f(x_1, x_2)\, dx_1\, dx_2$$

$$= \int_{x_1} x_1 f(x_1)\, dx_1 + \int_{x_2} x_2 f(x_2)\, dx_2$$

$$= E(x_1) + E(x_2) \tag{3-71}$$

without regard to the independence of x_1 and x_2.

The variance of $y = x_1 + x_2$ can be obtained in similar fashion as

$$\sigma_y^2 = E[(x_1 + x_2 - \mu_{x_1} - \mu_{x_2})^2] = E[((x_1 - \mu_{x_1}) + (x_2 - \mu_{x_2}))^2]$$

$$= E[(x_1 - \mu_{x_1})^2 + (x_2 - \mu_{x_2})^2 + 2(x_1 - \mu_{x_1})(x_2 - \mu_{x_2})] \tag{3-72}$$

$$= \sigma_{x_1}^2 + \sigma_{x_2}^2 + 2\sigma_{x_1 x_2}$$

Note that the variance of the sum is not simply the sum of variances but rather includes the addition of twice the covariance term. If the correlation coefficient r is available this relationship may be expressed as

$$\sigma_y^2 = \sigma_{x_1}^2 + \sigma_{x_2}^2 + 2r\sigma_{x_1}\sigma_{x_2} \tag{3-73}$$

In the event that x_1 and x_2 are uncorrelated, their covariance and correlation coefficient are zero. Hence, this expression reduces to

$$\sigma^2_{x_1 + x_2} = \sigma^2_{x_1} + \sigma^2_{x_2} \qquad x_1 \text{ and } x_2 \text{ uncorrelated} \qquad (3\text{--}74)$$

In the event that we have a linear combination of random variables, say $z = C_1 x_1 + C_2 x_2$, we can apply the results of the last section to obtain

$$\mu_z = C_1 E(x_1) + C_2 E(x_2) \qquad (3\text{--}75)$$

$$\sigma^2_z = C^2_1 \sigma^2_{x_1} + C^2_2 \sigma^2_{x_2} + 2C_1 C_2 \sigma_{x_1 x_2} \qquad (3\text{--}76)$$

These results can easily be extended to linear combinations of n univariate random variables. That is, if $z = C_1 x_1 + C_2 x_2 + \cdots + C_n x_n$, then

$$\mu_z = C_1 E(x_1) + C_2 E(x_2) + \cdots + C_n E(x_n) \qquad (3\text{--}77)$$

$$\sigma^2_z = \sum_{i=1}^{n} C^2_i \sigma^2_{x_i} + 2 \sum_{i=1}^{n-1} \sum_{j=i+1}^{n} C_i C_j \sigma_{x_i x_j} \qquad (3\text{--}78)$$

As noted for the two variable case, if all n random variables are uncorrelated the variance of their sum reduces to the sum of their variances. Techniques for developing the probability distributions for sums of independent random variables are discussed in Chapter 6.

Differences between Random Variables. The subtraction of one random variable from another can be viewed as a special case of the linear combination of random variables discussed above. That is, $y = x_1 - x_2$ can be viewed as $y = x_1 + C_2 x_2$ where $C_2 = -1$. It follows, then, that

$$E(x_1 - x_2) = E(x_1) - E(x_2) \qquad (3\text{--}79)$$

$$\sigma^2_{x_1 - x_2} = \sigma^2_{x_1} + \sigma^2_{x_2} - 2\sigma_{x_1 x_2} \qquad (3\text{--}80)$$

Obviously, if we have a linear combination of random variables containing both addition and subtraction, the general relationships developed in Equations 3–77 and 3–78 still hold. Suppose, for example, that $y = C_1 x_1 - C_2 x_2 + C_3 x_3$, then

$$E(y) = C_1 E(x_1) - C_2 E(x_2) + C_3 E(x_3)$$

and

$$\sigma^2_y = C^2_1 \sigma^2_{x_1} + C^2_2 \sigma^2_{x_2} + C^2_3 \sigma^2_{x_3} - 2C_1 C_2 \sigma_{x_1 x_2} + 2C_1 C_3 \sigma_{x_1 x_3} - 2C_2 C_3 \sigma_{x_2 x_3}$$

One further result concerning the sums and differences of random variables will be of use to us in future calculations. It can be shown that if x_1 and x_2 are both normally distributed, then $y = x_1 \pm x_2$ is also normally distributed. The mean and variance of the new distribution are obtained in the usual manner. The reader is cautioned, however, that this result applies only to reproductive distributions such as the normal distribution and is not true in general. Transform techniques for developing the general distribution when the x_i's are independent are discussed in Chapter 6.

Products and Quotients of Random Variables.   The expected value of the product of two random variables has already been calculated in Equation 3–68. All that is needed is to rearrange terms. That is,

$$E(x_1x_2) = E(x_1)\,E(x_2) + \sigma_{x_1x_2} \tag{3–81}$$

Note that in this case the mean of a product is equal to the product of the means *only* if the random variables are uncorrelated.

The variance of a product is more difficult to calculate. In the event that x_1 and x_2 are independent, we can resort to the expectation operation and use the fact that $E(x_1x_2) = E(x_1)\,E(x_2)$ for that case. That is,

$$\mathrm{Var}(x_1x_2) = E[(x_1x_2 - E(x_1x_2))^2]$$

$$= E[(x_1x_2)^2] - [E(x_1x_2)]^2$$

$$= E(x_1^2)\,E(x_2^2) - [E(x_1)\,E(x_2)]^2$$

But we know from the computational form of σ_x^2 that

$$E(x^2) = \sigma_x^2 + [E(x)]^2$$

therefore,

$$\mathrm{Var}(x_1x_2) = (\sigma_{x_1}^2 + \mu_{x_1}^2)(\sigma_{x_2}^2 + \mu_{x_2}^2) - \mu_{x_1}^2\,\mu_{x_2}^2$$

$$= \mu_{x_1}^2\,\sigma_{x_2}^2 + \mu_{x_2}^2\,\sigma_{x_1}^2 + \sigma_{x_1}^2\,\sigma_{x_2}^2 \tag{3–82}$$

for x_1 and x_2 independent.

In the event that the coefficient of variation of at least one of these variables is small, it is common practice to use the approximation of

$$\sigma_{x_1x_2}^2 \approx \mu_{x_2}^2\,\sigma_{x_1}^2 + \mu_{x_1}^2\,\sigma_{x_2}^2 \tag{3–83}$$

When the variables in a product are dependent we are as a practical matter forced to use an approximation. The approximation suggested by Springer *et al.* is[2]

$$\mathrm{Var}(x_1x_2) = \mu_{x_1}^2\,\sigma_{x_2}^2 + \mu_{x_2}^2\,\sigma_{x_1}^2 + 2\mu_{x_1}\mu_{x_2}\,r\sigma_{x_1}\sigma_{x_2}$$

$$= \mu_{x_1}^2\,\sigma_{x_2}^2 + \mu_{x_2}^2\,\sigma_{x_1}^2 + 2\mu_{x_1}\mu_{x_2}\,\sigma_{x_1x_2} \tag{3–84}$$

We are in similar difficulties with both the mean and variance of a quotient. Springer *et al.* suggest that reasonable approximations for quotients of the form $z = x_1/x_2$ are

$$\mu_z = \frac{\mu_{x_1}}{\mu_{x_2}} \tag{3–85}$$

---

[2] Clifford H. Springer, Robert E. Herlihy, Robert T. Mall, and Robert I. Beggs, *Probabilistic Models* (Homewood, Ill.: Richard D. Irwin, Inc., 1968), p. 122.

and

$$\sigma_z^2 = (\mu_{x_2})^{-2} \sigma_{x_1}^2 + \left(\frac{\mu_{x_1}}{\mu_{x_2}^2}\right)^2 \sigma_{x_2}^2 - 2(\mu_{x_2})^{-1} \left(\frac{\mu_{x_1}}{\mu_{x_2}^2}\right) \sigma_{x_1 x_2} \qquad (3\text{-}86)$$

For the special case of x_1 and x_2 independent, the expression for variance reduces to

$$\sigma_{x_1/x_2}^2 = \frac{(\mu_{x_2}^2 \sigma_{x_1}^2 + \mu_{x_1}^2 \sigma_{x_2}^2)}{\mu_{x_2}^4} \qquad (3\text{-}87)$$

A general formula for finding the approximate variance for compound functions of random variables can be developed from the first few terms of the well known Taylor's formula. The assumption which must be made is that the expected value of the compound random variable is approximately equal to the function evaluated with each random variable equal to its individual mean. That is, if

$$z = f(x_1, x_2, \ldots, x_n)$$

then

$$E(z) \approx f(\mu_{x_1}, \mu_{x_2}, \ldots, \mu_{x_n})$$

Taylor's formula for a function of n variables expanded about the points $a_1, a_2, \ldots, a_n$ is

$$F(x_1, x_2, \ldots, x_n) = F(a_1, a_2, \ldots, a_n) + \sum_{i=1}^{n} (x_i - a_i) F_i(a_1, \ldots, a_n)$$

$$+ \frac{1}{2} \sum_{i=1}^{n} \sum_{j=1}^{n} (x_i - a_i)(x_j - a_j) F_{ij}(a_1, \ldots, a_n) + R \qquad (3\text{-}88)$$

where

$$F_i = \frac{\partial F}{\partial x_i}$$

$$F_{ij} = \frac{\partial^2 F}{\partial x_i \partial x_j}$$

and R is a remainder term which will be considered negligible.

If we examine the argument in the expectation for variance, the Taylor series for that argument takes a simple form. Suppose that the compound random variable is z with mean μ_z. Then

$$\text{Var}(z) = E[(z - E(z))^2] = E[F(x_1, x_2, \ldots, x_n)]$$

Treating $F(x_1, x_2, \ldots, x_n)$ as the function to be expanded about the means (μ_i) of each of the variables x_i, we have

$$F(\mu_1, \mu_2, \ldots, \mu_n) = (z - \mu_z)^2 \approx 0$$

$$F_i(\mu_1, \mu_2, \ldots, \mu_n) = 2(z - \mu_z)\frac{\partial z}{\partial x_i} \approx 0$$

$$F_{ij}(\mu_1, \mu_2, \ldots, \mu_n) = 2\left(\frac{\partial z}{\partial x_i}\right)\left(\frac{\partial z}{\partial x_j}\right) + 2\frac{\partial^2 z}{\partial x_i \partial x_j}(z - \mu_z)$$

$$\approx 2\left(\frac{\partial z}{\partial x_i}\right)\left(\frac{\partial z}{\partial x_j}\right)\Bigg|_{x_i = \mu_i}$$

from which

$$F(x_1, x_2, \ldots, x_n) \approx \sum_{i=1}^{n} \sum_{j=1}^{n} (x_i - \mu_i)(x_j - \mu_j)\left(\frac{\partial z}{\partial x_i}\right)\left(\frac{\partial z}{\partial x_j}\right) \qquad (3\text{-}89)$$

where the partial derivatives are evaluated at $x_i = \mu_i$. Since the variance of z is the expected value of F, it follows that

$$\text{Var}(z) = \sum_{i=1}^{n} \sum_{j=1}^{n} E\left[(x_i - \mu_i)(x_j - \mu_j)\left(\frac{\partial z}{\partial x_i}\right)\left(\frac{\partial z}{\partial x_j}\right)\right]$$

$$= \sum_{i=1}^{n} \left(\frac{\partial z}{\partial x_i}\right)^2 \sigma_{x_i}^2 + 2\sum_{i=1}^{n-1} \sum_{j=i+1}^{n} \left(\frac{\partial z}{\partial x_i}\right)\left(\frac{\partial z}{\partial x_j}\right)\sigma_{x_i x_j} \qquad (3\text{-}90)$$

where all partial derivatives are evaluated at $x_i = \mu_i$. The approximations for variances of products and quotients previously noted can be developed from this formula.

To illustrate the procedure, let

$$z = x_1 + x_2 - x_3 x_4$$

and

$$\mu_z \approx \mu_1 + \mu_2 - \mu_3 \mu_4$$

then

$$\text{Var}(z) = \sigma_1^2 + \sigma_2^2 + \mu_4^2 \sigma_3^2 + \mu_3^2 \sigma_4^2$$

$$+ 2[\sigma_{12} - \mu_4 \sigma_{13} - \mu_3 \sigma_{14} - \mu_4 \sigma_{23} - \mu_3 \sigma_{24} + \mu_3 \mu_4 \sigma_{34}]$$

where the subscript x_i has been suppressed.

Table 3–2 summarizes the various formulas for means and variances of compound functions.

Approximate Distributions. We have gone to considerable length to develop expressions for the means and variances of compound random

TABLE 3-2

Means and Variances for Compared Random Variables

Function	Mean	Variance
$x_1 + x_2$	$\mu_{x_1} + \mu_{x_2}$	$\sigma_{x_1}^2 + \sigma_{x_2}^2 + 2\sigma_{x_1 x_2}$
$x_1 - x_2$	$\mu_{x_1} - \mu_{x_2}$	$\sigma_{x_1}^2 + \sigma_{x_2}^2 - 2\sigma_{x_1 x_2}$
$x_1 x_2$ (independent)	$\mu_{x_1} \mu_{x_2}$	$\mu_{x_1}^2 \sigma_{x_2}^2 + \mu_{x_2}^2 \sigma_{x_1}^2 + \sigma_{x_1}^2 \sigma_{x_2}^2$
$x_1 x_2$ (dependent)	$\mu_{x_1} \mu_{x_2} + \sigma_{x_1 x_2}$	$\mu_{x_1}^2 \sigma_{x_2}^2 + \mu_{x_2}^2 \sigma_{x_1}^2$
		$+ 2\mu_{x_1} \mu_{x_2} \sigma_{x_1 x_2}$ (approx.)
$\dfrac{x_1}{x_2}$ (independent)	$\dfrac{\mu_{x_1}}{\mu_{x_2}}$ (approx.)	$\dfrac{\mu_{x_2}^2 \sigma_{x_1}^2 + \mu_{x_1}^2 \sigma_{x_2}^2}{\mu_{x_2}^4}$ (approx.)
$\dfrac{x_1}{x_2}$ (dependent)	$\dfrac{\mu_{x_1}}{\mu_{x_2}}$ (approx.)	$(\mu_{x_2})^{-2}\sigma_{x_1}^2 + \left(\dfrac{\mu_{x_1}}{\mu_{x_2}^2}\right)^2 \sigma_{x_2}^2 -$
		$2\dfrac{\mu_{x_1}}{\mu_{x_2}^3} \sigma_{x_1 x_2}$ (approx.)

variables simply because they are valuable indicators of often inaccessible probability densities. In addition, two theorems provide access to useful probability information based solely on knowledge of the means and variances of distributions. One is known as Tchebycheff's inequality and the other as the central limit theorem. Both are discussed in nearly every text on probability and statistics.[3]

Tchebycheff's inequality states that

$$P(\mu - K < x < \mu + K) \geq 1 - \frac{\sigma^2}{K^2} \tag{3-91}$$

where x is any random variable having mean μ and variance σ^2. This permits us to place lower bounds on probability statements without knowing the probability density. For example, if we know that $\mu_x = 6$ and $\sigma_x = 2$, then the probability that x falls between 2 and 10 is

$$P(2 < x < 10) = P(6 - 4 < x < 6 + 4) \geq 1 - \frac{2^2}{4^2} = 0.75$$

The central limit theorem states that if $x_1, x_2, \ldots, x_n$ are independent random variables with means $\mu_1, \mu_2, \ldots, \mu_n$ respectively and variances $\sigma_1^2, \sigma_2^2, \ldots, \sigma_n^2$ respectively, then their sum for large n tends toward a normal

[3] See, for example, Richard Von Mises (edited and complemented by Hilda Geiringer), *Mathematical Theory of Probability and Statistics* (New York: Academic Press, 1964), pp. 115 and 279.

distribution, the mean and variance of which are found by summing the individual means and variances. That implies that the random variable

$$z = \frac{\sum_{i=1}^{n} x_i - \sum_{i=1}^{n} u_i}{\sqrt{\sum_{i=1}^{n} \sigma_i^2}} \tag{3-92}$$

is approximately normally distributed with zero mean and unit variance when n is large. Although in theory these results hold only for large n, some authors suggest that sample sizes as small as 10 are often sufficient to assume normality. The most common application for the central limit theorem is to make probability statements about the means of samples of a fixed size n, drawn from a population whose mean and variance is known. Each observation x_i has mean μ and variance σ^2. Assuming that the n observations in a sample are independent, we can multiply and divide Equation 3–92 on the right by $1/n$ to obtain

$$z_n = \frac{(1/n)(\sum_{i=1}^{n} x_i - \sum_{i=1}^{n} \mu)}{(1/n)\sqrt{n\sigma^2}} = \frac{\bar{x} - \mu}{\sigma/\sqrt{n}} \tag{3-93}$$

We are now in a position to make any desired probability statements about $\bar{x}$, the sample mean.

Other techniques for fitting distributions to sample data will be discussed in the next chapter.

SELECTED BIBLIOGRAPHY

CLARKE, A. BRUCE, AND DISNEY, RALPH L. *Probability and Random Processes for Engineers and Scientists*. New York: John Wiley & Sons, Inc., 1970.

DUNCAN, ACHESON J. *Quality Control and Industrial Statistics*, Part I. 3d ed. Homewood, Ill.: Richard D. Irwin, Inc., 1965.

FELLER, WILLIAM. *An Introduction to Probability Theory and Its Applications*, Vol. 1. 3d ed. New York: John Wiley & Sons, Inc., 1968.

HILLIER, FREDERICK S., AND LIEBERMAN, GERALD J. *Introduction to Operations Research*, Chap. iii. San Francisco, Calif.: Holden-Day, 1967.

LANING, J. HALCOMBE, JR., AND BATTIN, RICHARD H. *Random Processes in Automatic Control*, Chap. ii. New York: McGraw-Hill Book Co., Inc., 1956.

PARZEN, E. *Modern Probability Theory and Its Applications*. New York: John Wiley & Sons, Inc., 1960.

SPRINGER, CLIFFORD H.; HERLIHY, ROBERT E.; MALL, ROBERT T.; and BEGGS, ROBERT I. *Probabilistic Models*. Homewood, Ill.: Richard D. Irwin, Inc., 1968.

———. *Statistical Inference*. Homewood, Ill.: Richard D. Irwin. Inc., 1966.

VON MISES, RICHARD (edited and complemented by Hilda Geiringer). *Mathematical Theory of Probability and Statistics*. New York: Academic Press, 1964.

PROBLEMS

3-1 Draw Venn diagrams to illustrate each of the following events for general A and B:

a) $\overline{A \cup B}$

b) $(A \cup B)$

c) $\overline{A} \cap B$

d) $(\overline{A} \cap B) \cup (A \cap \overline{B})$

e) $\overline{A} \cap \overline{B}$

3-2 A coin is tossed three times. Describe the sample space.

a) Describe each of the following events in terms of points in the sample space:

i) Two or more heads.

ii) Only one tail.

iii) One or more tails.

b) Assuming that the coin is unbiased, calculate the probabilities of the following events:

i) One head.

ii) Two tails.

iii) One tail given that the first toss is a head.

3-3 An urn contains three black balls and two white balls. First one ball is selected and then a second selection is made from among the remaining four balls. Assume that all possible results have the same probability. Find the probability that a black ball will be selected.

a) The first time.

b) The second time.

c) Both times.

3-4 If two dice are tossed, what is the probability of each of the following events?

a) A total of seven is obtained.

b) A total of two is obtained.

c) A total of four is obtained.

3-5 A lot of 20 castings is known to contain 10 defective castings. If a sample of five is drawn from the lot, what is the probability that all five will be good?

3-6 An assembly operation for a new machine requires two independent tasks. The times for each task measured in days are represented by the random variables x_1 and x_2 whose distributions are as follows:

x_1	$f(x_1)$	x_2	$g(x_2)$
1	0.2	2	0.1
2	0.3	3	0.5
3	0.4	4	0.2
4	0.1	5	0.2

a) Calculate the mean and variance for each task.

b) Develop the cumulative distribution for total assembly time.

c) Find the probability that total assembly time will exceed five days.

d) If task one costs $50 per day and task two costs $60 per day, find the mean and variance for total assembly cost.

3–7   The number of defects in a new garment prior to grading is believed to be Poisson distributed with a mean of four. After grading a production lot of garments, class *B* goods are identified as those with more than three defects while all of the rest are identified as class *A*.

a) What portion of each lot will be class *A*?

b) What is the probability that a garment selected from the class *B* group will contain five defects?

c) What is the mean number of defects in a class *A* garment?

3–8   The weights of a certain population of male college students can be described by a normal distribution with a mean of 165 pounds and a variance of 400.

a) Establish limits, symmetric about the mean, within which 90 percent of the population is located.

b) What is the probability that a student selected at random from this population will weigh between 170 and 175 pounds?

c) If the football coach chooses four defensive linemen by random selection from this population, what is the probability that his "front four" will average over 200 pounds?

d) If we know that no one weighing less than 180 pounds is a candidate for the football team, what is the probability that a man on the team from this school will weigh over 200 pounds?

3–9   The number of units an operator can process is believed to be Poisson distributed with a rate of five per hour. The number of breakdowns per eight-hour shift for the conveyor serving this work station is also Poisson distributed with a mean of two.

a) Find the probability distribution for the number of units produced between breakdowns.

b) Calculate the mean and variance for units produced between breakdowns.

3–10   A generous employer has agreed to give each man a day off on his birthday. For purposes of analysis he is willing to assume that every year has 365 days and that each day is equally likely for a birthday. In order to provide work coverage in each department, he must know the probability that two or more persons will be off on the same day.

a) Calculate the probability that two or more employees in a department of *n* persons will have the same birthday.

b) Find the department size above which the probability will exceed 0.5 that two persons will have the same birthday.

3–11   Prove that the correlation coefficient is equal to zero for independent random variables.

3-12 Prove that $\sigma_{x+y} = \sigma_x + \sigma_y$ for perfectly correlated variables and that $\sigma_{x+y} = \sigma_x - \sigma_y$ for negatively correlated variables.

3-13 Using the Taylor's formula technique, prove that the relationships of Table 3-2 are valid.

3-14 A group of four assembly operators is paid on the basis of a group incentive plan in which rejected items are charged against total production at the rate of four good units reduction for every reject. In a recent day's production, out of four rejects, three were attributed to Sam who has been berated by his fellow workers. Was Sam justified in attributing his frequency of breakage to chance?

3-15 A certain product is produced on two machines. Actual production on each machine each day is measured by the discrete random variables x_1 and x_2. Each entry in the table below represents the joint probability, e.g., $p(x_1 = 0, x_2 = 0) = 0.1$

x_2 \ x_1	0	1
0	0.1	0
1	0.3	0.3
2	0.1	0.2

a) Find the marginal distributions of x_1 and x_2.
b) Find the conditional distribution of x_1 given $x_2 = 2$.
c) Are x_1 and x_2 independent random variables?
d) Find the probability distribution of $(x_1 + x_2)$.

3-16 The rth factorial moment of a distribution is defined to be $E[x^{(r)}]$. You have been told that the rth factorial moment of a particular distribution is $n^{(r)}p^r$ where n and p are parameters of the distribution. From this information establish the mean, variance, and third moment about zero. Show all calculations.

3-17 Given the following data:

Demand (D)	Lead Time (L)	Joint Probability $f(D, L)$
2	1	0.2
3	1	0.1
4	1	0.3
4	2	0.3
2	2	0.1

a) Calculate the marginal distribution for lead-time demand $f(D)$.
b) Calculate the conditional probabilities $f(L|D)$ for $L = 1$ and $D = 0, 1, 2, 3, 4, 5, \ldots$

3-18   The local UA campaign manager is attempting to establish an estimate for contributions coming for a particular zone of the city. They are soliciting from ambassadors (A), beatniks (B), clerks (C), dentists (D), engineers (E), firemen (F) garbagemen (G), hustlers (H), inmates (I), and janitors (J). In this district the number of potential donors in each class is known as well as miscellaneous statistics about past giving habits. Independence among donors is assumed.

Profession	Number	Statistics
A	1	Past contributions follow Poisson distribution with mean = $49
B	300	Totals from samples of 300 in which every donor who gave contributed $1, appear binomially distributed with mean = $30
C	100	Individuals contribute an average of $10 with standard deviation = $2
D	4	Contributions from the total group are exponentially distributed with standard deviation = $400
E	2	Individuals in the engineering profession average $100, have a standard deviation of $5, and follow the gamma distribution
F, G, H, I, J	10 in each group	Statistics on individuals from these professions indicate a mean contribution of $15 with a variance of 9.

a) Develop a table for mean and variance of contributions from each profession treated as a whole.

b) The UA goal for this zone is $3,000. What is the probability that the goal can be exceeded?

c) What goal should be established such that the probability of exceeding it is 95 percent.

d) Establish a lower bound for the probability that a hustler picked at random will contribute between $9 and $21.

3-19   The batch output for a particular production process consists of the total output from three independent operations whose operating times are random variables. Each hour that process No. 1 operates gives 5 gallons of yield. Each hour for process No. 2 gives 10 gallons of yield. Each hour for process No. 3 gives 4 gallons of yield.

The number of hours run time in a batch for process No. 1, (x_1) is distributed by

$$f(x_1 = k) = \frac{8!}{k!(8-k)!}(0.3^k)(0.7)^{8-k} \qquad 0 \le k \le 8$$

process No. 2. (x_2) by

$$g(x_2 = k) = \frac{4^k e^{-4}}{k!} \qquad k \ge 0$$

and process No. 3 (x_3) by

$$h(x_3 = k) = \begin{cases} 0.1 & k = 0 \\ 0.3 & k = 1 \\ 0.2 & k = 2 \\ 0.4 & k = 3 \end{cases}$$

Develop a probability interval for total process yield such that the probability of the total falling within the interval is at least 0.60.

3–20 One of the basic inventory models, which you will encounter in your studies, is a deterministic model of the form

$$K = \frac{\lambda A}{Q} + \frac{IQ}{2} + C\lambda$$

where
  K = average annual cost
  λ = annual demand rate
  Q = order quantity
  A = order cost
  I = carrying charge per unit of inventory
  C = purchase price per unit

Suppose that your *I.E.* department has developed data which indicate that λ, Q, and I are really random variables. Their distributions are unknown, but the following numbers are available:

Mean for each random variable, i.e., μ_λ, μ_Q, μ_I

Variance for each random variable, i.e., σ_λ^2, σ_Q^2, σ_I^2

Correlation coefficients $r_{\lambda Q}$, $r_{\lambda I}$, r_{QI}

O. R. Bravedo has suggested that it is an adequate approximation to suppose that

$$E(K) = \frac{\mu_\lambda A}{\mu_Q} + \frac{\mu_I \mu_Q}{2} + C\mu_\lambda$$

What he now needs is an expression for the variance of K.

a) Use your knowledge of Taylor's formula to develop an approximation for σ_K^2 which can be expressed as a function of the given statistics.

b) For the special case of $\mu_Q = 500$, $\sigma_Q^2 = 10^4$ $\mu_I = 25$, $\mu_I^2 = 36$, $r_{QI} = 0.2$, find an exact expression for the mean of $(IQ/2)$.

c) Now suppose $r_{QI} = 0$ in part (*b*). Find exact expressions for both the mean and variance of $(IQ/2)$.

3–21 Monte Carlo has a battlefield simulation ready to operate on site near the island of Nirvana. To operate the simulation he needs to sample from a normal distribution with mean 20 and variance 16. He has no way to directly generate the required normal observations. However, he can send out 10 man patrols to check the enemy stables. From old Prussian Army data he believes that the number of kicks inflicted on a man assigned to such a patrol will be distributed by a nonnormal distribution with a mean of 3.0 and variance 2.5.

a) Develop and justify a method for obtaining the necessary normal observations from patrol missions.

b) Illustrate your methods for the particular set of (1, 0, 3, 5, 6, 4, 2, 2, 0, 3) kicks suffered by the members of a patrol.

CHAPTER 4

Applications for Statistics

THE SCIENCE of statistics is often known by the layman only in terms of descriptive statistics. This branch of statistics is solely concerned with organizing facts from numerical data. One thinks of statistics in terms of the number of highway deaths last year, our gross national product, or total dollar value of sales for the company. But this is just a portion of the total science of statistics. There is another portion of statistics concerning matters of estimation and inference which is quite closely related to probability theory.

For our purposes we will consider the estimation of parameters obtained by experiment to be a problem in statistics. In fact there are two aspects to this problem which are often used to divide the field of statistics. One concerns the design of experiments and investigations while the other concerns statistical inference. Our major interest will be statistical inference, which provides measures of the uncertainty of conclusions drawn from experimental data.

Descriptive Statistics

Descriptive statistics are used to simplify and summarize data so that the information content of the data can be more easily comprehended. We have already mentioned summary data such as total highway deaths, gross national product, and total sales. Now we will look at slightly more sophisticated descriptions of such data.

Frequency. In Chapter 3 we worked extensively with probability distributions of random variables. The sample data counterparts of these theoretical distributions are the relative frequency distributions and their associated graphs, the relative frequency histograms.

The first step in organizing numerical data is to arrange it in ascending or descending order of magnitude. The resulting array may then be manipulated to obtain desired measures and grouped in various ways to offer graphic evidence of its underlying structure. The most common means of grouping data is to divide the range (largest value minus smallest) into a number of class intervals. The frequency associated with each class interval is simply the number of data points which fall within that interval. Relative frequency is obtained by dividing the absolute frequency of each class by the total number of data points in the array. As with the theoretical probability distributions, cumulative frequencies are obtained by counting all cases less than or equal to the point of interest.

The range is commonly divided into class intervals of equal size. When possible, class intervals are chosen such that their midpoints coincide with actually observed data but their boundaries do not. To illustrate these concepts, consider the time study data for tool crib service contained in Table 4–1.

TABLE 4–1

Tool Crib Service Time Measured in Minutes

1.6	1.8	2.0	2.1	2.4
1.6	1.8	2.0	2.1	2.4
1.7	1.8	2.0	2.2	2.5
1.7	1.9	2.0	2.2	2.6
1.8	2.0	2.1	2.3	2.7

The range for these data is 2.7–1.6, or 1.1 minutes, which we will divide into six class intervals. Since each data point is measured to the nearest 0.1 of a minute, class boundaries occurring at points which are odd multiples of 0.05 will not include the actual points. In addition, six intervals will provide cell frequencies greater than one. A tabular description of these data is given in Table 4–2. This information can be displayed graphically as shown in Figure 4–1.

TABLE 4–2

Class Boundaries		Frequencies		Cumulative Frequencies	
From	To	Absolute	Relative	Absolute	Relative
1.55	1.75	4	0.16	4	0.16
1.75	1.95	5	0.20	9	0.36
1.95	2.15	8	0.32	17	0.68
2.15	2.35	3	0.12	20	0.80
2.35	2.55	3	0.12	23	0.92
2.55	2.75	2	0.08	25	1.00

FIGURE 4–1

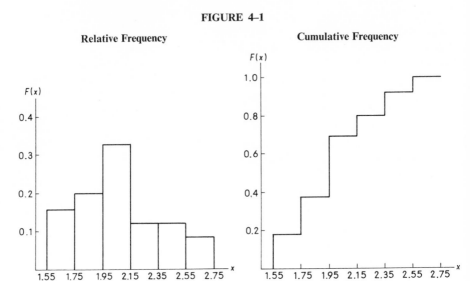

Relative Frequency   Cumulative Frequency

In the event that it is desirable to have each observed value of the sample data appear at the midpoint of a class interval, our interval width would be 0.1 minute. The resulting relative frequency distribution could then be used in the same manner as the theoretical distributions for random variables employed in the previous chapter. For the data given, the distribution would appear in bar chart form as shown in Figure 4–2. The advantages of grouping the data into larger class intervals for visual display should be obvious.

Order Statistics. The frequency distribution is just one way of describing a set of numbers $\{x_i\}$. Another way is to use numbers calculated in some way from the set $\{x_i\}$. Such numbers are called statistics. The simplest statistics to calculate are order statistics. These include the median, the range, and percentiles.

FIGURE 4–2

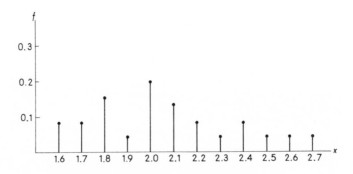

The term percentile is used in reference to a distribution of observations. For example, the 20th percentile, P_{20}, is defined as the value below which 20 percent of the distribution of values will fall. The easiest way to establish percentile numbers is to operate from the cumulative frequency polygon, which is obtained from the cumulative frequency distribution by connecting the tops of all bars with straight lines. The 20th percentile is read as the x value which has an f coordinant of 0.20. Note that this value, $P_{20} = 1.725$, as obtained from Figure 4–3, does not correspond exactly to any of the observed values of Table 4–1. This convention is adopted so that all percentiles are defined and all analysts will get the same number for any given percentile. Otherwise, one might argue from the definition that any number from 1.701 through 1.8 is the 16th percentile and that 1.801 is the 32nd percentile.

The median is the middle value in an ordered group of observations. Table 4–1 contains 25 observations. The middle value is the 13th member of the array, i.e., 2.0. If there is an even number of observations, the median is defined as the average of the two middle values. For the array 10, 12, 14, 17, 20, 21 the median is $(14 + 17)/2 = 15.5$.

In many cases there will be very little difference between the arithmetic mean and median, but they may differ widely. For example, suppose that four men are earning salaries of $5,000, $5,000, $7,000, and $27,000. The median is $6,000 while the mean is $11,000. The mode is yet another measure of central tendency. The mode is the value of the observation occurring most frequently. In our salary example the mode is $5,000. Thus we see that each

FIGURE 4–3

Cumulative Frequency Polygon

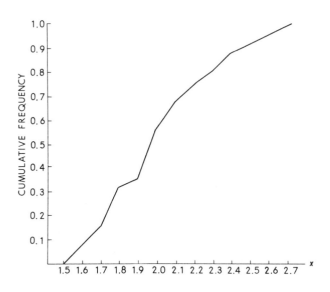

of the three statistics (mean, mode, and median) which purport to measure central tendency gives a different number.

Range is a simple measure of dispersion among the observations. It is defined as the largest value minus the smallest value in the ordered array. The range of salaries in the previous paragraph is $27,000 − $5,000 = $22,000. The range, coupled with a measure of central tendency such as the median, gives a description of a set of observations in very concise form. However, such measures are of limited use in performing the more sophisticated analyses associated with mathematical statistics.

Moment Statistics. Moment statistics provide useful information in describing observations and are vital to our future calculations. The best known moment statistics are the arithmetic mean and the standard deviation. In contrast to order statistics which use little information about the actual value of numbers in the set, moment statistics use the actual value of each number in the set being described.

The concept of sample moment statistics is a straightforward extension of the moments of a distribution introduced in Chapter 3. Indeed, if we consider the sample to be our entire population, the calculations are identical. For example, the tool crib data of Table 4–1 could be displayed in relative frequency form as:

x	$f(x)$	x	$f(x)$	x	$f(x)$	x	$f(x)$
1.6	$\frac{2}{25}$	1.9	$\frac{1}{25}$	2.2	$\frac{2}{25}$	2.5	$\frac{1}{25}$
1.7	$\frac{2}{25}$	2.0	$\frac{5}{25}$	2.3	$\frac{1}{25}$	2.6	$\frac{1}{25}$
1.8	$\frac{4}{25}$	2.1	$\frac{3}{25}$	2.4	$\frac{2}{25}$	2.7	$\frac{1}{25}$

The first moment about zero, which we now refer to as the sample mean ($\bar{x}$) is from Chapter 3,

$$\bar{x} = \sum_{x_i} x_i \, f(x_i) \tag{4-1}$$

The second moment about the mean, which we now call the sample variance (s^2), is in similar fashion

$$s^2 = \sum_{x_i} (x_i - \bar{x})^2 f(x_i) \tag{4-2}$$

For these data the mean and variance are

$$\bar{x} = 1.6(\tfrac{2}{25}) + 1.7(\tfrac{2}{25}) + \cdots + 2.7(\tfrac{1}{25}) = 2.052$$

and

$$s^2 = (1.6 - 2.052)^2 \, \tfrac{2}{25} + (1.7 - 2.052)^2 \, \tfrac{2}{25} + \cdots + (2.7 - 2.052)^2 \, \tfrac{1}{25}$$
$$\approx 0.089$$

So far, these calculations are indistinguishable from those performed in determining the mean, μ, and variance, σ^2, of a known distribution, $f(x)$. However, it is not necessary to develop the relative frequency distribution in order to determine sample moments. Instead, the usual procedure is to develop the moments directly from the raw data as

$$\bar{x} = \frac{1}{n} \sum_{i=1}^{n} x_i \qquad (4\text{-}3)$$

$$s^2 = \frac{1}{n} \sum_{i=1}^{n} (x_i - \bar{x})^2 \qquad (4\text{-}4)$$

where n is the number of data elements in the sample. In this form, the first moment $\bar{x}$ is easily recognized as the simple arithmetic average of the sample values. The second moment s^2 is in similar fashion the simple arithmetic average of the squared deviations of data elements from the mean.

The equivalence of the two forms of calculation can be seen by examining the relative frequency calculation for the mean in our example problem. Regrouping the terms of that expression,

$$\bar{x} = \tfrac{1}{25}[1.6(2) + 1.7(2) + \cdots + 2.7(1)]$$
$$= \tfrac{1}{25}[1.6 + 1.6 + 1.7 + 1.7 + \cdots + 2.7]$$
$$= \frac{1}{25} \sum_{i=1}^{25} x_i$$

Even though our sample was given as an ordered array, order is unimportant when calculating sample moments.

As was the case with our mathematical expectation calculations, a computational form of the variance can be obtained. Consider only the expression under the summation in Equation 4-4:

$$\sum_{i=1}^{n} (x_i - \bar{x})^2 = \sum_{i=1}^{n} (x_i^2 - 2x_i\bar{x} + \bar{x}^2)$$
$$= \sum_{i=1}^{n} x_i^2 - 2\bar{x} \sum_{i=1}^{n} x_i + \sum_{i=1}^{n} \bar{x}^2$$
$$= \sum_{i=1}^{n} x_i^2 - n\bar{x}^2 \qquad (4\text{-}5)$$

The computational form of the sample variance is then

$$s^2 = \frac{1}{n} \sum_{i=1}^{n} x_i^2 - \bar{x}^2 \qquad (4\text{-}6)$$

This calculation is particularly easy to perform on calculators or computers. Each data point is squared as read in and sums of their values and their squares are accumulated. After summing, division by n provides the necessary numbers for both mean and variance. In our example,

$$\sum_{i=1}^{n} x_i = 51.3$$

and

$$\sum_{i=1}^{n} x_i^2 = 107.49$$

from which

$$s^2 = \frac{1}{25}(107.49) - \left(\frac{51.3}{25}\right)^2 = 0.089$$

The statistic s^2 is a biased estimate of the population variance. By that we mean that its expected value is not equal to the population variance. Later we will introduce $\hat{\sigma}^2$ as the unbiased estimate of population variance where

$$\hat{\sigma}^2 = \frac{n}{n-1}s^2 = \frac{1}{(n-1)}(\Sigma x_i^2 - n\bar{x}^2)$$

The expected value of $\hat{\sigma}^2$ is σ^2.

Higher sample moments are calculated in straightforward fashion. The first term in the computational form of the variance is the second moment about zero. The jth moment about zero is

$$m_j = \frac{1}{n}\sum_{i=1}^{n}(x_i)^j \qquad (4\text{--}7)$$

Higher order moments about the mean (μ_j) can be developed exactly as we develop the variance. For example, the first four moments about $\bar{x}$ are

$$\mu_1 = 0 \cdot \qquad (4\text{--}8)$$

$$\mu_2 = m_2 - m_1^2 \qquad (4\text{--}9)$$

$$\mu_3 = m_3 - 3m_2 m_1 + 2m_1^3 \qquad (4\text{--}10)$$

$$\mu_4 = m_4 - 4m_3 m_1 + 6m_2 m_1^2 - 3m_1^4 \qquad (4\text{--}11)$$

Based on these calculations, the most important moment statistics are

$\bar{x}$ = arithmetic mean = m_1
s^2 = variance = μ_2
s = standard deviation = $\sqrt{\mu_2}$

Sampling Procedures

Nearly every model constructed by an operations engineer is based upon incomplete information. He may hypothesize that product demand has a certain known probability distribution or that the mean interval between machine breakdowns is x hours, but he rarely knows these items with absolute certainty. His belief in the validity of his assumptions is frequently based upon sample observations. Sampling theory provides the link between populations and samples drawn from them. In their more powerful applications, sample data are used to estimate population parameters and to test hypotheses about the population. This is quite different from using the sample data directly as a model for the probability distribution of an unknown universe.

Samples are selections made in some fashion from a larger population or universe. The population may be real or hypothetical. We are of course most interested in inferences about real populations, but to aid the process we can use our knowledge of what happens when hypothetical samples are drawn from hypothetical universes. Populations may also be finite or infinite. Making inferences about a finite population is more difficult because the universe is changed by the removal of finite samples. For that reason even for universes which are known to be finite, infinite hypothetical populations are often used as models whenever the sample size is small relative to the population size.

The principal reasons for sampling are economy and inaccessibility of populations. It is often cheaper to measure a limited portion of a population than to examine every member, even if that could be accomplished. Of course the economy of data collection must be balanced against the risk of erroneous conclusions, but statistical theory provides means of quantifying that risk. In addition to economic arguments, one is often forced to use sample data simply because it may be impossible to examine the entire population. For example, if the universe consists of all possible cycle times that will be produced by a worker operating an engine lathe, we can never collect all of the data. The best we can do is to perform a time study over a finite number of cycles and hope that this sample provides an accurate description of future performance.

Design of Sampling Experiments. Since the purpose of sampling is to learn something about a universe, it is important to make the sample as nearly representative of the universe as possible. Sampling is an experiment. The method of choosing a sample is called the design of the experiment. A general treatment of design of experiments is an advanced topic in mathematical statistics which is beyond the scope of this text. We will mention only the simplest commonsense procedures.

The human tendency is to introduce bias into a sampling procedure through the application of judgments in the process of collecting the sample. The temptation is to discard certain events as not being representative when selecting typical events from a larger collection. Sometimes such omissions are deliberate and in some sense justified. For example, in the time study procedures described in Chapter 2, it is common practice to discard extremely long observed element times if in the analyst's judgment there was an unusual event which caused the extra delay. Time study data represent extremely biased samples, and deliberately so. In general, however, when using classical statistics we would like to remove judgmental decisions from data collection.

The simplest design to accomplish this is the random sample. Later we will discuss Bayesian analysis, which can be used to make subjective and judgmental decisions about the data.

The basic idea of a random sample is that every element in the universe has an equal chance of being included in the sample. Theoretically, every item chosen should be measured and returned to the population before another selection is made. This means that a particular item may be chosen more than once in the same sample. Practically, if the population is large compared to the sample size, very little error is introduced by not returning each item to the population. In fact it may be impossible to do so if the item is changed or destroyed by the examination.

The safest way to generate a random sample is to use a table of random numbers to determine the order of selection of the sample from its population. Such a table consists of numbers chosen in a fashion similar to drawing numbered tags out of a box containing N uniquely identified tags. If for example, we wish to draw a sample of five orders from a file containing 100, the random numbers 60, 31, 14, 28, 24 would tell us that the 60th, 31st, etc., orders should be examined.

Sometimes the elements in the universe of interest are already arranged in random order. When that is true, systematic sampling can be used to produce random samples. In our order-pulling example, if there is no reason to suspect that the amount of the order should vary with its position in the file, selecting every 20th order until five are obtained should give a representative sample from our universe. This technique should be used with extreme care, however. If the orders are filed by date and every fifth one corresponds to a Monday sale, the sample will be extremely biased. Similar difficulties arise in work sampling studies where observations are made at fixed intervals of say 30 minutes. If the operation being observed is truly random, no difficulties arise. However, if there is a basic cycle with a mean occurrence time which is an even multiple of 30, a very biased view of the task under study will be obtained. When in doubt, the safest procedure is to use random sampling.

Stratified sampling is used when the population may be subdivided into several subpopulations or strata. The number of observations in the sample is apportioned among these strata. Within each stratum, random or systematic sampling is applied in the usual fashion. For example, if we want to know something about absenteeism among employees in a plant employing 300 women and 700 men, we might divide a proposed sample of 100 into a random sample of 30 selected from female personnel records and 70 from male personnel records. In this way we can be assured that our prior knowledge of population statistics will be utilized to give a more representative sample than a simple 100 records selected completely at random.

Sampling Distributions.   Anytime we calculate a statistic from sample data we are generating a new random variable. The probability distribution of a statistic obtained from a sample is called a sampling distribution. Since $\bar{x}$

and s^2 are the most commonly used statistics in operations engineering, we will stress the development of their distributions.

We could generate empirical approximations for sampling distributions. For example, suppose that a random sample of 10 cylinders is inspected from each day's production of several hundred. The mean ($\bar{x}$) and variance (s^2) of each sample of 10 are calculated and recorded. At the end of one hundred production days the array of one hundred sample means can be used to construct a relative frequency diagram for means. The array of variances can also be used to construct a relative frequency diagram for variances. These diagrams are empirical estimates of the sampling distributions for mean and variance. Statistics on the statistics can be calculated from these arrays. For instance, we can calculate a mean of the means ($\bar{\bar{x}}$) and a variance of the means ($s_{\bar{x}}^2$) by treating each of the sample means in our array as though it was a single observation from an unknown universe of mean values.

Sampling Distributions for the Mean. Fortunately, to develop probability statements about sample statistics, we can employ the theory of mathematical statistics to provide more expedient methods than enumeration of many samples. The first such application has already been introduced. Recall from Chapter 3 that the central limit theorem tells us that under very general conditions, the sum of n independent random variables will be normally distributed. We used that fact to demonstrate that means of samples of size n will be normally distributed, with the mean of the means equal to the population mean and the variance of the means equal to the population variance divided by the sample size.

As long as the sample is reasonably large, say greater than 30, the mean and variance of the sample can be used as estimates of the corresponding population parameters in applying the central limit theorem. Then, under very general conditions on the distribution function of individual samples,

$$z = \frac{\bar{x} - \hat{\mu}}{s/\sqrt{n}} \qquad (4\text{-}12)$$

will tend to be normally distributed with zero mean and variance of one. Thus we have our sampling distribution for means of large samples.

In the event that we know that the population being sampled is normally distributed with a specified mean and variance, the sample means will be normal regardless of sample size.

The use of the central limit theorem is acceptable only when we have large samples, say greater than 30, with sample estimates used for variance or smaller samples, say between 10 and 30, from a population with known variance. Otherwise, we should employ the t distribution as the sampling distribution for means.[1]

---

[1] See Acheson J. Duncan, *Quality Control and Industrial Statistics* (3d ed.; Homewood, Ill.: Richard D. Irwin, Inc., 1965), p. 128.

The t distribution (also known as "Students t") is given by

$$f(t) = \left(\frac{1}{\sqrt{\pi v}}\right) \frac{\Gamma[(v+1)/2]}{\Gamma(v/2)} \left(1 + \frac{t^2}{v}\right)^{-(v+1)/2} \tag{4-13}$$

where $-\infty < t < \infty$. The mean of this distribution is zero when the parameter $v > 1$. The variance is $v/(v-2)$ for $v > 2$. The t distribution arises from defining a random variable t as a function of a normally distributed random variable x and one which is chi-square distributed. The variable $t = x\sqrt{v}/\sqrt{\chi^2}$ is distributed by the t distribution. This relationship appears in the distribution of means since $(\bar{x} - \mu)\sqrt{n}/\sigma$ is normally distributed and $(n-1)\hat{\sigma}^2/\sigma^2$ has a χ^2 distribution. Furthermore, if $v = n - 1$, it follows that the statistic

$$t = \frac{\bar{x} - \hat{u}}{\sqrt{\hat{\sigma}^2}/\sqrt{n}} \tag{4-14}$$

where $\hat{\sigma}^2$ is an unbiased estimate of the variance, will be distributed according to the t distribution. The parameter $v = n - 1$ is called the number of "degrees of freedom" of the distribution. The degrees of freedom are those associated with the χ^2 component discussed in the next section. As n becomes large, this distribution approaches the normal. The t distribution is most useful for samples of less than 30 drawn from a normally distributed universe with an unknown variance. It can be applied under those circumstances exactly as we applied the normal sampling distribution.

Distribution of Sample Variances. Unfortunately, there is no general theorem regarding the form of the distribution of sample variance. However, if we are willing to assume that the population from which we are sampling is normal in form, then the distribution of sample variances has the form of a χ^2 distribution. The χ^2 distribution is given by

$$f(\chi^2) = \frac{(\chi^2)^{(k-2)/2} e^{-\chi^2/2}}{(2^{k/2})[(k/2) - 1]!} \tag{4-15}$$

where the parameter k refers to the number of degrees of freedom of the distribution. This distribution has a mean of k and variance of $2k$. For large values of k it approaches normality. The χ^2 statistic is given by

$$\chi^2 = \sum_{i=1}^{k} \left(\frac{x_i - \mu_i}{\sigma_i}\right)^2 \tag{4-16}$$

where μ_i and σ_i are the mean and variance of a normal distribution. The phrase "degrees of freedom" refers to the number of independent random variables whose squares are being added.

The sample variance is calculated from

$$s^2 = \frac{\sum_{i=1}^{n}(x_i - \bar{x})^2}{n}$$

If the x_i values are normally distributed with variance σ^2 we can form the statistic

$$\sum_{i=1}^{n} \frac{(x_i - \bar{x})^2}{\sigma^2} = \frac{ns^2}{\sigma^2} \tag{4-17}$$

which will be χ^2 distributed with $n - 1$ degrees of freedom. We have lost one degree of freedom by using $\bar{x}$ in the calculation of sample variance. There are only $n - 1$ independent squares in the sum.

Suppose for example that for training purposes we are to time 10 cycles of a process, which from past data we know has a normal distribution with process time variance of 20. The training director feels that, ideally, sample variance should be within 22 percent of the population variance of 20 in order to permit accurate evaluation of the trainee. We want to find the probability that sample variance will exceed 24.4. The χ^2 statistic is

$$\chi^2 = \frac{10(24.4)}{20} = 12.2$$

From the χ^2 tables reading at the line $k = n - 1 = 9$, we see that

$$P(\chi^2 > 12.2) = 0.20$$

Therefore the chance that sample variance will exceed 24.4 is 2 out of 10.

If we cannot assume that the parent population is normal, we may be reduced to characterizing the sampling distribution for variance by its mean and variance. To obtain the necessary estimates, we can use the techniques developed in Chapter 3 for finding the mean and variance of combinations of random variables. The mean of the sample variance is given by

$$E(s^2) = E\left[\frac{\sum_{i=1}^{n}(x_i - \bar{x})^2}{n}\right]$$

$$= \frac{1}{n}\left[E\left(\sum_{i=1}^{n} x_i^2\right) - nE(\bar{x}^2)\right]$$

Applying the rules for means of sums and products of random variables,

$$E(x_i^2) = \mu^2 + \sigma^2$$

and

$$E(\bar{x}^2) = \mu_{\bar{x}}^2 + \sigma_{\bar{x}}^2 = \mu^2 + \frac{\sigma^2}{n}$$

from which

$$E(s^2) = \frac{1}{n}\left[n(\mu^2 + \sigma^2) - n\left(\mu^2 + \frac{\sigma^2}{n}\right)\right]$$

or

$$E(s^2) = \left(\frac{n-1}{n}\right)\sigma^2 \qquad (4\text{-}18)$$

Thus we see that the mean of our sampling distribution for variance is equal to $(n-1)/n$ times the variance of the population from which the samples are drawn. The statistic s^2 is a biased estimator of the population variance since its expected value is not equal to σ^2. The unbiased estimate of σ^2 is $\hat{\sigma}^2 = [n/(n-1)]s^2$ since its expectation is equal to the population variance. An approximation to the variance of the sampling distribution can be obtained in similar fashion from

$$\mathrm{Var}(s^2) = E[(s^2 - E(s^2))^2]$$

$$= E\left[\left(\sum_{i=1}^{n} \frac{(x_i - \bar{x})^2}{n} - \left(\frac{n-1}{n}\right)\sigma^2\right)^2\right]$$

$$\approx \frac{\mu_4 - \mu_2^2}{n} \qquad (4\text{-}19)$$

where μ_4 and μ_2 refer to the moments about the mean for the parent population. At this point, if one is unwilling to make any further assumptions about the form of the underlying distribution, Tchebycheff's inequality can be applied to determine rough limits on probable variations in s^2. For a more complete discussion of this problem, the reader should consult a statistics text such as Duncan.[2]

Estimation Problems

There are two kinds of estimates commonly used by statisticians, the point estimate and the interval estimate. The term point estimate refers to a single number which gives an estimate of some unknown quantity. The term interval estimate refers to a pair of numbers between which the unknown quantity is believed to be. Interval estimates are usually accompanied by a measure of assurance that the interval includes the true parameter. This measure of assurance is called a confidence level.

Point Estimates. The most widely used method for obtaining point estimates is called the method of maximum likelihood. The principle of maximum likelihood recommends that one value of the parameter be selected as an estimate which if it were the true value would produce the highest probability of the observed sample results.

According to Duncan, the method of maximum likelihood is favored because the estimates it yields have good properties.[3] Maximum likelihood estimates are

---

[2] *Ibid.*, chap. vi.
[3] *Ibid.*, p. 454.

1. Consistent. The probability that the estimate deviates from the universe value by any predetermined amount decreases as the sample size increases.
2. Approximately normally distributed for large sample sizes.
3. Efficient. No other estimate which is approximately normally distributed in large samples has a smaller sampling variance.
4. Sufficient. No other estimate based upon the same data and independent of the maximum likelihood estimate can yield any further information about the universe parameter.
5. Best estimates. If x is a maximum likelihood estimate of X, then in general $f(x)$ is a maximum likelihood estimate of $f(X)$.

To use the method of maximum likelihood, we must be willing to assume that the observations in our sample came from a family of distributions completely specified except for the parameters. The method involves forming a likelihood function which represents the probability of observing the set of n sample observations as a function of the unknown parameters. This function is then maximized with respect to the parameters. For example, suppose that we will test fire 50 rounds from a new military weapon. If a round scores a bullseye we will record a one. If it misses we will record a zero. In mathematical terms this can be viewed as drawing a sample of 50 from a Bernouilli distribution where the density for each observation x_i is given by

$$f(x_i = x) = p^x(1 - p)^{1 - x} \qquad x = 0, 1 \qquad (4\text{--}20)$$

The Bernouilli distribution is a special case of the binomial where the parameter $n = 1$. The parameter p is to be estimated from the sample data.

The probability of acquiring the particular sequence of numbers appearing in the sample is

$$f(x_1, x_2, \ldots, x_{50}; p) = [p^{x_1}(1 - p)^{1 - x_1}][p^{x_2}(1 - p)^{1 - x_2}] \cdots [p^{x_{50}}(1 - p)^{1 - x_{50}}]$$

$$= \prod_{i=1}^{50} f(x_i; p) = p^{\Sigma x_i}(1 - p)^{50 - \Sigma x_i}$$

Since sums are easier to work with than products, let us maximize the logarithm of the likelihood function. The logarithm of the likelihood has its maximum at the same point as does the likelihood. Therefore let us maximize L, where

$$L = \log \prod_{i=1}^{n} f(x_i; p) = \sum_{i=1}^{n} \log f(x_i; p) \qquad (4\text{--}21)$$

For the binomial problem under consideration let $y = \Sigma x_i$, then

$$L = y \log p + (50 - y) \log(1 - p)$$

from which

$$\frac{dL}{dp} = \frac{y}{p} - \frac{50 - y}{1 - p} = 0$$

and

$$\frac{d^2 L}{d p^2} < 0$$

Therefore, the maximum likelihood estimate for p is

$$p = \frac{y}{50} = \frac{1}{50} \sum_{i=1}^{50} x_i = \bar{x}$$

which is as we would have suspected. We know that the mean and variance for a Bernoulli distribution are $\mu = p$ and $\sigma^2 = p(1 - p)$. We can now use the fact that for most functions, maximum likelihood estimates of functions of a parameter are equal to the functions evaluated with the parameter equal to its estimate, to obtain

$$\hat{\mu} = \frac{1}{n} \sum_{i=1}^{n} x_i$$

and

$$\hat{\sigma}^2 = \frac{1}{n} \sum_{i=1}^{n} x_i \left(1 - \frac{1}{n} \sum_{i=1}^{n} x_i \right)$$

Since the sample values are zero or one, it follows that $\Sigma x_i = \Sigma x_i^2$ and

$$\hat{\sigma}^2 = \frac{1}{n} \sum_{i=1}^{n} x_i^2 - \bar{x}^2 \tag{4-22}$$

What we have shown is that the first and second sample moments are maximum likelihood estimates for the corresponding population parameters.

The general rule for developing maximum likelihood estimates for multiple parameter populations is to form the function

$$L = \log \prod_{i=1}^{n} f(x_i; \theta_1, \theta_2, \ldots, \theta_k) \tag{4-23}$$

then take partial derivatives with respect to the unknown parameters θ_i. The resulting set of k equations,

$$\frac{\partial L}{\partial \theta_1} = \frac{\partial L}{\partial \theta_2} = \cdots = \frac{\partial L}{\partial \theta_k} = 0 \tag{4-24}$$

must then be solved simultaneously to obtain the maximum likelihood estimates $\theta_1, \theta_2, \ldots, \theta_k$.

Unbiased Estimates. An unbiased estimate of a population parameter is one whose expected value is equal to the parameter. That is, $\hat{\theta}$ is unbiased if

$$E(\hat{\theta}) = \theta$$

If $\hat{\theta}$ is not unbiased, the difference

$$b = E(\hat{\theta}) - \theta$$

is called the bias. Unfortunately, maximum likelihood estimators are not in general unbiased.

Throughout this chapter we have referred to sample mean and sample variance as estimators of population mean and variance. The sample mean is an unbiased estimator of population mean, but sample variance is a biased estimate of population variance.

We have already demonstrated the biased nature of sample variance in Equation 4–18. There we showed that

$$E(s^2) = \left(\frac{n-1}{n}\right)\sigma^2$$

where the factor $(n-1)/n$ is an indication of the magnitude of bias. We can correct for the bias in this estimate by defining

$$\hat{\sigma}^2 = \frac{n}{n-1}(s^2) \qquad\qquad (4\text{-}25)$$

It follows, then, that

$$E(\hat{\sigma}^2) = \frac{n}{n-1} E(s^2) = \sigma^2$$

as required of an unbiased estimate.

In some texts the sample variance is defined as the unbiased estimate $\hat{\sigma}^2$ by combining the multiplication factor and our definition of s^2. That is,

$$\hat{\sigma}^2 = \frac{n}{n-1}\left[\frac{1}{n}\sum_{i=1}^{n}(x_i-\bar{x})^2\right] = \frac{\displaystyle\sum_{i=1}^{n}(x_i-\bar{x})^2}{n-1} \qquad (4\text{-}26)$$

We will take care to distinguish between these two estimates of population variance ($\hat{\sigma}^2$ and s^2) even though for large values of n their difference is negligible. The formula for variance of a set of values,

$$s^2 = \sum_{i=1}^{n}\frac{(x_i-\bar{x})^2}{n}$$

is valid regardless of whether we are computing the variance for an entire population or for a sample from a population.

All of our discussion about estimates has implicitly assumed that we are sampling from an infinite population or that we have used sampling with replacement. There are additional corrections to be applied if our population size is small relative to the sample size. Springer et al., argue that if one is using a computer for the calculations, these sometimes complicated expressions should be routinely employed.[4] The interested reader is urged to

---

[4] Clifford H. Springer, Robert E. Herlihy, Robert T. Mall, Robert I. Beggs, *Statistical Inference* (Homewood, Ill.: Richard D. Irwin, Inc., 1966), pp. 221-22.

consult that text for discussion of these and other considerations for estimation. For the most part we will employ the simpler approximations already introduced.

Interval Estimates. We have seen that some kinds of point estimates have certain desirable properties, However, any estimate constructed from sample data is a random variable. This means that it is highly unlikely that a point estimate of a population parameter will be correct. What we often are interested in specifying is an interval that will have a high probability of including the universe value. Thus an engineer might estimate the yield strength of a certain steel as 30,000 psi ± 2,000. A cost accountant might estimate the labor cost for performing the yield test as $12 ± $3. The idea behind these estimates is that it is very unlikely that yield strength will fall outside the range 28,000 to 32,000 psi or that test costs will fall outside the range $9 to $15. The point estimates of 30,000 psi and $12 have been qualified by establishing an interval around each in which we feel the true values may lie.

Suppose, for example, that we draw a sample of four observations (2.7, 1.3, 1.9, 2.1) of inspection times from a normal distribution with a known variance of 0.36. The maximum likelihood estimate of the unknown population mean μ is the mean of the sample observations

$$\bar{x} = 2.0$$

In general, for samples of size 4, the statistic

$$z = \frac{\bar{x} - \mu}{\sigma/\sqrt{n}} = \frac{\bar{x} - \mu}{0.3}$$

will be normally distributed with $\mu = 0$, and $\sigma^2 = 1$. The probability that z lies between any two arbitrarily chosen numbers can be calculated. For example,

$$P(-1.96 < z < 1.96) = 0.95 \qquad (4\text{--}27)$$

as determined from the normal tables. This is easily converted into a probability statement involving μ. Since

$$-1.96 < \frac{\bar{x} - \mu}{0.3}$$

it follows that

$$\mu < \bar{x} + 0.3\,(1.96) = \bar{x} + 0.588$$

Similarly,

$$\frac{\bar{x} - \mu}{0.3} < 1.96$$

is equivalent to

$$\mu > \bar{x} - 0.588$$

We can therefore rewrite the probability statement 4–27 in the form

$$P(\bar{x} - 0.588 < \mu < \bar{x} + 0.588) = 0.95 \qquad (4\text{--}28)$$

which after substituting $\bar{x} = 2.0$ becomes

$$P(1.412 < \mu < 2.588) = 0.95 \qquad (4\text{--}29)$$

We can now make the statement that we are 95 percent certain that the two limits (1.412, 2.588) contain the true mean value between them.

The problems associated with confidence intervals are discussed at length by Mood and Graybill.[5] They are particularly careful to interpret the meaning of the confidence interval. Since μ is not a random variable stating that the probability that μ falls between 1.412 and 2.588 is 0.95 is meaningless. Either the indicated interval contains μ or it does not. What this statement does tell us is that the probabllity that the random interval $\bar{x} - 0.588$ to $\bar{x} + 0.588$ covers the true mean is 0.95. This means that if we draw 100 samples of four from the population and compute the random interval $\bar{x} - 0.588$ to $\bar{x} + 0.588$ for each sample, then on the average 95 of those intervals would be expected to contain the true mean μ.

The interval 1.412 to 2.588 is called a 95 percent confidence interval. Obviously we can obtain intervals with any desired degree of confidence by employing the properties of the normal distribution. Any numbers a and b such that the ordinants of those points include C percent of the area under the standard normal curve can be used to determine a confidence interval. Since the normal curve is symmetric about $z = 0$, the shortest confidence intervals are obtained by letting $b = -a$ as shown in Figure 4–4.

In general, if we know the variance of a normal population, the C percent confidence estimate for the mean is obtained from

$$P\left[\bar{x} - \frac{\sigma}{\sqrt{n}}(z_{(100-C)/2}) < \mu < \bar{x} + \frac{\sigma}{\sqrt{n}}(z_{(100-C)/2})\right] = \frac{C}{100} \qquad (4\text{--}30)$$

The term $z_{(100-C)/2}$ represents the critical z values from the standard normal curve which define C percent of the area under the curve. The critical values for 90 percent, 95 percent and 99 percent confidence are 1.645, 1.960, and 2.576, respectively.

Since we do not usually know the variance of the population from which we are sampling, a more accurate procedure is to employ the t distribution for our confidence interval estimates. Using the unbiased estimate for population variance,

$$\hat{\sigma}^2 = \frac{n}{n-1}s^2 = \frac{\sum_{i=1}^{n}(x_i - \bar{x})^2}{(n-1)}$$

---

[5] Alexander M. Mood, and Franklin A. Graybill, *Introduction to the Theory of Statistics* (New York: McGraw-Hill, Book Co., Inc., 1963), chap. xi.

FIGURE 4-4

A Confidence Interval

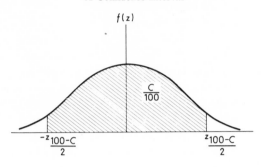

we have from Equation 4–14

$$t = \frac{\bar{x} - \mu}{\sqrt{\Sigma(x_i - \bar{x})^2/n(n-1)}} \tag{4-31}$$

which follows the distribution 4–13. Since this distribution is symmetric, we find confidence limits as we did with the normal. For instance, if we want to establish a 90 percent confidence interval for the mean of a population on the basis of a sample of size n, we must find a number $t_{0.05}$ such that

$$P(-t_{0.05} < t < t_{0.05}) = \int_{-t_{0.05}}^{t_{0.05}} f(t, n-1)\,dt = 0.90$$

Converting inequalities yields

$$P\left(\bar{x} - \frac{t_{0.05}\,\hat{\sigma}}{\sqrt{n}} < \mu < \bar{x} + \frac{t_{0.05}\,\hat{\sigma}}{\sqrt{n}}\right) = 0.90 \tag{4-32}$$

The critical t values are obtained from the tables of the t distribution with $n-1$ degrees of freedom. If n is sufficiently large (a common rule of thumb is $n > 30$), the normal distribution may be used as an approximation to the t distribution.

Confidence intervals for the variance of a normal distribution are obtained in straightforward fashion from the χ^2 distribution. Recall from Equation 4–17 that the statistic ns^2/σ^2 is χ^2 distributed. Following our usual arguments, we seek two numbers a and b such that

$$P(a < \chi^2 < b) = \int_a^b f(\chi^2)\,d\chi^2 = \frac{C}{100}$$

Converting inequalities we obtain

$$P\left(\frac{ns^2}{b} < \sigma^2 < \frac{ns^2}{a}\right) = \frac{C}{100} \tag{4-33}$$

from which the desired confidence interval can be computed.

The χ^2 distribution is not exactly symmetric, especially for a small number of degrees of freedom. However, as a practical matter Mood and Graybill recommend selecting a and b such that an equal area is cut from each tail of the distribution even though this may not be the shortest confidence interval.[6] If the χ^2 is tabulated in complementary cumulative form, then for 90 percent confidence we would choose $a = \chi^2_{0.95}$ and $b = \chi^2_{0.05}$ from a table of the χ^2 distribution with $n - 1$ degrees of freedom.

Determining the Sample Size. Since the width of our confidence interval estimates for the mean are obviously a function of sample size n, we will introduce an approximate technique for establishing the adequacy of sample size.

Consider a time study analyst who has just completed a preliminary study of an assembly operation. He has obtained 36 observations from which he has calculated a mean cycle time of $\bar{x} = 1.5$ minutes and a variance of $s^2 = 0.09$. If he duplicates his study the next day, what is the probability that the mean of the next study will fall between 1.4 and 1.6 minutes? Lacking any other information, let us assume that the population mean and variance are reasonably approximated by the sample data. Then for the next sample,

$$P(1.4 \leq \bar{x} \leq 1.6) = P\left(\frac{1.4 - 1.5}{0.05} \leq z \leq \frac{1.6 - 1.5}{0.05}\right)$$
$$= F(2) - F(-2)$$
$$= 0.9772 - 0.0228 = 0.9544$$

as obtained from the normal tables.

Now let us pose a slightly more difficult question. How large should the sample be if in a long history of time studies, the analyst wants to have 95 percent confidence that the error of his estimate will not exceed 10 percent of the mean.

Graphically, we are defining a portion of the real line which we believe will include the true population mean 95 percent of the time. For large sample sizes, $\bar{x}$ is normally distributed with mean μ and variance σ^2/n. Therefore, the confidence interval statement is

$$P\left(\bar{x} - \frac{1.96\sigma}{\sqrt{n}} \leq \mu \leq \bar{x} + \frac{1.96\sigma}{\sqrt{n}}\right) = 0.95$$

The error of the estimate from the confidence interval statement is $1.96\sigma/\sqrt{n}$. This error will be equal to $0.1\bar{x}$ if

$$\frac{1.96\sigma}{\sqrt{n}} = 0.1\bar{x}$$

from which

$$n = \left(\frac{1.96\sigma}{0.1\bar{x}}\right)^2 \tag{4-34}$$

[6] *Ibid.*, p. 254.

Since we do not usually know σ, we must use a sample estimate s as an approximation. For small values of n, the t distribution should be used instead of the normal to obtain the coefficient for $s/\sqrt{n}$.

To apply these results to the study problem, we will use $s = 0.3$ and $\bar{x} = 1.5$ and ignore the fact that they were originally estimated from a sample of 36. From Equation 4-34,

$$n = \left[\frac{(1.96)(0.3)}{(0.1)(1.5)} \right]^2 \approx 16$$

This tells us that a sample of 16 observations is sufficient to be 95 percent confident that the observed mean is within ± 10 percent of the true mean. Our original sample of 36 is more than adequate. If the indicated sample size had exceeded 36, we would be forced to collect more data, revise our estimates, and try the calculation again.

The general form of the sample size equation is

$$n = \left(\frac{Ds}{a\bar{x}} \right)^2 \tag{4-35}$$

where

D = the number of sigma units associated with the desired level of confidence.

s = a sample estimate of population standard deviation

$\bar{x}$ = a sample mean

a = accuracy desired

Hypothesis Testing

So far we have limited our discussion to the statistical problems of describing populations and estimating parameters. Now we will discuss methods for using those procedures to perform tests. This major area of statistical inference is called testing of hypotheses.

A statistical hypothesis is an assumption concerning some population. It usually takes the form of assigning values to one or more parameters of the population. For example, it may be hypothesized that the average life of a certain cutting tool is 200 machining hours. This is expressed as $H_0: \mu = 200$. The only way to be absolutely certain about the truth or falsity of such a hypothesis may be to examine the entire population of cutting tools. Since this may be impractical or impossible, we will resort to taking a sample from from the population and use the sample results to make the decision of whether or not to accept the hypothesis. Obviously there is some risk that an erroneous conclusion will be drawn when we employ such procedures. However, we now have sufficient background in statistics to quantify the risks we are taking.

There are some philosophical implications concerning where the risk level should be established and what it means to accept an hypothesis. However, for the moment let us simply ask the question: What is the chance that the sample results observed could occur if H_0 is really true? For example, suppose that we have a long history of production records which have established with reasonable certainty that the cutting tools now being used have a mean life of 200 hours with a standard deviation of 40. We now have the opportunity to purchase a different brand of tool at a slightly lower cost. In spite of the salesman's claim, our concern is that the cheaper tool will be of inferior quality with a reduced mean life. We are willing to assume that the variance will remain unchanged.

Suppose that 25 of the new tools are used on the production line as a comparison test to establish their worth. These 25 prove to have a mean of $\bar{x} = 180$ hours. The question now is: What is the chance that we could draw a sample of 25, whose mean is at least as low as $\bar{x} = 180$, from a population with a mean $\mu = 200$ and standard deviation $\sigma = 40$? From our knowledge of the sampling distribution for means,

$$z = \frac{\bar{x} - \mu}{\sigma / \sqrt{n}}$$

is normally distributed. The data of the problem yield a critical z value of

$$z = \frac{180 - 200}{40/5} = -2.5$$

From the normal tables,

$$P(\bar{x} < 180) = P(z < -2.5) = 0.0062$$

This indicates that in slightly over six times out of 1,000 we might indeed find a sample mean at least as low as 180 from a population with $\mu = 200$. If it is our opinion that this is too rare an event to support the hypothesis that the new tools have the same life characteristics as the old, we would reject H_0.

Error Types. The procedure outlined above does give us some feel for the risk of accepting the salesman's claim. However, a more satisfactory procedure may be to establish a critical region before the test is conducted, then accept or reject H_0 depending upon the sample results. In this way our risk level is predetermined and we are not put in a position or arguing with either the salesman or our conscience about the merits of the results. The critical region consists of all values of the test statistic where the decision is made to reject H_0.

In the process of establishing the critical region, two types of errors must be considered. A Type I error is committed if the hypothesis is really true but is rejected by the sample. A Type II error, is made if the hypothesis is accepted when it is not true. The risks asssociated with these errors are merely the probability of their occurrence. Thus α is referred to as the probability or risk of a Type I error and β as the risk of a Type II error. Ideally, we would like to minimize errors of decision. Practically, this is not a simple matter since for a given sample size, decreasing the risk of one type of error will lead to an increase in the second type error. The only way to reduce both types of error is to increase the sample size. If one type error is considered more serious than the other, a compromise may be reached in favor of limiting the more serious of the two.

The risk of Type II error can only be measured against some alternative hypothesis. Suppose, for example, that our alternative hypothesis in the cutting tool example is that the mean life of the cheap tool is 175 hours, expressed as $H_1 : \mu = 175$. Further suppose that we have established our critical region for samples of 25 as $\bar{x} < 185$. This means that if we observe a sample mean which is less than 185, we will reject $H_0 : \mu = 200$. Otherwise we will not reject it. The character of this test can best be appreciated by examining plots of the two hypothesized populations on the same axes.

Figure 4-5 presents the test information. The risk of Type I error for this test shown by area α in the figure is

$$P(\bar{x} < 185 \,|\, \mu = 200) = P\left(z < \frac{185 - 200}{8}\right) = 0.0304$$

The risk of the Type II error shown by area β is

$$P(\bar{x} \geq 185 \,|\, \mu = 175) = P\left(z \geq \frac{185 - 175}{8}\right) = 0.1057$$

Obviously we would obtain a different value of β if we proposed a different mean for H_1. A plot of β versus the mean of potential alternative populations is called the operating characteristic (OC) curve for a test. More will be said about OC curves in the chapter on quality control. Statisticians often prefer to plot $1 - \beta$, which they refer to as the power of a test.

Designing a Test. In the preceding discussion we have evaluated the risks involved by establishing an arbitrary critical region and sample size.

FIGURE 4-5

Testing a Hypothesis

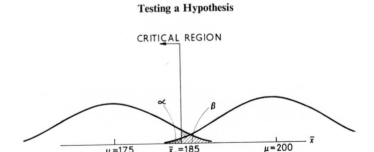

CRITICAL REGION

$\mu = 175$ $\bar{x}_c = 185$ $\mu = 200$

Let us now turn the problem around by attempting to establish a proper sample size and critical region to satisfy certain specified risks.

The information needed to design the test includes

1. The size of the shift in a parameter we wish to detect.
2. The variance of the population.
3. The risks (α and β) which we are willing to take.

In our example, suppose that we want to know if the mean life of the cheap tools is 25 hours less than our present tools. Both populations are assumed to have the same variability, $\sigma = 40$. Further suppose that we are willing to risk erroneously identifying the shift 5 percent of the time ($\alpha = 0.05$) and risk identifying a nonexistent shift 10 percent of the time ($\beta = 0.10$). (The error probabilities of 5 and 10 percent are commonly employed in hypothesis testing, although there is no reason to avoid other values if they seem more appropriate.)

We have sufficient information to form two equations in the two unknowns, $\bar{x}_c$ and n, which will specify our testing procedure. Based on $\alpha = 0.05$ we have

$$P(\bar{x} < \bar{x}_c \mid \mu = 200) = P\left(z < \frac{\bar{x}_c - 200}{40/\sqrt{n}}\right) = 0.05$$

from which

$$\frac{\bar{x}_c - 200}{40/\sqrt{n}} = -1.645 \qquad (4\text{–}36)$$

Based on $\beta = 0.10$ we have

$$P(\bar{x} \geq \bar{x}_c \mid \mu = 175) = P\left(z \geq \frac{\bar{x}_c - 175}{40/\sqrt{n}}\right) = 0.10$$

from which

$$\frac{\bar{x}_c - 175}{40/\sqrt{n}} = 1.282 \qquad (4\text{–}37)$$

Subtracting Equation 4–36 from 4–37, after clearing the denominator of each, gives

$$25 = 2.927\left(\frac{40}{\sqrt{n}}\right)$$

from which, after rounding, $n = 22$. Using this value in Equation 4–36 we have

$$\bar{x}_c = -1.645\left(\frac{40}{\sqrt{22}}\right) + 200 \approx 186$$

The decision rule is then: Choose a random sample of 22 cutting tools, and if the mean life of these is less than 186 hours, reject the hypothesis that they came from a population with mean 200 ($H_0: \mu = 200$); otherwise accept H_0.

This type of test design is called a one-tail test We have specified a critical region which falls on only one tail of the hypothesized distribution. A one-tail test was appropriate in our example because H_1 was on one side only of H_0. An alternative would be to construct a two-tailed test in which the risk α is split evenly between the tails. This would establish both upper and lower limits for our critical region when the alternative hypothesis is on both sides of H_0. Suppose, for example, that we want to conduct a two-tailed test for a sample of 25 when $\alpha = 0.05$, $H_0: \mu = 200$ and $H_1: \mu \neq 200$. Here we are interested in detecting differences in either direction. The appropriate probability statements are

$$P(\bar{x} > \bar{x}_u \mid \mu = 200) = \frac{\alpha}{2} = 0.025$$

and

$$P(\bar{x} < \bar{x}_L \mid \mu = 200) = \frac{\alpha}{2} = 0.025$$

These can be solved exactly as before from

$$\frac{\bar{x}_u - 200}{8} = 1.960$$

and

$$\frac{\bar{x}_L - 200}{8} = -1.960$$

The critical regions are then $\bar{x} > 215.68$ and $\bar{x} < 184.32$. Between the limits $\bar{x}_L$ and $\bar{x}_u$, H_0 is accepted. This decision rule is shown in Figure 4–6. As before, the risk of a Type II error can be established by finding the probability that drawn from an alternative population, the mean of a sample of 25 would fall between $\bar{x}_L$ and $\bar{x}_u$.

FIGURE 4–6

A Two-Tailed Test

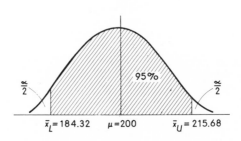

The parameter α is sometimes referred to as the level of significance. By choosing a 5 percent level of significance there are 5 chances in 100 that we would reject an hypothesis when it should be accepted. Alternatively, we are 95 percent confident that we have made the right decision.

General Strategy. For our purposes, the techniques of hypothesis testing have been amply demonstrated by the simple cutting tool example of the previous paragraphs. Since the parameter to be tested was the mean and since we assumed that the variance of our populations was known, the hypothesis tests were straightforward extensions of our knowledge of the normal sampling distribution for means. If we did not want to make the assumption that population variance was known, we could estimate variance from our sample and use the t distribution to determine the critical region for $\bar{x}$. If we were testing hypotheses about the variance of the population, the χ^2 distribution would be used, and so forth. The nature of the problem will indicate what test statistic is to be used, and we must consult the proper tables to establish the required critical region.

The general procedure for simple statistical experiments can be summarized as follows:

1. State the hypothesis to be tested, H_0, and its alternative, H_1.
2. Specify the risks of Type I and Type II errors, α and β.
3. Select the test statistic to test H_0.
4. Determine the sampling distribution for this test statistic under each of the hypotheses.
5. Calculate a sample size and establish a critical region on this test statistic which will satisfy the risk requirements.
6. Compute the value of the statistic from the observed sample values.
7. Accept or reject the hypothesis depending upon whether the computed statistic is outside or inside the critical region.

In practice, one frequently specifies α and the sample size n rather than design for a particular alternative H_1 and β. Under those conditions, all that is required is to calculate the critical region under the null hypothesis H_0.

A few of the more common testing situations are summarized in Table 4–2. For a more complete discussion of these and other tests, the reader is urged to consult Dixon and Massey or one of the other excellent texts listed in the Bibliography.[7]

Fitting a Distribution

Through our procedures of estimation, we already have methods to establish the values of parameters of underlying distributions on the basis of sample data. This may well be all the "fitting" we need if we only desire the

---

[7] Wilfred J. Dixon, and Frank M. Massey, Jr., *Introduction to Statistical Analysis* (New York: McGraw-Hill Book Co., Inc., 1951), chaps. vii, viii and ix.

TABLE 4-2
Hypothesis Tests

Test	Assumptions	Statistic	Distribution	Critical Region
1. $H_0: \mu = \mu_0$	σ^2 known	$z = \dfrac{\bar{x} - \mu_0}{\sigma/\sqrt{n}}$	Normal	$z \geq z_u$ $z \leq z_L$
2. $H_0: \mu \leq \mu_0$	σ^2 known	$z = \dfrac{\bar{x} - \mu_0}{\sigma/\sqrt{n}}$	Normal	$z \geq z_c$
3. $H_0: \mu = \mu_0$	σ^2 unknown	$t = \dfrac{\bar{x} - \mu_0}{\hat{\sigma}/\sqrt{n}}$	t_{n-1}	$t \geq t_u$ $t \leq t_L$
4. $H_0: \mu_1 = \mu_2$	$\sigma_1^2 = \sigma_2^2$ known	$z = \dfrac{\bar{x}_1 - \bar{x}_2}{\sigma\sqrt{1/n_1 + 1/n_2}}$	Normal	$z \leq z_L$ $z \geq z_u$
5. $H_0: \mu_1 = \mu_2$	$\sigma_1^2 = \sigma_2^2$ unknown	$t = \dfrac{\bar{x}_1 - \bar{x}_2}{\hat{\sigma}_p\sqrt{1/n_1 + 1/n_2}}$*	$t_{n_1 + n_2 - 2}$	$t \geq t_u$ $t \leq t_L$
6. $H_0: \sigma^2 = \sigma_0^2$	Normal population	$\chi^2 = \dfrac{ns^2}{\sigma_0^2}$	χ^2_{n-1}	$\chi^2 \leq \chi^2_L$ $\chi^2 \geq \chi^2_u$
7. $H_0: \sigma_1^2 = \sigma_2^2$	Normal populations	$F = \dfrac{\hat{\sigma}_1^2}{\hat{\sigma}_2^2}$	$F_{(n_1-1),\,(n_2-1)}$	$F \leq F_L$ $F \geq F_u$

* $\hat{\sigma}_p^2$ = Pooled estimate of $\sigma^2 = \dfrac{[(\Sigma x_{1i}^2 - (\Sigma x_{1i})^2/n_1 + \Sigma x_{2i}^2 - (\Sigma x_{2i})^2/n_2]}{(n_1 + n_2 - 2)}$

moments of a distribution without worrying too much about its form. However, when we want to make probability statements about a population, we need a method to test hypotheses about the form of the distribution. Here, hypothesis tests are conducted to establish the veracity of an equation for a curve based upon sample data.

The Chi-Square Test.   The term goodness of fit refers to the comparison of some observed sample distribution with a theoretical frequency distribution. Although there are several hypothesis tests which can be used in this context, the most widely used is the chi-square goodness-of-fit test. The χ^2 goodness-of-fit test is an hypothesis test which compares a set of sample frequencies with a set of frequencies that would be expected on the basis of some hypothesis about the distribution of the parent population. The statistic used to establish the critical region is

$$\chi^2 = \sum_{i=1}^{k} \left[\frac{(F_i - f_i)^2}{f_i} \right] \tag{4-38}$$

where

F_i = number of sample observations found in class interval i

f_i = number of observations expected under H_0

k = number of class intervals; k is usually selected so that no interval has $f_i < 5$

To illustrate the use of the test, suppose that we have collected automobile sales data for a particular dealer during a 100-day period. The mean of the sample data is 2.6 autos per day. Our hypothesis is that these data came from a Poisson distribution. If the population is in fact Poisson with $\mu = 2.6$, then we would expect on the average to sell one auto on 19.3 days during a 100-day study This comes from

$$P(x = 1 | \mu = 2.6) = 2.6e^{-2.6}/1! = 0.193$$

and

$$f_1 = n \, P(x = 1) = 100(0.193) = 19.3$$

This number $f_1 = 19.3$ is contrasted with the observed frequency $F_1 = 21$. Results for such comparisons for all possible values of daily sales are noted in Table 4–4. Sales days in which six or more units may be sold have been combined in an attempt to keep the theoretical frequency for each interval somewhere near the lower desirable limit of five.

The number of degrees of freedom associated with the test is equal to the number of cells, k, minus the number of conditions imposed by the fitting process. In this instance we have imposed two conditions, namely,

$$\Sigma f_i = \Sigma F_i$$

$$\bar{x} = \frac{\Sigma F_i x_i}{n}$$

TABLE 4-4

Calculations for the χ^2 Test of the Hypothesis
That Demand Is Poisson Distributed

Automobiles Sold	$F_i = Days$ Observed	$f_i = Days\ Expected$ from Poisson	$\dfrac{(F_i - f_i)^2}{f_i}$
0	8	7.4	0.049
1	21	19.3	0.150
2	23	25.1	0.177
3	18	21.8	0.662
4	6	14.1	4.650
5	11	7.4	1.751
6	10	3.2⎤ 4.9	5.310
≥7	0	1.7⎦	
			$\chi^2 = 12.749$

If we were attempting to fit a normal distribution whose variance must also be estimated from the sample data, we would lose a third degree of freedom. Checking the χ^2 tables for $k - 2 = 5$ degrees of freedom and a commonly used value of $\alpha = 0.05$, we find

$$P(\chi^2 > 11.07) = 0.05$$

Since our observed χ^2 value of 12.749 exceeds the boundary of our critical region ($\chi^2_c = 11.07$); we must reject at the 5 percent level of significance the hypothesis that our sales are being generated by a Poisson process. If χ^2 had been less than χ^2_c we would have accepted using the logic that samples drawn from the hypothesized population could reasonably be expected to yield such values. Any values less than χ^2_c are not rare events under the hypothesized conditions.

For a more complete discussion of the χ^2 goodness-of-fit test, the reader is urged to consult Duncan.[8]

Approximate Test. The operations engineer may be faced with sample data from a system for which he has no strong prior indication of the underlying distribution form. In this situation he may be reduced to matching moments with a general family of distributions in an attempt to obtain a reasonable candidate for further testing.

One of the most common quick tests is to compare the mean and variance of the sample data. If the mean and variance are approximately equal and the histogram is not terribly unrealistic, the analyst may be willing to make the assumption that the underlying distribution is Poisson. This technique is especially useful for small tactical models involving queues and inventories, since approximate solutions are often satisfactory and the Poisson assumption makes the models very easy to manipulate.

---

[8] Duncan, *op. cit.*, pp. 522–24.

In other situations we may be able to approximate empirical data with one of the members of the gamma or beta families of distributions. Recall that these functions acquire a wide variety of shapes as their parameter values change. For instance, suppose that we have sample data from which we have calculated $\bar{x} = 20$ and $s^2 = 36$. The gamma is a two-parameter distribution (a, b) of the form

$$f(x) = \frac{b(bx)^a}{a!} e^{-bx} \qquad x \geq 0 \qquad (4\text{-}39)$$

whose mean and variance are

$$\mu = \frac{a + 1}{b} \qquad (4\text{-}40)$$

$$\sigma^2 = \frac{a + 1}{b^2} \qquad (4\text{-}41)$$

Solving these equations for a and b we have

$$b = \frac{\mu}{\sigma^2} \qquad (4\text{-}42)$$

and

$$a = \left(\frac{\mu}{\sigma}\right)^2 - 1 \qquad (4\text{-}43)$$

We can now use our sample data to estimate the parameters as $b = \frac{20}{36}$ and $a = \frac{400}{36} - 1$. The adequacy of this fit can then be tested by the usual χ^2 goodness-of-fit procedure. Such procedures may not be terribly elegant but they do often provide needed analytic approximations for ill-defined underlying distributions.

Bayesian Techniques

In earlier sections we have treated a density function, say $f(x, \theta)$, where x is a random variable and θ is an unknown parameter which we hope to estimate from sample data. We have denied any prior knowledge of θ other than the general form of the space from which it is drawn. For example, in estimating the mean, we assumed only that it was a real number. When estimating the variance, we assumed only that it was a real number greater than zero, etc. In some operational situations, however, we may have additional information about θ which can be used to sharpen our estimates. For example, an operations engineer may have evidence that θ itself acts as a random variable for which he can postulate a realistic density function. Bayes estimators seek to make use of this additional information in estimating θ. The Bayes decision rule often makes use of probability and economic data. It says to compute the expected value of each act when conditional profits or losses as functions of possible states of the system are known and take the act with the most favorable expected value. In modern decision theory, prior information about probabilities may even be subjective. Estimates are revised as new data are presented.

Bayes Theorem. The postulated distribution for the parameter θ, say $g(\theta)$, is referred to as a prior or "a priori" distribution. After sample data have been observed and a sample statistic say X, calculated, our estimate of the form of the distribution may change. This revised distribution, $g(\theta \mid X)$, is called the posterior or "a posteriori" distribution of θ. The computation of the posterior probabilities is based upon Bayes theorem. Although techniques based upon Bayes theorem are receiving considerable emphasis in modern decision theory, their use in making probability statements about parameters predates the maximum likelihood and confidence interval arguments we have employed. For a more complete discussion of the classical uses of Bayes theorem, the reader should consult a text such as Cramer.[9] For the use of Bayesian analysis in modern decision theory, the reader should consult a text such as Schlaifer.[10]

The logic of Bayes theorem is easily developed through our knowledge of joint, marginal, and conditional probabilities. Recall that the joint probability (and density) of two events can be written as the product of a marginal and a conditional probability. For the estimation problem, assuming discrete random variables, let

$g(\theta)$ $=$ prior probability of θ

$g(\theta \mid X) =$ posterior probability of θ

$f(X \mid \theta) =$ conditional probability of obtaining sample statistic X from a population with parameter θ

$h(X,\theta)$ $=$ joint probability of X and θ

We know that

$$h(X, \theta) = g(\theta \mid X)f(X) = f(X \mid \theta)\, g(\theta) \qquad (4\text{-}44)$$

from the general relationships among joint, marginal, and conditional probabilities. Rearranging terms we have

$$g(\theta \mid X) = \frac{f(X \mid \theta)\, g(\theta)}{f(X)} \qquad (4\text{-}45)$$

But the marginal probability of X, $f(X)$, can be obtained from

$$f(X) = \sum_{\theta} h(X, \theta) = \sum_{\theta} f(X \mid \theta)\, g(\theta) \qquad (4\text{-}46)$$

[9] Harald Cramer, *Mathematical Methods of Statistics* (Princeton: Princeton University Press, 1946), p. 508.
[10] R. Schlaifer, *Analysis of Decisions under Uncertainty* (New York: McGraw-Hill Book Co., Inc., 1969).

Therefore the final statement of Bayes theorem is

$$g(\theta \mid X) = \frac{f(X \mid \theta)g(\theta)}{\sum_\theta f(X \mid \theta)\, g(\theta)} \tag{4-47}$$

In the event that the random variables are continuous, these same symbols can be used to represent their densities. We merely replace the summation with an integration.

One of the oldest methods for using Bayes theorem in estimation involves maximizing posterior probability for point estimates or establishing intervals on the basis of $g(\theta \mid X)$. Although this technique is useful, it should be pointed out that modern Bayesian estimates are not the same as the maximum posterior probability estimates. The modern approach is discussed later. For example, suppose that we are manufacturing TV tubes on a 24-hour per day basis. Past records indicate that the first shift produces an average of 12 percent defective tubes, the second shift 15 percent defective, and the third 18 percent defective. Furthermore, 0.5 of our total production comes from the first shift, 0.3 from the second, and 0.2 from the third. A particular lot is being prepared for shipment. We know that it was produced on a single shift, but we do not know which one. A sample of 50 tubes drawn from the lot reveals 8 defective tubes. The question to be answered is: What is our estimate for lot percent defective?

If we use maximum likelihood techniques, our estimate for lot percent defective is $p = \frac{8}{50} \times 100 = 16$ percent. However, this ignores the information we already have concerning our manufacturing process. Using the Poisson approximation to the binomial, we can develop the necessary statements for Bayes theorem from

$$P(\bar{x} = 8 \mid p = 0.12) = f(X \mid \theta_1) = 0.1033$$
$$P(\bar{x} = 8 \mid p = 0.15) = f(X \mid \theta_2) = 0.1373$$
$$P(\bar{x} = 8 \mid p = 0.18) = f(X \mid \theta_3) = 0.1318$$
$$P(p = 0.12) = g(\theta_1) = 0.5$$
$$P(p = 0.15) = g(\theta_2) = 0.3$$
$$P(p = 0.18) = g(\theta_3) = 0.2$$

Applying these to Equation 4-47, we obtain the following posterior probabilities:

$$g(p = 0.12 \mid \bar{x} = 8) = \frac{f(8 \mid 0.12)g(0.12)}{f(8 \mid 0.12)g(0.12) + f(8 \mid 0.15)g(0.15) + f(8 \mid 0.18)g(0.18)}$$

$$= \frac{(0.1033)(0.5)}{(0.1033)(0.5) + (0.1373)(0.3) + (0.1318)(0.2)}$$

$$= 0.433$$

$$g(p = 0.15 \mid \bar{x} = 8) = 0.346$$
$$g(p = 0.18 \mid \bar{x} = 8) = 0.221$$

Since the maximum posterior probability is $g(p = 0.12 \mid \bar{x} = 8)$, our estimate for p is $p = 0.12$ in spite of a sample fraction defective which is closer to 0.15. In this instance, our prior knowledge of the process has overshadowed the sample information. We would have made an identical prediction before any samples were drawn. This technique is most useful if the only possible values of p are 0.12, 0.15, and 0.18. If these values are themselves only estimates, other decision methods may be in order.

An alternative procedure, and one which would be followed by a modern Bayesian, would be to calculate the expected value of p based upon its posterior distribution. That is,

$$E(p \mid \bar{x} = 8) = \sum_p g(p \mid \bar{x} = 8)p$$
$$= (0.12)(0.433) + (0.15)(0.346) + (0.18)(0.221) = 0.1436$$

Thus the Bayesian estimate in modern terms would be $p = 0.1436$.

In later more sophisticated uses, Bayes theorem has been employed to develop estimators for the common population parameters, such as mean and variance. Modern Bayesian estimates make use of a loss function, $L(\hat{\theta}, \theta)$. A particular decision function is then established for $\hat{\theta}$ such that risk, $R = E[L(\hat{\theta}, \theta)]$, is minimized. $L(\hat{\theta}, \theta)$ indicates how much would be lost if we select $\hat{\theta}$ as our estimate when the true parameter value is θ. For example, we might select our loss function for an estimate of the mean, μ, as the squared error

$$L(\hat{\mu}, \mu) = (\hat{\mu} - \mu)^2$$

The Bayes estimator is then the value of $\hat{\mu}$, as a function of the sample observations $x_1, x_2, \ldots, x_n$, which minimizes

$$v(\hat{\mu}; x_1, \ldots, x_n) = \int_{-\infty}^{\infty} (\hat{\mu} - \mu)^2 h(\mu \mid x_1, \ldots, x_n) \, d\mu \qquad (4\text{-}48)$$

where the function h is the posterior density. The usual methods of calculus are employed to obtain $\hat{\mu}$. This technique is described in detail by Mood and Graybill.[11]

Application as a Decision Aid.   Bayesian techniques are often introduced in the context of modern decision theory. In this context, a convenient way to characterize a decision problem is by means of a decision matrix. One form for such a matrix has the decision maker's alternatives, a_i, listed as row headings, possible future states of nature, S_j, listed as column headings and measures of outcome $V(\theta_{ij})$ appearing as cell entries.

When the state of nature, S_j, is a random variable, we may select the alternative action, a_i, which minimizes our expected loss

$$E[L(a_i)] = \sum_j V(\theta_{ij}) f(S_j) \qquad (4\text{-}49)$$

---

[11] Mood and Graybill, *op. cit.*, pp. 187–92.

When $f(S_j)$ is interpreted as a prior distribution, it is said that we have used the Bayes principle to select the course of action. We may use experimental evidence to revise our estimates of the probabilities $f(S_j)$ by means of Bayes theorem. If we use this posterior distribution of S_j to calculate the appropriate expected values, we are said to be employing Bayes procedures. Hillier and Lieberman have a concise discussion of the process.[12]

To illustrate Bayes procedures, suppose that we must decide which of two customers shall receive the lot of TV tubes discussed in the previous example. Customer A expects to receive lots which are 12 percent defective. Each percentage point over that costs our company a penalty of $100. Customer B expects to receive lots which are 15 percent defective. If they are of poorer quality, we pay a flat penalty of $350. If they are of better quality, we lose a price premium of $100 per percentage point. The decision matrix, expressed in terms of dollar costs to our company, is shown in Figure 4–7.

FIGURE 4–7

A Shipment Decision

	S_1: 12% Defective	S_2: 15% Defective	S_3: 18% Defective
a_1: Ship to A	0	$300	$600
a_2: Ship to B	$300	0	$350

Prior to collecting any sample data, the expected costs of the alternatives were

$$E(a_1) = 0(0.5) + \$300(0.3) + \$600(0.2) = \$210$$

$$E(a_2) = \$300(0.5) + 0(0.3) + \$350(0.2) = \$220$$

The Bayes principle tells us to select a_1, that is ship to customer A for minimum expected loss. After examining the sample data in which 8 defective tubes were found in a sample of 50, we use the posterior distribution of S_i developed in the last section to obtain

$$E(a_1 \mid \bar{x}) = 0(0.423) + \$300(0.346) + \$600(0.221) = \$236.40$$

$$E(a_2 \mid \bar{x}) = \$300(0.423) + 0(0.346) + \$350(0.221) = \$204.25$$

Now our decision has been reversed. The Bayes principle tells us to use a_2 and ship to customer B for minimum expected cost in light of our experimental evidence.

A Bayesian approach often permits an analyst to take advantage of subjective estimates of probabilities of future events. It is at this point that

---

[12] Frederick S. Hillier and Gerald J. Lieberman, *Introduction to Operations Research* (San Francisco: Holden-Day, 1967), pp. 82–89.

modern decision theory departs most radically from traditional statistics. From a decision theory point of view, it is acceptable to use any reasonable information, including management judgment, to establish a prior distribution. These initial estimates are then updated through the use of Bayes theorem as experimental evidence is collected. This is a decided departure from the pure statistics view which would not admit subjective estimates as legitimate data when establishing a probability density.

Analysis of Variance

In earlier sections of this chapter we discussed methods for testing for significant differences between two means. However, in designing experiments it frequently is necessary or desirable to design the experiment in such a way that several factors can be studied simultaneously. In such a situation it would not be good statistical procedure to investigate the differences among the various means by performing a series of t tests. For example, if we wanted to use the t test to test differences among five means, we would have to compute 10 t values. In general, we would have as many t values, v_t, in comparing n means as there are possible combinations of n things taken two at a time. That is,

$$v_t = C_2^n = \frac{n!}{(n-2)!\,2!} \tag{4-50}$$

If we were to use a significance level of 5 percent for each such test, the level of significance for testing the hypothesis of no difference in the means of a group would be much higher. Even if all samples are from the same population, on the average 5 percent of the t values will exceed the critical level. Treating this as a binomial distribution with $n = 10$ and $p = 0.05$, the probability that one or more of the t values will exceed the critical level is

$$P(x \geq 1) = \sum_{x=1}^{10} C_x^{10}(0.05)^x(1 - 0.05)^{10-x} = 0.4013$$

With this testing procedure, the hypothesis of all means equal would be rejected when true over 40 percent of the time.

The analysis of variance is a more efficient statistical technique than running a series of t tests. It is used to discern whether or not there is enough difference among a set of sample means to suspect that one or more of them may be from a unique population. The null hypothesis to be tested is that the samples come from populations having the same mean values. However, the basis for the test is the decomposition of the statistical variance of the original data, hence the name analysis of variance (ANOVA).

The Basic Linear Model.   Let us begin our discussion with the simplest single-factor experiments. Suppose that we want to establish whether or not there are any performance differences among three secretaries in a typing pool.

Assume for the moment that they all type letters which are assigned to them at random. Performance is measured by the time it takes to type a single letter. Table 4-6 gives the results of a time study of their efforts.

TABLE 4-6

Letter Typing Data in Minutes

Secretary 1	Secretary 2	Secretary 3
9.2	7.6	7.7
8.8	8.4	7.0
9.0	8.2	6.8
8.2	7.8	8.0
9.8		7.3
		8.2

Every entry in this table represents a single observation x_{ij}. The basic model proposed is that each such observation is the sum of a common effect, μ, for the whole experiment; the treatment effect, t_j, associated with secretary j and a random error, e_{ij}, present in the ith observation on the jth treatment. The model then becomes

$$x_{ij} = \mu + t_j + e_{ij} \qquad (4\text{-}51)$$

We will follow the discussion presented by Hicks, who employs the dot notation.[13] A dot signifies a sum over all observations in a population. Thus $T_{..}$ is the sum of all observations in the table, $T_{.j}$ is the sum of all observations in column j, $\mu_{.j}$ is the mean of all possible observations in column j, or $E(x_{ij})$, etc.

In the basic model, we could view the treatment effect as being a deviation from the common effect for the whole experiment. Similarly e_{ij} can be viewed as the difference between the observed value x_{ij} and the effect of treatment j. Thus we can rewrite Equation 4-51 as

$$x_{ij} = \mu + (\mu_{.j} - \mu) + (x_{ij} - \mu_{.j})$$

or alternatively

$$x_{ij} - \mu = (\mu_{.j} - \mu) + (x_{ij} - \mu_{.j}) \qquad (4\text{-}52)$$

which is an identity true for all values of x_{ij}.

The means in this expression are unknown. However, we can use our knowledge of estimation theory to obtain sample estimates for each of the

---

[13] Charles R. Hicks, *Fundamental Concepts in the Design of Experiments* (New York: Holt, Rinehart & Winston, 1964), chap. iii.

treatment means $\mu_{.j}$ and the grand mean μ. Using only the data from column j we can estimate the treatment mean as

$$\bar{x}_{.j} = \frac{\sum_i x_{ij}}{n_j} = \frac{T_{.j}}{n_j} \tag{4-53}$$

In similar fashion, the grand mean is estimated from

$$\bar{x}_{..} = \frac{\sum_i \sum_j x_{ij}}{N} = \frac{T_{..}}{N} \tag{4-54}$$

where $N = \sum_j n_j$

Substituting these sample statistics for their corresponding population parameters yields

$$x_{ij} - \bar{x}_{..} = (\bar{x}_{.j} - \bar{x}_{..}) + (x_{ij} - \bar{x}_{.j}) \tag{4-55}$$

If both sides of Equation 4–55 are squared, then summed over both i and j we obtain

$$\sum_{j=1}^{k} \sum_{i=1}^{n_j} (x_{ij} - \bar{x}_{..})^2 = \sum_{j=1}^{k} \sum_{i=1}^{n_j} (\bar{x}_{.j} - \bar{x}_{..})^2 + \sum_{j=1}^{k} \sum_{i=1}^{n_j} (x_{ij} - \bar{x}_{.j})^2 \tag{4-56}$$

This is the expression which Hicks refers to as "the fundamental equation of analysis of variance."[14] It demonstrates that the total sum of squared deviations from the grand mean can be decomposed into the sum of squared deviations of treatment means from the grand mean and the sum of squared deviations within treatments. The importance of this observation is that it permits us to develop three unbiased estimates of population variance under the null hypothesis that $\mu_{.1} = \mu_{.2} = \cdots = \mu_{.k}$ or $t_j = 0$ for all j. The test statistic for ANOVA is a ratio of two of these estimates.

If we divide the term on the left of Equation 4–56 by $N - 1$, we have the usual unbiased estimate for population variance:

$$\sigma^2 = \frac{\sum_{j=1}^{k} \sum_{i=1}^{n_j} (x_{ij} - \bar{x}_{..})^2}{(N - 1)} \tag{4-57}$$

We could also estimate population variance by first estimating the variance of means drawn from a common population, $\sigma_{\bar{x}}^2$, then use for samples of size n,

$$\sigma_x^2 = n\sigma_{\bar{x}}^2$$

An unbiased estimate for the variance of means is given by

$$\hat{\sigma}_{\bar{x}}^2 = \frac{\sum_{j=1}^{k} (\bar{x}_{.j} - \bar{x}_{..})^2}{(k - 1)}$$

from which

$$\hat{\sigma}_x^2 = \frac{\sum_{j=1}^{k} n_j (\bar{x}_{.j} - \bar{x}_{..})^2}{(k - 1)} \tag{4-58}$$

---

[14] *Ibid.*, p. 25.

This expression can be obtained by dividing the first term on the right of Equation 4–56 by $(k - 1)$. The third unbiased estimate for population variance is obtained by pooling estimates of variance from each of the k treatments. That is, since

$$\frac{\sum_{i=1}^{n_j}(x_{ij} - \bar{x}_{.j})^2}{(n_j - 1)}$$

is an estimate of variance within the jth treatment and we assume that all k variances are equal, we obtain the pooled estimate

$$\hat{\sigma}_x^2 = \frac{\sum_{j=1}^{k}\sum_{i=1}^{n_j}(x_{ij} - \bar{x}_{.j})^2}{(N - k)} \qquad (4\text{–}59)$$

This is the last term in Equation 4–56 divided by $(N - k)$.

Obviously the three estimates for population variance described above are not independent. However, it can be shown that the estimates of Equations 4–58 and 4–59 will yield two independent, chi-square distributed, unbiased estimates of σ^2 when $\mu_{.1} = \mu_{.2} = \cdots = \mu_{.k}$. The ratio of two such unbiased estimates of the same variance forms the sample statistic F which will be distributed according to the F distribution with $(k - 1)$, $(N - k)$ degrees of freedom. The F distribution can be viewed as a special case of the beta distribution. The two parameters of the F distribution are called degrees of freedom. The number of degrees of freedom of the variate contained in the numerator of F is always quoted first. The test of the hypothesis $H_0: \mu_{.1} = \mu_{.2} = \cdots = \mu_{.k}$ is carried out by forming the ratio

$$F_{k-1, N-k} = \frac{\sum_{j=1}^{k} n_j(\bar{x}_{.j} - \bar{x}_{..})^2 / (k - 1)}{\sum_{j=1}^{k}\sum_{i=1}^{n_j}(x_{ij} - \bar{x}_{.j})^2 / (N - k)} \qquad (4\text{–}60)$$

Using a one-tail test, H_0 is rejected if $F \geq F_{1-\alpha}$ where the significance level α represents the area to the right of $F_{1-\alpha}$. In this test, the sum of squares between treatments is always put into the numerator. As Hicks suggests, a significant F then indicates that the difference between means has something in it besides the estimate of the variance.[15] The supposition is that there is a real difference in treatment means ($\mu_{.1}$, $\mu_{.2}$, etc.) and H_0 should be rejected.

To facilitate the computation of F, it is common practice to rewrite the sums in terms of treatment totals. A standard format for recording ANOVA results is shown in Table 4–7

The critical assumption behind this test is that the observations are from normal populations with equal variances for all treatments (homogeneous variance). However, it has been shown that moderate violations of the assumptions of normal distribution and equal variance will have little influence on ANOVA.

---

[15] *Ibid.*, p. 27.

TABLE 4–7

ANOVA Table for Single Factor ANOVA

Source of Variation	Degrees of Freedom	Sum of Squares (SS)	Mean Square
Between treatments (t_j)	$k-1$	$\dfrac{\sum_{j=1}^{k} T_{.j}^2}{n_j} - \dfrac{T_{..}^2}{N}$	$\dfrac{SS_t}{k-1}$
Error (e_{ij})	$N-k$	$\displaystyle\sum_{j=1}^{k} \sum_{i=1}^{n_j} x_{ij}^2 - \dfrac{\sum_{j=1}^{k} T_{.j}^2}{n_j}$	$\dfrac{SS_e}{N-k}$
Totals	$N-1$	$\displaystyle\sum_{j=1}^{k} \sum_{i=1}^{n_j} x_{ij}^2 - \dfrac{T_{..}^2}{N}$	

Returning to the data of Table 4–6, we see that the observed mean typing times per letter by secretary are

$$\bar{x}_{.1} = \frac{\sum_{i=1}^{5} x_{i1}}{5} = 9.0$$

$$\bar{x}_{.2} = \frac{\sum_{i=1}^{4} x_{i2}}{4} = 8.0$$

$$\bar{x}_{.3} = \frac{\sum_{i=1}^{6} x_{i3}}{6} = 7.5$$

The sample means are obviously different, but we do not yet know if this difference is statistically significant. The hypothesis to be tested is

$$H_0: \mu_{.1} = \mu_{.2} = \mu_{.3}$$

Between secretaries, variation gives the estimate

$$\hat{\sigma}_t^2 = \frac{[\sum_{j=1}^{3} T_{.j}^2/n_j - T_{..}^2/N]}{2}$$

$$= \frac{[(45)^2/5 + (32)^2/4 + (45)^2/6 - (122)^2/15]}{2} = 36.45$$

The estimate from the error term is

$$\hat{\sigma}_e^2 = \frac{[\sum_{j=1}^{3} \sum_{i=1}^{n_j} x_{ij}^2 - \sum_{j=1}^{3} T_{.j}^2/n_j]}{12}$$

$$= \frac{[1001.82 - 998.50]}{12} = 0.28$$

The test statistic is then

$$F = \frac{\hat{\sigma}_t^2}{\hat{\sigma}_e^2} = \frac{36.45}{0.28} \approx 130$$

Choosing a significance level of 0.05, the critical value from the F table is

$$F_{2,\,12} = 3.89$$

Since our test statistic is much larger than 3.89, we reject the null hypothesis and conclude that there is indeed a significant difference among secretaries.

Higher Order Analyses. The model discussed in the previous section was concerned only with differences among secretaries. It is easy to imagine, however, that we may be overlooking much information contained in the data which could be used to test other factors. For example, suppose that four executives use this secretary pool and that entries in the first four rows of Table 4–6 represent times recorded for different combinations of executives and secretaries. The entry $x_{22} = 8.4$ says that it took secretary number two 8.4 minutes to type a letter from executive number two. Similarly, $x_{23} = 7.0$ says that it took secretary number three 7.0 minutes to type a letter from the same executive. We could perform a two-way analysis of variance to test simultaneously for differences among secretaries and among executives. The basic model becomes

$$x_{ij} = \mu + t_i + c_j + e_{ij} \tag{4-61}$$

where

μ = an overall mean

t_i = a row effect (executive bias)

c_j = a column effect (secretary bias)

e_{ij} = a random residual normally distributed with zero mean and variance σ^2

In this model it is possible that either the t_i's or the c_j's or both may be zero. If by hypothesis the t_i's are zero we can make independent estimates of σ^2 from (1) the variation between row means (executive means) and (2) the residual variance in a manner similar to the one-way ANOVA. The ratio of these estimates is used in an F test to test the hypothesis of no executive bias. In similar fashion, an estimate of σ^2 based on column means is used together with the residual variance to test for secretary bias.

In the event that we have more than one observation for each executive-secretary combination, we can add another test by examining the interaction effect. The model now becomes

$$x_{ijk} = \mu + t_i + c_j + t_{ij} + e_{ijk} \tag{4-62}$$

where t_{ij} represents the interaction or joint executive-secretary bias.

Still another dimension could be added if there were several different brands of typewriters in use in the secretary pool. By moving secretaries from machine to machine and assigning each secretary at least one letter from every executive, we could use the same data to test for (1) differences among secretaries, (2) differences among executives, (3) differences among typewriters, and (4) interaction effects. Such a model without the interactions would appear as

$$x_{ijk} = \mu + t_i + c_j + r_k + e_{ijk} \tag{4-63}$$

With interactions the model would be

$$x_{ijk} = \mu + t_i + c_j + r_k + t_{ij} + t_{ik} + t_{kj} + t_{ijk} + e_{ijk} \tag{4-64}$$

As before, the strategy is to develop independent estimates of the variance by considering each factor in turn. These estimates are then used to form ratios with the estimate for variance from the error term, which are in turn used in F tests. The details on such designs are contained in several of the texts listed at the end of this chapter.

SELECTED BIBLIOGRAPHY

CRAMER, HARALD. *Mathematical Methods of Statistics*. Princeton: Princeton University Press, 1946.

DIXON, WILFRID J., AND MASSEY, FRANK J. JR. *Introduction to Statistical Analysis*. New York: McGraw-Hill Book Co., Inc., 1951.

DUNCAN, ACHESON J. *Quality Control and Industrial Statistics*. 3d ed. Homewood, Ill.: Richard D. Irwin, Inc., 1965.

HICKS, CHARLES R. *Fundamental Concepts in the Design of Experiments*. New York: Holt, Rinehart & Winston, 1964.

HOAG, R., AND CRAIG, A. *Introduction to Mathematical Statistics*. 2d ed. New York: McGraw-Hill Book Co., Inc., 1965.

MOOD, ALEXANDER M., AND GRAYBILL, FRANKLIN A. *Introduction to the Theory of Statistics*. 2d ed. New York: McGraw-Hill Book Co., Inc., 1963.

MORRIS, WILLIAM T. *Management Science a Baysian Introduction*. Englewood Cliffs, N.J.: Prentice-Hall, Inc., 1968.

SCHLAIFER, R. *Analysis of Decisions under Uncertainty*. New York: McGraw-Hill Book Co., Inc., 1969.

SPIEGEL, MURRAY A. *Theory and Problems of Statistics*. New York: Schaum Publishing Co., 1961.

SPRINGER, CLIFFORD H.; HERLIHY, ROBERT E.; MALL, ROBERT T.; AND BEGGS, ROBERT I. *Statistical Inference*. Homewood, Ill.: Richard D. Irwin, Inc., 1966.

PROBLEMS

4–1   In the following table the time (in seconds) for 40 observations of a critical job cycle are recorded.

a) Construct a frequency distribution with five-second class intervals. Use the first-class mark (midpoint) as 120.

b) Construct a histogram from this data.

c) Construct a frequency polygon from this data.

d) What is the range?

e) What is the median?

f) What is the mode?

g) What is the mean?

h) What is the standard deviation?

i) Establish a 95 percent confidence interval for mean cycle time based on this data.

j) Determine the number of observations necessary to be 95 percent confident that the population mean lies within ± 10 percent of the observed sample mean.

128	149	156	144	142	150	145	138
135	152	153	136	147	140	173	146
165	154	119	163	176	138	126	168
144	140	148	135	147	142	158	146
157	145	125	150	132	135	164	161

4–2   Given the following data:

4, 6, 5, 4, 2, 4, 6, 5, 4, 5, 5, 7, 4, 3, 4, 1, 6, 3, 4, 2

Find:

a) Mean.

b) Mode.

c) Median.

d) Range.

e) Standard deviation.

f) Plot a histogram for this data.

g) Assuming that this data came from a normal distribution, calculate the 95 percent confidence interval for the population mean.

h) Determine the number of readings required for a confidence of 95 percent that the mean of the population is within ± 5 percent of the sample mean.

4–3   Given that the population of times from which I am sampling is distributed according to the normal distribution with $\mu = 2$, $\sigma = 0.5$, find the probability that a single observation will fall in the range of 1.7 to 2.4.

4–4   Given that I have observed a task 10 times and have calculated $\bar{x} = 3.5$, $s_x = 0.7$, determine the sample size I *should* collect to be 99 percent confident that the population mean falls within ± 20 percent of the sample mean.

4–5   During the analysis of data for a particular sample of a three-element cycle the following quantities have been calculated:

Element	No. of Readings	Mean Element Time ($\bar{x}$)	Variance (s_x^2)
1	400	0.05 min.	0.0009
2	400	0.10	0.0036
3	400	0.08	0.0064

a) What is the coefficient of variation for each element?

b) Based on the above data would you say the observer has obtained an adequate sample size? If not how many cycles should he study? (Assume a desired confidence level of 99 percent and accuracy of ±10 percent.)

c) What accuracy was achieved for element 1 assuming 95 percent confidence?

d) How confident are we that the *actual* time for element 2 is within ±6 percent of the observed sample mean?

4-6   During the analysis of data for a particular sample of a three-element job the following quantities have been calculated:

Element	No. of Readings	$\Sigma(x_i)$	$\Sigma(x_i^2)$
1	300	12 min.	0.75
2	500	25	1.70
3	450	18	0.90

a) What is the mean time for each element?

b) What is the standard deviation for each element?

c) What is the coefficient of variation for each element?

d) Based on the above data would you say the observer has obtained an adequate sample size? If not, how many cycles should he study for 99 percent confidence and an accuracy of ±5 percent?

e) How confident are you that the actual time for element 2 is within ±6 percent of the observed sample mean?

4-7   A work sampling study of the activities of a local bar-maid has been conducted. Observations made at random intervals revealed 20 instances of chatting with customers and 80 instances of other activities. Based on this pilot study, calculate 68 percent confidence limits for the true proportion of time she is engaged in conversation.

4-8   A bottleneck operation has been subjected to a pilot study with a resulting mean observed time of 0.04 minutes and a variance of 0.0009. On the basis of this pilot study:

a) How many observations should you make to be 99 percent confident of an accuracy of ±5 percent relative to the estimated mean?

b) How confident are you that the element above is within ±7½ percent of the observed sample mean if this sample consisted of 400 observations?

4-9   Ben Commerce has become convinced that the telephone in his girl's dorm is tied up a disproportionate amount of time. To test his belief he placed 100 phone calls at random times during the day. He got through on 20 of his attempts. Calculate for Ben the 95 percent confidence limits for the true proportion of time the line is open.

4-10   Joe College has tried all quarter to reach his instructor. Being a good industrial engineer he has recorded his efforts which show that only 8 calls out of 40 attempted at random intervals during the quarter were successful. Calculate for Joe the 95 percent confidence limits for the true portion of time his instructor is available.

4-11 Consider the following time study data:

Element	Mean Observed	Elemental Standard Data	Variance
1	0.12 min.	—	0.0004
2	0.20	0.22	0.0016
3	1.40	—	0.0049

From work sampling data,
Number of observations working, 88
Number of observations allowable idleness, 12
a) Calculate an estimate for the number of observations necessary to be 95 percent confident that the true percent idle time falls between 10 percent and 14 percent.
b) Estimate the number of observations necessary to guarantee with 99 percent confidence at least 10 percent accuracy in the observed times for the *elements* listed. (Note: You only need *one* estimate, not three.)
c) Determine a standard time for this job.

4-12 In measuring the performance of a bottleneck operation, the time study department has taken a sample of size 20 with a resulting mean time of 6.0 minutes and a variance of 9.0. To maintain balance in the system it has been estimated that a true mean in the range of 5.4 to 6.6 will be satisfactory. How many readings do I need to be 95 percent confident that the true mean does fall within the indicated range?

4-13 As a first guess at describing measurements from a machining experiment, the local production engineer estimates that individual measurements are approximately uniformly distributed on the interval 1.005 to 1.010 inches.
a) What is the expected value of a single measurement?
b) What is the variance for this population?
c) Establish a 99 percent confidence interval for the mean of a sample of size 16 drawn from the above population.

4-14 Given the following time study sheet:

Element	Cycle 1	2	3	4	5	Standard Data Time
1. Man	0.16	0.20	0.17	0.19	0.18	
2. Machine	0.21	0.27	0.25	0.24	0.23	0.24
3. Man	0.18	0.16	0.15	0.17	0.19	
4. Man	0.15	0.09	0.12	0.14	0.10	0.10
5. Machine	0.16	0.14	0.15	0.13	0.17	0.15
6. Man	0.13	0.10	0.15	0.16	0.11	0.10

Company practice is to rate machine elements at 133 percent. A work sampling study indicates 40 allowable instances of personal time, unavoidable delays, etc., and 360 instances of productive work during the observations. Employees are given a 30-minute lunch period which is not accounted for in the above work sampling study.

a) Compute the sample size which will give ± 10 percent accuracy with 95 percent confidence for the actual percent of allowances.

b) Compute 99 percent confidence limits for percent allowance.

c) What are the mean elemental times?

d) What is the normal cycle time?

e) What is the standard in pieces per hour?

4-15   The Wipeout Skateboard Company is attempting to determine a standard for their product demonstrators. Stopwatch observations indicated the following information concerning the demonstration procedure:

Element	No. of Observations (N)	Mean Observed Time (x)	Variance (s^2)
1. Position board	100	0.20	0.15
2. Mount board	100	0.10	0.04
3. Descend hill	81	0.40	0.09
4. Recover board	64	0.73	0.04
5. Return to top	49	1.60	0.36
6. Bandage sore knees (occurs once every 5 cycles)	16	6.00	0.81

Element No. 3 is considered to be machine controlled and is rated at 100 percent. A work sampling study indicated 7 instances of allowable personal time and 28 instances of productive work. Standard data for element 5 indicates a normal time of 1.80 minutes and for element 1, 0.25 minutes.

a) What rating factor will you use?

b) Calculate the normal time per round trip.

c) Calculate a standard time in minutes per trip.

d) How many observations are needed to be 99 percent confident that the true mean time to recover a board lies between 0.71 and 0.75 minutes?

4-16   It has been proposed that the departmental secretary be studied in order to establish a reasonable estimate of the time required to perform various tasks. A preliminary work sampling study has been conducted with the following results:

Activity	Number of Observations
Typing exams	52
Typing letters	68
Talking on the phone	40
Delays	22
Personal time	18

The above observations occurred at random over a five-day period. (The normal workday is eight hours.) During that time, six exams, 40 letters, and 98 telephone calls were handled. The average rating factor was 120 percent.

a) Determine the "mean observed time" for typing an exam. (Time in minutes.)

b) Determine the "normal time" for processing a phone call. (Time in minutes.)

c) Determine the "standard" in terms of letters per hour for typing letters.

d) On the basis of the estimates given, determine the sample size necessary to be 90 percent confident that the proper allowance percent (delays plus personal time) falls between 17 percent and 23 percent.

4–17 Prove that Equations 4–10 and 4–11 are valid.

4–18 Prove that the sample mean $\bar{x}$ is an unbiased estimate of the population mean μ.

4–19 Toss a coin 10 times, recording 1 every time it comes up heads and 0 every time it comes up tails.

a) Calculate the sample mean and variance of the number of heads observed.

b) Repeat this experiment 20 times.

c) Plot a relative frequency diagram for mean number of heads observed after 5, 10, and 20 experiments.

d) Assuming that the central limit theorem is valid for such small sample sizes, compare the frequency diagrams of part (*c*) with the distribution predicted by the central limit theorem. Use the sample estimates for population mean and variance.

e) Compare the results of parts (*c*) and (*d*) with the theoretically correct distribution anticipated from 10 tosses of an unbiased coin.

4–20 Samples of size *n* have been taken from a normal distribution. Demonstrate the development of maximum likelihood estimators for the mean and variance.

4–21 Samples of size *n* are to be taken from the uniform distribution over the interval *a* to *b*. Find the maximum likelihood estimators for *a* and *b* as well as the mean and variance for the population.

4–22 An engineer has tested four sheets of a new alloy for hardness. He has obtained readings of 40, 38, 41, and 37 on the Rockwell *c* scale. Are these consistent with the suppliers claim of a hardness of 42 at the 0.05 level? (Assume normality.)

4–23 Two technicians have been presented samples of a drug from presumably similar laboratories. Technician *A* has measured the sulphur content in five vials as 24, 21, 26, 28, and 26 milligrams. Technician *B* has measured the content of four vials as 30, 31, 28, and 26 milligrams. The process traditionally exhibits a variance of 9. Are the two technicians measuring the same thing at the 5 percent level of significance?

4–24 Company policy states that customer orders to be filled from stock shall be processed within 48 hours of their receipt. A study of order processing reveals that the average process time is 37 hours with a variance of 25. This variance is assumed to be constant for all items although the mean may shift. Determine the risk of a Type I error if a department is cited for altering the process whenever an order exceeds the 48-hour limit. Construct an OC curve for the implied hypothesis test.

4-25   Management has expressed the view that roughly 60 percent of the time customer arrivals are governed by a Poisson process with a mean of 6 per hour. The rest of the time they are governed by a Poisson process with a mean arrival rate of 8 per hour. A sample of one hour's data yields seven arrivals. A second sample yields eight arrivals.

a) What is your view of the arrival processes after the first sample?

b) What is your view after the second sample?

c) What is the Bayesian estimate of the average arrival rate in view of all of the data at hand?

CHAPTER 5

Fourier Analysis and Transform Techniques

THE PURPOSE of this chapter is to introduce the basic elements of commonly used transformations. Fourier transforms, Laplace transforms, exponential transforms, z transforms, and geometric transforms exhibit many of the same properties. Their common heritage can be traced to the Fourier series representation of a function. Since many of the operating principles learned for one transform apply to the others, we will concentrate on the Laplace transform for continuous functions and the z and geometric transforms for integral valued functions.

In the traditional courses in engineering mathematics the Laplace transformation has been introduced as a powerful method for solving linear differential equations. In similar manner the z and geometric transforms can be thought of as powerful methods for solving linear difference equations. Although these uses are of undeniable value to the modern operations engineer, transform techniques gain even more importance in the analysis of feedback control systems, in the manipulation of probability distributions, and in the ability to model system dynamics. In every application the transforms permit reduction of complex mathematical operations to simpler algebraic problems. For example, it will be shown that higher order derivatives can be transformed into simple algebraic expressions involving the Laplace transform. After the desired manipulation has been performed, the expression may be inverted to recover the function of interest. Similarly, the calculation of the probability distribution for a sum of independent random variables can be changed from the convolution integral or sum to a simple product of transforms.

In the present chapter we shall consider the origin and manipulation of various transformation techniques. In the following chapter we shall examine their use in systems analysis and probability modeling.

FOURIER SERIES

In the study of many physical systems one often encounters periodic disturbances such as forces, torques, voltages, etc. In the study of management systems, periodic effects are generated by payday schedules, holidays, seasonal factors, etc. When such periodic phenomena can be reduced to expressions involving simple sine and cosine waves, they are more easily manipulated. When nonperiodic functions are encountered, the exponential form of the Fourier series leads to the Fourier integral. From this the usual transform pairs for the Fourier transform are readily apparent.

Simple Periodic Functions

An Approximation for Discontinuous Functions.   In nearly every basic calculus course the student is introduced to the Taylor series expansion for analytic functions. This is usually expressed in the form

$$f(t) = \sum_{j=0}^{\infty} \frac{f^{(j)}(a)}{j!} (t - a)^j \tag{5-1}$$

where $f(t)$ is the function of interest and $f^{(j)}(t)$ is the jth derivative of that function. The expansion is said to have occurred about the point $t = a$. When performing engineering calculations it is often convenient to use just the first few terms of this series as an approximation for more complicated functions. The reader may recall that for a Taylor series representation of a function to exist, the function and its derivatives must be continuous and the remainder after n terms as n approaches infinity must be zero.

A Fourier series representation of a function is in a sense more general in that discontinuous, periodic functions which have no Taylor series representation can be developed in Fourier series. For most practical applications, questions of convergence are covered by a theorem due to Dirchlet which says roughly that if $f(t)$ is a bounded periodic function with at most a finite number of points of discontinuity, then the Fourier series of $f(t)$ converges to $f(t)$ at all points where $f(t)$ is continuous and to the average value of the right- and left-hand limits of $f(t)$ at each point where $f(t)$ is discontinuous.[1] This implies that discontinuous functions such as that shown in Figure 5-1 can be represented by a Fourier series even though the Taylor series expansion of this function does not exist.

---

[1] C. R. Wylie, Jr., *Advanced Engineering Mathematics* (2d ed.; New York: McGraw-Hill Book Co., Inc., 1960), p. 248.

FIGURE 5-1

A Discontinuous Periodic Function

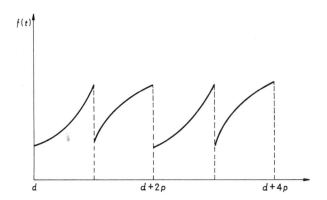

The trigonometric form of the Fourier series representation of a periodic function $f(t)$ with period $2p$ is

$$f(t) = a_0 + \sum_{n=1}^{\infty} a_n \cos\left(\frac{n\pi t}{p}\right) + b_n \sin\left(\frac{n\pi t}{p}\right) \qquad (5\text{-}2)$$

where

$$a_0 = \frac{1}{2p} \int_d^{d+2p} f(t)\, dt \qquad (5\text{-}2a)$$

$$a_n = \frac{1}{p} \int_d^{d+2p} f(t) \cos\left(\frac{n\pi t}{p}\right) dt \qquad (5\text{-}2b)$$

$$b_n = \frac{1}{p} \int_d^{d+2p} f(t) \sin\left(\frac{n\pi t}{p}\right) dt \qquad (5\text{-}2c)$$

The expressions for a_n and b_n are the so-called Euler formulas. For a discussion of the development of these formulas, the reader is referred to Wylie.[2]

A function is said to have period $2p$ if

$$f(t + 2pn) = f(t) \qquad (5\text{-}3)$$

where n is any integer. The simplest periodic functions to work with have period 2π. Examples of such functions are the sine, cosine, and tangent functions.

---

[2] *Ibid.*, chap. vii.

Example.   The function

$$f(t) = \begin{cases} 3 & -4 < t < 0 \\ 0 & 0 < t < 2 \\ 2 & 2 < t < 4 \end{cases}$$

which repeats itself again over the next interval of eight units can be viewed as a periodic function in which $p = 4$. The coefficients for the Fourier series representation of this function are obtained from

$$a_0 = \frac{1}{(2)(4)} \left[\int_{-4}^{0} 3 \, dt + \int_{0}^{2} 0 \, dt + \int_{2}^{4} 2 \, dt \right] = 2$$

$$a_1 = \frac{1}{4} \left[\int_{-4}^{0} 3 \cos \left(\frac{\pi t}{4} \right) dt + \int_{2}^{4} 2 \cos \left(\frac{\pi t}{4} \right) dt \right] = -\frac{2}{\pi}$$

$$a_2 = \frac{1}{4} \left[\int_{-4}^{0} 3 \cos \left(\frac{2\pi t}{4} \right) dt + \int_{2}^{4} 2 \cos \left(\frac{2\pi t}{4} \right) dt \right] = 0$$

$$b_1 = \frac{1}{4} \left[\int_{-4}^{0} 3 \sin \left(\frac{\pi t}{4} \right) dt + \int_{2}^{4} 2 \sin \left(\frac{\pi t}{4} \right) dt \right] = -\frac{4}{\pi}$$

$$b_2 = \frac{1}{4} \left[\int_{-4}^{0} 3 \sin \left(\frac{2\pi t}{4} \right) dt + \int_{2}^{4} 2 \sin \left(\frac{2\pi t}{4} \right) dt \right] = -\frac{2}{\pi}$$

The resulting Fourier series representation of $f(t)$ contains as its first few terms

$$f(t) = 2 - \frac{2}{\pi} \cos \left(\frac{\pi t}{4} \right) - \frac{4}{\pi} \sin \left(\frac{\pi t}{4} \right) - \frac{2}{\pi} \sin \left(\frac{\pi t}{2} \right)$$

The discontinuous function $f(t)$ together with its continuous approximation is shown in Figure 5–2. Note that the continuous approximation approaches the midpoint of the extremes at the points of discontinuity. Even with this very crude approximation it can be seen that the areas under the two curves are very nearly equal. The reader is invited to carry out the calculation of additional terms in the Fourier series for this function to demonstrate that the continuous approximation falls progressively closer to the actual function as the number of terms is increased.

Half-Range Expansions

In many applications it is desirable to obtain a smooth trigonometric representation of a nonperiodic function defined over a finite interval $(0, p)$. In such instances a Fourier series may be employed treating the function as though it is periodic with a period $2p$. The coefficients are calculated in the usual manner, and the resulting series representation will converge to the original function in the interval $(0, p)$.

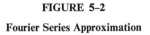

FIGURE 5-2

Fourier Series Approximation

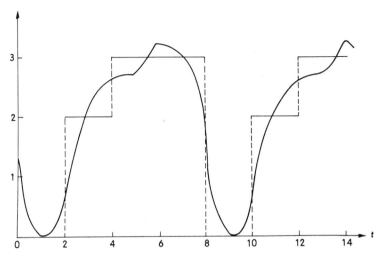

Since one may not care what form the periodic extension of the function assumes outside the interval $(0, p)$, it is often convenient to force the extension to be either odd or even. A function is odd if

$$f(-t) = -f(t) \qquad (5\text{-}4a)$$

for all t. A function is even if

$$f(-t) = f(t) \qquad (5\text{-}4b)$$

for all t. From these definitions it is easy to see that $\sin(x)$ is an odd function and $\cos(x)$ is an even function.

When an even extension of the nonperiodic function $f(t)$ defined over the interval $(0, p)$ is assumed, the coefficients of the Fourier series reduce to

$$a_n = \frac{2}{p} \int_0^p f(t) \cos\left(\frac{n\pi t}{p}\right) dt$$

$$b_n = 0 \qquad (5\text{-}5a)$$

When an odd extension is assumed, the Fourier coefficients become

$$a_n = 0$$

$$b_n = \frac{2}{p} \int_0^p f(t) \sin\left(\frac{n\pi t}{p}\right) dt \qquad (5\text{-}5b)$$

The fact that half of the terms go to zero in odd and even functions can also be used to advantage when obtaining the Fourier series representation of periodic functions which can be identified as odd or even.

Example.   Consider the function

$$f(t) = \begin{cases} 3t & 0 < t < 4 \\ 2 & 4 < t < 6 \\ 0 & \text{elsewhere} \end{cases}$$

If we wish to approximate $f(t)$ with a continuous function to facilitate calculation, an expression for the half-range expansion with an even extension would be

$$(t) = a_0 + \sum_{n=1}^{k} a_n \cos\left(\frac{n\pi t}{p}\right)$$

$$= \frac{2}{6}\left[\int_0^4 3t\, dt + \int_4^6 2\, dt\right] + \frac{2}{6}\left[\int_0^4 3t \cos\left(\frac{\pi t}{6}\right) dt + \int_4^6 2\cos\left(\frac{\pi t}{6}\right) dt\right]\cos\left(\frac{\pi t}{6}\right)$$

$$+ \frac{2}{6}\left[\int_0^4 3t \cos\left(\frac{\pi t}{3}\right) dt + \int_4^6 2\cos\left(\frac{\pi t}{3}\right) dt\right]\cos\left(\frac{\pi t}{3}\right) + \cdots$$

Numerical Methods

In many engineering applications data may be collected during an experiment. It is unlikely that an accurate mathematical expression which describes these data will be known by the analyst. Furthermore, the resulting time series may for logical reasons tend to exhibit marked periodic tendencies. The Fourier series offers an easy method for fitting a smooth periodic function to these data.

The Trapezoidal Rule.   The calculation of the Fourier coefficients proceeds exactly as before except that now we must employ numerical integration. The simplest means of numerically integrating a function $g(t)$ is by the trapezoidal rule. In this technique one can consider the integral of the function $g(t)$ to represent the area under the curve. The area is approximated by a series of trapezoids with bases of length $g(t)$ and $g(t + \Delta t)$ and altitudes of Δt. The area of one such trapezoid is then

$$\text{Area} = \left[\frac{g(t) + g(t + \Delta t)}{2}\right]\Delta t \qquad (5\text{--}6)$$

The total area under the curve $g(t)$ over the interval $0 \le t \le N$ can then be expressed as

$$\text{Area} = \sum_{t=0}^{N} \left[\frac{g(t) + g(t + \Delta t)}{2}\right]\Delta t \qquad (5\text{--}7)$$

where the index on the sum increments in units of Δt. The geometry of this calculation is illustrated in Figure 5–3.

FIGURE 5–3

Numerical Integration

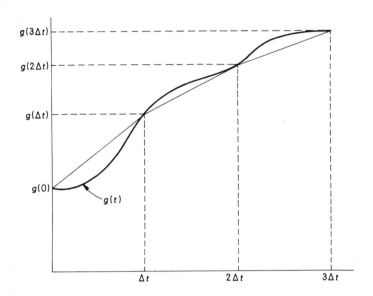

Determining the Fourier Coefficients.   When attempting to calculate the Fourier coefficients from empirical data, the function $g(t)$ is not known at any points except $g(0)$, $g(\Delta t)$, $g(2\Delta t)$, etc. These points are then used to define the trapezoids. For example, suppose that we have seven data points $[g(0), g(1), \ldots, g(6)]$ which we believe come from a periodic process whose period is $2p = 6$. The Fourier coefficients (a_n) for a function passing through these points are given by

$$a_n = \frac{1}{3}\left[\frac{g(0)}{2}\cos\left(\frac{n\pi 0}{3}\right) + g(1)\cos\left(\frac{n\pi 1}{3}\right) + g(2)\cos\left(\frac{n\pi 2}{3}\right) + g(3)\cos\left(\frac{n\pi 3}{3}\right) \right.$$

$$\left. + g(4)\cos\left(\frac{n\pi 4}{3}\right) + g(5)\cos\left(\frac{n\pi 5}{3}\right) + \frac{g(6)}{2}\cos\left(\frac{n\pi 6}{3}\right)\right]$$

$$(5\text{–}8)$$

The b_n coefficients are calculated in similar fashion by replacing the cosine terms with the corresponding sine terms in Equation 5–8.

If one permits the number of terms in the Fourier series to be arbitrarily large, there is an infinite number of ways in which the Fourier series $F(t)$ can take on the values of the sample data. Therefore, we shall assume that the number of terms in the expansion is limited to N where $N \le p$ when the period is $2p$. The following Nth partial sum then can be used to approximate the empirical data:

$$g(t) \approx a_0 + \sum_{n=1}^{N} \left(a_n \cos \left(\frac{n\pi t}{p} \right) + b_n \sin \left(\frac{n\pi t}{p} \right) \right) \qquad (5\text{-}9)$$

When an even number of data points are available and $N = p$, the partial sum shown gives a trigonometric polynomial which assumes the values $F(t) = g(t)$ and the error is zero.[3] This form of the Fourier series is particularly valuable in analyzing economic data from known seasonal phenomena. Fourier analysis plays an important role in many forecasting models. For examples of this application see Brown.[4]

Fourier Integral

Exponential Form of the Fourier Series. From trigonometry we know that the sine and cosine functions have the exponential equivalents

$$\sin (x) = \frac{e^{ix} - e^{-ix}}{2i} \qquad (5\text{-}10)$$

$$\cos (x) = \frac{e^{ix} + e^{-ix}}{2} \qquad (5\text{-}11)$$

where $i^2 = -1$. Using these identities the Fourier series representation of $f(t)$ shown in Equation 5-2 may be rewritten as

$$f(t) = \sum_{n=-\infty}^{\infty} c_n e^{in\pi t/p} \qquad (5\text{-}12)$$

where

$$c_n = \frac{1}{2p} \int_{d}^{d+2p} f(t) e^{-in\pi t/p} dt$$

The details of this conversion are contained in Wylie.[5] This now gives us an alternate means of presenting the same information for a Fourier series.

Nonperiodic Functions. So far all of our discussion has concerned periodic functions or periodic extensions of functions defined over a limited range. Since many practical problems do not involve periodic functions, it is desirable to generalize the method of Fourier series to include nonperiodic functions. Essentially this involves starting with a function $f(t, T)$ of period T and letting T approach infinity. The resulting function $f(t)$ then is no longer periodic. This will permit us to manipulate such functions as probability density functions which are not periodic. In its limiting form, the

[3] Erwin Kreyszig, *Advanced Engineering Mathematics* (2d ed.; New York: John Wiley & Sons, Inc., 1967), p. 463.

[4] Robert A. Brown, *Smoothing Forecasting and Prediction of Discrete Time Series* (Englewood Cliffs, N.J.: Prentice-Hall, Inc., 1963).

[5] Wylie, *op. cit.*, p. 262.

Fourier series leads us to the development of transform pairs which play important roles in our future modeling efforts. Now we will briefly sketch the extension of Fourier series representations of periodic functions to non-periodic functions.

The Fourier series representation of $f(t, T)$ in exponential form is

$$f(t, T) = \frac{1}{T} \sum_{n=-\infty}^{\infty} \left[\int_{-T/2}^{T/2} f(t, s) e^{-iw_n s} ds \right] e^{iw_n t} \qquad (5\text{–}13)$$

where

$$w_n = \frac{2n\pi}{T}$$

Note that the increment in w_n, Δw_n can be expressed as

$$\Delta w = w_{n+1} - w_n = \frac{2\pi}{T} \qquad (5\text{–}14)$$

Therefore, $f(t, T)$ can be rewritten as

$$f(t, T) = \frac{1}{2\pi} \sum_{n=-\infty}^{\infty} \left[\int_{-T/2}^{T/2} f(t, s) e^{-iw_n s} ds \right] e^{iw_n t} \Delta w \qquad (5\text{–}15)$$

This expression contains a sum of the form

$$\sum_{n=-\infty}^{\infty} g(w_n) \Delta w$$

which under very general conditions can in the limit be written as

$$\lim_{\Delta w \to 0} \sum_{n=-\infty}^{\infty} g(w_n) \Delta w = \int_{-\infty}^{\infty} g(w) dw \qquad (5\text{–}16)$$

In our expression for the Fourier series of $f(t, T)$, then

$$\lim_{T \to \infty} f(t, T) = \lim_{\Delta w \to 0} \frac{1}{2\pi} \sum_{n=-\infty}^{\infty} g(w_n) \Delta w$$

or

$$f(t) = \frac{1}{2\pi} \int_{-\infty}^{\infty} \left[e^{iwt} \int_{-\infty}^{\infty} f(s) e^{-iws} ds \right] dw \qquad \begin{array}{l} \text{Fourier} \\ \text{Int.} \end{array} \qquad (5\text{–}17)$$

This is the so-called Fourier integral. It is a valid representation of the non-periodic function $f(t)$ provided that in every finite interval $f(t)$ satisfies the Dirchlet conditions of being a bounded function with a finite number of discontinuities and that the improper integral

$$\int_{-\infty}^{\infty} |f(t)| dt$$

exists.

It is well to note at this point that any function satisfying the Dirchlet conditions does have a Fourier series representation. Furthermore, that representation is unique. This fact will permit us later on to manipulate transformations with some confidence that the resulting functions can be inverted to obtain the unique answer desired.

Fourier Transform Pairs

Alternate Forms of the Fourier Integral.   The Fourier integral given by Equation 5–17 can be written several different ways. For example,

$$f(t) = \frac{1}{2\pi} \int_{-\infty}^{\infty} g(w)e^{iwt}\,dw$$

where

$$g(w) = \int_{-\infty}^{\infty} f(t)e^{-iwt}\,dt \tag{5-18}$$

or

$$f(t) = \frac{1}{\sqrt{2\pi}} \int_{-\infty}^{\infty} c(w)e^{iwt}\,dw$$

where

$$c(w) = \frac{1}{\sqrt{2\pi}} \int_{-\infty}^{\infty} f(t)e^{-iwt}\,dt \tag{5-19}$$

When written in this manner each of the pairs 5–18 and 5–19 constitutes what is known as a Fourier transform pair.

Note that the coefficient function $g(w)$ is completely equivalent to $f(t)$ since if we know $g(w)$ we can reconstruct $f(t)$ by carrying out the indicated integration. In effect we have two different representations of the same function. They are often characterized as one function in the time domain and one in the frequency domain. Extensive tables of transform pairs have been constructed for engineering use. The function $g(w)$ is often referred to as the "Fourier transform" of $f(t)$, and $f(t)$ is referred to as the "inverse Fourier transform" of $g(w)$. The transform and its inverse will be given the symbols $\mathscr{F}[f(t)]$ and $\mathscr{F}^{-1}[g(w)]$ respectively.

THE LAPLACE TRANSFORM

Much of the information concerning manipulation of all transforms can be obtained from a detailed study of one. The particular transform to receive most of our attention is the Laplace transform.

Fourier to Laplace Transforms

Unilateral Transform Pairs.   In many applications of the Fourier integral the function to be represented is identically zero before $t = 0$. In this case the general Fourier transform pair becomes the unilateral Fourier transform pair

$$f(t) = \mathscr{F}^{-1}[g(w)] = \frac{1}{2\pi} \int_{-\infty}^{\infty} g(w)e^{iwt} \, dw$$

$$g(w) = \mathscr{F}[f(t)] = \int_{0}^{\infty} f(t)e^{-iwt} \, dt \qquad (5\text{--}20)$$

This transform may be useful in many applications but may be meaningless in others. For example, the unit step function

$$u(t) = \begin{cases} 0 & t < 1 \\ 1 & t > 1 \end{cases}$$

has as its Fourier transform

$$\mathscr{F}[u(t)] = \int_{0}^{\infty} e^{-iwt} \, dt = \frac{e^{-iwt}}{-iw} \Big|_{0}^{\infty} = \frac{\cos wt - i \sin wt}{-iw} \Big|_{0}^{\infty}$$

This expression is meaningless since both the sine and cosine oscillate without limit as t approaches infinity.

Convergence Factor.   In order to insure the convergence of the unilateral transform pair, the transform $\mathscr{F}[f(t)]$ must be multiplied by e^{-at}. The new transform is then

$$T[f(t)] = \int_{0}^{\infty} f(t) e^{-at-iwt} \, dt \qquad (5\text{--}21)$$

This transform will converge for functions such as the unit step cited above. By redefining the binomial term $s = a + iw$, the unilateral Fourier transform pair modified by the convergence factor becomes the Laplace transform pair

$$F(s) = \mathscr{L}[f(t)] = \int_{0}^{\infty} f(t)e^{-st} \, dt \qquad (5\text{--}22)$$

$$f(t) = \mathscr{L}^{-1}[F(s)] = \frac{1}{2\pi i} \int_{a-i\infty}^{a+i\infty} F(s)e^{st} \, ds \qquad (5\text{--}23)$$

The symbols $\mathscr{L}[f(t)]$ and $\mathscr{L}^{-1}[F(s)]$ will be used to denote the Laplace transform and its inverse respectively. For a more detailed discussion of the relationship of Laplace to Fourier transforms see Wylie.[6]

Note that the transformation variable s in the Laplace transform is a complex number. The complex inversion formula for $\mathscr{L}^{-1}[F(s)]$ requires

---

[6] *Ibid.*, pp. 285–88.

contour integration which is not generally an easy task. For that reason it is common practice to resort to tables of transform pairs and a few simple theorems for finding inverse transforms. This is the approach we will employ.

The existence of the Laplace transform for a function $f(t)$ is given by the following theorem from Kreyszig.[7]

Theorem: Let $f(t)$ be a function which is piecewise continuous on every finite interval in the range $t \geq 0$ and satisfies

$$|f(t)| \leq Me^{\alpha t} \qquad \text{for all } t \geq 0$$

and for some constants α and M. The Laplace transform of $f(t)$ exists for all $s > \alpha$.

Functions satisfying this condition are said to be of exponential order. For our purposes we will treat the variable s as a dummy variable and assume that the integral defining the Laplace transform will be uniformly convergent for the set of s values of interest to us. For the most part our calculations will employ s values in the interval $[0, 1]$. The functions we will employ are of exponential order and do converge over the indicated range of s.

It should be noted that if the Laplace transform of a function exists, it is unique. Conversely if two continuous functions have the same transform they are identical.

Transforms of Elementary Functions

Applying the Definition. One can easily construct a simple table of transform pairs by carrying out the integration indicated by the definition of the Laplace transform of a function $f(t)$. For example, suppose that the transform of the function

$$f(t) = \begin{cases} k & t \geq 0 \\ 0 & \text{elsewhere} \end{cases}$$

is desired. Operating from the definition

$$\mathscr{L}[k] = \int_0^\infty ke^{-st}\,dt$$

$$= -\frac{k}{s}e^{-st}\Big|_0^\infty = \frac{k}{s}$$

In similar fashion the transform of the function

$$f(t) = \begin{cases} t & t \geq 0 \\ 0 & \text{elsewhere} \end{cases}$$

---

[7] Kreyszig, *op. cit.*, p. 196.

is given by

$$\mathscr{L}[t] = \int_0^\infty t e^{-st} \, dt$$

Integrating by parts, let $u = t$ and $dv = e^{-st} \, dt$, then

$$\int u \, dv = uv - \int v \, du$$

or

$$\mathscr{L}(t) = \frac{-te^{-st}}{s} \bigg|_0^\infty + \frac{1}{s} \int_0^\infty e^{-st} \, dt = \frac{1}{s^2}$$

Once the indicated transforms have been obtained by integration or other means, they are available for our use just as we use tables of integrals. A brief table of transform pairs is given in Table 5–1.

TABLE 5–1

Some Elementary Functions $f(t)$ and Their Laplace Transforms $\mathscr{L}(f)$

No.	$f(t)$	$\mathscr{L}(f)$	No.	$f(t)$	$\mathscr{L}(f)$
1	1	$\dfrac{1}{s}$	6	e^{at}	$\dfrac{1}{(s-a)}$
2	t	$\dfrac{1}{s^2}$	7	$\cos wt$	$\dfrac{s}{(s^2+w^2)}$
3	t^2	$\dfrac{2!}{s^3}$	8	$\sin wt$	$\dfrac{w}{(s^2+w^2)}$
4	t^n	$\dfrac{n!}{s^{n+1}}$	9	$\cosh at$	$\dfrac{s}{(s^2-a^2)}$
	$(n = 1, 2, \ldots)$				
5	t^a	$\dfrac{\Gamma(a+1)}{s^{a+1}}$	10	$\sinh at$	$\dfrac{a}{(s^2-a^2)}$
	(a positive)				

Reprinted with permission from Erwin Kreyszig, *Advanced Engineering Mathematics* (2d ed.: New York: John Wiley & Sons, Inc., 1967), p. 194.

Very complete tables of transform pairs are available in most advanced engineering math texts and in handbooks such as that published by the National Bureau of Standards.[8] Now if we have need to determine the Laplace

---

[8] M. Abramowitz, and I. A. Stegun (ed.), *Handbook of Mathematical Functions*, AMS55 (Washington, D.C.: U.S. Department of Commerce, National Bureau of Standards, U.S. Government Printing Office, 1964).

transform of e^{at}, we simply refer to the appropriate table entry to find that

$$\mathscr{L}(e^{at}) = \frac{1}{s-a}$$

It is unnecessary to carry out the integration. Conversely if our calculations yield a transform $6/s^4$, the time function can be recovered from pair 4 in Table 5–1. That is

$$\mathscr{L}[f(t)] = \frac{6}{s^4} = \frac{3!}{s^{3+1}}$$

therefore

$$f(t) = t^3$$

Special Properties of Laplace Transforms

It is often possible to obtain transforms of more complex functions from a knowledge of simpler ones by observing certain basic theorems about the technique. Similarly, the inverse transformation may be expedited by taking advantage of such theorems. Results of a number of theorems will be presented here without proof. They have been selected on the basis of their usefulness in practical applications. The interested reader is referred to texts such as Kreyszig for their development.[9]

Linearity. The Laplace transform is a linear operator. This means that the transform of a function made up of a linear combination of other functions is a linear combination of the transforms of the component functions.

$$\mathscr{L}[af(t) + bg(t)] = a\mathscr{L}[f(t)] + b\mathscr{L}[g(t)] \qquad (5\text{–}24)$$

For example, the transform of

$$f(t) = 5 + 2t + 3t^2$$

is

$$\mathscr{L}[f(t)] = 5\mathscr{L}(1) + 2\mathscr{L}(t) + 3\mathscr{L}(t^2)$$

$$= \frac{5}{s} + \frac{2}{s^2} + \frac{6}{s^3}$$

The fact that the Laplace transform is a linear operator also suggests a means of facilitating the inverse transformation. Any time that a transform to be inverted can be expressed as a sum of simpler transforms whose inverses are recognized, the time function is easily obtained. A common technique for splitting some transforms into sums of simple transforms is partial fraction expansion.

---

[9] Kreyszig, *op. cit.*, chap. iv.

Partial Fraction Expansion. During the analysis of many systems, transforms of the form

$$F(s) = \frac{A(s)}{B(s)} \tag{5-25}$$

will appear. Here $F(s)$ represents the Laplace transform and $A(s)$ and $B(s)$ are polynomials in s. When the degree of the numerator is less than the degree of the denominator, such fractions are called proper rational fractions.

From algebra, when the denominator can be factored into a product of linear terms, we know that the fraction can be expressed as a sum of separate terms each having as its denominator a factor of the original denominator. The values of the numerators must be determined. For example, suppose that we must evaluate the following inverse transform:

$$\mathscr{L}^{-1}\left[\frac{s+2}{s^3 - 9s}\right] = \mathscr{L}^{-1}\left[\frac{s+2}{s(s+3)(s-3)}\right]$$

By partial fraction expansion

$$\frac{s+2}{s(s+3)(s-3)} = \frac{c_1}{s} + \frac{c_2}{s+3} + \frac{c_3}{s-3}$$

where c_1, c_2, and c_3 are to be determined. The numerators can be determined by reducing the right side to a common denominator, equating like powers of s, and solving the set of resulting equations. In the numerator

$$s + 2 = c_1(s+3)(s-3) + c_2(s)(s-3) + c_3(s)(s+3)$$

$$= c_1(s^2 - 9) + c_2(s^2 - 3s) + c_3(s^2 + 3s)$$

from which

$$c_1 + c_2 + c_3 = 0 \qquad \text{from } s^2 \text{ coefficients}$$

$$-3c_2 + 3c_3 = 1 \qquad \text{from } s^1 \text{ coefficients}$$

$$-9c_1 = 2 \qquad \text{from } s^0 \text{ coefficients}$$

Solving simultaneously yields

$$c_1 = -\tfrac{2}{9}$$

$$c_2 = -\tfrac{1}{18}$$

$$c_3 = \tfrac{5}{18}$$

The indicated inverse transformation has now been reduced to

$$\mathscr{L}^{-1}\left(\frac{s+2}{s^3 - 9s}\right) = -\frac{2}{9}\,\mathscr{L}^{-1}\left(\frac{1}{s}\right) - \frac{1}{18}\,\mathscr{L}^{-1}\left(\frac{1}{s+3}\right) + \frac{5}{18}\,\mathscr{L}^{-1}\left(\frac{1}{s-3}\right)$$

From Table 5–1 the time function is obviously

$$f(t) = -\tfrac{2}{9} - \tfrac{1}{18}e^{-3t} + \tfrac{5}{18}e^{3t}$$

When the denominator $B(s)$ can be factored into n distinct roots, the transform $F(s)$ is said to have n simple or first-order poles. In the previous example the roots are $s = 0$, $s = -3$, and $s = 3$. These are the values of s which will make the denominator zero. Whenever the transform has only first-order poles a_k, the coefficients c_k can also be calculated from

$$c_k = \lim_{s \to a_k} (s - a_k) F(s) \tag{5-26}$$

In the previous example

$$c_1 = \lim_{s \to 0} \frac{(s)(s + 2)}{s(s + 3)(s - 3)} = -\frac{2}{9}$$

$$c_2 = \lim_{s \to -3} \frac{(s + 3)(s + 2)}{s(s + 3)(s - 3)} = -\frac{1}{18}$$

$$c_3 = \lim_{s \to 3} \frac{(s - 3)(s + 2)}{s(s + 3)(s - 3)} = \frac{5}{18}$$

When the denominator of $F(s)$ has a factor which is repeated k times, $F(s)$ is said to have a kth order pole. Such a pole will contribute k terms in the partial fraction expansion. Suppose that the transform in the previous example is modified slightly such that

$$F(s) = \frac{s + 2}{s(s + 3)(s - 3)^3}$$

then it is said to have simple poles at $s = 0$ and $s = -3$ and a third-order pole at $s = 3$. The partial fraction expansion now becomes

$$F(s) = \frac{c_1}{s} + \frac{c_2}{s + 3} + \frac{c_{31}}{(s - 3)^3} + \frac{c_{32}}{(s - 3)^2} + \frac{c_{33}}{s - 3}$$

The coefficients $c_1 = -\frac{2}{81}$ and $c_2 = -\frac{1}{648}$ can be obtained by exactly the same limit argument previously used. The coefficients c_{31}, c_{32}, and c_{33} are obtained from

$$c_{31} = \lim_{s \to 3} (s - 3)^3 F(s) = \frac{5}{18}$$

$$c_{32} = \lim_{s \to 3} \frac{d(s - 3)^3 F(s)}{ds} = -\frac{27}{324}$$

$$c_{33} = \lim_{s \to 3} \frac{1}{2} \frac{d^2(s - 3)^3 F(s)}{ds^2} = -\frac{17}{648}$$

In general, the nth coefficient for terms resulting from a kth order repeated root a_j will be

$$c_{jn} = \frac{1}{(n - 1)!} \lim_{s \to a_j} \frac{d^{n-1}(s - a_j)^k F(s)}{ds^{n-1}} \tag{5-27}$$

Denominators with more than one repeated root lead to similar calculations for each repeated factor.

$$\frac{A(s)}{(s-a_1)^m(s-a_2)^n} = \frac{c_{11}}{(s-a_1)^m} + \frac{c_{12}}{(s-a_1)^{m-1}}$$

$$+ \cdots + \frac{c_{1m}}{s-a_1} + \frac{c_{21}}{(s-a_2)^n} + \cdots + \frac{c_{2n}}{s-a_2}$$

Complex Shifting. When a function $f(t)$ with a known transform $F(s)$ is multiplied by a factor e^{at}, the transform of the resulting function can be expressed in terms of the known transform.

$$\mathscr{L}[e^{at}f(t)] = F(s-a) \tag{5-28}$$

This relationship implies that multiplication of the original function by e^{at} is equivalent to replacing the argument s with $s-a$ in the transform. For example

$$\mathscr{L}(t^2e^{3t}) = \mathscr{L}(t^2)\Big|_{s=s-3}$$

From Table 5–1

$$\mathscr{L}(t^2) = F(s) = \frac{2}{s^3}$$

therefore

$$\mathscr{L}(t^2e^{3t}) = \frac{2}{(s-3)^3}$$

Transform of a Derivative. The Laplace transform is especially helpful in solving higher order linear differential equations. The transform of the nth order derivative of a function $f(t)$ is related to the transform of $f(t)$ and the initial conditions of the system by

$$\mathscr{L}[f^{(n)}(t)] = s^n F(s) - s^{n-1} f(0) - \cdots - sf^{(n-2)}(0) - f^{(n-1)}(0) \tag{5-29}$$

where $f^{(j)}(0)$ represents the jth derivative of $f(t)$ evaluated at $t = 0$. In this manner the n initial conditions which are normally used to solve for n constants in the solution of an nth order linear differential equation are carried along throughout the solution.

Suppose it is necessary to find the Laplace transform of the third derivative of the function

$$f(t) = t^3$$

when it is known that

$$F(s) = \frac{6}{s^4}$$

and

$$f(0) = f^1(0) = f^2(0) = 0$$

Then

$$\mathscr{L}\left[\frac{d^3(t^3)}{dt^3}\right] = s^3 \frac{6}{s^4} = \frac{6}{s}$$

which agrees with $\mathscr{L}(6)$ obtainable from Table 5-1.

Integration. There are two important problems in integration which we often face. One is the evaluation of cumulative distributions. The other is the convolution operation.

The Laplace transform of the integral of a function $f(t)$ is related to the transform of $f(t)$ by

$$\mathscr{L}\left[\int_0^t f(r)\,dr\right] = \frac{1}{s}\,\mathscr{L}[f(t)] \qquad (5\text{-}30)$$

Suppose we need to know the transform of the cumulative distribution of the random variable t when $f(t)$ is known to be negative exponential with parameter μ. Then

$$\mathscr{L}[f(t)] = \mathscr{L}[\mu e^{-\mu t}] = \frac{\mu}{s + \mu}$$

and

$$\mathscr{L}\left[\int_0^t f(r)\,dr\right] = \frac{\mu}{s(s + \mu)}$$

Convolution. The convolution of two functions $f(t)$ and $g(t)$ is defined by the convolution (or Faltung) integral

$$\int_0^t f(r)g(t - r)\,dr$$

One of the most useful results of Laplace transform theory is that the transform of a convolution is equal to the product of the transforms of the functions being convolved.

$$\mathscr{L}\left[\int_0^t f(r)g(t - r)\,dr\right] = \mathscr{L}[f(t)]\mathscr{L}[g(t)] \qquad (5\text{-}31)$$

A similar statement can be made for discrete transforms of the convolution sum introduced in future discussions. In every case, the transform of the convolution is equal to the product of the transforms of the functions being convolved.

The convolution integral appears in the analysis of linear systems and in evaluating sums of independent random variables. For example, the density for the sum of two independent random variables is the convolution of the densities of those variables. We shall have much more to say about this important topic in the next chapter.

Shifting on the Time Axis.   From time to time in our work we will find it necessary to shift the origin of a function to a new point on the time axis. Such a shift is readily performed in the transform domain by

$$\mathscr{L}[f(t-a)u(t-a)] = e^{-as}F(s) \qquad (5\text{-}32)$$

where $F(s)$ is the transform of $f(t)$ with its origin at $t = 0$, a is the number of units the origin has been shifted to the right, and $u(t-a)$ is a unit step function at $t = a$. The unit step is included with the shifted function $f(t-a)$ to insure that the nonnegative restriction on the Laplace transform is not violated, i.e., the function is zero to the left of $t = a$. This theorem answers the question of how the *transform* changes when the t argument of the function is replaced by $t - a$. Conversely, Equation 5–28 answers the question of how the *function* changes when the argument s of the transform is replaced by $s - a$.

Multiplication and Division by t.   The reader may recall that differentiation and integration of a function $f(t)$ were accomplished in the transform domain by multiplication and division of the transform by s. In similar fashion multiplication and division of $f(t)$ by t may be accomplished by differentiation and integration of the Laplace transform.

$$\mathscr{L}[tf(t)] = -\frac{d}{ds}F(s) \qquad (5\text{-}33)$$

$$\mathscr{L}\left[\frac{f(t)}{t}\right] = \int_{s}^{\infty} F(s)\,ds \qquad (5\text{-}34)$$

As before these relationships may be used to evaluate transforms of functions containing components $f(t)$ whose transforms are already known.

Initial and Final Values.   In many practical applications it may not be necessary to know the value of a function over all possible values of t. Instead, we may be interested in such questions as: What is the output of the system after a very long operating period? Initial and final values for some functions can be determined directly from their transforms without going through the inversion process. When $f(t)$ and $f'(t)$ are Laplace transformable and $f(t)$ is not an oscillating function,

$$\lim_{s\to\infty} sF(s) = \lim_{t\to 0} f(t) \qquad (5\text{-}35)$$

$$\lim_{s\to 0} sF(s) = \lim_{t\to\infty} f(t) \qquad (5\text{-}36)$$

Equation 5–35 is the so-called initial-value theorem which says that the behavior of $f(t)$ in the neighborhood of $t = 0$ corresponds to the behavior of $sF(s)$ in the neighborhood of $s = \infty$. Similarly Equation 5–36 is the final-value theorem which says that the behavior of $f(t)$ in the neighborhood of $t = \infty$ corresponds to the behavior of $sF(s)$ in the neighborhood of $s = 0$.

Proofs of these relationships are contained in Thomson.[10]

Suppose that it is known that the transform of the output of a particular system is

$$F(s) = \frac{161}{s(5s + 10)} + \frac{10}{(5s + 10)}$$

Then the value of $f(t)$ at $t = 0$ is

$$\lim_{t \to 0} f(t) = \lim_{s \to \infty} sF(s) = \lim_{s \to \infty} \left(\frac{161}{5s + 10} + \frac{10}{5 + 10/s} \right) = 2$$

The terminal value of $f(t)$ at $t = \infty$ is

$$\lim_{t \to \infty} f(t) = \lim_{s \to 0} sF(s) = 16.1$$

Note that it was not necessary to identify the entire function $f(t)$ to obtain these values.

It is necessary, however, to determine the location of the roots of the denominator for the transform. When the real portion of the roots are negative, these theorems will work. When the real portion of any root is positive they will give erroneous results. In this example the roots of the denominator are $s = 0$ and $s = -2$. Since neither is positive the theorem works. If on the other hand we attempt to use the final value theorem on

$$F(s) = \frac{1}{s - 3}$$

with the positive root $s = 3$, we obtain

$$\lim_{s \to 0} sF(s) = 0$$

However, the inverse transform of this function is

$$f(t) = e^{3t}$$

which obviously grows beyond bounds as $t \to \infty$. The theorem is not applicable in this case.

Solution of Differential Equations

So far our discussion of Laplace transforms has been limited to the mechanics of obtaining the transforms of given functions and inverting specified transforms to obtain the corresponding functions of time. We are now in a position to use these skills in the solution of meaningful problems.

The Subsidiary Equation.   Using the basic relationships discussed so far,

---

[10] William T. Thomson, *Laplace Transformation* (2d ed.; Englewood Cliffs, N.J.: Prentice-Hall, Inc., 1960), pp. 20–21.

it is an easy matter to reduce an ordinary linear differential equation with constant coefficients to an algebraic equation of the transform. Such an equation of the transform is called the subsidiary equation of the given differential equation.

Suppose that we have a physical system whose behavior can be described by the equation

$$\frac{d^2 y}{dt^2} - 9y = e^{2t} \qquad \text{where } y(0) = y'(0) = 0$$

Here the function $y(t)$, which is to be determined, can be thought of as the response function for the system. The expression on the right, e^{2t}, is sometimes called the driving function. The subsidiary equation is formed by taking transforms of both sides of the equation.

$$\mathscr{L}\left(\frac{d^2 y}{dt^2}\right) - 9\mathscr{L}(y) = \mathscr{L}(e^{2t})$$

which reduces to

$$s^2 \mathscr{L}(y) - sy(0) - y'(0) - 9\mathscr{L}(y) = \frac{1}{s-2}$$

Solving for $\mathscr{L}(y)$ we obtain

$$\mathscr{L}(y) = \frac{1}{(s-2)(s^2-9)} = \frac{1}{(s-2)(s+3)(s-3)}$$

$$= \frac{-\frac{1}{5}}{s-2} + \frac{\frac{1}{30}}{s+3} + \frac{\frac{1}{6}}{s-3}$$

from which

$$y(t) = \tfrac{1}{30} e^{-3t} + \tfrac{1}{6} e^{3t} - \tfrac{1}{5} e^{2t}$$

A Caution to the Reader. It is well to observe at this time that we have presented many diverse facts about Laplace transforms without carefully following their development and noting the subtleties contained in their use. In particular, we have said very little about the values of s required to achieve convergence. We pretend that the integral converges for all s of interest. Most of the rules presented work for most well-behaved functions. When problems are encountered which will not yield to the tools discussed, the reader is urged to consult a higher level math text containing the necessary rigor. Ours is a brute-force pragmatic attack in which we may employ the techniques of Laplace transforms as though they are always valid and fall back on more rigorous analysis only when answers are unobtainable or violate our engineering intuition.

DISCRETE TRANSFORMS

The use of Laplace transforms as discussed in the preceding section assumes that the functions being manipulated are piecewise continuous. However, in many applications we may be interested in working with sampled functions defined as a train of impulses each having an area equal to the function at the sampling instant or with point functions such as discrete probability distributions. In such cases we need discrete transformations which can be manipulated by rules similar to those developed for Laplace transforms. Two such transformations are the z transform and the geometric transform. They are power series transformations of a function $f(n)$ with an integral argument n into functions of the complex variable z. The variable z serves the same purpose as the variable s in the Laplace transformation.

The z Transformation

A Discrete Analog of the Laplace Transform. There is some confusion in the literature concerning the proper terminology for this class of transforms. We will adopt the form suggested by Beightler, Mitten, and Nemhauser and reserve the term z transform for the power series transformation with negative exponents for z.[11] Accordingly, we will define the z transform as

$$Z[f(n)] = \sum_{n=0}^{\infty} f(n)z^{-n} \qquad (5\text{-}37)$$

Here we are assuming that n is a nonnegative integral-valued variable whose range is zero to infinity unless otherwise noted. Aseltine has developed the z transform by taking the Laplace transform of sampled data functions.[12] In this case the complex variable z is equivalent to e^s used in the Laplace transform. The z transform then can be viewed as the Laplace transform for functions of integral valued variables.

Developing Tables of Transform Pairs. As was true for the Laplace transform, finding z transforms of functions and their inverses is most easily accomplished by using certain fundamental properties of the transform and a table of transform pairs.

Transforms for elementary functions can be obtained by straightforward application of the definition. For example, the z transform of

$$f(n) = \begin{cases} c & n \geq 0 \\ 0 & n < 0 \end{cases}$$

[11] C. S. Beightler, L. G. Mitten, and G. C. Nemhauser, "A Short Table of Z-Transforms and Generating Functions," *Operations Research*, Vol. 9, No. 4 (July–August 1961), p. 575.
[12] John A. Aseltine, *Transform Method in Linear System Analysis* (New York: McGraw-Hill Book Co., Inc., 1958), p. 247.

becomes

$$Z[f(n)] = \sum_{n=0}^{\infty} cz^{-n} = c(1 + z^{-1} + z^{-2} + \cdots)$$

The infinite sum in brackets is of the form of a geometric series with an argument $r = 1/z$. If $r^2 < 1$ it is a well-known fact that the limit of the sum of an infinite number of terms in this sequence is

$$S_{\infty} = \frac{1}{1 - r} \tag{5-38}$$

Applying the relationship to our particular sequence gives

$$Z(c) = \frac{c}{1 - (1/z)} = \frac{cz}{z - 1} \tag{5-39}$$

We can also build up a table of pairs by expansion of rational fractions of z. For example, by long division

$$\frac{z}{z - c} = 1 + cz^{-1} + c^2z^{-2} + \cdots$$

If we compare this with the definition of the z transform it is obvious that the sum shown represents the transform of $f(n) = c^n$. Therefore,

$$Z(c^n) = \frac{z}{z - c} \tag{5-40}$$

and we have another entry for our table. Furthermore, if we replace the constant c with e^b we immediately obtain the transform for $f(n) = e^{bn}$.

$$Z(e^{bn}) = \frac{z}{z - e^b} \tag{5-41}$$

Further extensions of these basic relationships are left as exercises for the reader. A short list of transform pairs and basic theorems is contained in Table 5–2.

Operating Rules. As was true of the Laplace transform the formulas contained in Table 5–2 are valid only for those values of z for which the series converges.

A number of rules presented for Laplace transforms find direct parallels in the theory of z transforms. For example, both are linear operators, therefore

$$Z[af(n) + bg(n)] = aZ[f(n)] + bZ[g(n)] \tag{5-42}$$

Shifting on the n axis is easily accomplished in transform domain by letting $g(n) = f(n - k)$ then

$$Z[f(n-k)] = z^{-k}Z[f(n)] \tag{5-43}$$

TABLE 5-2

Geometric and z Transforms

Definition	Function $f(n)$	Geometric Transform $G[f(n)] = \sum_{n=0}^{\infty} f(n)z^n$	z Transform $Z[f(n)] = \sum_{n=0}^{\infty} f(n)z^{-n}$
1	$ag(n) + bh(n)$	$a\,G[g(n)] + b\,G[h(n)]$	$a\,Z[g(n)] + b\,Z[h(n)]$
2	$g(n+k)$	$z^{-k}\,G[g(n)] - \sum_{r=0}^{k-1} g(r)z^{r-k}$	$z^{k}\,Z[g(n)] - \sum_{r=0}^{k-1} g(r)z^{k-r}$
3	$g(n-k)u(n-k)$	$z^{k}\,G[g(n)]$	$z^{-k}\,Z[g(n)]$
4	$c^{an}\,g(n)$	$G[g(n)]\big|_{z=caz}$	$Z[g(n)]\big|_{z=z/ca}$
5	$\sum_{r=0}^{n} g(r)h(n-r)$	$G[g(n)]\,G[h(n)]$	$Z[g(n)]\,Z[h(n)]$
6	$\Delta g(n) = g(n+1) - g(n)$	$z^{-1}[(1-z)\,G(g(n)) - g(0)]$	$(z-1)\,Z[g(n)] - z\,g(0)$
7	$f(n) = \begin{cases} 1(n=k) \\ 0(n \neq k) \end{cases}$	z^{k}	z^{-k}
8	c	$\dfrac{c}{1-z}$	$\dfrac{cz}{z-1}$
9	n	$\dfrac{z}{(1-z)^2}$	$\dfrac{z}{(z-1)^2}$
10	n^2	$\dfrac{z(1+z)}{(1-z)^3}$	$\dfrac{z(1+z)}{(z-1)^3}$
11	n^3	$\dfrac{z(z^2+4z+1)}{(1-z)^4}$	$\dfrac{z(z^2+4z+1)}{(z-1)^4}$
12	n^k	$\dfrac{z\,dG[g(n)]}{dz}$ with $g(n) = n^{k-1}$	$-\dfrac{z\,d\,Z[g(n)]}{dz}$ with $g(n) = n^{k-1}$
13	c^n	$\dfrac{1}{1-cz}$	$\dfrac{z}{z-c}$
14	nc^n	$\dfrac{cz}{(1-cz)^2}$	$\dfrac{cz}{(z-c)^2}$
15	$n^2 c^n$	$\dfrac{cz(1+cz)}{(1-cz)^3}$	$\dfrac{cz(z+c)}{(z-c)^3}$
16	$n^k c^n$	$\dfrac{z\,d\,G[g(n)]}{dz}\bigg|_{z=cz}$ with $g(n) = n^{k-1}$	$\dfrac{-z\,d\,Z[g(n)]}{dz}\bigg|_{z=z/c}$ with $g(n) = n^{k-1}$
17	$\binom{n+k}{k}c^n$	$\dfrac{1}{(1-cz)^{k+1}}$	$\dfrac{z^{k+1}}{(z-c)^{k+1}}$
18	$\binom{b}{n}c^n a^{b-n}$	$(a+cz)^b$	$\dfrac{(az+c)^b}{z^b}$

TABLE 5–2 (Continued)

Defini-tion	Function $f(n)$	Geometric Transform $G[f(n)] = \sum_{n=0}^{\infty} f(n)z^n$	z Transform $Z[f(n)] = \sum_{n=0}^{\infty} f(n)z^{-n}$
19	$\dfrac{c^n}{n}$ $n = 1, 2, 3 \ldots$	$-\ln(1 - cz)$	$\ln z - \ln(z - c)$
20	$\dfrac{c^n}{n!}$	e^{cz}	$e^{c/z}$
21	$\sin(nc)$	$\dfrac{z \sin c}{z^2 + 1 - 2z \cos c}$	$\dfrac{z \sin c}{z^2 + 1 - 2z \cos c}$
22	$\cos(nc)$	$\dfrac{1 - z \cos c}{z^2 + 1 - 2z \cos c}$	$\dfrac{z(z - \cos c)}{z^2 + 1 - 2z \cos c}$

Adapted with permission of the editor from C. S. Beightler, L. G. Mitten, and G. L. Nemhauser, "A Short Table of Z-Transforms and Generating Functions," *Operations Research*, Vol. 9, No. 4 (July–August, 1961), pp. 576–77.

Even calculatio involving the discrete analog of a derivative, the forward difference, can often be expedited by employing the z transform. The first forward difference is defined as

$$\Delta f(n) = f(n + 1) - f(n) \tag{5-44}$$

The transform of this difference is related to the transform of the function $f(n)$ by

$$Z[f(n + 1) - f(n)] = Z[f(n + 1)] - Z[f(n)] = \sum_{n=0}^{\infty} f(n + 1)z^{-n} - Z[f(n)]$$

$$= \sum_{j=1}^{\infty} f(j)z^{-j}z - Z[f(n)] = zZ[f(n)] - zf(0) - Z[f(n)]$$

from which

$$Z[\Delta f(n)] = (z - 1)Z[f(n)] - zf(0) \tag{5-45}$$

Note the direct parallel with Equation 5-29 which shows the Laplace transform of the derivative of a function in terms of the transform of the original function.

These and other operating rules are summarized for the convenience of the reader in Table 5-2.

Example. Consider the problem of determining the z transform of the following function:

$$f(n) = (n - 4)^2 u(n - 4) + \left(\frac{c^n}{n!}\right)\left(\frac{c}{n + 1} - 1\right)$$

where $u(n - 4)$ represents a unit step function at the point $n = 4$.

Although there are a number of ways to carry out the transformation, we will attempt to employ several of the relationships discussed above. First we recognize that $f(n)$ is a sum of two separate functions $g(n)$ and $h(n)$ where

$$g(n) = (n - 4)^2 u(n - 4)$$

$$h(n) = \frac{c^n}{n!}\left(\frac{c}{n+1} - 1\right)$$

Therefore, our transformation problem is reduced to one of finding separate transforms for $g(n)$ and $h(n)$ by the linearity property of z transforms. That is,

$$Z[f(n)] = Z[g(n)] + Z[h(n)]$$

Second, the function $g(n)$ can be related to the function n^2 which has been shifted four units to the right. From Equation 5–43 we know that

$$Z[(n - 4)^2 u(n - 4)] = z^{-4} Z(n^2)$$

Furthermore, from definition 10 in Table 5–2 we know that

$$Z(n^2) = \frac{z(1 + z)}{(z - 1)^3}$$

The transform for the function $g(n)$ must then be

$$Z[(n - 4)^2 u(n - 4)] = \frac{z^{-3}(1 + z)}{(z - 1)^3}$$

Third, with careful examination we can recognize the function $h(n)$ as

$$h(n) = \Delta \frac{c^n}{n!}$$

From Equation 5–45 we know that

$$Z[h(n)] = (z - 1)Z\left(\frac{c^n}{n!}\right) - z$$

Using definition 20 from Table 5–2 yields

$$Z\left(\frac{c^n}{n!}\right) = e^{c/z}$$

The transform of $h(n)$ then becomes

$$Z[h(n)] = (z - 1)e^{c/z} - z$$

Now we are in a position to bring all of the components together to complete the transformation of the function $f(n)$.

$$Z[f(n)] = \frac{z^{-3}(1 + z)}{(z - 1)^3} + (z - 1)e^{c/z} - z$$

Note that by judicious use of our tables and a few basic theorems relative to z transforms we have obtained the transform of a rather formidable expression without evaluating a single sum.

The Geometric Transform

Relationship to the Exponential Transform.   Just as the z transform can be considered as a discrete version of the Laplace transform, the geometric transform can be considered as a discrete version of the exponential transform. The exponential transform for continuous functions is defined as

$$E[f(t)] = \int_{-\infty}^{\infty} f(t)e^{st}\, dt \qquad (5-46)$$

It operates much the same as the Laplace transform we have been using except that it is defined for functions having negative as well as positive arguments and the complex variable s is carried as a positive exponent. There is also a bilateral Laplace transform which is defined from $-\infty$ to $+\infty$. However, since the exponential transform is widely used in probability theory, we will use the exponential transform in preference to the bilateral Laplace. We shall have more to say about the exponential transform in the next chapter when we discuss moment generating functions.

The geometric transform for a function $f(n)$ with an integral argument n is defined as

$$G[f(n)] = \sum_{n = -\infty}^{\infty} f(n)z^n \qquad (5-47)$$

The geometric transform bears exactly the same relationship to the exponential transform as the z transform bears to the Laplace transform. The complex variable z carries a positive exponent, and it is possible for the argument n to range from minus to plus infinity.

The confusion of terminology is even further compounded in the case of the geometric transform. We are employing the same terminology as Howard who refers to the relationship defined by Equation 5–47 as a geometric transform.[13] Beightler, Mitten, and Nemhauser on the other hand use the term generating function for this transformation.[14] To complete the

---

[13] Ronald A. Howard, "System Analysis of Linear Models," appearing in H. E. Scarf, D. M. Gilford, and M. W. Shelley, *Multistage Inventory Models and Techniques* (Stanford, 1963), chap. vi.

[14] Beightler *et al., op. cit.,* p. 576.

confusion Brown terms the same transformation a z transform.[15] The reader is urged to examine the mathematical definition carefully before employing one of several available tables on " z transforms."

Using the Transform. In the event that the function being transformed is defined for a negative argument n, the geometric transform is required. However, if the function is defined only for nonnegative n, then either the z or geometric transform may be employed. The choice is one of personal taste and compatability with related analyses.

Since most of the functions routinely encountered in systems analysis and operations engineering are normally zero to the left of the origin, it is convenient to redefine the geometric transform as

$$G[f(n)] = \sum_{n=0}^{\infty} f(n)z^n \qquad (5\text{-}48)$$

where $n \geq 0$. In this form a set of identities parallel to those available for the z transform is easily developed. Table 5-2 contains both the z and geometric transforms for a number of commonly encountered functions. The methods of analysis are identical. The reader is urged to demonstrate this for himself by obtaining the geometric transform of the function $f(n)$ used in the last section to illustrate the z transform.

Inversion of Transforms

As was true in the case of Laplace transforms, finding the inverse of either z or geometric transforms may require a combination of good tables, keen insight, and considerable skill. The easiest method is obviously to use a table of transform pairs. However, no table can cover all possible cases. Beightler, Mitten, and Nemhauser suggest five methods for finding the inverse when it cannot be obtained from a table.[16]

1. Application of basic theorems.
2. Partial fraction expansion.
3. Long division.
4. Contour integration.
5. Maclaurin series expansion.

Basic Theorems. Formulas 1 through 5 of Table 5-2 are general theorems which may be applied in any sequence or recursively. For example, suppose it is necessary to find the inverse of the geometric transform.

$$G[f(n)] = \frac{1}{1 - c^3 z} + \frac{cz^4}{(1 - cz)^2}$$

[15] Brown, *op. cit.*, p. 408.
[16] Beightler *et al.*, *op. cit.*, p. 577.

The first term can be recognized as $G[g(n)] = 1/(1 - az)$ where the argument a has been replaced by c^3. From definition 13 in Table 5–2

$$G^{-1}\left(\frac{1}{1 - az}\right) = a^n$$

therefore

$$G^{-1}\left(\frac{1}{1 - c^3z}\right) = (c^3)^n = c^{3n}$$

The second term can be written as

$$\frac{cz^4}{(1 - cz)^2} = z^3 \left[\frac{cz}{(1 - cz)^2}\right]$$

From definition 14 in Table 5–2 the term in square brackets has as its inverse

$$G^{-1}\left[\frac{cz}{(1 - cz)^2}\right] = nc^n$$

Since the transform of this known function has been multiplied by z^3 the shifting theorem contained in definition 3 shows us that

$$G^{-1}\left[\frac{z^3(cz)}{(1 - cz)^2}\right] = (n - 3)c^{n-3}u(n - 3)$$

Finally, by utilizing the linearity property of geometric transforms we have

$$f(n) = c^{3n} + (n - 3)c^{n-3}u(n - 3)$$

Where

$$u(n - 3) = \begin{cases} 0 & n < 3 \\ 1 & n \geq 3 \end{cases}$$

Partial Fractions. Whenever the transform to be inverted is expressed as a ratio of polynomials in which the degree of the numerator is less than the degree of the denominator, it may be expanded as a sum of simpler transforms. When the degree of the numerator is larger than the degree of the denominator, one can use long division to reduce the numerator to a degree smaller than the denominator. This is exactly the same approach used in inverting Laplace transforms. Once the partial fraction expansion is obtained the transform is inverted by resorting to tables or the theorems cited.

For example, consider the transform

$$G[f(n)] = \frac{5 - 13z}{3z^2 - 4z + 1}$$

Factoring the denominator yields

$$\frac{5 - 13z}{3z^2 - 4z + 1} = \frac{5 - 13z}{(1 - 3z)(1 - z)}$$

which from our knowledge of partial fractions can be written as

$$\frac{c_1}{1-3z} + \frac{c_2}{1-z} = \frac{1}{1-3z} + \frac{4}{1-z}$$

From definitions 8 and 13 the inverse transform becomes

$$f(n) = 3^n + 4$$

Long Division. Any desired number of terms of the inverse of a transform whose numerator and denominator are polynomials can be obtained by long division. In this instance the function $f(n)$ evaluated at a particular n appears as the coefficient of the corresponding power of z. For example, by long division

$$\frac{1}{1-2z} = 1 + 2z + 4z^2 + 8z^3 + \cdots$$

from which $f(0) = 1$, $f(1) = 2$, $f(2) = 4$, etc. This result is consistent with definition 13 in Table 5–2 which shows

$$G^{-1}\left(\frac{1}{1-2z}\right) = 2^n$$

Maclaurin Series Expansion. From algebra we know that it is possible to obtain a power series expansion for many functions in the form

$$f(x) = \sum_{j=0}^{\infty} \frac{x^j f^{(j)}(0)}{j!}$$

where $f^{(j)}(0)$ represents the jth derivative of $f(x)$ evaluated at $x = 0$. This expansion is called Maclaurin's series. Since the series consists of a sum of terms of the form of x^j times a coefficient, we are again in a position to obtain any desired number of terms of the time function corresponding to a given transform. Here we treat the transform as a function of the variable z and take derivatives with respect to z.

For example, suppose we want to find the inverse of the geometric transform

$$G[f(n)] = e^{2z}$$

The Maclaurin Series for this function is

$$G[f(n)] = 1 + 2z + \frac{(2z)^2}{2!} + \frac{(2z)^3}{3!} + \cdots$$

from which the coefficient of z^n is

$$f(n) = \frac{2^n}{n!}$$

This result is consistent with definition 20 in Table 5–2.

Uses for Discrete Transforms

Geometric and z-transforms find many important uses in the field of operations engineering. They are helpful in the solution of difference equations and differential difference equations. In addition we will employ them in the analysis of discrete control systems and to study probability distributions for discrete random variables. Such transforms are especially helpful in characterizing complex distributions involving random sums of random variables and in determining the moments of such distributions. Examples of these and other applications of the z and geometric transforms appear throughout the remainder of the text and hence will not be repeated here.

SELECTED BIBLIOGRAPHY

ABRAMOWITZ, M., AND STEGUN, I. A. (eds.). *Handbook of Mathematical Functions, AMS 55*. Washington, D.C.: U.S. Department of Commerce, National Bureau of Standards, U.S. Government Printing Office, 1964.

ASELTINE, JOHN A. *Transform Method in Linear System Analysis*. New York: McGraw-Hill Book Co., Inc., 1958.

BEIGHTLER, C. S.; MITTEN, L. G.; AND NEMHAUSER, G. L. "A Short Table of z-Transforms and Generating Functions," *Operations Research*, Vol. 9, No. 4 (July–August 1961), pp. 574–78.

BROWN, ROBERT G. *Smoothing, Forecasting and Prediction of Discrete Time Series*. Englewood Cliffs, N.J.: Prentice-Hall, Inc., 1963.

CRAIG, EDWARD J. *Laplace and Fourier Transforms for Electrical Engineers*. New York: Holt Rinehart & Winston, 1964.

HOWARD, RONALD A. "System Analysis of Linear Models" appearing in SCARF, H. E., *et al. Multistage Inventory Models and Techniques*. Stanford, 1963.

KREYSZIG, ERWIN. *Advanced Engineering Mathematics*. 2d ed. New York: John Wiley & Sons, Inc., 1967.

THOMSON, WILLIAM T. *Laplace Transformation*, 2d ed. Englewood Cliffs, N.J.: Prentice-Hall, Inc., 1960.

WYLIE, C. R., JR. *Advanced Engineering Mathematics*. 2d ed. New York: McGraw-Hill Book Co., Inc., 1960.

PROBLEMS

5-1 *a*) By considering the identity below, show that any function $f(t)$ can be written as the sum of an odd and even function:

$$f(t) = \frac{f(t) + f(-t)}{2} + \frac{f(t) - f(-t)}{2}$$

b) Express each of the following functions as the sum of an odd and an even function:

$$i)\ \ e^{2t} \qquad ii)\ \ \frac{t^2}{1-t} \qquad iii)\ \ \frac{t+1}{t-2}$$

5-2   The numbers of requests for flu shots at the University Health Center on the first of each month during the past year are given in the table below. Assume that for our purposes all months are of equal length. Determine the third partial sum Fourier approximation to these data. Plot the approximate function and the actual data points on the same graph. Use your results to estimate the number of shots on July 15.

Date	Requests	Date	Requests
Jan. 1	82	July 1	40
Feb. 1	84	Aug. 1	39
Mar. 1	79	Sept. 1	43
Apr. 1	71	Oct. 1	53
May 1	59	Nov. 1	65
June 1	47	Dec. 1	75

5-3   *a)* The output $f(t)$ for a control system is $\sin(5t)$. Find the Fourier series representation of $f(t)$.

b) Use the formal definition of the Laplace transform to find $\mathscr{L}[f(t)]$. You may use the fact that

$$\int e^{ax} \sin bx \, dx = \frac{e^{ax}}{a^2 + b^2}(a \sin bx - b \cos bx)$$

5-4   The Fourier series representation of a function is known to be

$$f(t) = g(t) + h(t)$$

where $g(t)$ is even, $h(t)$ is odd, and

$$f(t) = 1.0 + \cos(3t) + 3\sin(2.5t) + 2\cos(6t) + 9\sin(5t)$$
$$+ 3\cos(9t) + 27\sin(7.5t) + 4\cos(12t) + \cdots$$

a) Find a general expression for the nth term of the expansion of $h(t)$.

b) Find a closed form for the Fourier approximation for $g(t)$ using the 19th partial sum. Show all calculations.

5-5   A chemical processing plant operates around the clock for five days and then is stopped for clean-up and recharging for a similar period. While in operation, the plant produces at a constant rate of 3,000 pounds per day. When stopped the rate is obviously zero. Since production rate over time is a discontinuous function it is desirable to have a continuous approximation to this function for purposes of analysis.

a) Find the Fourier coefficients corresponding to the production rate function.

b) Write the corresponding Fourier series.

c) How should the production function $F(x)$ be defined over one complete cycle if it is desirable that the Fourier series converge to $F(x)$ throughout the interval?

5-6   The base sales of a new product appear to be increasing as a linear function of time, i.e., bt, where t is measured in months. In addition there is a seasonal factor best described by $c \sin(\pi t/6)$.

a) What is the primative period of the seasonal factor?

b) Consider sales for a one-year period only. Develop the first two nonzero terms of the half range expansion for *total* sales (i.e., base plus seasonal) when the periodic extension is *odd*. Leave in integral form.

5-7   1969 base sales for a local watering hole were S_0 per day. During 1970, base sales for the first of the month have doubled each month (through July). Because they are located adjacent to a large plant which pays its employees twice each month, management feels that there is also a cyclical effect best described by a superimposed sine wave with amplitude k. The first peak in cyclical sales occurred on January 1, 1970. The plant is a defense contractor, and the watering hole feels that sales are bound to decline in 1971. They predict that consumption will fall off such that January 15, 1971, data will be the same as December 15, 1970.

a) Assuming that time is measured in months and that data is available for daily consumption, develop an expression for forecasting sales $S(t)$ for the balance of 1970 ($t = 0$, implies January 1, 1970).

b) Develop the Fourier series approximation to the sales function applicable through 1971. (Leave in integral form.)

5-8   Arrests for narcotics violations in the jungle of a prominent Chinese institution are listed by month in the table below:

Month	Arrests
September	5
October	9
November	23
December	53

Local police are studying these data to see if meaningful inferences concerning the rise and fall of left-wing groups can be drawn.

Agent 001 has information from SMASH to indicate that these data represent one-half period of a periodic process which can be described by an " even " function. Develop the first two nonzero terms of the Fourier expansion of this function. What is the length of the " primative " period for this function? What is your estimate for January arrests?

5-9   The Master's degrees in Social Unrest issued by the Relentless Institute of Terror since its founding in 1960 are listed below:

Year	Degrees Granted
1960	300
1961	297
1962	304
1963	315
1964	324
1965	325
1966	312

Local insurance companies are studying these data to determine the probable effect on fire insurance rates.

Suppose that these data are to be approximated by a series of sine terms over the interval of 1960 through 1963. Use your knowledge of harmonic analysis to establish the estimating function, i.e., work with the raw data, not a polynomial fit to the data.

5–10   The function $f(t)$ is known to have the following Fourier series representation:

$$f(t) = 0.5 + \cos\frac{\pi t}{3} + \frac{1}{2}\sin\frac{\pi t}{3} + 2\cos\frac{2\pi t}{3} + \frac{1}{3}\sin\frac{2\pi t}{3} + 3\cos\pi t + \frac{1}{4}\sin\pi t + \cdots$$

a) If this function is assumed to have been expressed as a sum of an odd and an even function, what is the Fourier expansion for the odd component?

b) Develop a closed form expression for the sum of all terms through frequency 10π for the even component.

5–11   Vy Bration has some data on surface roughness from a machining operation which appears to be periodic with period of four seconds. His initial data points are

t	$s(t)$
0	10
1	12
2	11
3	9

a) Find the amplitude of the second harmonic under the assumption that this process exactly repeats itself every four seconds.

b) What can you tell Vy about the frequency of potential trouble sources in this process?

c) What is the Fourier series representation which will exactly pass through the indicated data points?

5–12   Find the Laplace transforms of the following functions:

a) $t^2 - 2$ *b*) $a\cos(2t)$

c) $e^{-2t}\cos t$ *d*) $e^{-t}\sin^2 t$

e) $e^{-at}\sin wt$ *f*) $f(t)$

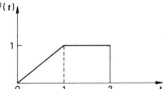

5–13   Show that

a) $\mathcal{L}(te^{at}) = \dfrac{1}{(s-a)^2}$ *b*) $\mathcal{L}(e^{at}\sin wt) = \dfrac{w}{(s-a)^2 + w^2}$

5–14 Find $f(t)$ if $\mathscr{L}[f(t)]$ equals

$$a) \quad \frac{3}{s+2} \qquad b) \quad \frac{1}{s^2+9} \qquad c) \quad \frac{s+2}{(s+2)^2+w^2}$$

5–15 Using the differentiation theorem show

$$a) \quad \mathscr{L}(t\cos wt) = \frac{s^2-w^2}{(s^2+w^2)^2} \qquad b) \quad \mathscr{L}(te^{at}) = \frac{1}{(s-a)^2}$$

5–16 Using the integration theorem find $f(t)$ if $\mathscr{L}[f(t)]$ equals

$$a) \quad \frac{1}{s(s-2)} \qquad b) \quad \frac{1}{s^2(s+1)} \qquad c) \quad \frac{1}{s^2}\left(\frac{s-1}{s+1}\right)$$

5–17 Use the relationship $\mathscr{L}[tf(t)] = -F'(s)$ to find the transform of

$$a) \quad te^t \qquad b) \quad t^2 e^{2t}$$
$$c) \quad t\sin 3t \qquad d) \quad t^2 e^{-t}$$

5–18 Use the relationship $\mathscr{L}\left[\dfrac{f(t)}{t}\right] = \displaystyle\int_s^\infty F(r)\,dr$ to find $f(t)$ if $\mathscr{L}(f)$ is

$$a) \quad \frac{2s}{(s^2+1)^2} \qquad b) \quad \ln\frac{s^2+1}{(s-1)^2}$$

5–19 Represent the following functions in terms of unit step functions and find their Laplace transforms.

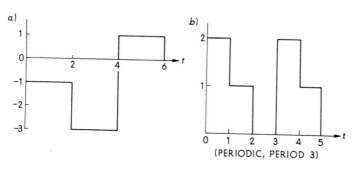

5–20 Find the Laplace transforms of the following periodic functions (period 2π)

$$a) \quad f(t) = 2\pi - t \qquad 0 < t < 2\pi \qquad\qquad b) \quad f(t) = t^2 \qquad 0 < t < 2\pi$$

5-21   Use the convolution property of Laplace transforms to solve the following problems:

a) Find $\mathscr{L}^{-1}\left[\dfrac{1}{(s-1)(s-2)}\right]$

b) Find $\mathscr{L}^{-1}\left[\dfrac{s}{(s^2+a^2)^2}\right]$

c) Find $\mathscr{L}^{-1}\left[\dfrac{1}{s^2(s+1)^2}\right]$

d) Solve the integral equation for $y(t)$:

$$y(t)=t^2+\int_0^t y(u)\sin(t-u)\,du$$

5-22   Use the convolution property of Laplace transforms to solve the following problems:

a) Find $\mathscr{L}^{-1}\left[\dfrac{1}{(s+a)(s+b)}\right]$

b) Find $\mathscr{L}^{-1}\left[\dfrac{1}{(s^2+4s+13)^2}\right]$

c) Find $\mathscr{L}^{-1}\left[\dfrac{1}{s(s^2+1)}\right]$

5-23   Solve the following integral equation for $y(t)$:

$$\int_0^t \frac{y(u)}{\sqrt{t-u}}\,du=1+t+t^2$$

5-24   The system equation for a simple RL circuit is given below:

$$L\frac{dI(t)}{dt}+RI(t)=E(t)$$

Consider the system at rest with initial condition $I(0)=0$. If the system is subjected to a driving force $E(t)=k$ determine the flow of current as a function of time $[I(t)]$.

5-25   The cumulative production output for Generous Motors skates can be described by the following differential equation:

$$\frac{d^2x}{dt^2}+5\frac{dx}{dt}+4x=e^t \qquad 0<t<10$$

where $x(t)=$ cumulative output in units up to time t after job setup. Under the assumption that the system must be initialized with a setup, find the cumulative output function $x(t)$ for $0<t<10$.

5-26 Perform the following calculations, if possible. If the indicated operations are impossible, prove it.

a) $\mathscr{L}\,(e^{t^2}) = ?$

b) $\mathscr{L}^{-1}\left[\dfrac{2e^{-\pi s} + 2e^{-\pi s/2}}{(s^2 + 4)(1 - e^{-\pi s})}\right] = ?$ (sketch the resulting function)

c) $\lim\limits_{t \to \infty} f(t) = ?$ when $\mathscr{L}[f(t)] = \dfrac{s^2 + bs + c}{s^3 + sd^2 + 3s^2 + 3d^2}$

5-27 From the elementary theory of queues it is well known that the steady-state equations for an unlimited single channel exponential queuing system are

$$(\lambda + \mu)p_n = \lambda p_{n-1} + \mu p_{n+1} \qquad n > 0$$
$$\lambda p_0 = \mu p_1$$

Where λ = arrival rate, μ = service rate, p_i = probability of i in the system

a) Develop the geometric transform for p_i.
b) Using this transform, calculate the expected value for number in the system.
c) Using the transform, calculate the variance for number in the system.
d) Ignore the probability implications and assume that $(\lambda + \mu)f(n) = \lambda f(n-1) + \mu f(n+1)$ holds for all $n \ge 0$. Use geometric transform techniques to develop an expression for $f(n)$ as a function of $f(0)$.

5-28 O. R. Student is an analyst for the Only Sore Undergrads Athletic Department. As a keen observer of human affairs he has noted that long lines tend to accumulate at the athletic ticket office this time of year. He recognizes that the number in line at any one time can be predicted only in a probability sense and that this probability statement changes as the day progresses. The equation he uses to describe this phenomenon is

$$\frac{d P_n(t)}{dt} = a[P_{n-1}(t) - P_n(t)]$$

where $P_n(t)$ represents the probability of n in line at time t. He further notes that $P_0(0) = 1$ and $P_n(0) = 0$ when $n > 1$. Having once taken IE 798I he recognizes this as a differential equation in t and a difference equation in n. You must now determine $P_n(t)$ for O. R. Student by *utilizing your knowledge of Laplace and geometric transforms.*

CHAPTER **6**

Transform Techniques in Systems Analysis and Probability Modeling

IN THE LAST chapter we discussed the mechanics of manipulating a number of different transforms. It is the purpose of this chapter to employ some of the special characteristics of transforms in linear system analysis and probability modeling.

The Impulse Response Function

The unit impulse or delta function plays a key role in understanding the use of transforms in system analysis. We will consider both the Dirac delta function for use with the Laplace transform and a simple unit pulse for use with the discrete transforms.

The Impulse and System Operators. Let us first consider the analysis of a linear system operating on discrete time functions, i.e., functions defined on the integers that can take on nonzero values only at the points 0, 1, 2, 3, ... Linear systems exhibit the properties of time invariance and superposition as discussed below. Our discussion is patterned after the excellent treatment by Howard.[1]

We will consider a system to be an operator that acts on one function to

---

[1] Ronald A. Howard, "System Analysis of Linear Models" in H. E. Scarf, D. M. Gilford, and M. W. Shelly (eds.), *Multistage Inventory Models and Techniques* (Stanford: Stanford University Press, 1963).

194

FIGURE 6-1

Function of a System

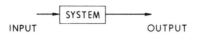

INPUT   OUTPUT

produce another. Our mathematical operators have their physical counter-parts in the black boxes popularized in recent years as the building blocks for complex systems. Figure 6-1 can be thought of as a simple single element or as a very intricate system performing many operations on the input signal before displaying the output. For our purposes, the role of system analysis will be to develop a mathematical operator which can characterize actions performed on any given input signal by a proposed system.

We shall begin by supposing that the response of a system to a unit impulse is known. For example, in a particular inventory control system it has been observed that a sale of one unit of stock on day zero will generate a replacement order for that stock five days later. The sale of one unit is our input signal, a unit impulse at time zero. The replacement order is our output signal, another pulse five days later. The stock replenishment system is our black box for which we have just observed an impulse response function, the replenishment order being the "impulse response." Note that the control system being discussed is operating on information, not physical goods. The system has mathematical functions flowing in and out, not items of inventory. For that reason, a second system, say a demand forecasting system, could operate from the same input signal without loss of information.

Let

$h(n) =$ impulse response function $output$

$I(n - k) =$ unit impulse at n equals k $input$

$S[f(n)] =$ the system operator

Then

$$h(n) = S[I(n - 0)]$$

which for our simple delay system becomes

$$h(n) = I(n - 5)$$

This says that the system response to a unit impulse at the origin is a second pulse displaced five time units. This is commonly referred to as a pure time lag system.

The systems of concern to us will be considered to be time invariant. This means that if the system responds to a signal at time zero with a response function $h(n)$, then it will respond to the same signal received at time k with a response function $h(n - k)$. In other words, translating the origin of the input signal moves the origin of the output signal by the same number of units. In our simple inventory example, a unit sold on day 5 would lead to a requisition on day 10 due to the time invariance of the system.

```
          ┌─────────┐
────────▶│ SYSTEM  ├────────▶
          └─────────┘
  I(n-5)              h(n-5)=I(n-10)
```

A second important property of linear systems is sometimes referred to as superposition. This means that a series of signals being input to a system will elicit a response function which is the sum of the effects of the responses to each signal acting alone. Furthermore if an input signal is multiplied by a constant, the resulting output will be multiplied by the same constant. In our inventory example suppose that three units are sold at time zero and two units are sold at time one. The response to the sale of three units will be $3h(n)$. The response to the sale of two units will be $2h(n - 1)$. The total system response function to the sales vector input is

$$3h(n) + 2h(n - 1)$$

where $h(n)$ is the known impulse response function.

Continuing the same line of reasoning it is easy to imagine any given discrete input function $f(n)$ as a vector whose components $f(k)$ are each multiplied by an impulse function delayed by k time units. In the preceding paragraph we could have depicted the sales vector as

$$f(n) = [3I(n - 0), 2I(n - 5)]$$

In general

$$f(n) = [f(0)I(n - 0), f(1)I(n - 1), \ldots, f(k)I(n - k) \cdots] \qquad (6\text{--}1)$$

Recall that the superposition principle permits us to multiply the impulse response by the same factor as the input and to add component responses. The system response $g(n)$ at time n to any arbitrary input function $f(n)$ is then simply the weighted sum of a series of impulse responses delayed by an appropriate time.

$$g(n) = \sum_{k=0}^{n} f(k)h(n - k) \qquad (6\text{--}2)$$

This is the convolution sum introduced in the preceding chapter. The functions being convolved are the input function $f(n)$ and the impulse response function $h(n)$. The development of the convolution is depicted in Figure 6–2.

Note that we have completely characterized the behavior of linear, time-invariant systems by a single mathematical function, the impulse response.

FIGURE 6–2

The Development of Convolution

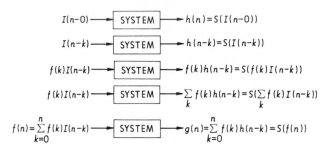

Adapted with the permission of the publisher from Ronald A. Howard, "System Analysis of Linear Models" in H. E. Scarf, D. M. Gilford, and M. W. Shelly (eds.), *Multistage Inventory Models and Techniques* (Stanford: Stanford University Press, 1963).

This means that once we know how such a system responds to a unit impulse signal at time zero, we can determine its response to any discrete input function by the convolution operation.

The Transfer Function

Use of Transforms. The convolution sum developed above is not always an easy mathematical operation to carry out even when $f(n)$ and $h(n)$ are well-defined functions. For that reason we will resort to either the z or geometric transform.

In the previous chapter we saw that the convolution of two functions in time domain reduced to a simple product of transforms in frequency domain. (See Equation 5 in Table 5–2.) The transform of the response of a system to an arbitrary input signal is then simply the product of the transform of the input signal and the transform of the impulse response function. Either z or geometric transforms may be used. That is,

$$T[g(n)] = T[f(n)]T[h(n)] \qquad (6\text{–}3)$$

where $T(\cdot)$ represents the transformation operation.

Because of its importance in system analysis the transform of $h(n)$ is given the special name *transfer function.* Now if we know the transfer function for a system we can predict how that system will respond to any input signal by multiplying the transform of the input by the transfer function and inverting. The ultimate goal is to develop rules for constructing increasingly complex control systems by combining simple linear systems with known transfer functions. The transfer function for the total system then gives a complete characterization of that system.

Example. A particular system has been subjected to a unit impulse input and observed to give a response of

$$2^n(n + 1)$$

From Table 5–2, the z transform of the impulse response function is

$$Z(2^n n + 2^n) = \frac{2z}{(z - 2)^2} + \frac{z}{z - 2}$$

which reduces to the transfer function

$$T = \frac{z^2}{(z - 2)^2}$$

A new input signal

$$f(n) = \frac{3^n}{n!}$$

will lead to an output $g(n)$ whose transform is

$$Z[g(n)] = \frac{z^2 e^{3/z}}{(z - 2)^2}$$

The Delta Function. The analysis of continuous systems is carried out in much the same manner as the analysis of discrete systems. The system is characterized by its impulse response function which can be convolved with an arbitrary input to obtain the resulting output. Equivalently the transform of the impulse response may be multiplied by the transform of the new input to get the transform of the new output. The transform of the impulse response is again referred to as the *transfer function.*

The impulse function used to analyze continuous systems takes a slightly different form. This is the Dirac delta function with the properties[2]

$$\delta(t - a) = 0 \qquad t \neq a \tag{6-4}$$

$$\int_0^\infty \delta(t - a)\,dt = 1 \tag{6-5}$$

It can be defined as the limiting area of a rectangle of width E and height $1/E$ as E approaches zero.

A literal interpretation of the delta function in any physical system causes some difficulties. It is a function of zero width, infinite height, and area one. It might be approximated by a very brief pulse of very large magnitude but could never be exactly reproduced by a physical system. For our purposes it is a mathematical convenience which will enable us to better understand the convolution operation in system analysis.

---

[2] William Tyerell Thomson, *Laplace Transform* (2d ed., Englewood Cliffs, N.J.: Prentice-Hall, Inc., 1960), p. 27.

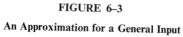

FIGURE 6–3

An Approximation for a General Input

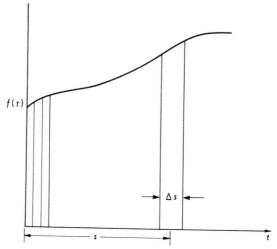

We will characterize the response of a system to an impulse input, in this case the delta function, as $h(t)$ where t is a continuous variable. Now, following the argument of Aseltine, consider an arbitrary input function $f(t)$ to be a series of impulses of magnitude $f(s) \Delta s$ as shown in Figure 6–3.[3] The response to a single unit impulse occurring at time s is known to be $h(t - s)$ by the time invariant property of the system. The total response to a number of such pulses each multiplied by $f(s) \Delta s$ is

$$\sum_{s=\Delta s}^{t} h(t - s) f(s) \Delta s$$

by the superposition principle.

Under very general conditions the above sum, expressed in the limit as Δs approaches zero, becomes

$$g(t) = \int_{0}^{t} f(s)h(t - s)\,ds \qquad (6\text{–}6)$$

This is the Faltung or convolution integral, introduced in Chapter 5. Using the Laplace transform the transform of the output is seen to be

$$\mathscr{L}[g(t)] = \mathscr{L}[f(t)]\mathscr{L}[h(t)] \qquad (6\text{–}7)$$

The Laplace transform of $h(t)$ is the transfer function.

---

[3] John A. Aseltine, *Transform Method in Linear System Analysis* (New York: McGraw-Hill Book Co., Inc., 1958), p. 135.

The Transfer Function as a Ratio of Transforms. The Laplace transform of the delta function takes a particularly simple form. From the definition of the delta function, it is obvious that the integral of any argument times the delta function at $t = a$ will simply be the integrand evaluated at $t = a$.

$$\int_0^\infty f(t)\delta(t-a)\,dt = f(a)\int_{a-\varepsilon}^{a+\varepsilon}\delta(t-a)\,dt = f(a) \tag{6-8}$$

Applying this to the definition of the Laplace transform of an impulse at the origin yields

$$\mathscr{L}[\delta(t-0)] = \int_0^\infty e^{-st}\delta(t-0)\,dt = 1 \tag{6-9}$$

Similarly the transform of a delta function displaced a units to the right is

$$\mathscr{L}[\delta(t-a)] = \int_0^\infty e^{-st}\delta(t-a)\,dt = e^{-as} \tag{6-10}$$

Recall that our definition of the impulse response function required that the system be excited by a delta function at time zero. The transform of the input is then unity. The transform of the response to this input we previously called a transfer function.

Since it may not be feasible to approximate the delta function as input for a system to be analyzed, we will employ an alternate definition of the transfer function as

$$\text{Transfer function} = \frac{\mathscr{L}(\text{output})}{\mathscr{L}(\text{input})} \tag{6-11}$$

when the system is initially at rest. This implies that we can excite the system with a known function $f(t)$, observe the response $g(t)$ elicited by that function, and form the ratio of their transforms to obtain the transfer function. Note that this definition of the transfer function is consistent with our use of the transform of the impulse response function. When the input function is a delta function at the origin

$$\text{Transfer function} = \frac{\mathscr{L}(\text{out})}{\mathscr{L}(\text{in})} = \frac{\mathscr{L}[h(n)]}{\mathscr{L}[\delta(t-0)]}$$

But

$$\mathscr{L}[\delta(t-0)] = 1$$

therefore the transfer function defined as a ratio of transforms is equivalent to the Laplace transform of the impulse response function.

A similar analysis can be performed for discrete systems using the impulse function since

$$Z[I(n-0)] = \sum_{n=0}^\infty I(n-0)z^{-n} = 1$$

and

$$G[I(n - 0)] = \sum_{n=0}^{\infty} I(n - 0)z^n = 1$$

In other words, for continuous systems the transfer function can be viewed as the transform of the impulse response function or the ratio of the Laplace transform of an output to the transform of its associated arbitrary input. In like manner, for discrete systems, the transfer function can be viewed as the z or geometric transform of the impulse response function or as the ratio of the transform of an output to the transform of its associated input.

Example. A particular information system operates on an input signal by taking the first forward difference of that signal. For one input function, with value zero when $n = 0$, the system has been observed to give the response function

$$g(n) = 2n + 1$$

Using our knowledge of difference equations and geometric transforms, we must determine the unknown input function and a transfer function for the system.

The difference equation to be satisfied is

$$f(n + 1) - f(n) = 2n + 1$$

A subsidiary equation in the geometric transform of $f(n)$ is formed by taking the transform of both sides of this difference equation (see Table 5–2).

$$\frac{1}{z}[G(f(n)) - f(0)] - G[f(n)] = \frac{2z}{(1 - z)^2} + \frac{1}{1 - z}$$

Solving for the geometric transform of $f(n)$ yields

$$G[f(n)] = \frac{z(z + 1)}{(1 - z)^3}$$

Reference to Table 5–2 reveals that this is the transform of the well-known function

$$f(n) = G^{-1}[f(n)] = n^2$$

Therefore the input signal which generated the observed output must have been n^2.

The transfer function for this system is most easily obtained from the ratio of transforms of the observed output and calculated input.

$$\text{Transfer function} = \frac{G[g(n)]}{G[f(n)]} = \frac{(z + 1)/(1 - z)^2}{z(z + 1)/(1 - z)^3} = \frac{1 - z}{z}$$

Compound Systems

So far we have discussed techniques for analysis of simple linear systems consisting of a single element. Now we will consider more complex systems consisting of a number of independent linear systems configured in various ways to produce a desired result. The basic building blocks will be series, parallel, and feedback loop connections. Detailed discussions of the development of these elements are contained in Brown[4] and Howard.[5]

Goals of System Analysis. One purpose of the system analysis approach we are pursuing is to reduce complex systems with many elements to an equivalent single element system with a known transfer function. In so doing it is necessary to know the impulse response or transfer functions of each element viewed independently. From this the behavior of any given configuration of a number of such elements can be determined analytically. This is the analysis function: to analyze the behavior of a well-defined system.

Design is the companion of engineering analysis. The second purpose of our study is to provide a means of suggesting alternative ways to construct systems to perform some well-defined task. Obviously analysis and design cannot be separated. They represent two pieces of a continuous cycle. The building block concept of system elements and their reduction to single transfer functions represent mathematical analysis and design to parallel the physical experiments traditionally conducted by engineers when designing a new product.

Elements in Series. The single element system consists of a system operator which receives an input signal, performs an operation based on that signal, and produces an output signal. We can consider the functions involved to be either discrete or continuous. If discrete, we have employed the convolution sum and z or geometric transforms to relate input to output. If continuous, we have employed the convolution integral and Laplace transforms to relate input to output. In the following discussion we will use general functions recognizing that the same operations hold for discrete and continuous systems.

If two elements are connected in series, the output for element number 1 becomes the input for element number 2. Suppose that we know the impulse response function for each element operating independently, say $h_1(t)$ and $h_2(t)$. An input signal $f(t)$ for the compound system would progress through the system as

[4] Robert G. Brown, *Smoothing, Forecasting and Prediction of Discrete Time Series* (Englewood Cliffs, N.J.: Prentice-Hall, Inc., 1963), pp. 406–9.
[5] Howard, *op. cit.*, pp. 153–62.

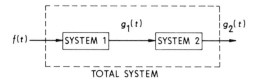

TOTAL SYSTEM

The output for subsystem 1 is

$$g_1(t) = f(t) * h_1(t)$$

where $f * h$ connotes the convolution operation. Now since $g_1(t)$ serves as input to subsystem 2, the output for subsystem 2 and the total system is

$$g_2(t) = g_1(t) * h_2(t) = f(t) * h_1(t) * h_2(t) \qquad (6\text{–}12)$$

The convolution operation is commutative, associative, and distributive. This then permits us to replace the two elements in series with a single element whose impulse response is

$$h(t) = h_1(t) * h_2(t) \qquad (6\text{–}13)$$

Equivalently the transfer function for two elements in series may be expressed as

$$\text{Transfer function} = T[h_1(t)]T[h_2(t)] \qquad (6\text{–}14)$$

where $T(\cdot)$ denotes the transformation operation appropriate for the systems used. This may be extended to n such elements in series by taking the n-fold convolution or the product of n transfer functions.

Elements in Parallel. A parallel configuration of elements permits several operations to be performed simultaneously on the same input signal after which the component outputs are summed. Two systems in parallel could be represented as

Total System

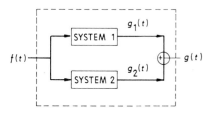

It is well to note that the arrows on this diagram represent a flow of information. The fork in the flow of the signal $f(t)$ does not mean that $f(t)$ has been split into two parts. It simply means that subsystems 1 and 2 both

have access to the same input signal. On the output side all signals flowing into a node are additive.

From the diagram

$$g(t) = g_1(t) + g_2(t)$$

where

$$g_1(t) = f(t) * h_1(t)$$

and

$$g_2(t) = f(t) * h_2(t)$$

therefore

$$g(t) = f(t) * [h_1(t) + h_2(t)]$$

This means that we can replace two elements in parallel with a single element system whose impulse response function is

$$h(t) = h_1(t) + h_2(t) \qquad \text{parallel} \qquad (6\text{--}15)$$

Similarly, the transfer function for elements in parallel is

$$\text{Transfer function} = T[h_1(t)] + T[h_2(t)] \qquad (6\text{--}16)$$

Obviously these results are extended to as many subsystems as desired by adding the appropriate number of impulse response functions or transfer functions.

Feedback Loops.   The simplest feedback loop is one in which the output signal becomes a function of itself:

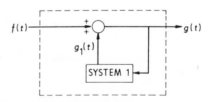

In this case, the output $g(t)$ is fed back through a subsystem which produces a new output $g_1(t)$ which is in turn added to the external input $f(t)$. An automatic controller on a machine tool which makes adjustments based on the current diameter of the part being manufactured functions in this manner.

The total system output as shown in the diagram can be expressed as

$$g(t) = f(t) + g(t) * h_1(t)$$

There is no simple way to replace this convolution by some equivalent response function as we did with parallel and series connections. However, we can obtain the transfer function for a single simple element which will replace the feedback loop.

Taking transforms

$$T[g(t)] = T[f(t)] + T[g(t)]T[h_1(t)]$$

from which

$$T[g(t)] = \frac{T[f(t)]}{1 - T[h_1(t)]}$$

The transfer function for a simple element connecting $f(t)$ and $g(t)$ is defined as

$$\text{Transfer function} = \frac{T[g(t)]}{T[f(t)]}$$

The transfer function for a simple element which will perform the function of the feedback loop is then

$$\text{Transfer function} = \frac{1}{1 - T[h_1(t)]} \qquad (6\text{--}17)$$

where $T[h_1(t)]$ is the transfer function of the element contained in the loop.

More complex feedback loops may be constructed by inserting one element connecting input to output and a second element connecting output to input.

Total System

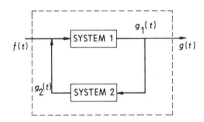

The transfer function for a simple element to replace this loop is

$$\text{Transfer function} = \frac{T[h_1(t)]}{1 - T[h_1(t)]T[h_2(t)]} \qquad (6\text{--}18)$$

An explanation of this function is detailed in Howard[6] and elsewhere.

We are now in a position to determine the transfer function for any combination of parallel, series, and feedback systems. Once the transfer function is known, total system response to any given input signal can be obtained.

---

[6] *Ibid.*, p. 163.

Example. A compound system is composed of two types of elements A and B arranged as shown:

Total System

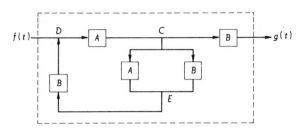

Elements A and B have known transfer functions $T[h_A(t)]$ and $T[h_B(t)]$. Determine the transfer function for a single element connecting the functions $f(t)$ and $g(t)$ which will duplicate the configuration of A and B elements shown.

The first step is to reduce all easily recognized subconfigurations to single elements. The subsystem connecting nodes C and E is a parallel hookup.

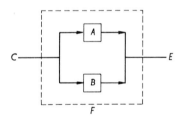

The transfer function for an equivalent single element, say F, is from Equation 6–16

$$T[h_F(t)] = T[h_A(t)] + T[h_B(t)]$$

If we examine the system between nodes C and D, this new element F is connected in series with another element B.

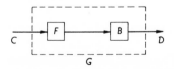

From Equation 6–14 the equivalent transfer function for this subsystem is

$$T[h_G(t)] = T[h_F(t)]T[h_B(t)] = [T(h_A(t)) + T(h_B(t))]T[h_B(t)]$$

The original system has now been reduced to that of a two-element feedback loop connected in series with a simple element B.

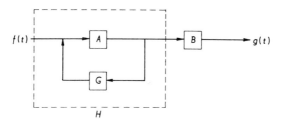

The feedback loop can be replaced by a simple element with a transfer function given by Equation 6–18.

$$T[h_H(t)] = \frac{T[h_A(t)]}{1 - T[h_A(t)]T[h_G(t)]}$$

Finally, combining this with the last series element B gives the total system transfer function of

$$T[h_S(t)] = \frac{T[h_A(t)]T[h_B(t)]}{1 - T[h_A(t)][T(h_A(t)) + T(h_B(t))]T[h_B(t)]}$$

Now it is possible to determine the transform of the output of this composite system when subjected to an arbitrary input $f(t)$.

$$T[g(t)] = T[f(t)]T[h_S(t)]$$

We will return to the role of transfer functions in system analysis in later chapters on model building. Simplified examples of their use are contained in the problems at the end of this chapter.

Transforms in Probability Modeling

Many discussions in probability modeling center around the use of moment generating functions, characteristic functions, and probability generating functions. Although the reader is often not appraised of the fact, these tools from probability theory are in reality simple transforms of the type discussed throughout the last chapter. The function being transformed is the probability density function. When applied to probability densities, the transforms have additional properties which enable us to calculate moments, distributions for sums of random variables, cumulative distributions, etc., directly from the transforms. The purpose of this section is to demonstrate the application of the various transforms in a probability context.

The Characteristic Function. The characteristic function $C(s)$ corresponding to a probability density function $f(x)$ is defined as the expected value of

e^{isx}.[7] The expectation may be written in terms of a Stieltjes integral to give a definition which includes both continuous and discontinuous cases.

$$C(s) = E(e^{isx}) = \int_{-\infty}^{\infty} e^{isx} \, d \, F(x) = \int_{-\infty}^{\infty} e^{isx} f(x) \, dx \qquad (6\text{–}19)$$

where i is the imaginary number $\sqrt{-1}$, $f(x)$ is the probability density function for x, and $F(x)$ is the cumulative distribution. When $F(x)$ is continuous the Stieltjes integral reduces to the Riemann integral as noted. For our purposes we will only use the characteristic function when $f(x)$ is continuous. Hence the Riemann integral will suffice.

We have encountered the characteristic function before. This is the Fourier integral introduced in Chapter 5. Relating the characteristic function to Equation 5–18, we could refer to it as the "inverse Fourier transform" of the probability density function. Recall from our discussion of the Fourier integral that the only requirements for this transform to exist are that there be at most a finite number of discontinuities in the function and that the improper integral

$$\int_{-\infty}^{\infty} |f(x)| \, dx$$

exist. Since $f(x)$ is a probability density function the improper integral always equals one. Hence the characteristic function exists for all probability distributions. The same is not true of the moment generating function and the probability generating function. For that reason, together with the fact that the characteristic function is unique, it is the most general transform to use in theoretical calculations in which the form of the distribution is not specified.

Developing Moments from the Characteristic Function. In some applications the characteristic function may be developed from a series of calculations involving a number of random variables. The resulting function may be extremely difficult to invert to obtain the probability density. However, the moments of the probability distribution are readily obtainable directly from the characteristic function.

Let us begin by taking the first derivative of the characteristic function with respect to s.

$$\frac{dC(s)}{ds} = \int_{-\infty}^{\infty} ixe^{isx} f(x) \, dx$$

If we evaluate this derivative with the argument $s = 0$ we have

$$\frac{dC(s)}{ds}\bigg|_{s=0} = i \int_{-\infty}^{\infty} x f(x) \, dx$$

---

[7] See for example, William Feller, *An Introduction to Probability Theory and Its Applications* (New York: John Wiley & Sons, Inc., 1966), Vol. II, chap. xv.

6—Transform Techniques in Systems Analysis and Probability Modeling   209

This is obviously i times the mean, or the first moment about zero, of $f(x)$. By taking higher order derivatives we have the general term

$$\frac{d^r C(s)}{ds^r} = i^r \int_{-\infty}^{\infty} x^r e^{isx} f(x)\, dx$$

The rth moment about zero is then

$$E(x^r) = \frac{C^{(r)}(0)}{i^r} \tag{6-20}$$

where $C^{(r)}(0)$ represents the rth derivative of the characteristic function evaluated at $s = 0$. Note that we can generate the moments without knowing the form of the parent distribution.

Once we know the moments about zero the variance or second moment about the mean and any other higher order moments about the mean can be obtained from the appropriate identity.

For example,

$$\text{Var}(x) = E[(x - \mu)^2] = E(x^2) - [E(x)]^2$$

therefore

$$\text{Var}(x) = \frac{C^{(2)}(0) - [C^{(1)}(0)]^2}{i^2}$$

Example. The normal distribution with mean μ and variance σ^2 is given by

$$f(x) = \frac{1}{\sqrt{2\pi}\,\sigma} \exp\left[\frac{-(x - \mu)^2}{2\sigma^2}\right] \tag{6-21}$$

The characteristic function for this distribution is

$$C_n(s) = \exp\left(i\mu s - \frac{\sigma^2 s^2}{2}\right) \tag{6-22}$$

The first derivative of $C_n(s)$ with respect to s yields

$$\frac{dC_n(s)}{ds} = (i\mu - s\sigma^2)\exp\left(i\mu s - \frac{\sigma^2 s^2}{2}\right)$$

Evaluating the derivative at $s = 0$ we have

$$C^{(1)}(0) = i\mu = iE(x)$$

The second derivative is

$$\frac{d^2 C_n(s)}{ds^2} = [-\sigma^2 + (i\mu - \sigma^2 s)^2]\exp\left(i\mu s - \frac{\sigma^2 s^2}{2}\right)$$

from which

$$C^{(2)}(0) = -\sigma^2 + (i\mu)^2 = i^2 E(x^2)$$

The variance is

$$\mathrm{Var}(x) = \frac{C^{(2)}(0) - [C^{(1)}(0)]^2}{i^2}$$

$$= \frac{[-\sigma^2 + (i\mu)^2] - (i^2\mu^2)}{i^2}$$

$$= \sigma^2$$

as expected for this distribution.

The Moment Generating Function. The usual definition of the moment generating function of the random variable x when x is continuously distributed is the expected value of e^{sx}.

$$M(s) = E(e^{sx}) = \int_{-\infty}^{\infty} e^{sx} f(x)\, dx \tag{6-23}$$

This is the function we earlier termed the exponential transform of $f(x)$. As long as this transform does exist it is unique. In other words, if two random variables have the same moment generating function, then they have the same density function.

Although handy for manipulations, it is important to recognize that unlike the characteristic function, not every probability distribution has a moment generating function since e^{sx} is not bounded. In addition, the exponential transform is not as widely used in other fields as are the Fourier and Laplace transforms. This may make it more difficult to invert the moment generating function in the event that the density function must be recovered.

When we are concerned with a nonnegative random variable x, it may be expedient to use the Laplace transform of the density function $f(x)$ as a moment generating function. In this case

$$\mathscr{L}[f(x)] = \int_{0}^{\infty} e^{-sx} f(x)\, dx \tag{6-24}$$

When the problem permits the use of the Laplace transform one has the added advantage of being able to use widely available handbooks. This greatly simplifies the task of inversion when the probability density function must be recovered.

Developing Moments from the Moment Generating Function. The rth moment about zero is generated by the same method employed for the characteristic function, namely, taking derivatives. The first derivative of $M(s)$ with respect to s is

$$\frac{dM(s)}{ds} = \int_{-\infty}^{\infty} x e^{sx} f(x)\, dx$$

Evaluating this derivative at $s = 0$ gives

$$M^{(1)}(0) = \int_{-\infty}^{\infty} xf(x)\, dx = E(x) \tag{6-25}$$

Continuing this process through r derivatives gives the general expression for the rth moment about zero.

$$E(x^r) = M^{(r)}(0) \tag{6-26}$$

If the moment generating function is expanded by a Taylor series expansion about $s = 0$, the moments of the distribution appear as coefficients of the terms $s^r/r!$

$$M(s) = 1 + M^{(1)}(0)s + \frac{M^{(2)}(0)s^2}{2} + \cdots + \frac{M^{(r)}(0)s^r}{r!} \cdots \tag{6-27}$$

When the Laplace transform is used as a moment generating function for nonnegative random variables, the calculation is the same except that the rth derivative at $s = 0$ gives the rth moment about zero multiplied by $(-1)^r$. That is,

$$\mathscr{L}^{(r)}[f(x)] = \int_0^{\infty} (-1)^r x^r e^{-sx} f(x)\, dx$$

from which

$$\mathscr{L}^{(r)}[f(x)]\Big|_{s=0} = (-1)^r E(x^r) \tag{6-28}$$

Example.   The probability density for the gamma distribution is

$$f(x) = \begin{cases} b^{a+1}\Gamma(a+1)^{-1}x^a e^{-bx} & x > 0 \\ 0 & x \le 0 \end{cases} \tag{6-29}$$

The Laplace transform of this density is

$$\mathscr{L}[f(x)] = \frac{1}{(1 + s/b)^{a+1}} \tag{6-30}$$

The moments of the gamma may be obtained from the derivatives of the transform.

$$E(x) = (-1)\mathscr{L}^{(1)}[f(x)]\Big|_{s=0} = \frac{(a+1)(1 + s/b)^{-a-2}}{b}\Big|_{s=0} = \frac{a+1}{b}$$

$$E(x^2) = \mathscr{L}^{(2)}[f(x)]\Big|_{s=0} = \frac{(a+2)(a+1)(1 + s/b)^{-(a+3)}}{b^2}\Big|_{s=0} = \frac{(a+1)(a+2)}{b^2}$$

The variance then becomes

$$\mathrm{Var}(x) = E(x^2) - [E(x)]^2 = \frac{(a+1)(a+2)}{b^2} - \left(\frac{a+1}{b}\right)^2 = \frac{a+1}{b^2}$$

In this instance the moments are more easily obtained from the Laplace transform than by carrying out the integration implied by their definition even though the density is well defined.

The Probability Generating Function. The term *generating function* for the random variable x with cumulative distribution $F(x)$ may be defined as

$$G(s) = E(s^x) = \int_{-\infty}^{\infty} s^x \, dF(x) \tag{6-31}$$

This is similar to the previously defined moment generating function in which the argument e^{sx} is replaced by s^x. Clearly both the moment generating function and generating function can be regarded as special cases of the characteristic function. However, for our purposes we will employ a more restricted class of such functions. We will use the term probability generating function to denote the geometric transform of the probability distribution function for discrete random variables assuming only the integer values $k = 0, 1, 2, \ldots$. That is,

$$G(s) = \sum_{x=0}^{\infty} s^x f(x) \tag{6-32}$$

The term probability generating function arises from the fact that the relative frequency for any particular value of x can be " generated " by taking derivatives. In this sense it behaves much like the moment generating function. Note that from the definition

$$G(s) = f(0) + f(1)s + f(2)s^2 + f(3)s^3 + \cdots$$

If we permit the variable s to take on the value zero we have

$$G(0) = f(0) + f(1) \cdot 0 + f(2) \cdot 0 + \cdots = f(0)$$

and we have recovered the relative frequency with which x equals zero directly from the generating function.

Now let us examine the derivatives of $G(s)$ with respect to s. Note that even though this function is discrete in x it can be considered to be continuous in s. The first derivative is

$$G'(s) = 0 + f(1) + 2f(2)s + 3f(3)s^2 + \cdots$$

which when evaluated at $s = 0$ gives

$$G'(0) = f(1)$$

The second derivative evaluated at $s = 0$ gives

$$G''(0) = 2f(2)$$

Continuing through the general nth derivative, we have

$$\left. \frac{d^n G(s)}{ds^n} \right|_{s=0} = n! f(n)$$

By now it should be obvious that we can "generate" the probability distribution $f(x)$ through as many values of x as desirable by taking an appropriate number of derivatives. That is,

$$f(x = n) = \frac{1}{n!} \frac{d^n G(s)}{ds^n} \bigg|_{s=0} \tag{6-33}$$

This is often the easiest way to invert the transform of a given function when extensive tables are not available. Obviously we can never recover the entire distribution $f(x)$ when x can take on an infinite number of values, but we can recover the first few terms of the probability vector.

Example.   The random variable x has a mean μ and is Poisson distributed.

$$f(x) = \frac{\mu^x e^{-\mu}}{x!} \tag{6-34}$$

The probability generating function for x is

$$G(s) = \sum_{x=0}^{\infty} s^x \frac{\mu^x e^{-\mu}}{x!}$$

which can be written as

$$G(s) = e^{-\mu} \sum_{x=0}^{\infty} \frac{(\mu s)^x}{x!}$$

The summation can be recognized as the power series expansion of $e^{\mu s}$, that is,

$$e^{\mu s} = \sum_{x=0}^{\infty} \frac{(\mu s)^x}{x!}$$

The closed form expression for the probability generating function for the Poisson distributed random variable x is then

$$G(s) = e^{-\mu(1-s)} \tag{6-35}$$

Now let us reverse the problem and suppose that we have a generating function

$$G(s) = e^{(s-1)/5}$$

which we have not recognized as the transform of a Poisson distribution with mean 0.2.

The probability that $x = 0$ can be obtained from

$$f(0) = G(0) = e^{(0-1)/5} = 0.8187$$

The probability that $x = 1$ can be recovered from

$$f(1) = G'(0) = \tfrac{1}{5} e^{(0-1)/5} = 0.1637$$

The probability that $x = 2$ is

$$f(2) = \tfrac{1}{2}G''(0) = \tfrac{1}{2}(\tfrac{1}{5})(\tfrac{1}{5})e^{(0-1)/5} = 0.0164$$

and so forth. A check with a table of the Poisson distribution reveals that these are in fact the correct values.

Moments from the Probability Generating Function. In addition to generating the probability distribution, the function $G(s)$ can be used to generate the moments of that distribution. However, unlike the moment generating function the probability generating function does not yield the power moments about zero in a one-step calculation. The derivatives of $G(s)$ evaluated now at $s = 1$ will give us the factorial moments of the distribution.

The expression x, n factorial will be taken to mean

$$x^{(n)} = x(x - 1) \cdots (x - n + 1) \tag{6-36}$$

The expected value of $x^{(n)}$ is referred to as the nth factorial moment of x. Returning to the definition of $G(s)$ and its derivatives we have

$$G(s) = \sum_{x=0}^{\infty} s^x f(x)$$

$$G'(s) = \sum_{x=0}^{\infty} x s^{x-1} f(x)$$

$$G''(s) = \sum_{x=0}^{\infty} x(x - 1)s^{x-2} f(x)$$

$$\frac{d^n G(s)}{ds^n} = \sum_{x=0}^{\infty} x(x - 1) \cdots (x - n + 1)s^{x-n} f(x)$$

Replacing the argument s with the integer one we have the nth factorial moment

$$E(x^{(n)}) = \frac{d^n G(s)}{ds^n} \bigg|_{s=1} \tag{6-37}$$

In most of our work we will be more interested in the power moments of a distribution. The conversion of factorial to power moments can be carried out through the use of Stirling numbers of the second kind as discussed by Miller.[8] However, since most of our work will be confined to the first two moments of the distribution, we will not use the general Stirling number conversions but rather work directly with the definition.

Since

$$x^{(1)} = x$$

---

[8] Kenneth S. Miller, *An Introduction to the Calculus of Finite Differences and Difference Equations* (New York: Henry Holt & Co., Inc., 1960), p. 16.

the expected value of x is given by

$$E(x) = E(x^{(1)}) = G'(s)\Big|_{s=1} \qquad (6\text{-}38)$$

The expected value of $x^{(2)}$ is

$$E(x^{(2)}) = E(x^2) - E(x) = G''(s)\Big|_{s=1}$$

from which

$$E(x^2) = E(x^{(2)}) + E(x^{(1)})$$

$$= G''(1) + G'(1) \qquad (6\text{-}39)$$

This information can now be used to recover the variance directly from the probability generating function.

$$\text{Var}(x) = E(x^2) - [E(x)]^2$$
$$= G''(1) + G'(1) - [G'(1)]^2 \qquad (6\text{-}40)$$

Example. From Equation 6–35 we know that the probability generating function for the Poisson distribution is

$$G(s) = e^{-\mu(1-s)}$$

The mean of the distribution is

$$G'(s)\Big|_{s=1} = \mu e^{-\mu(1-s)}\Big|_{s=1} = \mu$$

The second factorial moment is

$$G''(s)\Big|_{s=1} = \mu^2 e^{-\mu(1-s)}\Big|_{s=1} = \mu^2$$

from which the variance is

$$\text{Var}(x) = G''(1) + G'(1) - [G'(1)]^2$$
$$= \mu^2 + \mu - \mu^2 = \mu$$

as expected.

Compound Distributions

So far our discussion of the probability implications of transforms has indicated that once the transform of a distribution is known, the moments of the distribution can be obtained by taking derivatives. In addition we have shown how a finite number of terms for a discrete distribution can be obtained without going through the inversion process. These techniques may be of use when we are working with a single known probability distribution. However, they gain their real power when used with compound distributions whose transforms can be obtained in straightforward fashion but may be difficult to invert. In this section we will use the convolution property of transforms to obtain probability statements about sums of random variables and random sums of random variables.

Sum of Random Variables. Consider the two independent random variables x and y distributed by $f(x)$ and $g(y)$ where

$$(xf) = \begin{cases} 0.5 & x = 0 \\ 0.3 & x = 1 \\ 0.2 & x = 2 \\ 0 & \text{elsewhere} \end{cases}$$

$$g(y) = \begin{cases} 0.2 & y = 0 \\ 0.4 & y = 1 \\ 0.3 & y = 2 \\ 0.1 & y = 3 \\ 0 & \text{elsewhere} \end{cases}$$

If we form a new random variable z where

$$z = x + y$$

the distribution of z can be obtained by an exhaustive list of all possible combinations of x and y. For example, let the probability distribution for z be $h(z)$ then

$$h(0) = f(0)g(0) = 0.10$$
$$h(1) = f(0)g(1) + f(1)g(0) = 0.26$$
$$h(2) = f(0)g(2) + f(1)g(1) + f(2)g(0) = 0.31$$
$$h(3) = f(0)g(3) + \cdots + f(3)g(0) = 0.22$$
$$h(4) = f(0)g(4) + \cdots + f(4)g(0) = 0.09$$
$$h(5) = f(0)g(5) + \cdots + f(5)g(0) = 0.02$$

In performing this calculation we have in effect convolved the two distributions f and g. This operation could have been represented by the convolution sum

$$h(z) = \sum_{k=0}^{z} f(k)g(z - k) \tag{6-41}$$

If the random variables x and y had been continuously distributed, the distribution of their sum could be obtained from the convolution integral.

$$h(z) = \int_{0}^{z} f(x)g(z - x)\, dx \tag{6-42}$$

From our previous work with transforms we know that the convolution operation with the functions f and g is equivalent to the multiplication of their transforms. The transform of $h(z)$ is then

$$T[h(z)] = T[f(x)]T[g(y)] \qquad (6\text{-}43)$$

where $T(\cdot)$ represents the general transformation operation. Geometric or z transforms will be used when x and y are discrete, and Laplace transforms, characteristic functions, or moment generating functions will be used when x and y are continuous.

This same operation may be continued to cover a sum of n independent random variables x_i with distributions $f_i(x_i)$

$$T[h(z)] = T(f_1(x_1))T[f_2(x_2)] \cdots T[f_n(x_n)] \qquad (6\text{-}44)$$

In the event that the x_i variables are identically distributed by $f(x)$ this reduces to

$$T[h(z)] = T^n[f(x)] \qquad (6\text{-}45)$$

The moments of the sum may be obtained from the transform or by employing the expected value arguments of Chapter 3.

Example. The parts department of a local factory carries two spare tubes for their closed circuit TV monitor. Each tube now in stock is believed to have a life-span following an exponential distribution with a mean of 100 days. The tube presently installed in the monitor has life remaining which is gamma distributed with mean 48 and variance 16. The monitor runs 24 hours per day.

Let us first determine the number of days stock contained in the spare parts supply. Days stock d is the sum of two random variables x_1 and x_2 representing the life of spare tubes 1 and 2. The life distribution for the spares is

$$f(x) = 0.01e^{-0.01x} \qquad (6\text{-}46)$$

which has a Laplace transform of

$$\mathscr{L}[f(x)] = \int_0^\infty 0.01e^{-0.01x}e^{-sx}\,dx$$

$$= \frac{0.01}{0.01 + s} \qquad (6\text{-}47)$$

Since number of days stock is

$$d = x_1 + x_2$$

the transform of the distribution $h(d)$ is from Equation 6-45

$$\mathscr{L}[h(d)] = \left[\frac{0.01}{0.01 + s}\right]^2 \qquad (6\text{-}48)$$

The expected value and the variance for number of days spare stock can be obtained from the derivatives

a) $E(d) = -\mathscr{L}'[h(d)]\Big|_{s=0} = -2\left[\dfrac{0.01}{0.01 + s}\right]\left[\dfrac{-0.01}{(0.01 + s)^2}\right]\Big|_{s=0}$

$= 2/0.01 = 200$

b) $E(d^2) = \mathscr{L}''[h(d)]\Big|_{s=0} = \left[\dfrac{2(0.01)}{(0.01 + s)^2}\right]\left[\dfrac{0.01}{(0.01 + s)^2}\right]$

$+ \dfrac{2[2(0.01)(0.01 + s)]}{(0.01 + s)^4}\Big|_{s=0}$

$= 2 \times 10^4 + 4 \times 10^4 = 6 \times 10^4$

c) $\mathrm{Var}(d) = E(d^2) - [E(d)]^2$

$= 6 \times 10^4 - 4 \times 10^4 = 2 \times 10^4$

Comparing Equation 6–48 with Equation 6–30 we see that the distribution $h(d)$ is really a gamma distribution with parameters $a = 1$ and $b = 0.01$. This holds for the general case. A sum of n identically distributed exponential variables with mean μ will be gamma distributed with parameters

$$a = n - 1$$

and

$$b = \frac{1}{\mu}$$

The total life t of the monitor is the sum of the life of the present tube x_0 and the existing stocks.

$$t = x_0 + x_1 + x_2$$

The transform of the distribution $g(t)$ is

$$\mathscr{L}[g(t)] = \mathscr{L}[f(x_0)]\mathscr{L}[f(x_1)]\mathscr{L}[f(x_2)]$$

where x_0 is gamma distributed and x_1 and x_2 are exponentially distributed. The parameters of the gamma are related to the mean and variance by

$$b = \frac{\mu}{\sigma^2} = \frac{48}{16} = 3$$

and

$$a = \left(\frac{\mu}{\sigma}\right)^2 - 1 = \left(\frac{48}{4}\right)^2 - 1 = 143$$

The total transform of $g(t)$ then becomes

$$\mathscr{L}[g(t)] = \left[\frac{3}{3+s}\right]^{144} \left[\frac{0.01}{0.01+s}\right]^2$$

Although the inverse of this transform is not so easily accomplished, the moments are readily obtainable from the appropriate derivatives. The development of the mean and variance are left as an exercise for the reader.

Random Sums of Random Variables. We are often interested in sums of identically distributed independent random variables in which the number of terms in the sum is itself a random variable. Let S_N be such a sum, then

$$S_N = x_1 + x_2 + \cdots + x_N$$

where the x_i's share a common distribution $f(x)$ and the variable N is distributed by $g(n)$. Following the argument of Feller[9] we can see from the fundamental formula for conditional probabilities that

$$P(S_N = j) = \sum_{n=0}^{\infty} P(N = n)P(x_1 + x_2 + \cdots + x_n = j) \qquad (6\text{-}49)$$

If we assume that both the x_i's and N are discrete random variables, the distribution for $S_N = j$, say $h(j)$, is given by

$$h(j) = \sum_{n=0}^{\infty} g(n)[f(x)]^{n*} \qquad (6\text{-}50)$$

where $[f(x)]^{n*}$ represents the n-fold convolution of $f(x)$.

The probability generating function of $h(j)$, $H(s)$, may be written in terms of the generating function of $f(x)$, $F(s)$, as

$$H(s) = \sum_{j=0}^{\infty} h(j)s^j = \sum_{n=0}^{\infty} g(n)F(s)^n \qquad (6\text{-}51)$$

by the convolution property of transforms. The right side of this equation is the Taylor expansion of $G(s)$, the generating function for $g(n)$, with the argument s replaced by $F(s)$. That is,

$$H(s) = G[F(s)] \qquad (6\text{-}52)$$

This nesting process can be continued for an arbitrary number of random sums of random variables as long as each of the variables is discrete and possesses a known generating function.

Example. An inventory system operates with a replenishment lead time of n days distributed by $h(n)$. The number of customers y per day is distributed by $k(y)$. Each customer may require a random number of units of stock x

---

[9] William Feller, *An Introduction to Probability Theory and Its Applications* (3d ed.; New York: John Wiley & Sons, Inc., 1968), Vol. I, pp. 268–69.

distributed by $g(x)$. The distributions have been estimated to be

$$h(n) = \frac{10!}{n!(10-n)!}(0.4)^n(0.6)^{10-n} \qquad 0 \le n \le 10$$

$$k(y) = \frac{(5)^y e^{-5}}{y!} \qquad y \ge 0$$

$$g(x) = \begin{cases} 0.9 & x = 1 \\ 0.1 & x = 2 \\ 0 & \text{elsewhere} \end{cases}$$

The associated probability generating functions are

$$H(s) = \sum_{n=0}^{10} h(n)s^n = (0.4s + 0.6)^{10}$$

$$K(s) = \sum_{y=0}^{\infty} k(y)s^y = e^{-5(1-s)}$$

$$G(s) = \sum_{x=1}^{2} g(x)s^x = 0.9s + 0.1s^2$$

Consider first the number of units demanded each day. Each customer requires x units, and there are y customers per day. Daily demand d then is the sum of units demanded by customer one plus units demanded by customer two, etc.

$$d = x_1 + x_2 + \cdots + x_y$$

The probability generating function for d is from Equation 6–52

$$D(s) = K[G(s)] = \exp[-5(1 - 0.9s - 0.1s^2)]$$

Consider now the number of units demanded during a lead time. The random variable u is made up of a random number of days n in each of which a random number of units d are demanded. That is,

$$u = d_1 + d_2 + \cdots + d_n$$

from which

$$U(s) = H[D(s)]$$

Finally we can write this three-way compounding in terms of the transforms of our original distribution as

$$U(s) = H[K(G(s))]$$

$$= [0.4 \exp[-5(1 - 9s - 0.1s^2)] + 0.6]^{10}$$

In theory, an exact expression for the lead time demand distribution could be obtained by inverting $U(s)$. As a practical matter, portions of the probability distribution are most easily calculated from the power series expansion of $U(s)$. If only the moments are desired, they may be obtained by applying Equations 6–38 through 6–40.

Random Sums of Continuously Distributed Random Variables. In the previous paragraphs we saw that random sums of discrete random variables could be represented by an appropriate nesting of probability generating functions. In the event that the components in the sum are continuous rather than discrete we must revert to the concept of conditional events.

Suppose that our random sum S_N consists of a random number N of terms where each term takes on the value x with probability $f(x)$, a continuous distribution. For any fixed number of terms n the Laplace transform of the distribution of the sum $h(y)$ is given by

$$\mathscr{L}[h(y)] = [\mathscr{L}(f(x))]^n \qquad (6\text{–}53)$$

Let us consider this to be a conditional transform and rewrite it as

$$\mathscr{L}(s \mid n) = [\mathscr{L}(f(x))]^n \qquad (6\text{–}54)$$

The unconditional transform $\mathscr{L}(s)$ can then be obtained from

$$\mathscr{L}(s) = \sum_{n=0}^{\infty} g(n)\mathscr{L}(s \mid n) \qquad (6\text{–}55)$$

Example. The number of users n on a particular water main in one day is distributed by

$$g(n) = \begin{cases} 0.4 & n = 2 \\ 0.6 & n = 3 \\ 0 & \text{elsewhere} \end{cases}$$

Each customer requires x gallons of water where x is uniformly distributed between 50 and 100 gallons.

The Laplace transform of the distribution for usage per customer is

$$\mathscr{L}[f(x)] = \int_{50}^{100} \frac{1}{50} e^{-sx} \, dx$$

$$= \frac{[e^{-50s} - e^{-100s}]}{50s}$$

The transform for daily usage is then

$$\mathscr{L}(s) = \sum_{n=0}^{\infty} g(n)\mathscr{L}(s \mid n)$$

$$= 0.4 \left\{ \frac{[e^{-50s} - e^{-100s}]}{50s} \right\}^2$$

$$+ 0.6 \left\{ \frac{[e^{-50s} - e^{-100s}]}{50s} \right\}^3$$

Note that the total distribution is continuous. Therefore, to obtain moments we would evaluate the derivatives of $\mathscr{L}(s)$ at $s = 0$ in accordance with Equation 6–28.

This transform is relatively easy to invert. Working with the sum of two uniformly distributed variables

$$\mathscr{L}(s \mid 2) = \frac{1}{2500} \left(\frac{1}{s^2} \right) [e^{-50s} - e^{-100s}]^2$$

$$= \frac{1}{2500} \left(\frac{1}{s^2} \right) [e^{-100s} - 2e^{-150s} + e^{-200s}]$$

The inverse transform of $1/s^2$ is $f(x) = x$ as can be confirmed from the table in Chapter 5. By the second shifting theorem for Laplace transforms multiplying the transform of a function by e^{-as} shifts that function on the t axis by a units. Applying these results to $\mathscr{L}(s \mid 2)$ reveals

$$f(s) = \frac{1}{2500}[(x - 100)u(x - 100) - 2(x - 150)u(x - 150)$$
$$+ (x - 200)u(x - 200)]$$

or

$$f(x) = \begin{cases} \dfrac{(x - 100)}{2500} & 100 \leq x < 150 \\[3mm] \dfrac{(200 - x)}{2500} & 150 \leq x \leq 200 \\[3mm] 0 & \text{elsewhere} \end{cases}$$

Inversion of the balance of the function $\mathscr{L}(s)$ is left as an exercise for the reader.

SELECTED BIBLIOGRAPHY

ASELTINE, JOHN A. *Transform Method in Linear System Analysis.* New York: McGraw-Hill Book Co., Inc., 1958.

BROWN, ROBERT G. *Smoothing, Forecasting and Prediction of Discrete Time Series.* Englewood Cliffs, N.J.: Prentice-Hall, Inc., 1963.

FELLER, WILLIAM. *An Introduction to Probability Theory and Its Applications,* Vol. II. New York: John Wiley & Sons, Inc., 1966.

———. *An Introduction to Probability Theory and Its Applications* Vol. I. 3d ed. New York: John Wiley & Sons, Inc., 1968.

HOWARD, RONALD A. "System Analysis of Linear Models," *Multistage Inventory Models and Techniques.* (eds, H. E. SCARF, D. M. GILFORD, and M. W. SHELLY). Stanford: Stanford University Press, 1963.

MILLER, KENNETH S. *An Introduction to the Calculus of Finite Differences and Difference Equations.* New York: Henry Holt & Co., 1960.

THOMPSON, WILLIAM TYRRELL, *Laplace Transform.* 2d ed. Englewood Cliffs, N.J.: Prentice-Hall, Inc., 1960.

PROBLEMS

6-1 A compound system consisting of two simple elements has been construc-ted. The z transform of the output from element 1 when an impulse function has been imposed is known to be

$$Z[h_1(n)] = \frac{z^2}{(z-a)^2}$$

The second element standing alone has exhibited an impulse response function of

$$h_2(n) = \sin\left[\pi(0.5n+1)\right]$$

These two elements are linked together in the following fashion:

$$f(n) \longrightarrow \boxed{Z[h_1(n)]} \longrightarrow \boxed{Z[h_2(n)]} \longrightarrow g(n)$$

Element 1   Element 2

a) Determine the transfer function for each of the elements.

b) Determine a single transfer function which could be used in place of the two series elements.

c) Determine the impulse response for element number 1.

d) Determine the response of the system to an input of the form:

$$f(0) = 1$$
$$f(1) = 3$$
$$f(2) = 2$$
$$f(3) = 3$$
$$f(4) = 4$$
$$f(n) = 0 \quad n > 4$$

Note: Answer to part (*d*) may may be left in transform form.

6-2 A load is being driven by a constant force A. The driving force is being consumed by three factors: the acceleration imparted to the load (force = mass $\times$ acceleration), the wind resistance (force = $c \times$ velocity), and friction which is independent of speed but increases with distance traveled. This friction caused by the bearings picking up grit consumes a force $Kx(t)$ where $x(t)$ measures distance traveled by time t.

a) If the load has no initial velocity what is the limit of the distance it will move. (Use your knowledge of transforms to achieve a solution.)

b) As a designer you can influence the mass of the vehicle, the wind resistance and bearing design. For purposes of maximizing distance traveled, which of the variables should receive your attention?

6-3 A rocket plant wishes to install its own exotic fuel generator. The only generator on the market has a 15-gallon reservoir. When a gallon of fuel is sud-denly dipped from a full reservoir, reservoir deficiency (r) has been observed to vary continuously according to

$$r = e^{-0.5t}$$

where t is time in hours.

The plant produces rockets continuously from 8 A.M. to 4 P.M. and has found that the demand for fuel during that period can be adequately described by the function

$$f(t) = 10e^{-0.1t}$$

Prove whether or not a single generator will supply the needs of the plant.

6-4 *a*) The impulse response for a discrete linear system has been observed to be $h(n)$. A new input function $f(n)$ is to be presented to the system. From the accompanying data of $f(n)$ and $h(n)$, calculate the response of the system to this new input.

n	$h(n)$	$f(n)$
0	1	0
1	0	2
2	3	3
3	0	1
≥ 4	0	0

b) Using the data of problem (*a*), find the response of the system to an input of the form

$$f(n) = \cos\left[\frac{\pi}{3}(n+2)\right]$$

Utilize the z transform in your solution.

6-5 Consider a manufacturing process in which the in-process inventory exhibits hourly fluctuations of the form

$$f(t) = \begin{cases} 2kt & 0 < t < 0.5 \text{ hours} \\ k & 0.5 < t < 1.0 \text{ hour} \end{cases}$$

Furthermore, it has been noted that during a recent period of rising demand represented by

$$s(t) = e^{2t}$$

power requirements for this process were

$$r(t) = t^3$$

a) Develop an even half-range expansion to represent $f(t)$ as a continuous function during one hour. (Leave your answer in integral form.)

b) Develop the transform of the power requirements function for this system when it is subjected to demand $s_1(t)$ as shown below:

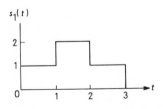

6–6   Two black boxes have been hooked up as shown below:

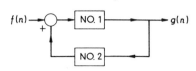

Box No. 1 was subjected to an input of $\sin [(\pi/2)n]$ and gave a response of $\cos [(\pi/2)(n-1)]$.

Box No. 2 was subjected to an input $\delta (n)$ and gave a response of $(0.5)^{n-1}$.

   a) Determine the impulse response function for box No. 1.

   b) Determine the transfer function for box No. 2.

   c) Determine the response transform for the total system when subjected to an input of $f(n) = n$.

   Note: All functions are sampled functions, i.e., $n = 0, 1, 2, \ldots$ Use z transforms in your solutions.

6–7   Given the following "black box" system:

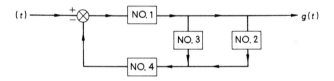

Preliminary analysis reveals the following characteristics for each of these boxes when subjected to various inputs.

$$\text{Box No. 1:} \frac{\mathscr{L} \text{ (out)}}{\mathscr{L} \text{ (in)}} = 1$$

$$\text{Box No. 2:} \frac{\mathscr{L} \text{ (in)}}{\mathscr{L} \text{ (out)}} = \frac{(s+3)^2(s-1)}{s}$$

$$\text{Box No. 3: Impulse response} = \sin \left[\frac{\pi}{2}(t+1) \right]$$

$$\text{Box No. 4: Characteristic function} = s^3$$

   a) Calculate a single transfer function to replace boxes 2, 3, and 4.

   b) Calculate the impulse response function for box No. 2.

   c) Calculate the system transfer function.

d) Determine the response of the system to an input of the form $f(t)$ shown below [$f(t)$ is periodic with period 5]. Leave in transform notation.

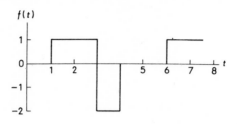

6–8   Consider the following linear system composed of six independent elements:

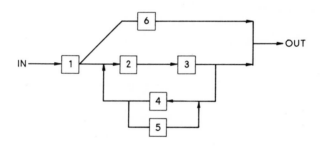

The following data are known about these systems:

(1)   All systems are linear and continuous. Laplace transforms are to be used in the analysis.
(2)   Element No. 1 has a transfer function of ln $[(s-2)/(s-3)]$.
(3)   Element No. 2 has a transfer function of $e^{-4s}/(s+4)$.
(4)   Element No. 3 multiplies its input by a factor of 5.
(5)   When elements No. 4 and No. 5 were subjected to inputs of cos $(3t)$, they gave responses of sin $(3t)$.
(6)   When the system as a whole was subjected to an impulse function it responded with

$$g(t) = \tfrac{1}{3}\,(5e^{5t} - 2e^{2t})$$

a) Find the impulse response functions for elements 1, 2, 3, 4.
b) Using functional notation only (i.e., $H(s) = f[H_1(s), H_2(s), \ldots, H_6(s)]$), develop an expression for the total system transfer function.
c) Find the transfer function for element No. 6.

6–9 Consider the following system of elements with known impulse response functions, $h_i(t)$:

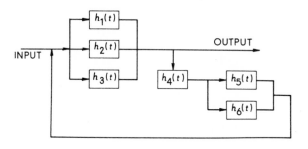

where

$$h_1(t) = h_2(t) = h_3(t) = (te^{-t})^3$$

$$h_4(t) = \int_0^t h_1(\tau)\, d\tau$$

$$\mathcal{L}[h_5(t)] = \frac{1}{(s+2)^2} \qquad h_5(0) = 0$$

$$h_6(t) = \frac{d\, h_5(t)}{dt}$$

a) Using functional notation only, i.e., $h_1(t)$, $H_1(s)$, etc., develop the transfer function for a single element which will perform all of the functions of the six elements given.

b) Using Laplace transforms develop the transform of the output from two such systems in series when subjected to an input of the form

$$\tfrac{1}{4}(1 - \cos 2t)$$

(The result is to be expressed as a function of the single variable s).

6–10 Consider a system initially at rest which receives an impulse function as an input. The response transform is known to be

$$\bar{r}(s) = \frac{e^{-2s}}{(s + 2i)(s - 2i)}$$

Nothing is known about the internal workings of the system other than the fact that it is linear.

a) Determine the transfer function for the system.

b) Determine the impulse response function $r(t)$.

c) Determine the response of this system to an input of the form shown below:

$$f(t) = \begin{cases} u\,(t - 3) + 2t & 0 < t < 5 \\ 6 & t \geq 5 \end{cases}$$

6–11   Consider the following "black box" system:

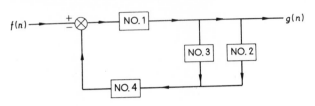

Preliminary analysis reveals the following characteristics for each of these boxes when subjected to various sampled functions inputs:

$$\text{Box No. 1:} \frac{Z(\text{out})}{Z(\text{in})} = 1$$

$$\text{Box No. 2:} \frac{Z(\text{in})}{Z(\text{out})} = \frac{1}{3} z^{-2}(z^2 + 1)$$

$$\text{Box No. 3: Impulse response function} = \sin \left[\frac{\pi}{2}(n+1) \right]$$

$$\text{Box No. 4: Characteristic function} = z^2$$

where $Z(f)$ implies the z transform of f.

  a) Calculate a single equivalent transfer function to replace boxes 2, 3, and 4.
  b) Calculate the system transfer function.
  c) Assume that another box with transfer function $(z^2 + 1)/(z^2 + 4)$ is being considered as a system. If the input to this box is $\delta(n)$, calculate its response when $n = 6$, i.e., $g(6)$.

6–12   A compound system is composed of two types of elements, A and B, arranged as shown:

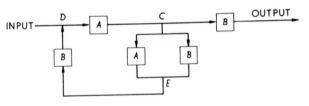

The impulse responses of the elements are

n	$A(n)$	$B(n)$
0	0	2
1	1	0
2	1	1
≥ 3	0	0

a) Find the transfer function of a single "black box" which will replace this system using functional notation, i.e., $T[A(n)]$ and $T[B(n)]$.

b) Evaluate the transfer function for the particular functions $A(n)$ and $B(n)$ given.

6–13   A certain linear system can be described by the following difference equation when subjected to a driving function $f(n) = 2 + 6n^2$

$$\Delta^2 y(n) + 3\Delta y(n) + 6y(n) = f(n)$$

where $y(0) = 0$, $y(1) = 0$.

a) Use your knowledge of *z transforms* to determine $y(n)$.

b) From your knowledge of impulse response functions, what would be the value of the output at $n = 4$ if this system is subjected to an impulse at $n = 0$?

6–14   Consider the following linear system composed of seven independent elements:

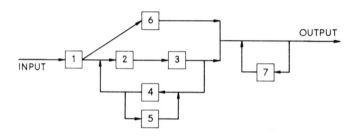

The following data is known about these systems:

(1)   All are continuous systems to be analyzed by Laplace transforms.

(2)   Element No. 1 has a transfer function of $e^{-3s}/(s + 4)$.

(3)   Element No. 2 has a transfer function of $1/(s + 0.5)^2$.

(4)   Element No. 3 multiplies its input by a factor of 4.

(5)   Elements Nos. 4, 5, and 7 are identical. When subjected to an input of $f(t) = \cos(3t)$ each gives a response of $g(t) = \sin(3t)$.

a) Find the impulse response functions for elements 1, 2, 3, and 4.

b) Find a single transfer function for the total system using functional notation (i.e., $H(s) = f[H_1(s), H_2(s), \dots, H_7(s)]$.

c) Suppose that for one particular configuration on element No. 6 the total system has an impulse response of $(1/2)(e^{4t} - e^{2t})$. Find the transfer function for element No. 6.

6–15   Suppose that the transfer function for a system expressed in terms of *z* transforms is known to be:

$$\frac{-z^3 + z^2 km}{kz^5 - kz^3 + 5z^3 - 5z^5}$$

Find the steady state behavior of the system when subjected to unit impulse input at $n = 0$.

6-16 A linear control system which was originally at rest has been excited by a function $f(t)$. The function $y(t)$ measures deviations of the control variable from its desired target. The Laplace transform of $y(t)$ has been calculated as

$$Y(s) = \frac{3s \div (s^3 + s^2 + 5s + 5)}{s^2 - 6s + 25}$$

At this point no clearing of fractions has been performed. This represents the ratio of transforms obtained directly from the solution to a differential equation.

a) Find the driving function for this system expressed in terms of a convolution integral. You do not need to complete this integration.

b) Find the transfer function for this system.

c) Find the terminal value of the impulse response function associated with this system.

d) Suppose that a compound system consisting of three subsystems, like the one described above, connected in series is subjected to an input of the form

$$f(t) = t \left[e^{7t} + \frac{t^2}{6} \right]$$

Find the transform of the output for the compound system.

6-17 Consider an intermediate storage tank which must hold the output from a certain chemical process. Next Friday a walkout by plant employees is expected. At that time nothing more will be used from the tank. However, the plant engineers have no way to shut off the chemical process which feeds it. At the time of the walkout the number of gallons, a, in the tank will be a random variable with density $f(a)$. Daily output, b, for the process is a random variable, with density $g(b)$.

a) Given that the strike will last only one day, develop an expression for the probability density for tank level at the end of the strike. State all assumptions.

b) Company negotiators are uncertain about the length of the strike (n) but have estimated that its duration will be distributed by $h(n)$. Determine the p.d.f. for tank level at the end of the strike.

c) Suppose that tank capacity is 150 gallons,

$$f(a) = \frac{1}{100} \qquad 0 \le a \le 100$$

$$g(b) = \frac{b}{200} \qquad 0 \le b \le 20$$

$$h(n) = \frac{1}{5} \qquad n = 1, 2, 3, 4, 5$$

What is the probability that the tank will overflow with a one-day strike? With the uncertain strike, what will be the expected tank level at the strike's end?

6-18 The management of a local bar has observed that the probability of their door opening in less than time t after the arrival of a customer may be approximated by

$$1 - (2.718)^{-10t}$$

In addition they have noted that customers always arrive either singly or in pairs. The probability that a single customer enters when the door opens is 0.8. Once inside, a customer may drink up to three beers according to the following distribution:

x Beers	Probability of x
0	0.1
1	0.3
2	0.4
3	0.2

a) Develop the probability generating function for the number of door openings in one hour.

b) Develop the probability generating function for the number of beers consumed by a pair of customers.

c) Develop the probability generating function for the number of beers served per hour. (Leave your answer in functional notation, i.e., do *not* expand to a single function of s.)

d) Suppose that the generating function for the probability that beers served per hour exceed x is given by

$$\frac{1}{1-s} - \frac{e^{(5s-5)}}{1-s}$$

Calculate the mean number of beers per eight-hour shift.

6–19 A certain electronic system has been captured by the friendly forces. The internal mechanism is known to have multiple components of type 1, the life of each of which is a random variable continuously distributed by

$$f(x_1) = 0.2e^{-x_1/5} \qquad x_1 > 0$$

where x_1 is measured in hours.

These components are arranged such that as soon as one component fails, the next component of the same type begins to function. The number of such components in the system is a random variable believed to be distributed by

$$g(n) = \frac{3^n}{4^{(n+1)}} \qquad n = 0, 1, 2 \ldots$$

As long as the system continues to function, the enemy will be unaware that friendly forces are in the area. Once it ceases to function, it will take t hours before it will be detected by the enemy. The time t is a discrete random variable with the geometric transform given by

$$F_t(z) = \frac{(e^{4z})^2}{e^8}$$

a) Find the probability that two successive components will fail in less than four hours.

b) Use your knowledge of sum calculus to find the geometric transform of the number of components in the system.

c) Find the transform of the density for the number of hours until total electronic system failure. Express in closed form.

d) Find the mean and variance for total time remaining before enemy detection.

6–20   The local Rose control squad has three basic weapons at its disposal. They are night sticks, chemical mace, and hairspray confiscated from unruly coeds. Each member of the squad carries one night stick and one mace. The number of hairsprays each carries is a random variable distributed by

$$h(n) = \begin{cases} 0.6 & n = 1 \\ 0.3 & n = 2 \\ 0.1 & n = 3 \end{cases}$$

The number of students which can be handled by a night stick (x_1) is a discrete random variable distributed by

$$f(x_1) = (0.3)^{x_1}(0.7) \qquad x_1 \geq 0$$

The number handled by a mace (x_2) is distributed by

$$g(x_2) = \frac{(8)^{x_2} e^{-8}}{(x_2)!} \qquad x_2 \geq 0$$

The number handled by a can of hairspray (x_3) is distributed by

$$k(x_3) = \frac{2^{x_3}}{(3)^{x_3+1}} \qquad x_3 \geq 0$$

a) Develop the geometric transforms for each of the four distributions h, f, g, and k. Identify them as $H(z)$, $F(z)$, $G(z)$, and $K(z)$.

b) What is the mean number of students handled by a single can of hairspray? What is the variance? (Use your transform to obtain a solution.)

c) Using functional notation only [i.e., $H(z)$, $F(z)$, etc.] develop the probability generating function $S(z)$ for the number of students which can be handled by a single squad member.

d) Suppose that the number of squad members (m) is also a random variable distributed by

$$j(m) = \begin{cases} 0.5 & m = 1 \\ 0.3 & m = 2 \\ 0.2 & m = 3 \end{cases}$$

Find the probability generating function for total students handled and establish the probability that a squad cannot control any students. (Do not simplify.)

6–21   A careful study of the consumption of beer on wet campuses reveals that the number of gallons (x) consumed each day by a single floor of students is continuously distributed by

$$f(x) = \begin{cases} \dfrac{2(2x)^9 e^{-2x}}{9!} & x \geq 0 \\ 0 & x < 0 \end{cases}$$

The number of floors (r) in a wet dorm is distributed by

$$h(r) = \begin{cases} 0.5 & r = 3 \\ 0.3 & r = 5 \\ 0.2 & r = 6 \\ 0 & \text{elsewhere} \end{cases}$$

The number of days in a term is Poisson distributed with a mean of 12. (Student unrest makes term length a random variable.)

a) Determine the Laplace transform of $f(x)$.

b) Determine the second factorial moment for gallons of beer consumed in a wet dorm each day.

c) Determine an appropriate transform for the distribution of gallons of beer consumed per term in a wet dorm. (Set it up but do not carry out to closed form.)

6-22 The generating function for $\{q_j\}$ where $q_j =$ probability that $n > j = \sum_{n=j+1}^{\infty} p_n$ and $\{p_j\}$ is the distribution of n is given by

$$Q(s) = \frac{1 - P(s)}{1 - s}$$

Use your knowledge of geometric transforms to develop this relationship beginning with a difference equation involving p_j and q_j.

CHAPTER 7

Forecasting and Stochastic Processes

FORECASTING implies the prediction of some future event. The weatherman provides a forecast of the expected weather over the next few hours. The salesman provides a forecast of the number of units he expects to sell next month. The economist provides a forecast of the expected gross national product next year. The military planner provides a forecast of expected performance capabilities of airborne weapon systems over the next 10 years. All such predictions carry the title of forecast even though they may vary widely in the analysis performed, the form of the data used, and the accuracy obtained.

The operations engineer is in the business of providing quantitative aids for management decisions. Many of the models discussed in this text are sterile without accurate estimates or forecasts of the magnitude and direction of critical parameter changes during future time periods. The forecasting techniques encountered are every bit as diverse as those associated with the professionals mentioned in the previous paragraph. The operations engineer may be asked for advice concerning inventory levels which require forecasts of future demand. He may be asked for advice concerning capital investment alternatives which require forecasts of interest rates, general employment levels, and national economic development. He may be asked for advice concerning the development of new product lines which require forecasts of market potential, technological feasibility, and plant capacity.

The point is that anyone who is involved with describing future events must of necessity employ some sort of forecasting device. Unfortunately, many practitioners of operations engineering truncate their sophisticated analysis short of an accurate description of the data which will ultimately control system performance. They may take as given that demand is Poisson, that the economy will continue to grow at roughly the current rate, or that methods of providing power for industrial use will remain unchanged. They are not to be condemned for assumptions about the future, which are explicitly stated and qualified, but rather for failure to recognize the nature of the forecasts accepted and to use the best techniques available to sharpen their estimates. The purpose of this chapter is to demonstrate some of the techniques available to assist the operations engineer in forecasting future events. For the most part, these techniques are short-range forecasting devices. Their value diminishes as the planning horizon increases.

General Approaches

For our purposes, we will identify four major topics of interest to those who must generate forecasts. They are:

1. Expert opinion.
2. Time series analysis.
3. Prediction by association.
4. Stochastic processes.

It will soon become evident that these are not necessarily mutually exclusive classifications.

From the point of view of the operations engineer, expert opinion is the least quantifiable technique used to obtain forecasts. In its simplest form, the use of expert opinion implies that the analyst requires estimates of future events which are beyond his area of technical competence. He accepts the economist's prediction of growth of the economy and the product manager's view of sales potential for a new product. This says nothing about the rigor of the analysis used to reach the opinions offered by the experts. It only says that for his purposes, the operations engineer has taken the forecasts as given. In the case of economic forecasts, the opinions of the experts may be founded on very complete analyses of vast amounts of historical data or they may be nothing more than intuitive guesses on the part of product managers with years of unquantified experience to draw upon. In either case, the operations engineer may not look beyond the opinion offered.

As he becomes more familiar with the veracity of various experts he routinely employs, the operations engineer may begin to modify their opinions before using them as data for his models. For example, if a particular sales manager habitually overestimates demands for his product, the engineer may multiply his prediction of next year's demand by an appropriate factor to bring it in line with historical performance. In another instance he may seek the opinions of several experts and use as his prediction a weighted average of their forecasts. This practice might be reasonable for estimating sales potential of a new product where a number of salesmen are polled. Salesman A with 15 year's experience estimates 400 units per year; salesman B with 10 years' experience estimates 300 units per year; and C with 5 years' experience estimates 600 units. Perhaps the analyst feels that the weight given each prediction should be proportional to the experience of the expert. In that case he might estimate sales as

$$S = \frac{(15)(400) + (10)(300) + 5(600)}{30} = 400 \text{ units per year}$$

Expert opinion can also be used to advantage to modify forecasts obtained by formal analysis of historical data. For example, both time series analysis and prediction by association assume that the same underlying process which has controlled the system in the past will continue to control it in the immediate future. The numbers obtained from such forecasts are valid only as long as this assumption holds. However, certain experts within the company may have information concerning new advertising campaigns, introduction of competitive products, political changes, etc., which may substantially modify the way a system performs. These data should be accounted for in preparing the final forecast for product demand.

The balance of this chapter concerns methods which can be used to extract useful information from historical data. They are mathematical techniques used to model an underlying system which generates observed data. They are closely related to the problems of statistical estimation discussed in earlier chapters.

TIME SERIES ANALYSIS

A common means of displaying performance information about a system is to plot the output of the system as a function of time. One finds plots of stock price indices in the financial section of the daily newspaper, plots of weekly sales in the sales manager's office, and plots of weekly production in the plant superintendent's office. In each instance we have a graphical display of time series. Figure 7–1 illustrates such a series for product demand.

The object is to provide a mathematical model, together with proper parameter estimates, which will (1) provide an historical description of the data and (2) be used to extrapolate past performance to future time periods. By examining Figure 7–1, for instance, we might conclude that the process is completely random in the sense that knowledge of units sold this week in no way influences units sold next week. In that case we might suppress the time dependence and simply treat each data point $x(t)$ as an independent observation drawn from an unknown probability distribution. The techniques of Chapter 4 could then be used to estimate parameters such as the mean and variance of the distribution. Forecasting would take the form of a confidence interval statement about next week's demand. We already have the knowledge necessary to carry out this form of prediction.

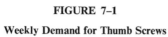

FIGURE 7-1

Weekly Demand for Thumb Screws

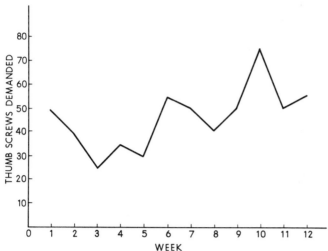

The more usual concept of a forecasting scheme is one which attempts to track a time varying signal. To many persons this connotes a single point estimate of future values. However, to take full advantage of our modeling techniques we need some indication of the probability distribution of these estimates, even though they may be functions of time. It is a rare event when the time series is completely deterministic so that a pattern once discovered will exactly reproduce itself in the future. All forecasting schemes ultimately, then, require probability statements about the accuracy of the prediction.

Curve Fitting

In some applications it may be desirable to find an analytic expression which will exactly pass through each of the points plotted for an empirical time series. In others, we may want to find the parameters for the best-fitting member of a family of proposed curves. Proposing a family of curves means that a model to describe the data has been selected. Parameters for the model must be selected so that the model in some sense fits the data. Our criterion for best fit will be minimum squared difference between actual and theoretical curves. Squared difference is used in preference to simple differences or absolute difference to prevent wide discrepancies on both sides from canceling each other's effect and because it is easier to handle mathematically.

Exact Fit.   One very powerful technique for fitting an analytic expression to a set of empirical data was introduced in Chapter 5. There we discussed the Fourier series as an approximation to other functional forms. It was noted that most functions could be approximated by the sum of a number of sine and cosine terms. When the function to be approximated is represented by $2N$ equally spaced data points, which we believe come from a periodic process of period $2N$, we saw that

$$g(t) = a_0 + \sum_{n=1}^{N} \left(a_n \cos \frac{n\pi t}{p} + b_n \sin \frac{n\pi t}{p} \right) \qquad (7\text{--}1)$$

would pass through each of the data points. Here, a_n and b_n are determined by numerical integration. (See Equation 5–8.)

We could also develop a polynomial which would pass through each of our empirical data points by employing the difference calculus. What we seek is the polynomial of lowest degree which will pass through every point. It is well known that if we have $(n + 1)$ equally spaced data points, there exists a polynomial of degree not exceeding n which has this property. We can employ a difference table and Newton's formula to establish the desired function.[1]

Let the first forward difference of $f(t)$ be defined as

$$\Delta f(t) = f(t + 1) - f(t) \qquad (7\text{--}2)$$

Higher order differences are defined in terms of differences of differences. Thus the second difference of $f(t)$ is

$$\Delta^2 f(t) = \Delta f(t + 1) - \Delta f(t)$$

and the nth difference is

$$\Delta^n f(t) = \Delta^{n-1} f(t + 1) - \Delta^{n-1} f(t) \qquad (7\text{--}3)$$

Let us further define t, n-factorial as

$$t^{(n)} = \frac{t!}{(t - n)!} = t(t - 1)(t - 2)\cdots(t - n + 1) \qquad (7\text{--}4)$$

where n and t are integers. Then, as suggested by Miller,[2] we can use Newton's formula in the form

$$f(t) = f(0) + \Delta f(0)t^{(1)} + \frac{\Delta^2 f(0)t^{(2)}}{2!} + \cdots + \frac{\Delta^n f(0)t^{(n)}}{n!} \qquad (7\text{--}5)$$

to find a polynomial passing through the data points. This is sometimes referred to as Newton's forward interpolation formula since we are focusing our attention on the initial data point, $f(0)$.

For example, suppose that sales records for the first five weeks after introducing a new product are available to us. The first step is to form a

---

[1] See Kenneth S. Miller, *The Calculus of Finite Differences and Difference Equations* (New York: Henry Holt & Co., Inc., 1960), chap. i.
[2] *Ibid.*, chap. i.

difference table in which column n represents the nth difference of $f(t)$. Table 7–1 is the difference table for our hypothetical example. The entries

TABLE 7–1

A Difference Table

Week	Sales $f(t)$	$\Delta f(t)$	$\Delta^2 f(t)$	$\Delta^3 f(t)$	$\Delta^4 f(t)$	$\Delta^5 f(t)$
0	0	9	−5	3	−1	1
1	9	4	−2	2	0	
2	13	2	0	2		
3	15	2	2			
4	17	4				
5	21					

in this table follow the definitions. For example, $\Delta^2 f(1) = \Delta f(2) - \Delta f(1) = 2 - 4 = -2$. The reader should try other entries to verify his understanding.

The next step is to form the factorial polynomial according to Equation 7–5.

$$f(t) = 0 + 9t^{(1)} + \frac{(-5)t^{(2)}}{2} + \frac{3t^{(3)}}{6} + \frac{(-1)t^{(4)}}{24} + \frac{t^{(5)}}{120}$$

Since most people are more comfortable working with power polynomials, we could expand it into the appropriate fifth degree power polynomial as

$$f(t) = 9t - \frac{5(t)(t-1)}{2} + \frac{3(t)(t-1)(t-2)}{6} - \frac{t(t-1)(t-2)(t-3)}{24}$$
$$+ \frac{t(t-1)(t-2)(t-3)(t-4)}{120}$$

Such a function is certainly not easy to work with and in fact may be an extremely poor predictor if we attempt to forecast future sales by straightforward extrapolation of the curve $f(t)$. It may be much better to suppose that there is an underlying process, say of the form

$$f(t) = a + bt \tag{7-6}$$

generating the data, which includes some random noise. The random noise prevents an exact fit for the simpler hypothesized model.

Method of Least Squares. The method of least squares begins with the premise that the underlying process generating a particular time series can be described by a well-defined function $f(t)$. Among the class of polynomial models, the function may be a straight line as in Equation 7–6 or a quadratic of the form

$$f(t) = a + bt + ct^2 \tag{7-7}$$

or any polynomial of higher degree. As a practical matter, however, Brown suggests that one rarely finds need for a polynomial of higher degree than the quadratic.[3]

In some systems we might have reason to believe that strong seasonal factors are present and therefore desire a periodic model of the system. In this case our function takes the form of Equation 7–1. It can be shown that the best fit in terms of total squared error for functions of this class is obtained by using the Fourier coefficients for a_n and b_n. For both the transcendental and polynomial models the parameters are chosen to minimize

$$e = \sum_{t=1}^{n} [\hat{f}(t) - f(t)]^2 \qquad (7\text{–}8)$$

where $\hat{f}(t)$ is the theoretical estimate corresponding to the actual data $f(t)$. Obviously, different combinations of these functions could be used. The best function is that one with the lowest value of e. In any given application, however, we may develop only the best straight line or the best parabola without establishing precisely which family is more appropriate.

FIGURE 7–2

Least Squares Method

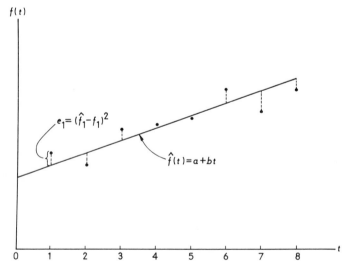

PROBLEM: Find a and b to minimize

$$e = \sum_{t=1}^{n} [\hat{f}(t) - f(t)]^2$$

[3] Robert G. Brown, *Smoothing, Forecasting and Prediction of Discrete Time Series* (Englewood Cliffs, N.J.: Prentice-Hall, Inc., 1963), p. 62.

Let us illustrate the procedure for establishing a least square curve by developing expressions for a and b in an equation for a straight line. Figure 7-2 shows how the time series relates to the proposed straight-line model. For each time t we can calculate the difference between the data observed and our proposed model of the data.

$$D(t) = \hat{f}(t) - f(t) = a + bt - f(t) \tag{7-9}$$

The sum of the squares of all such $D(t)$ values is our criterion.

$$D = \sum_{t=1}^{n} [D(t)]^2 = \sum_{t=1}^{n} [a + bt - f(t)]^2 \tag{7-10}$$

In this expression, t and $f(t)$ are known values. The parameters a and b are treated as variables which must be assigned values to minimize D. Applying the usual methods of calculus we require that

$$\frac{\partial D}{\partial a} = \frac{\partial D}{\partial b} = 0$$

from which

$$\frac{\partial D}{\partial a} = \sum_{t=1}^{n} 2[a + bt - f(t)] = 0 \tag{7-11}$$

$$\frac{\partial D}{\partial b} = \sum_{t=1}^{n} 2[a + bt - f(t)]t = 0 \tag{7-12}$$

Dividing each equation by 2 and combining terms yields

$$an + b \sum_{t=1}^{n} t - \sum_{t=1}^{n} f(t) = 0$$

$$a \sum_{t=1}^{n} t + b \sum_{t=1}^{n} t^2 - \sum_{t=1}^{n} t f(t) = 0$$

from which

$$a = \frac{\Sigma t^2 \Sigma f(t) - \Sigma t \Sigma t f(t)}{n \Sigma t^2 - (\Sigma t)^2} \tag{7-13}$$

$$b = \frac{n \Sigma t f(t) - \Sigma t \Sigma f(t)}{n \Sigma t^2 - (\Sigma t)^2} \tag{7-14}$$

We can use identities from the sum calculus to speed the calculation of the parameters a and b. It is well known that[4]

$$\sum_{t=1}^{n} t = \frac{n(n+1)}{2} \tag{7-15}$$

$$\sum_{t=1}^{n} t^2 = \frac{n(n+1)(2n+1)}{6} \tag{7-16}$$

---

[4] See for example, L. B. W. Jolley, *Summation of Series* (New York: Dover Publications, 1961), p. 4.

Therefore, we can rewrite the equations for a and b as

$$a = \frac{2(2n + 1)\Sigma f(t) - 6\Sigma t f(t)}{2n(2n + 1) - 3n(n + 1)} \qquad (7\text{--}17)$$

$$b = \frac{12\Sigma t f(t) - 6(n + 1)\Sigma f(t)}{2n(n + 1)(2n + 1) - 3n(n + 1)^2} \qquad (7\text{--}18)$$

We now have the information necessary to write the equation for the best-fitting trend line through a time series.

Let us use the data of Table 7–1 to illustrate the calculation. Here, we have

t	$f(t)$	$tf(t)$
1	9	9
2	13	26
3	15	45
4	17	68
5	21	105
	$\Sigma f(t) = 75$	$\Sigma t f(t) = 253$

from which

$$a = \frac{2(11)(75) - 6(253)}{10(11) - 15(6)} = 6.6$$

$$b = \frac{12(253) - 6(6)(75)}{10(6)(11) - 15(36)} = 2.8$$

The equation for the trend line is then

$$\hat{f}(t) = 6.6 + 2.8t$$

The accuracy of this fit is illustrated by Figure 7–3.

It is interesting to compare this simple linear function with the fifth degree polynomial we previously developed for these data. The fifth degree polynomial does pass through every data point while the straight line is only approximately correct. However, if we attempt to extrapolate each of these functions into future time periods, the straight line will likely give a more accurate forecast in the sense of closer agreement between model and data. This is because the linear model is more likely to be representative of the underlying process. Variations from the straight line can be viewed as random disturbances whose exact patterns are unlikely to be repeated in future periods.

If we have reason to suspect that a quadratic equation of the form $\hat{f}(t) = a + bt + ct^2$ will provide a better model for a time series, we can establish estimates for the coefficients by exactly the same techniques demonstrated for the linear function. The quantity to be minimized is

$$D = \sum_{t=1}^{n} [a + bt + ct^2 - f(t)]^2 \qquad (7\text{--}19)$$

FIGURE 7–3

Least Squares Trend Line

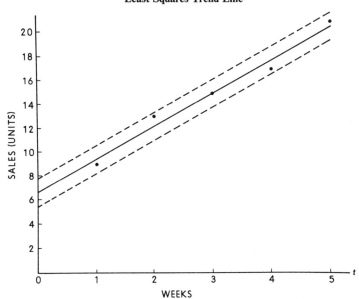

The actual calculation of a, b, and c will be left as an exercise for the reader. Obviously this same procedure could be used to calculate the best-fitting equation for a large number of classes. We could include $\log t$, $\sin t$, etc. The only restriction is that the coefficients a, b, c, d, etc., must enter the equation linearly.

An approximate method for choosing between a linear and quadratic model when the characteristics of the underlying process are unknown, for example, is to establish the least squares equation for both curves, calculate the sum of squared differences, and choose the smaller of the two. Alternatively, we could entertain the possibility of each curve, then test for the statistical significance of each coefficient. Such tests are similar to the tests for significance of parameters as outlined in Chapter 4.

One means of identifying the need for a change in the trend line is to establish control limits about the projection. The expression $\hat{f}(t)$ is a mean value. It is the expected value of the dependent variable for any given value of the independent variable t. The standard deviation of the least squares estimate (sometimes called the standard error of estimate) can be approximated by

$$s = \left[\frac{\sum_{t=1}^{n}(\hat{f}(t) - f(t))^2}{n}\right]^{1/2} \tag{7–20}$$

Within the accuracy of our numbers, assuming that the error is normally distributed, it is approximately true that 95 percent of the data will fall within $\pm 2s$ of the line $\hat{f}(t)$. For the data of Table 7–1, we have a standard error of estimate of approximately 0.6. The 95 percent control limits ($\pm 2s$) are shown by the dotted lines in Figure 7–3. We can use these limits to signal a change in the underlying process and consequent need for a change in our forecasting equation. We simply project the existing curve and its control limits into the future. As each new sales figure becomes available, we can plot it on the graph. If a number of such points fall outside our limits, we must develop a new trend line to serve as the forecast. This line is then projected in similar fashion.

Trend Following

The techniques discussed so far are best used when we have the total history of a process which we believe will remain stable in future time periods. However, the most common forecasting problems occur with systems that are continually changing. The straight-line equation developed over the first five weeks' data may be completely inappropriate for a forecast covering weeks 20 through 25. By that time the slope may have changed drastically, the intercept may be different, or an entirely different curve may be in order. What we need is a continually moving picture of the time series which will emphasize the most recent data and respond quickly to genuine changes in the underlying process. Two techniques used to accomplish this are the moving average and exponential smoothing.

Moving Average. In its simplest form a moving average supposes that the underlying process generating a time series is locally constant. However, the data include elements of random noise. The model for each observation is then

$$f(t) = a + e(t) \qquad (7\text{–}21)$$

and the curve to be estimated is

$$\hat{f}(t) = a \qquad (7\text{–}22)$$

Let us again consider the data of Table 7–1. Suppose that we are viewing the system after only three weeks of sales data have been collected. With this limited information we might project future sales as being equal to the arithmetic average of sales to date. That is,

$$(t) = \frac{\sum_{t=1}^{3} f(t)}{3} = \frac{37}{3} = 12\frac{1}{3}$$

This means that we would forecast sales for week 4 at $12\frac{1}{3}$ units. Now suppose that it is one week later. We now have four weeks' worth of actual data which we could average to obtain $\hat{f}(t)$. However, since we feel that the process may be changing over time, let us stick to a three-week moving average. We now use the average of weeks 2, 3, and 4 to estimate sales for week 5.

$$\hat{f}(5) = \frac{\sum_{t=2}^{4} f(t)}{3} = \frac{45}{3} = 15$$

Figure 7-4 illustrates how the three-week moving average tracks the time series, which has now been expanded to 10 weeks' worth of data. Here we are projecting only one week into the future with our forecasts. Note how the forecast lags the changes in direction of the time series. Obviously, if the underlying process is changing very rapidly, projections farther into the future will be greatly in error. We can affect the sensitivity of the forecast to changing conditions by altering the number of terms included in our moving average. Increasing n will cause the forecast to change more slowly. Decreasing n will cause it to respond more rapidly to changing conditions. The choice of n is a compromise which must be tempered by the desire to follow genuine changes without showing violent fluctuations in response to random noise in the data.

FIGURE 7-4

Forecasting with a Three-Week Moving Average

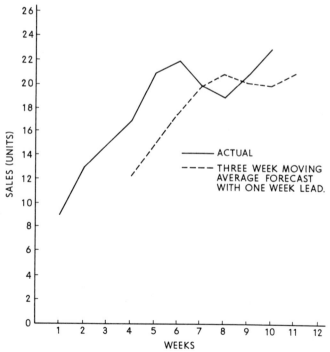

ACTUAL

THREE WEEK MOVING AVERAGE FORECAST WITH ONE WEEK LEAD.

SALES (UNITS)

WEEKS

We could use the concept of a moving average to fit a linear or quadratic model as well as the constant one. Here we would simply perform the least squares calculations using the n most recent data points. The forecast $\hat{f}(t)$ would be revised as each new element in the time series became available. Such a procedure would give more accurate tracking than the simple moving average if a large trend was evident.

Simple Exponential Smoothing. Exponential smoothing is a mathematical technique designed to provide the benefits of moving average without carrying the vast amount of data required for moving average calculations. This device has become quite popular for short-term forecasting in recent years. For an excellent discussion of this and other forecasting matters, the reader is urged to consult the text by Brown.[5] Our discussion draws heavily upon his ideas.

First-order, or simple, exponential smoothing is appropriate for forecasting time series which can be assumed to be locally constant. The basic model of Equation 7–21 describes the data. The smoothed function is written in terms of a recursive relationship.

Let

$S(t)$ = smoothed value at time t
$f(t)$ = observed data at time t
α = exponential smoothing constant $(0 \leq \alpha \leq 1)$

then

$$S(t) = S(t - 1) + \alpha \left[f(t) - S(t - 1) \right] \qquad (7\text{–}23)$$

When written in this form, it is apparent that our forecast for period t, which we obtain from

$$\hat{f}(t) = S(t - 1)$$

is modified by a fraction of its error to obtain the forecast for period $t + 1$,

$$\hat{f}(t + 1) = S(t)$$

By selecting a large α, we cause the system to respond rapidly to differences between actual and forecast conditions. By selecting a small α, on the other hand, the forecast will change relatively slowly from one period to the next. Hence we achieve a smoothing effect on the original time series data. Brown suggests that the smoothing constant will generally be some number between 0.01 and 0.3. In terms of the average age of the data, the smoothing constant can be related to an equivalent number of terms in a moving average calculation. For example, $\alpha = 0.5$ gives results equivalent to a three-period moving average. A value of $\alpha = 0.3$ corresponds roughly to $n = 6$ and $\alpha = 0.01$ corresponds roughly to $n = 200$.[6]

---

[5] Robert G. Brown, *Smoothing, Forecasting and Prediction of Discrete Time Series* (Englewood Cliffs, N.J.: Prentice-Hall, Inc., 1963).
[6] *Ibid.*, pp. 106–8.

For ease of data manipulation, the simple exponential smoothing equation may be written as

$$S(t) = \alpha f(t) + (1 - \alpha)S(t - 1) \qquad (7\text{-}24)$$

By expanding the terms on the right, it can be shown that $S(t)$ is a linear combination of all past observations from the beginning of the time series. Furthermore, the newest data receives the highest weight with the weight given to older elements decreasing exponentially with the age of the data

$$S(t) = \alpha f(t) + (1 - \alpha)[\alpha f(t - 1) + (1 - \alpha)S(t - 2)]$$

$$= \alpha f(t) + \alpha(1 - \alpha)f(t - 1) + \alpha(1 - \alpha)^2 f(t - 2) + \cdots + (1 - \alpha)^t f(0).$$

$$= \alpha \sum_{j=0}^{t-1} (1 - \alpha)^j f(t - j) + (1 - \alpha)^t f(0) \qquad (7\text{-}25)$$

Since our model is that $y = f(t) = a + e(t)$, we want the expected value of S to be equal to the expected value of y. This is demonstrated by

$$E(S) = \alpha \sum_{j=0}^{\infty} (1 - \alpha)^j E(y)$$

$$= \alpha E(y) \frac{1}{1 - (1 - \alpha)} = E(y)$$

Thus the smoothed value can be viewed as an average, which gives us another method for estimating the coefficient in a constant model.

$$S(t) = \hat{a}(t)$$

We can illustrate the use of simple exponential smoothing by using the data from Figure 7-4. To initialize the system, we could select $S(0)$ as a subjective estimate of anticipated sales or move the origin to week 3, for example, and use the average of the first three weeks' sales for $S(0)$. However, let us for the time being treat $S(0) = 9$ and proceed. If we let $\alpha = 0.3$, our first estimate is

$$S(1) = \hat{f}(2) = 0.3(9) + 0.7(9) = 9$$

The second estimate is

$$S(2) = \hat{f}(3) = 0.3(13) + 0.7(9) = 10.2$$

and so forth. Note that once we have calculated $S(t)$, we no longer need any data from periods 0 through t. All we require for the next forecast is $S(t)$, $f(t + 1)$, and α. This leads to a considerable savings in computer storage over weighted moving average techniques.

The results of the exponential smoothing calculations for α values of 0.1, 0.3, and 0.5 are summarized in Figure 7-5. Note that we have avoided a large transient condition which would occur if we initialized with $S(0) = 0$.

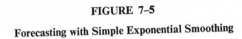

FIGURE 7–5

Forecasting with Simple Exponential Smoothing

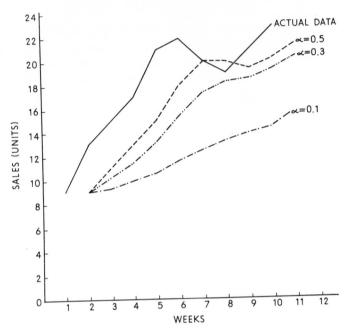

The choice of $S(0) = 9$ is in no way optimum, but it does bring the forecasts in line more quickly. Note also that the small smoothing constants cause the forecasts to lag the time series rather badly. Since α must be fairly large to even come close to the series, we might suspect that a constant model is not the one to use. A casual examination of the graph indicates that there is a trend present and suggests that a more appropriate model might be

$$f(t) = a + bt + e(t) \qquad (7\text{--}26)$$

We will now examine smoothing techniques for fitting this model to the data.

Correcting for Trend. The inability of first-order exponential smoothing to adequately track a time series, which contains a significant trend, can easily be demonstrated with the transform techniques discussed in Chapters 5 and 6. For this analysis we treat the forecasting device as a linear system which receives a time series as input and produces a smoothed function $S(t)$ as output.

The simple exponential smoothing system is illustrated in block diagram form by Figure 7–6. The signal $f(t)$ is operated on by a subsystem which multiplies the signal by α. The output from this subsystem is then passed

FIGURE 7-6

A Simple Exponential Smoothing System

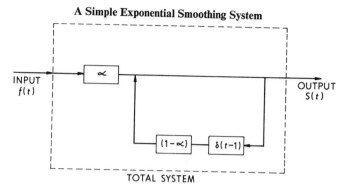

through a feedback loop containing a delay element and another multiplier element, $(1 - \alpha)$, in series. Total system output, $S(t)$, appears after the feedback loop. From Chapter 5, we can develop a transfer function in terms of geometric transforms for the total system as follows:

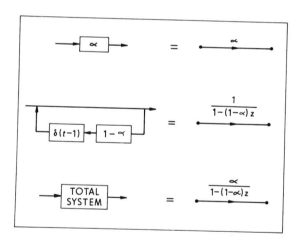

The transfer function for our forecasting system is then

$$T[h(t)] = \frac{\alpha}{1 - (1 - \alpha)z} \qquad (7\text{-}27)$$

If the input signal is in fact a constant $f(t) = a$, the transform of the input is

$$T(\text{in}) = \sum_{t=0}^{\infty} az^t = \frac{a}{1 - z}$$

Since the transform of the output is the product of the transfer function and the transform of the input, the output transform is

$$T(\text{out}) = T(\text{in})T[h(t)] = \frac{\alpha a}{(1 - z)[1 - (1 - \alpha)z]} \qquad (7\text{-}28)$$

The final value theorem for geometric transforms tells us that

$$\lim_{z \to 1} (1 - z)T[f(t)] = \lim_{t \to \infty} f(t) \qquad (7\text{-}29)$$

From Equation 7-28 it follows that the steady-state response of our forecasting system to a constant input is

$$\lim_{z \to 1} \frac{(1 - z)\alpha a}{(1 - z)[1 - (1 - \alpha)z]} = a$$

as we had hoped.

Now suppose that we are using the same forecasting system when the input signal is actually $f_1(t) = a + bt$. The geometric transform of this new input signal is

$$T[f_1(t)] = \frac{a}{1 - z} + \frac{bz}{(1 - z)^2} \qquad (7\text{-}30)$$

The system response to this signal has the transform

$$T(\text{out}) = T[f_1(t)] \, T[h(t)] = \frac{\alpha a}{(1 - z)[1 - (1 - \alpha)z]} + \frac{\alpha bz}{[1 - (1 - \alpha)z](1 - z)^2}$$

$$(7\text{-}31)$$

Following the usual procedure for partial fraction expansion, this reduces to

$$T(\text{out}) = \frac{a}{1 - z} - \frac{(1 - \alpha)a}{1 - (1 - \alpha)z} + \frac{(1 - \alpha)b}{1 - (1 - \alpha)z} + \frac{b}{(1 - z)^2} - \frac{b + [(1 - \alpha)/\alpha]b}{1 - z}$$

Inverting term by term yields the response to the linear input of

$$S(t) = a - (1 - \alpha)^{t+1} a + \frac{(1 - \alpha)^{t+1} b}{\alpha} + b(t + 1) - b - \left(\frac{1 - \alpha}{\alpha}\right)b$$

$$= a + bt - \left(\frac{1 - \alpha}{\alpha}\right)b - (1 - \alpha)^{t+1} a + \frac{(1 - \alpha)^{t+1} b}{\alpha} \qquad (7\text{-}32)$$

As t becomes large the last two terms in this expression will approach zero. The single smoothing operator, then, in the limit will respond to a linear input as

$$\lim_{t \to \text{large}} S(t) = a + bt - \left(\frac{1 - \alpha}{\alpha}\right)b \qquad (7\text{-}33)$$

In this form, it is obvious that the forecasting scheme will contain a constant bias of $b(1 - \alpha)/\alpha$. To eliminate this bias, it is necessary to estimate the value of the trend coefficient, b. If we call this value $\hat{b}$, the correct estimate for a system with a linear trend would be

$$C(t) = S(t) + \left(\frac{1 - \alpha}{\alpha}\right)\hat{b} \qquad (7\text{-}34)$$

There are several ways, enumerated below, to estimate the coefficient b and adjust the forecast for trend. The simplest method is to treat the magnitude of trend, $\hat{b}$, as the difference between two successive estimates, say

$$\hat{b} = S(t - 1) - S(t - 2)$$

Now if we want to move one time period into the future, we must add b units to our current estimate of the data. The estimating equation then becomes

$$S(t) = S(t - 1) + [S(t - 1) - S(t - 2)]$$
$$+ \alpha[f(t) - (S(t - 1) + S(t - 1) - S(t - 2))] \qquad (7\text{-}35)$$

or

$$S(t) = \alpha f(t) + 2(1 - \alpha)S(t - 1) - (1 - \alpha)S(t - 2) \qquad (7\text{-}36)$$

This is sometimes referred to as second-order exponential smoothing since it uses the two preceding values of the smoothed statistic to compute the next period's estimate.

If we find it necessary to project our estimates more than one period into the future, we can redefine the origin to be the present time t. The projection for period $t + T$ would then be

$$\hat{f}(t + T) = \hat{a} + \hat{b}\,T$$
$$= S(t) + [S(t) - S(t - T)]$$
$$= 2S(t) - S(t - T) \qquad (7\text{-}37)$$

Here we are assuming that the intercept estimate, $\hat{a}$, is the current value of $S(t)$ and that the total slope shown over the last T time periods will be the same for the next T periods. For the special case of a forecast which projects only one period into the future, we have

$$\hat{f}(t) = S(t - 1) + [S(t - 1) - S(t - 2)]$$
$$= 2S(t - 1) - S(t - 2) \qquad (7\text{-}38)$$

Another technique used to analyze a trend is to smooth the trend estimates in the same manner that we smoothed the estimates for the constant term. The apparent trend for a single period is

$$b = S(t - 1) - S(t - 2)$$

An exponentially smoothed average for trend would be

$$\hat{b}(t) = \beta[S(t-1) - S(t-2)] + (1-\beta)\hat{b}(t-1) \qquad (7\text{-}39)$$

where the smoothing constant is β. The forecast for period t is then

$$\hat{f}(t) = S(t-1) + \hat{b}(t)$$

$$= \alpha f(t-1) + (1-\alpha)S(t-2)$$

$$+ \beta[S(t-1) - S(t-2)] + (1-\beta)[\hat{b}(t-1)] \qquad (7\text{-}40)$$

Alternatively, we could retain our simple smoothing operator and estimate $\hat{b}$ from Equation 7–39 to obtain the smoothed value

$$C(t) = S(t) + \frac{1-\alpha}{\alpha}\,\hat{b}(t) \qquad (7\text{-}41)$$

in accordance with Equation 7–34. The forecast for period $t+1$ would then be

$$\hat{f}(t+1) = C(t) + \hat{b}(t)$$

$$= S(t) + \frac{\hat{b}(t)}{\alpha} \qquad (7\text{-}42)$$

where $S(t)$ is the simple smoothed average without trend adjustment.

One other technique, discussed by Brown,[7] is to pass the time series signal through two simple smoothing systems as indicated below:

The resulting signal, $S^{(2)}(t)$, defines double exponential smoothing as

$$S^{(2)}(t) = \alpha S(t) + (1-\alpha)S^{(2)}(t-1) \qquad (7\text{-}43)$$

Brown shows that these results can be used to estimate $\hat{a}(t)$ and $\hat{b}(t)$ as

$$\hat{a}(t) = 2S(t) - S^{(2)}(t)$$

$$\hat{b}(t) = \left(\frac{\alpha}{1-\alpha}\right)[S(t) - S^{(2)}(t)]$$

from which the forecast T periods in the future is

$$\hat{f}(t+T) = \hat{a}(t) + T\hat{b}(t) \qquad (7\text{-}44)$$

We have discussed four different exponential smoothing techniques for adjusting for trends. They are

1. Second-order smoothing (Equations 7–36 and 7–38).
2. Trend smoothing (Equation 7–40).

[7] *Ibid.*, p. 128.

3. Simple smoothing with smoothed trend adjustment (Equation 7–42).
4. Double smoothing (Equations 7–43 and 7–44).

The results of each technique applied to the data of Figure 7–5 are summarized in Table 7–2. A comparison of their accuracy can be made from Figure 7–7.

TABLE 7–2

Alternative Methods for Forecasting under Trend Conditions
(all smoothing constants = 0.3, initial slope = 4)

| | | Forecasting Method* | | | | | | | |
| | | (1) | | (2) | | (3) | | (4) | |
t	$f(t)$	$S(t)$	$\hat{f}(t)$	$S(t)$	$\hat{f}(t)$	$S(t)$	$\hat{f}(t)$	$S(t)$	$\hat{f}(t)$
1	9	9		9		9		9	
2	13	10.2	9	14.2	9	10.2	9	9.4	9
3	15	12.5	11.4	18.4	14.2	11.6	11.4	10.1	11.3
4	17	15.5	14.8	22.3	18.4	13.2	13.8	11.0	13.7
5	21	19.2	18.5	26.1	22.3	15.5	16.3	12.4	16.3
6	22	22.7	22.9	28.4	26.1	17.5	20.0	13.9	19.9
7	20	24.4	26.2	28.7	28.4	18.3	22.8	15.2	22.6
8	19	24.0	26.1	27.7	28.7	18.5	22.8	16.2	22.7
9	21	22.8	23.6	26.5	27.7	19.3	21.9	17.1	21.8
10	23	22.0	21.6	26.2	26.5	20.4	22.5	18.1	22.4
11			21.2		26.2		23.7		23.7

* Method 1: Second order smoothing.
  Method 2: Trend smoothing.
  Method 3: Simple smoothing with smoothed trend adjustment.
  Method 4: Double smoothing.

From the data shown, it is obvious that methods 3 and 4 give essentially the same results when α and β are equal. The choice of which technique to use is a compromise between computational convenience and demonstrated tracking ability for the time series under study.

We could add a fifth technique which is a special version of the least squares method for fitting a straight line to a set of data. In the present context, we would calculate the regression curve each period using only the n most recent data points rather than the entire set. In this manner we would follow a changing trend in much the same fashion as simple moving average follows changes in process levels.

Accounting for Cycles. Periodic phenomena add another dimension to the forecasting problem. When there are definite periodicities present, trigonometric models of the Fourier series type should be employed. However, one should be careful not to falsely identify random fluctuations in a time series as evidence of a periodic system. To do so would unnecessarily complicate

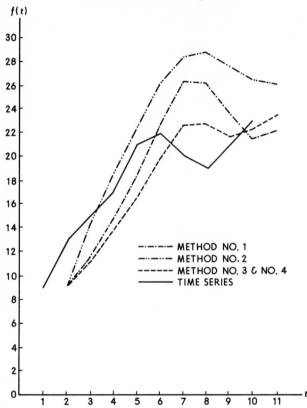

FIGURE 7–7

Forecasting with Trend Adjustments

the model and lead to spurious predictions for future events. Brown cautions that "trigonometric models should be used only where there is a known underlying cause that gives rise to a periodic phenomenon."[8] Common causes for periodicity are the occurrence of holidays or changes in predominant weather patterns in a marketing area. If we are marketing toys, for example, we might expect strong seasonal demand at Christmas with a trough at mid-year. If we are marketing snow tires, we might expect strong seasonal demand in the autumn. In each instance there is ample historical and logical evidence to support the thesis that the same general demand pattern will repeat itself on a 12-month cycle.

Later in this chapter we will also introduce the autocorrelation function which may be helpful in identifying potential cycles in the data. Such analyses

---

[8] *Ibid.*, p. 74.

only highlight regularities in the data which may be obscured in the basic time series plot. They do not replace the need for searching for underlying causes but rather offer guidance on where to search.

Consider the following hypothetical delivery data for one year for a new-car dealer:

Month	Cars Delivered	Month	Cars Delivered
January	50	July	74
February	62	August	40
March	84	September	60
April	90	October	92
May	80	November	81
June	75	December	62
		January	52

Having been exposed to model changeovers and spring buying rushes for a number of years, the dealer believes quite strongly that his business follows a six-month cycle with peaks occurring in the spring and autumn. For that reason, the model proposed for these data is periodic with

$$f(t) = a_0 + a_1 \cos\left(\frac{\pi t}{3}\right) + b_1 \sin\left(\frac{\pi t}{3}\right) \tag{7-45}$$

where 2π corresponds to the full period of six months. One month then equals $\pi/3$ radians. The coefficients a_0, a_1, and b_1 are the Fourier coefficients described in Chapter 5. They must be estimated by numerical integration of the given time series. Note that only those terms of frequency $\pi/3$ are included from the total spectrum possible with the Fourier series. This is in keeping with our premise that the only periodic phenomenon present has a period of six months and that we want the simplest model possible. Frequency $\pi/3$ assures us that in 12 months the system will go through two cycles, i.e., two cycles per year.

Following the arguments of Equation 5–8 from Chapter 5, we have for the first six months,

$$a_0 = \frac{1}{6}\left[\frac{f(0)}{2} + \sum_{i=1}^{5} f(i) + \frac{f(6)}{2}\right]$$

$$a_n = \frac{1}{3}\left[\frac{f(0)}{2} + \sum_{i=1}^{5} f(i) \cos\left(\frac{n\pi i}{3}\right) + \frac{f(6)}{2} \cos\left(2n\pi\right)\right] \qquad n > 0$$

$$b_n = \frac{1}{3}\left[\sum_{i=1}^{5} f(i) \sin\left(\frac{n\pi i}{3}\right)\right] \tag{7-46}$$

Treating the first January as the origin we can calculate a_0, for example, as

$$a_0 = \tfrac{1}{6}[25 + 62 + 84 + 90 + 80 + 75 + 37] = 76.5$$

In similar fashion, $a_1 = -13.8$ and $b_1 = -2.6$. The forecast for future months is then

$$\hat{f}(t) = 76.5 - 13.8 \cos\left(\frac{\pi t}{3}\right) - 2.6 \sin\left(\frac{\pi t}{3}\right) \tag{7-47}$$

The adequacy of this forecast for the given data is illustrated by Figure 7-8.

As with the coefficients in our constant and trend models, the coefficients for the trigonometric model can be updated as each new data point becomes available. Since our model assumes a six-month period, we could form a moving window which always looks at one complete cycle defined over the

FIGURE 7-8

Forecasting with a Trigonometric Model

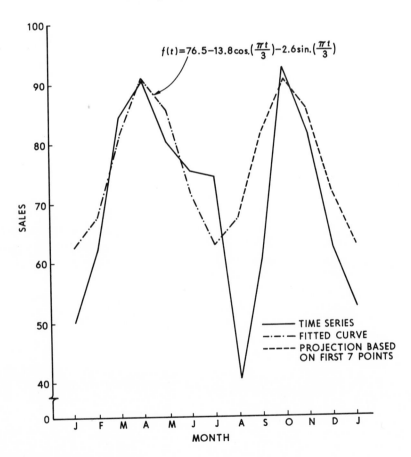

most recent data. If we recalculate a_0, a_1, and b_1 using the most recent seven data points necessary to define one complete period, we accomplish the same thing as we did with a moving average in earlier calculations. Exponential smoothing may also be used to estimate the coefficients. The interested reader is urged to consult Brown.[9]

Another technique commonly employed in highly seasonal industries is to construct a base series and relate current observations to that series. This procedure is discussed by Buffa and others.[10]

We might take, as our base series, last year's demand. A demand ratio of actual demand in each period to the base series demand for that period is calculated and smoothed. The forecast then consists of the expected ratio times the base series demand.

Let

$$R(t) = \text{demand ratio for period } t$$
$$f(t) = \text{actual demand for period } t$$
$$B(t) = \text{base series demand for period } t$$

then

$$R(t) = \frac{f(t)}{B(t)} \tag{7-48}$$

which gives a smoothed estimate of

$$D(t) = \alpha R(t) + (1 - \alpha)D(t - 1) \tag{7-49}$$

Unlike exponential smoothing, the statistical properties of this technique are not studied.

Where there may be changes in the average level of the process for seasonal systems, the smoothed estimate $D(t)$ must be modified by an appropriate trend adjustment. The trend modification can be performed by any of the techniques of the last section. For example, let us define the apparent trend as

$$b(t) = D(t) - D(t - 1)$$

with a smoothed average of

$$\hat{b}(t) = \beta b(t) + (1 - \beta)\hat{b}(t - 1)$$
$$= \beta[D(t) - D(t - 1)] + (1 - \beta)\hat{b}(t - 1) \tag{7-50}$$

Our forecast for period $t + 1$ would then be

$$\hat{f}(t + 1) = \left[D(t) + \left(\frac{1 - \alpha}{\alpha}\right)\hat{b}(t)\right]B(t + 1) \tag{7-51}$$

[9] *Ibid.*, chaps. xi and xii.
[10] Elwood S. Buffa, *Production—Inventory Systems: Planning and Control* (Homewood, Ill.: Richard D. Irwin, Inc., 1968), pp. 40–43.

TABLE 7-3

Calculation of Seasonal Forecasts Where $\alpha = \beta = 0.3$ and $D(0) = 1.00$

Month	t	Demand $f(t)$	Base $B(t)$	Ratio $R(t)=f(t)/B(t)$	Smoothed Ratio $D(t)$	Trend $b(t)$	Smoothed Trend $b(t)$	Trend Adjusted Ratio $D(t)$	No Trend Forecast	Forecast with Trend
Jan.	1	52	50	1.04	1.01	0.01	0.003	1.02		
Feb.	2	70	62	1.13	1.05	0.04	0.014	1.08	62.7	63.3
Mar.	3	89	84	1.06	1.05	0	0.010	1.07	88.2	90.8
Apr.	4	95	90	1.06	1.05	0	0.007	1.07	94.5	96.4
May	5	86	80	1.08	1.06	0.01	0.008	1.08	84.0	85.6
June	6	83	75	1.11	1.08	0.02	0.012	1.11	78.0	81.0
July	7	80	74	1.08	1.08	0	0.008	1.10	80.0	82.2
Aug.	8	47	40	1.17	1.11	0.03	0.015	1.15	43.2	44.0
Sept.	9	66	60	1.10	1.11	0.03	0.020	1.16	66.7	69.1
Oct.	10	100	92	1.09	1.10	0.01	0.011	1.13	102.0	106.8
Nov.	11	90	81	1.12	1.11	0.01	0.011	1.14	89.1	91.5
Dec.	12	70	62	1.13	1.12	0.01	0.011	1.15	68.9	70.8
Jan.	13		52						58.4	59.8

Alternatively, if we are willing to assume that the true ratio from period to period will remain unchanged, we can use as our forecast

$$\hat{f}(t + 1) = D(t)B(t + 1) \qquad (7\text{--}52)$$

To illustrate these procedures, let us treat the auto demand data used with the trigonometric model as our base series. Forecasts are made one month in advance for the succeeding year's data as illustrated in Table 7–3 and Figure 7–9. For the data given, it is obvious that both the no-trend and trend adjustment forecasts give reasonable approximations to the time series. Had the general upward trend been more pronounced, the trend adjustment would have shown a better fit.

FIGURE 7–9

Forecasting with a Base Series

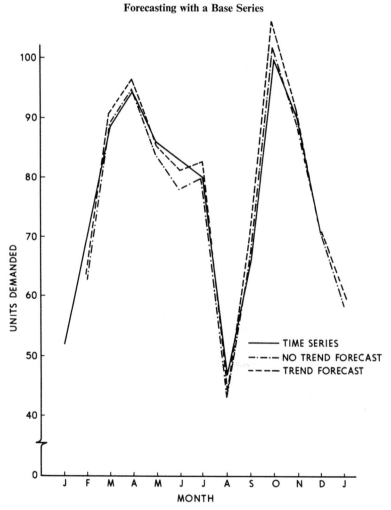

Probability Statements. We have examined several methods for developing models to describe a time series. These ranged from the exact fit polynomials and transcendental functions to be applied to deterministic systems, through the best fit techniques of regression and exponential smoothing. The choice of the particular model to use depends upon the analyst's view of the underlying process and the computational facilities at hand. The model should be no more complex than absolutely necessary to capture the salient features of the system.

Each of the forecasting techniques examined was based upon an expected value. Since the forecast obtained is for the mean of the process, we can expect actual data points to be spread about the forecasted value. As long as there are random effects present, it would be a rare event to have a forecasted value agree exactly with the data as it develops. The operations engineer may therefore find it desirable to provide probability statements to supplement the point estimates of the usual forecasting schemes.

An approximate measure of the error distribution can be obtained by studying the sequence of observed forecasting errors $\{f(j) - \hat{f}(j)\}$ where $f(j)$ represents actual demand for period j and $\hat{f}(j)$ is the forecast for that period. Ordinarily $\hat{f}(j)$ will be based upon data occurring through period $(j - 1)$. This sequence of numbers can be considered as a random sample from a single error distribution. The sample mean $\bar{x}$ and variance s^2 are then considered to be estimates of μ_e and σ_e^2 from that distribution. If we want to make probability statements about demand for the next period, we shall say that demand $f(t + 1)$ is a random variable drawn from a population with

$$\mu = \hat{f}(t + 1) + \mu_e \qquad (7\text{--}53)$$

$$\sigma^2 = \sigma_e^2 \qquad (7\text{--}54)$$

If $\mu_e = 0$, the forecasting method is called unbiased. In effect we are asserting that the probability distribution for demand in period $(t + 1)$ is identical with the error distribution superimposed on the forecast.

For example, consider the no-trend forecast of Table 7–3. The sequence of errors from February through December is

$$(70 - 62.7, 89 - 88.2, 95 - 94.5, 86 - 84, 83 - 78, 80 - 80, 47 - 43.2,$$

$$66 - 66.7, 100 - 102, 90 - 89.1, 70 - 68.9)$$

$$= (7.3, 0.8, 0.5, 2.0, 5.0, 0, 3.8, -0.7, -2.0, 0.9, 1.1)$$

The unbiased estimates for error mean and variance are

$$\mu_e = \frac{\sum_{t=2}^{12} e(t)}{11} = \frac{18.7}{11} = 1.7$$

$$\sigma_e^2 = \frac{\sum_{t=2}^{12} (e(t))^2 - 11\mu_e^2}{10} = \frac{100.2 - 31.8}{10} = 6.84$$

If we further make the bold assumption that the error distribution is approximately normal, the probability distribution for January demand will be normal with

$$\mu = \hat{f}(13) + 1.7 = 58.4 + 1.7 = 60.1$$

$$\sigma = (6.84)^{1/2} = 2.61$$

The 95 percent probability interval for demand in January would then be

$$P[55.0 < f(t) < 65.2] = 0.95$$

The no-trend forecast is slightly biased in this example, as we could surmise from Figure 7–9.

PREDICTION BY ASSOCIATION

We will use the expression "prediction by association" to connote those forecasting schemes which use the knowledge of one variable to predict the value of another. So far, our discussion has been limited to systems with time as the only independent variable. We will now consider those techniques which are commonly employed to predict the value of a desired dependent variable as a function of related independent variables other than time.

Regression and Correlation

In previous sections of this chapter we employed the method of least squares to develop a regression line to fit a linear relationship of the form

$$f(t) = a + bt$$

to time series data. Now we will use the same technique to fit a straight line to scatter diagrams which do not necessarily involve a single time series. For example, we might want to predict aircraft sales in year $(t + 2)$ as a function of student pilot starts in year (t). We could plot sales $x(t + 2)$ versus pilot starts $y(t)$ and perform our regression analysis on those data. Throughout this section we will refer exclusively to linear regression.

The Regression Equation. The coefficients for the least squares line through a set of points (x, y) can be developed from Equations 7–13 and 7–14. We merely replace t with x and $f(t)$ with y in those equations to obtain

$$\hat{a} = \frac{\Sigma x^2 \Sigma y - \Sigma x \Sigma xy}{n\Sigma x^2 - (\Sigma x)^2} \qquad (7\text{-}55)$$

$$\hat{b} = \frac{n\Sigma xy - \Sigma x \Sigma y}{n\Sigma x^2 - (\Sigma x)^2} \qquad (7\text{-}56)$$

from which

$$\hat{y} = \hat{a} + \hat{b}x \qquad (7\text{-}57)$$

In many forecasting applications, the number pairs (x, y) will be taken from two time series. Ideally we would like a series $x(t)$ which leads the series $y(t)$ by some amount. When this occurs, we can use the regression line to predict future events $y(t + j)$ on the basis of current knowledge of our leading indicator $x(t)$.

Consider the aircraft sales prediction problem. Table 7–4 shows the hypo-

TABLE 7–4

Hypothetical Data for Aircraft Sales Prediction

Year	Student Starts	Aircraft Sales	Coordinants $x(t-2), y(t)$
1	8,000	900	—
2	9,000	800	—
3	11,000	900	8,000, 900
4	10,000	1,000	9,000, 1,000
5	9,000	1,100	11,000, 1,100
6	12,000	1,200	10,000, 1,200
7	13,000	1,000	9,000, 1,000
8	11,000	900	12,000, 900
9	12,000	1,100	13,000, 1,100
10	13,000	1,200	11,000, 1,200

thetical data for one manufacturer. It is this manufacturer's hypothesis that today's students will enter the new aircraft market in two years. The regression line is predicated on that hypothesis.

The regression coefficients for these data after coding in units of 1,000 are

$$\hat{a} = \frac{(881)(8.4) - (83)(87.6)}{8(881) - (83)^2} = 0.812$$

$$\hat{b} = \frac{(8)(87.6) - (83)(8.4)}{8(881) - (83)^2} = 0.0226$$

The prediction equation is then

$$\hat{y}(t) = 0.812 + 0.0226x(t - 2)$$

where $\hat{y}(t)$ and $x(t)$ are measured in units of 1,000. On the basis of the data shown, the sales prediction for year 11 would be

$$\hat{y}(11) = 0.812 + 0.0226x(9)$$
$$= 0.812 + 0.0226(12) = 1,083 \text{ aircraft}$$

and for year 12

$$\hat{y}(12) = 0.812 + 0.0226x(10)$$
$$= 0.812 + 0.0226(13) = 1,106 \text{ aircraft}$$

Confidence Intervals. As with all of the forecasting schemes of this chapter, the regression equation is based upon expected values. The sample coefficients $\hat{a}$ and $\hat{b}$ are point estimates of the unknown population coefficients a and b. Following the arguments of Bowker and Lieberman, we will examine the statistical nature of the regression line under the following assumptions:[11]

1. $E(y) = a + bx$
2. σ_y^2 is constant for all x.
3. y is normally distributed.
4. The estimations are based upon a random sample.

Bowker and Lieberman show that the variance of a and b can be related to the variance of y by

$$\sigma_b^2 = \frac{\sigma_y^2}{\sum_{i=1}^{n}(x_i - \bar{x})^2} \tag{7-58}$$

$$\sigma_a^2 = \sigma_y^2 \left(\frac{1}{n} + \frac{\bar{x}^2}{\sum_{i=1}^{n}(x_i - \bar{x})^2} \right) \tag{7-59}$$

However, since σ_y^2 is seldom known, we must use the sample estimate for variance about the line.

$$s_{y|x}^2 = \frac{\sum_{i=1}^{n}(y_i - \hat{y}_i)^2}{n - 2} \tag{7-60}$$

We are now in a position to make confidence interval statements and test hypotheses about a and b.

Recall from Chapter 4 that when the population variance is unknown, the distribution for means will tend to follow the t distribution. Furthermore since we are using the n data points to estimate two constants, the number of degrees of freedom will be $(n - 2)$. The 90 percent confidence interval for a would be, for example,

$$\hat{a} \pm t_{0.05;\, n-2} \left[s_{y|x} \left(\frac{1}{n} + \frac{\bar{x}^2}{\sum_{i=1}^{n}(x_i - \bar{x})^2} \right)^{1/2} \right] \tag{7-61}$$

We can also use this information to test for the significance of each of the coefficients. For example, suppose that we want to establish whether or not the coefficient b is really significant. In other words, we want to know if there is a statistically significant trend in the data. The null hypothesis is that $b = 0$. For a significance level of α, the hypothesis that $b = 0$ is rejected whenever

$$\left| \frac{\hat{b} - 0}{s_b} \right| \geq t_{\alpha/2;\, n-2} \tag{7-62}$$

---

[11] Albert H. Bowker and Gerald J. Lieberman, *Engineering Statistics* (Englewood Cliffs, N.J.: Prentice-Hall, Inc., 1959), pp. 246–74.

To illustrate this calculation, consider again the data of Table 7–4. In computational form

$$s_{y|x}^2 = \frac{\Sigma y^2 - (\hat{a}\Sigma y + \hat{b}\Sigma xy)}{(n-2)} \tag{7-63}$$

from which

$$s_b^2 = \frac{\Sigma y^2 - (\hat{a}\Sigma y + \hat{b}\Sigma xy)}{(n-2)(\Sigma x_i^2 - n\bar{x}^2)} \tag{7-64}$$

Applying this to our data we have

$$s_b^2 = \frac{8.92 - (0.812)(8.4) - (0.0226)(87.6)}{6[881 - 8(10.375)^2]}$$

$$= \frac{0.12}{126} = 0.000953$$

The test statistic is

$$\frac{\hat{b}}{s_b} = \frac{0.0226}{0.0308} = 0.723$$

From the t distribution we find that

$$t_{0.025;6} = 2.447$$

Since

$$\frac{\hat{b}}{s_b} = 0.723 < 2.447$$

we cannot reject the hypothesis that $b = 0$. On the basis of our limited data, the supposed linear relationship between student starts and aircraft sales does not appear to be significant. From this information, one might argue that the best projection for aircraft sales for years 11 and 12 is simply the average annual sales to date.

$$\hat{f}(11) = \hat{f}(12) = \frac{\Sigma_{i=3}^{10} x_i}{8} = 1050 \text{ units}$$

Let us hasten to point out, however, that the average annual sales to date may not be the best possible of all predictors for aircraft sales. Our example has been based upon a simple regression equation relating sales to student starts. Had we proposed other factors related to sales, such as number of airports constructed, we might have used multiple regression techniques. These could reveal that other factors together with student starts might indeed be significant indicators of sales.

Correlation Analysis. A commonly used measure of the degree to which two variables are related is the sample correlation coefficient. Recall from our earlier discussion of probability theory that the correlation coefficient is related to variances and covariance by

$$\rho = \frac{\sigma_{xy}}{\sigma_x \sigma_y}$$

The sample estimate for this quantity is

$$r = \frac{\sum_{i=1}^{n} (x_i - \bar{x})(y_i - \bar{y})}{[\sum_{i=1}^{n} (x_i - \bar{x})^2 \sum_{i=1}^{n} (y_i - \bar{y})^2]^{1/2}} \tag{7-65}$$

which may be expressed in computational form as

$$r = \frac{\Sigma xy + n\bar{x}\bar{y}}{[(\Sigma x^2 - n\bar{x}^2)(\Sigma y^2 - n\bar{y}^2)]^{1/2}} \tag{7-66}$$

As we noted earlier, r may range between -1 and $+1$. When the correlation is positive, one variable tends to increase as the other increases. When it is negative, one variable tends to decrease as the other increases. A high absolute value of r indicates a high degree of association while a small value indicates little association between the variables.

In our aircraft sales example the correlation coefficient is

$$r = \frac{[87.6 - 8(10.375)(10.5)]}{[(881 - 8(10.375)^2)(8.92 - 8(1.05)^2)]^{1/2}}$$

$$\approx \frac{0.5}{1.37} = 0.365$$

This would seem to indicate a rather weak relationship between the variables. The significance of this correlation coefficient can be tested by

$$\left| \frac{r}{(1 - r^2)^{1/2}} \right| (n - 2)^{1/2} \geq t_{\alpha/2; n-2} \tag{7-67}$$

as described by Bowker and Lieberman.[12] If the test statistic exceeds the critical value, the null hypothesis $H_0: \rho = 0$ is rejected. For the given data

$$\left| \frac{r}{(1 - r^2)^{1/2}} \right| (n - 2)^{1/2} = \left| \frac{0.365}{(1 - 0.365^2)^{1/2}} \right| 6^{1/2} = 1.03$$

which is considerably less than $t_{0.025; 6} = 2.447$. This means that the correlation coefficient is not statistically significant at the 0.05 level. Since the correlation coefficient could have been derived from the slope of the regression line, it contains no additional information. For this problem the significance test for $\rho = 0$ is equivalent to testing whether the slope $b = 0$.

---

[12] Bowker and Lieberman, *op. cit.*, p. 274.

Autocorrelation. The term autocorrelation is used to denote the correlation coefficient calculated for succeeding values of the same function. For example, we might seek to correlate sales which are spread three months apart. If we achieved a significant correlation, we might suspect that our data is seasonal with a three-month cycle.

The autocorrelation function is sometimes referred to as the set of values for the autocovariance for all lags $k = 0, 1, 2, \ldots$. When displayed in normalized form the autocorrelation function is simply the set of autocorrelation coefficients. Let the autocovariance for data spaced k units apart be given by

$$R_{xx}(k) = \frac{\sum_{i=k+1}^{n} (x_i - \bar{x})(x_{i-k} - \bar{x})}{n - k - 1} \qquad (7\text{–}68)$$

When the lag is zero, this expression reduces to the sample variance

$$s^2 = R_{xx}(0) = \frac{\sum_{i=k+1}^{n} (x_i - \bar{x})^2}{n - k - 1} \qquad (7\text{–}69)$$

In normalized form, the autocorrelation function is equivalent to the auto-correlation coefficients

$$r(k) = \frac{R_{xx}(k)}{R_{xx}(0)} \qquad (7\text{–}70)$$

To facilitate computation with data which may have a long-term trend, Brown recommends fitting a straight line to the data before calculating auto-covariances.[13] The data are adjusted to zero expected value by establishing $y(t) = x(t) - \hat{x}(t)$. This removes the trend effect and leaves only variations about the trend line to be analyzed for possible correlation patterns. The autocovariances are then computed for y.

By plotting the autocorrelation function for a set of data, we may be able to identify significant cycles in the process by noting where the correlation function reaches maximum values. This technique often uncovers cyclical patterns which may be obscured by the noise inherent in the basic time series data. More elegant analysis is also possible by taking the Fourier transform of the autocovariance function. This yields the power spectrum by which the frequencies present and their amplitudes are revealed.

MARKOV PROCESSES

Most of the material of this chapter has concerned stochastic processes. The term stochastic implies that a probability function is generating an ordered sequence of events. In our consideration of time series we developed

---

[13] Brown, *op. cit.*, p. 395.

stochastic models for portions of the process. We supposed that the system could be modeled by a combination of a deterministic model, such as a straight line, and a superimposed stochastic model, which described random variations about the deterministic model. For our purposes, stochastic models are those models involving probability statements which are time dependent.

In this section we will turn our attention to a special class of stochastic processes known as Markov processes. This is a very fertile area for many types of system models including queueing and inventory models. The reason for introducing Markov processes in a forecasting chapter is to emphasize the idea that they are powerful models for predicting future states in many time varying random processes.

The Markov Property

The basic concepts of a Markov process are those of the state of the system and state transitions. If at time n the event E_k occurs, the system is said to be in state E_k. If at time $n + 1$ event E_j occurs, the system is said to have undergone a transition from state E_k to E_j. The probability of that particular transition, p_{kj}, is called a one-stage transition probability. For example, suppose that a man currently owns a convertible defined by state 1. At his next trade he may again purchase a convertible with probability 0.4 or he may purchase a two-door sedan with probability 0.6 and enter state 2. The stages or trials are defined by each occurrence of a trade.

The Markov property can be viewed as a first-order generalization of the common probability modeling assumption of independent trials. In our time series analysis, for example, the magnitude of the random component at time n was assumed to be independent of the magnitude at time $n + 1$. The series of values obtained for the random component can be viewed as resulting from a sequence of independent trials or experiments in which each value is drawn from a normally distributed population. In a Markov process, however, the outcome of a trial is assumed to be dependent upon the immediately preceding trial, but independent of all other past events. In terms of probability statements, the Markov property can be stated as

$$P(x_n = j \mid x_1 = k_1, x_2 = k_2, \dots x_{n-1} = i) = P(x_n = j \mid x_{n-1} = i) \quad (7\text{-}71)$$

where x_i is the outcome of the ith trial.

Chapman-Kolmogorov Equation. The conditional probabilities illustrated by Equation 7-71 are the transition probabilities for a Markov process. The probability of moving from state i to state j is the conditional probability that state j will occur on the next trial given that i has just occurred. Symbolically,

$$p_{ij} = P(x_n = j \mid x_{n-1} = i) \quad (7\text{-}72)$$

Assuming that trials are defined by discrete increments, we can build up conditional probability distributions for transitions over long intervals from those over short intervals by means of the Chapman-Kolmogorov equation.[14]

$$P(x_n = y \mid x_k = x) = \int_{-\infty}^{\infty} P(x_m = z \mid x_k = x)P(x_n = y \mid x_m = z)\, dz \quad (7\text{–}73)$$

If the state variables are also discrete this could be expressed as

$$p_{xy}^{(n-k)} = \sum_z p_{xz}^{(m-k)} p_{zy}^{(n-m)} \quad (7\text{–}74)$$

where $p_{ij}^{(r)}$ represents the probability of moving from i to j in r transitions. For example, we could consider the probability of moving from state x to state y in five transitions to be made up of two segments of a chain of events. The first segment might lead to some intermediate state z after two transitions while the second segment would lead from z to y in the remaining three transitions. Since z may be any possible intervening state, we must sum over all z to obtain the total probability of moving from x to y in five transitions via two segments of two and three transitions.

The idea that transition probabilities over long time intervals can be built up recursively from transition probabilities over shorter intervals is of fundamental importance to our analysis of Markov processes.

Markov Chains. Markov processes which are discrete in time with a discrete state space are called Markov chains. If the number of states is finite, they are referred to as finite Markov chains. The balance of this chapter concerns finite Markov chains. Since we are dealing with a discrete state space, we shall denote the possible states of the system by the integers. Thus $x_n = k$ means that the system is in state k at time n.

A Markov process is said to be stationary if the transition probabilities do not change over time. Thus for a stationary process the probability of moving from i to j in the nth transition is the same as it is for the first transition. For example, if we consider brand switching by consumers to be a Markov process, the probability of a switch from brand A to B might be independent of the number of purchases previously made by a consumer. If so, the process is stationary. On the other hand, the probability of moving from A to B on the second purchase might be different than it was on the first because of price changes, coupon offers, etc. In that case the process is non-stationary. In a sense we can view the transition probabilities as being conditioned upon the trial number.

Thanks to the Chapman-Kolmogorov equation, all we need to completely specify a stationary finite Markov chain is a probability vector defining the initial state of the system and a complete set of one-stage transition probabilities. If we want to know the probability of the system moving from state i

---

[14] D. R. Cox and H. D. Miller, *The Theory of Stochastic Processes* (New York: John Wiley & Sons, Inc., 1968), p. 17.

to state j in n steps (or stages), we can view it as moving from i to k in $n - 1$ steps then from k to j in the last step.

$$p_{ij}^{(n)} = \sum_k p_{ik}^{(n-1)} p_{kj} \tag{7-75}$$

By recursion we could develop $p_{ij}^{(2)}$, $p_{ij}^{(3)}$, etc., from this relationship. If the probability of the system being initialized in state i is $v_i(0)$, the probability of finding it in state j after n steps is given by

$$v_j(n) = \sum_i P(\text{start in } i) P(\text{move } i \text{ to } j \text{ in } n \text{ steps})$$

$$= \sum_i v_i(0) p_{ij}^{(n)} \tag{7-76}$$

This calculation can best be performed by use of matrix algebra. Let the initial probability distribution be given by the vector

$$V(0) = [v_1(0), v_2(0), \ldots, v_m(0)]$$

where v_i is the probability of the system being in state i. Let the set of one-stage transition probabilities p_{ij} be given by the matrix

$$P = [p_{ij}] = \begin{pmatrix} p_{11} & p_{12} & \cdots & p_{1m} \\ p_{21} & p_{22} & \cdots & p_{2m} \\ \vdots & & & \\ p_{m1} & p_{m2} & \cdots & p_{mm} \end{pmatrix}$$

The matrix P is square with nonnegative elements which when summed across any row equal one. Such a matrix of transition probabilities is called a stochastic matrix.

If we want to determine the probability that a three-state system will occupy state one after one transition we can calculate

$$v_1(1) = v_1(0) p_{11} + v_2(0) p_{21} + v_3(0) p_{31}$$

But this is nothing more than the first element of the vector which results when we multiply the vector $V(0)$ times the matrix P. Similarly $v_2(1)$ is the product of $V(0)$ times the second column of P, i.e., the second element of the vector $V(0)P$. In general

$$V(1) = V(0)P \tag{7-77}$$

will give the probability distribution for possible states of the system after one transition.

It follows that if we know the probability vector $V(n)$ after n transitions, we should be able to calculate the vector for $n + 1$ transitions by

$$V(n + 1) = V(n)P \tag{7-78}$$

This is the fundamental equation for calculations involving stationary Markov chains.

By recursion, we can develop an expression for $V(n)$ as a function of $V(0)$ since

$$V(1) = V(0)P$$
$$V(2) = V(1)P = V(0)P^2$$
$$V(3) = V(2)P = V(0)P^3$$

and in general

$$V(n) = V(0)P^n \tag{7-79}$$

This calculation accomplishes the summation indicated by Equation 7-76. The elements of the nth power of P are the n-stage transition probabilities $p_{ij}^{(n)}$. The product of the vector $V(0)$ and the jth column of P^n is the jth element of the vector $V(n)$. The vector product is

$$v_j(n) = v_1(0)p_{1j}^{(n)} + v_2(0)p_{2j}^{(n)} + \cdots + v_m(0)p_{mj}^{(n)}$$
$$= \sum_{i=1}^{m} v_i(0)p_{ij}^{(n)}$$

which is equivalent to Equation 7-76.

Steady-State Solutions. In many applications one may be interested in the behavior of a process over an infinite planning horizon. In automobile marketing, for example, we might be interested not only in the share of the market captured by different body styles over the next model year but also the ultimate share for each if conditions remain the same over an extended period. If such a process has a limiting state probability distribution, which is independent of starting conditions, it is said to be completely ergodic. The limiting distribution is referred to as the steady-state or equilibrium distribution.

Before attempting to calculate the steady-state solution, we need some assurance that such a solution exists. For finite chains, such assurance is easy to acquire. State j is said to communicate with state k if it is possible to reach k from j in a finite number of transitions. If all states communicate with every other state, the Markov chain is said to be irreducible. A periodic chain has the property that if the chain starts in state j it can only occupy state j again at time $t, 2t, 3t, \ldots$, where the integer t is the period of the system. This means that $p_{jj}^{(n)}$ vanishes except when n is an integral multiple of t. States with period 1 are called aperiodic. A finite, irreducible, aperiodic Markov chain is ergodic. This assures us that any chain which can be so classified does have a stationary distribution, independent of initial conditions, with nonzero probabilities of being in any state.

An equilibrium or steady-state solution implies that the probability vector defining the state distribution does not change with subsequent transitions. If the system is in equilibrium at stage n, this means that

$$V(n) = V(n + 1) = V(n + 2) \cdots$$

Let us suppress the argument n to signify that equilibrium has been reached. The fundamental Equation 7–78 then reduces to

$$VP = V \qquad (7\text{–}80)$$

Verbally we might say that the vector V has been passed through the transition matrix P to yield the vector V again.

$$V \longrightarrow \boxed{P} \longrightarrow V$$

In this problem we treat the elements of the vector V as unknowns. The indicated multiplication then yields m linear homogeneous equations in the m unknowns, $v_1, v_2, v_3, \ldots, v_m$.

$$v_1 p_{11} + v_2 p_{21} + v_3 p_{31} + \cdots + v_m p_{m1} = v_1$$

$$v_1 p_{12} + v_2 p_{22} + v_3 p_{32} + \cdots + v_m p_{m2} = v_2$$

$$\vdots$$

$$v_1 p_{1m} + v_2 p_{2m} + v_3 p_{3m} + \cdots + v_m p_{mm} = v_m \qquad (7\text{–}81)$$

Since these equations are homogeneous we require the additional equation

$$v_1 + v_2 + \cdots + v_m = 1 \qquad (7\text{–}82)$$

to achieve a solution. This relationship follows from the definition of a probability distribution. The solution procedure then consists of replacing one of the equations in 7–81 with 7–82 and solving the resulting set of m nonhomogeneous equations for the unknowns $v_1, v_2, \ldots, v_m$.

To illustrate this calculation, suppose that we have the following transition matrix:

$$P = \begin{pmatrix} 0.2 & 0.6 & 0.2 \\ 0.3 & 0.3 & 0.4 \\ 0.5 & 0.2 & 0.3 \end{pmatrix}$$

from which the product VP leads to

$$0.2v_1 + 0.3v_2 + 0.5v_3 = v_1$$

$$0.6v_1 + 0.3v_2 + 0.2v_3 = v_2$$

$$0.2v_1 + 0.4v_2 + 0.3v_3 = v_3$$

Replacing the first equation with $\sum v_i = 1$, the set of equations to be solved can be written in terms of the augmented coefficient matrix as

$$\begin{array}{cccc} v_1 & v_2 & v_3 & k \\ \begin{pmatrix} 1 & 1 & 1 & \bigg| & 1 \\ 0.6 & -0.7 & 0.2 & \bigg| & 0 \\ 0.2 & 0.4 & -0.7 & \bigg| & 0 \end{pmatrix} \end{array}$$

This set of equations can be solved in a number of different ways. By matrix algebra we have

$$AV' = K$$

from which

$$A^{-1}AV' = A^{-1}K$$

or

$$V' = A^{-1}K \tag{7-83}$$

where A^{-1} is the inverse of the unaugmented coefficient matrix. For the data given

$$A^{-1} = \begin{pmatrix} 0.328 & 0.088 & 0.720 \\ 0.368 & -0.072 & 0.320 \\ 0.304 & -0.160 & -0.104 \end{pmatrix}$$

from which

$$V' = \begin{pmatrix} 0.328 & 0.088 & 0.720 \\ 0.368 & -0.072 & 0.320 \\ 0.304 & -0.160 & -0.104 \end{pmatrix} \begin{pmatrix} 1 \\ 0 \\ 0 \end{pmatrix} = \begin{pmatrix} 0.328 \\ 0.368 \\ 0.304 \end{pmatrix}$$

Therefore

$$v_1 = 0.328$$
$$v_2 = 0.368$$
$$v_3 = 0.304$$

in the steady state.

Special States.   In the last section we were careful to specify the requirements for a completely ergodic process which will always yield a stationary distribution in the limit. However, it is worth noting the equation $VP = V$ can be used with any finite Markov chain as long as one is careful about the manner of interpreting the resulting probabilities (v_i).

For example, the matrix

$$P = \begin{pmatrix} 0.2 & 0.8 \\ 0 & 1 \end{pmatrix}$$

represents a Markov chain with a transient state. It does not satisfy the irreducible requirement since there is no way for the system to move from state 2 to state 1. State 2 is a trapping state, and state 1 is transient in that it will be impossible for the system to be in that state after an infinite number of transitions. The steady-state equations yield

$$0.2v_1 + 0v_2 = v_1$$
$$0.8v_1 + 1v_2 = v_2$$

from which $v_1 = 0$, $v_2 = 1$ as expected. This distribution is stationary but does not satisfy the formal requirements for an ergodic process.

Even a periodic process can be treated with these equations. The matrix

$$P = \begin{pmatrix} 0 & 1 \\ 1 & 0 \end{pmatrix}$$

represents a process with period 2. If the system starts in state 1 it will return to state 1 after 2 transitions. Obviously the limit $\lim_{n \to \infty} V(n)$ has no meaning in such a system. If n is odd and the system started in state 1 we have

$$V(n) = (1, 0)$$

while if n is even we have

$$V(n) = (0, 1)$$

However, applying the steady-state equations yields

$$V = (\tfrac{1}{2}, \tfrac{1}{2})$$

Obviously this cannot be the probability of finding the system in state i at some specific future time, since if that time is even we know $v_1 = 0$, $v_2 = 1$. However, we can interpret $v_1 = \tfrac{1}{2}$, $v_2 = \tfrac{1}{2}$ as the relative frequency with which each state is occupied over a long history of transitions.

Finally, consider the system with a matrix

$$P = \begin{pmatrix} 1 & 0 & 0 \\ 0.2 & 0.3 & 0.5 \\ 0 & 0 & 1 \end{pmatrix}$$

If we know that the system starts in state 1 or state 3, obviously it will remain there. If it starts in state 2 it will eventually be trapped in either state 1 or state 3. Applying the steady-state equations yields $v_2 = 0$ with v_1 and v_3 any values which sum to one.

The point is that the equation $VP = V$ can be used with any finite Markov chain to achieve meaningful results although not always stationary results. Stationarity can be checked by treating $V = V(n)$ then calculating

$$V(n)P = V(n + 1)$$

If $V(n + 1) = V$, the distribution is stationary.

Transform Solutions. It is possible to develop expressions for the time dependent state probability vector $V(n)$ by using the geometric transform techniques discussed in Chapters 5 and 6. For an excellent treatment of this technique, the reader is urged to consult Howard.[15]

The geometric transform of a matrix or vector can be obtained by taking

---

[15] Ronald A. Howard, *Dynamic Programming and Markov Processes* (Cambridge, Mass.: Massachusetts Institute of Technology Press, 1960), pp. 7–16.

the transform of every element in the array. In that sense we can view the transform of the vector $V(n)$ as

$$G[V(n)] = [G(v_1(n)), G(v_2(n)), \ldots, G(v_m(n))] \qquad (7\text{–}84)$$

Furthermore, we can treat the basic Markov recursion equation as a difference equation in n to be solved by transform methods.

The equation to be solved for $V(n)$ is

$$V(n + 1) = V(n)P$$

Applying definition 2 from Table 5–2 we have on the left

$$G[V(n + 1)] = z^{-1}[G(V(n)) - V(0)] \qquad (7\text{–}85)$$

Since the matrix P is a matrix of real numbers, we can treat P as a constant. The transform of the right side then becomes

$$G[V(n)P] = G[V(n)]P \qquad (7\text{–}86)$$

This leads to the subsidiary equation

$$z^{-1}[G(V(n)) - V(0)] = G[V(n)]P \qquad (7\text{–}87)$$

in the single unknown $G[V(n)]$.

Applying the rules of matrix algebra, we can rearrange terms to obtain

$$G[V(n)] - zG[V(n)]P = V(0)$$

$$G[V(n)][I - zP] = V(0) \qquad (7\text{–}88)$$

where I is the identity matrix. Since the square matrix $(I - zP)$ always has an inverse, we can obtain the solution

$$G[V(n)] = V(0)(I - zP)^{-1} \qquad (7\text{–}89)$$

The vector $G[V(n)]$ is the transform of the desired probability vector $V(n)$. Finally, to recover $V(n)$ we must invert $G[V(n)]$ element by element.

Let us illustrate the technique with the simple matrix

$$P = \begin{pmatrix} 0.2 & 0.8 \\ 0 & 1 \end{pmatrix}$$

so that

$$(I - zP) = \begin{pmatrix} 1 - 0.2z & -0.8z \\ 0 & 1 - z \end{pmatrix}$$

The inverse is

$$(I - zP)^{-1} = \begin{pmatrix} \dfrac{1 - z}{(1 - 0.2z)(1 - z)} & \dfrac{0.8z}{(1 - 0.2z)(1 - z)} \\[2ex] 0 & \dfrac{1 - 0.2z}{(1 - 0.2z)(1 - z)} \end{pmatrix}$$

By partial fraction expansion of each element this reduces to

$$(I - zP)^{-1} = \begin{pmatrix} \dfrac{0}{1-z} + \dfrac{1}{1-0.2z} & \dfrac{1}{1-z} + \dfrac{-1}{1-0.2z} \\[2mm] \dfrac{0}{1-z} + \dfrac{0}{1-0.2z} & \dfrac{1}{1-z} + \dfrac{0}{1-0.2z} \end{pmatrix}$$

$$(I - zP)^{-1} = \frac{1}{1-z}\begin{pmatrix} 0 & 1 \\ 0 & 1 \end{pmatrix} + \frac{1}{1-0.2z}\begin{pmatrix} 1 & -1 \\ 0 & 0 \end{pmatrix} \tag{7-90}$$

If we denote the inverse transform of $(I - zP)^{-1}$ by $A(n)$ we have, from identities 8 and 13 in Table 5–2

$$A(n) = \begin{pmatrix} 0 & 1 \\ 0 & 1 \end{pmatrix} + (0.2)^n \begin{pmatrix} 1 & -1 \\ 0 & 0 \end{pmatrix} \tag{7-91}$$

Returning to Equation 7–89 we see that the desired vector is

$$V(n) = V(0)A(n) \tag{7-92}$$

Obviously, the $A(n)$ matrix is nothing more than the nth power of our transition matrix P^n expressed in closed form.

Howard makes several observations about the form of $A(n)$.[16] He notes that among its components will always be at least one stochastic matrix arising from a term in the transform of the form $1/(1 - z)$. If the process is completely ergodic, there will be exactly one stochastic matrix, the rows of which will be identical vectors representing the steady-state probability distribution for the process. The remaining terms in $A(n)$ are multiplied by coefficients of the form c^n, nc^n, n^2c^n, etc., where c is less than one. These terms represent the transient components of the process.

In our example problem, if the system starts in state 1, the probability vector after n transitions is

$$V(n) = (1, 0)\begin{pmatrix} 0.2^n & 1 - 0.2^n \\ 0 & 1 \end{pmatrix} = (0.2^n, 1 - 0.2^n) \tag{7-93}$$

Since state 2 is a trapping state, the probability of finding the system in state 2, given that it starts in state 2, is obviously unity.

In a sense, one can view the row vectors comprising the steady-state portion of $A(n)$ as being conditional distributions. For example, suppose that we treat the 3 by 3 matrix previously introduced.

$$P = \begin{pmatrix} 1 & 0 & 0 \\ 0.2 & 0.3 & 0.5 \\ 0 & 0 & 1 \end{pmatrix}$$

---

[16] Ibid., p. 11.

from which

$$(I - zP)^{-1} = \frac{1}{1 - z} \begin{pmatrix} 1 & 0 & 0 \\ \frac{2}{7} & 0 & \frac{5}{7} \\ 0 & 0 & 1 \end{pmatrix} + \frac{1}{1 - 0.3z} \begin{pmatrix} 0 & 0 & 0 \\ -\frac{2}{7} & 1 & -\frac{5}{7} \\ 0 & 0 & 0 \end{pmatrix}$$

and

$$A(n) = \begin{pmatrix} 1 & 0 & 0 \\ \frac{2}{7} & 0 & \frac{5}{7} \\ 0 & 0 & 1 \end{pmatrix} + (0.3)^n \begin{pmatrix} 0 & 0 & 0 \\ -\frac{2}{7} & 1 & -\frac{5}{7} \\ 0 & 0 & 0 \end{pmatrix} \qquad (7\text{-}94)$$

The second row of this matrix is the probability distribution of states after n transitions given that the system started in state 2. This says that in the limit, if we start in state 2 we will wind up in state 1 with probability $\frac{2}{7}$ and in state 3 with probability $\frac{5}{7}$. As expected from the P matrix, the first and third rows of $A(n)$ tell us that if we start in state 1 or state 3 we will finish in those states with probability one.

At this point it should be apparent that transform techniques offer considerable insight into the behavior of Markov processes as well as providing closed form solutions for the state probability vector. However, as noted by the simple two by two example above, the use of transforms may require considerable calculation on the part of the analyst. For that reason they are normally reserved for the study of systems in which the characteristics of the transient solution are of prime importance.

SELECTED BIBLIOGRAPHY

Bowker, Albert H., and Lieberman, Gerald J. *Engineering Statistics*, chap. ix. Englewood Cliffs, N.J.: Prentice-Hall, Inc., 1959.

Brown, Robert G. *Smoothing, Forecasting and Prediction of Discrete Time Series.* Englewood Cliffs, N.J.: Prentice-Hall, Inc., 1963.

Buffa, Elwood S. *Production—Inventory Systems*, chap. ii. Homewood, Ill.: Richard D. Irwin, Inc., 1968.

Cox, D. R., and Miller, H. D. *The Theory of Stochastic Processes*, chaps. ii, iii, and iv. New York: John Wiley & Sons, Inc., 1968.

Eilon, Samuel. *Elements of Production Planning and Control.* chap. vi. New York: Macmillan Co., 1962.

Feller, William. *An Introduction to Probability Theory and Its Applications*, chaps. xiv, xv, and xvi. 2d ed., New York: John Wiley & Sons, Inc., 1957.

Howard, Ronald A. *Dynamic Programming and Markov Processes.* Cambridge, Mass.: Massachusetts Institute of Technology Press, 1960.

Kemeny, J., and Snell, L. *Finite Markov Chains*. Princeton, N.J.: D. Van Nostrand Co., Inc., 1959.

Montgomery, Douglas C. "An Introduction to Short-Term Forecasting." *Journal of Industrial Engineering*, Vol. XIX, No. 10 (October, 1968), pp. 500–503.

Winters, P. R. " Forecasting Sales by Exponentially Weighted Moving Averages." *Management Science*, Vol. 6, No. 3 (April, 1960), pp. 324–42.

PROBLEMS

7-1 Arrests for narcotics violations in the jungle of a prominent Chinese institution are listed by month in the table below:

Month	Arrests
September	5
October	9
November	23
December	53

Local police are studying these data to see if meaningful inferences concerning the rise and fall of left-wing groups can be drawn.

Agent 000 believes these data can be extrapolated for several months in the future. Develop for 000 a *power* polynomial of lowest degree which will fit these data.

7-2 Data have been collected to determine the relationship between the ambient air temperature and the average number of students involved in demonstrations by the "Sanctuary for Delinquent Students." These data are summarized below:

Ambient temperature (°F):	20	30	40	50	60	70
Average students per demonstration	7	13	43	145	367	757

a) Develop a polynomial which can be used to estimate the number of students per demonstration for all temperatures between 20° and 70° F.

b) Socio Comment, the new university analyst, feels that a better model for describing these data is one of the form

$$f(t) = a + b \cos \frac{\pi(t - 20)}{50}$$

Develop for Socio the value of the coefficients a and b which minimize the total square error of predicted students relative to observed students.

7-3 A study has revealed that the number of books reviewed and accepted by Snap Tech College Library has followed the following pattern since the founding of the college:

Year	Books Received (In Thousands)
1890	0
1900	2
1910	7
1920	15
1930	26
1940	40
1950	57
1960	77

The capacity of the library is 500,000 volumes. Assuming that this pattern of acquisition will continue, when do you predict that more library capacity will be needed?

7-4 The Master's degrees in Social Unrest issued by the Relentless Institute of Terror since its founding in 1960 are listed below:

Year	Degrees Granted
1960	300
1961	297
1962	304
1963	315
1964	324
1965	325
1966	312

Local insurance companies are studying these data to determine the probable effect on fire insurance rates.

a) Assuming that these data can be extrapolated over the immediate future, develop a factorial polynomial to serve as an estimating function for number of degrees granted per year. (Let 1960 be year zero.)

b) Use your knowledge of sum calculus to estimate the total number of R.I.O.T. degree holders you expect to see turned out over the life of the institution, i.e., until it ceases operation.

7-5 Computa Error Ltd. is being examined for possible takeover by Giant Electronic Brains. One element to consider is the stock price movement noted below. All prices are end-of-week bid prices:

Week: 1 2 3 4 5 6 7 8 9 10 11 12 13 14 15 16 17 18 19 20

Price: 78 74 80 79 80 78 79 80 84 83 82 79 80 82 81 83 85 86 88 90

Ima Forecaster has several models she wants to evaluate for these data:

a) As a first cut, fit the best curve of the form $a + bt$ to the given data.

b) An assistant has suggested that weekly data are too fine for this analysis. He wants to fit a curve to the average monthly (four weeks) prices. Establish the best curve of the form $a + bt$ for the assistant.

c) Determine an exact fit polynomial for the revised monthly data. Plot this curve, the actual data, and the straight line on the same axes.

d) Comment on the curves (*b*) and (*c*) as potential forecasters of future price movement.

7-6 Ima Forecaster has need of estimates for the parameters *a*, *b*, and *c* in a model of the form

$$f(t) = a + bt + ct^2$$

She hopes to use this model to describe a time series of stock prices. Use the method of least squares to develop estimating equations for *a*, *b*, and *c* as functions of the observed data points.

7-7 Use the results of Problems 7-6 and 7-5(a) to determine the best choice between a linear and a quadratic model to describe the data of 7-5.

7-8 The following time series is available for 10 years' sales of a popular aircraft manufacturer. All numbers are expressed in millions of dollars:

Year:	1960	1961	1962	1963	1964	1965	1966	1967	1968	1969
Sales:	100	80	82	83	124	150	210	220	265	280

a) Plot the results of forecasting with one-, two-, and three-year moving averages against the actual data, when the forecast lead is one year.

b) Perform the same moving average calculations for a two-year projection.

c) Develop a three-year moving average forecast which includes a trend correction. Plot this new forecast with a one-year projection, together with the straight moving average, on the same axes as the original data.

7-9 A popular mutual fund has provided the following record over 18 years for the total value of shares initially acquired for $10,000:

End of Year .	1	2	3	4	5	6	7	8	9
Value:	$8,800	$8,000	$8,200	$10,000	$11,600	$13,000	$13,500	$13,300	$12,700

End of Year:	10	11	12	13	14	15	16	17	18
Value:	$13,100	$14,700	$16,200	$16,600	$16,000	$19,700	$22,400	$22,800	$21,600

a) Estimate the value of the stock for each of the years given, employing simple exponential smoothing with a constant of 0.3. Assume that forecasts were always prepared one year in advance.

b) From this information estimate the 95 percent probability interval for stock value in year 19.

7-10 Using the data of Problem 7-9 and second order-exponential smoothing, prepare forecasts for the years 19 through 25.

a) Plot the forecasted values on the same axes as the actual data which turned out to be:

Year:	19	20	21	22	23	24	25
Actual:	$24,900	$26,600	$26,400	$31,000	$27,600	$32,000	$35,100

b) Estimate 95 percent probability intervals for the value in year 19 and year 25. From this information, comment upon the accuracy of your forecast.

7-11 Modify the example illustrated in Figure 7-8 by developing a one-month lead forecast for the second six-month period. Calculate the coefficients of the trigonometric model by using the most recent seven data points in a manner similar to simple moving averages. Plot the results of this moving trigonometric projection on the same axes with the actual time series and the static projection of Figure 7-8.

7-12 An operations engineer is attempting to establish a relationship between the price paid per lot for fasteners and the number which will be defective in the lot.

A sample of 16 lots of different fastener brands yields the following data:

Lot:	1	2	3	4	5	6	7	8	9
Defectives:	87	66	78	48	60	41	60	44	18
Price:	$2.30	$3.00	$1.00	$7.00	$2.00	$6.40	$4.00	$2.50	$6.00

Lot:	10	11	12	13	14	15	16
Defectives:	25	32	53	34	65	28	10
Price:	$7.40	$7.10	$6.80	$3.80	$6.10	$4.50	$8.00

a) Use linear regression to develop an estimating equation for defectives as a function of price.

b) Calculate the correlation coefficient.

c) Establish whether or not the coefficient of the linear term is significant at the 5 percent level.

7–13 A certain well-known forecasting model functions by modifying an observed sequence of numbers such that the output from the system at time *t* is equal to the output at the previous period plus a fraction "*a*" of the difference between the observed data at time *t* and the previous forecast. Let the observed input be given by $D(t)$ and the modified value by $F(t)$ where *t* is discrete.

a) Write a difference equation relating these functions.

b) Draw a complete flow graph with simple, as opposed to compound, elements to describe the action of this system.

c) Find the impulse response function for this system.

d) Using *z* transforms, find the response transform of this system to a signal of the form

$$D(t) = \frac{1}{b^t}$$

7–14 Clair Voyant has developed a scheme for tracking a time varying signal $f(t)$ by responding so that the rate of change of the response signal $r(t)$ is proportional to the difference between the response and the signal being tracked. The proportionality constant is "*a*." The signal $f(t)$ is made up of a deterministic portion plus a random noise element $e(t)$.

a) Write a differential equation which will describe the behavior of Clair's system.

b) Find the Laplace transform of the function $r(t)$.

c) For the special case of $f(t) = b + ct$, find response function $r(t)$ if the system is initially at rest.

d) How would you redesign Clair's system so that as *t* becomes large the response signal would accurately track an input of the form $b + ct$?

7–15 The brand switching probabilities for customers purchasing competing products A and B at the end of each year are believed to be the following:

A to A...0.2   B to A...0.6
A to B...0.8   B to B...0.4

Brand A currently controls 0.7 of the market.

a) Calculate the market shares after one and two transitions.

b) Determine the long-range market share for each product.

c) Check the long-range distribution for stationarity.

7-16 Analyze the Markov chain of Problem 7-15 using transform techniques.

7-17 A commercial loan officer receives applications for loans which he must process within a five-day period. At any day within the life of the application he can take no action, agree to grant the loan, or reject the application. However, if he does not act by the end of the fifth day, the loan is automatically rejected. From past records it appears that loan applications which are less than two days old are accepted with probability 0.2 on any given day. They are never rejected at that age. Applications which are 2, 3, or 4 days old are equally likely to be accepted or rejected and may be allowed to age one more day with probability 0.4. A five-day old application will be accepted with probability 0.1.

a) Model this system as a Markov process. Assume that decisions are made at times 0, 1, ..., 5.

b) Calculate the probability that a new application will be accepted at the end of day 2.

c) Calculate the probability that a three-day-old application will ultimately be accepted.

d) Calculate the average number of days an application will remain in the system before a decision is made.

e) If the bank receives four applications in the amounts of $500, $1,000, $2,000 and $2,500, calculate the expected amount of money loaned.

7-18 A market analysis concerning consumer behavior in auto purchases has been conducted. Body styles traded in and purchased have been recorded by a particular dealer with the following results:

Number of Customers	Trade
200	Two-door sedan for 2-door sedan
100	Two-door sedan for 4-door sedan
80	Two-door sedan for stationwagon
20	Two-door sedan for convertible
300	Four-door sedan for 4-door sedan
100	Four-door sedan for stationwagon
50	Convertible for convertible
150	Convertible for 2-door sedan
80	Stationwagon for 4-door sedan
120	Stationwagon for stationwagon

These data are believed to be representative of average consumer behavior. Develop a model and answer the following:

a) What is the probability that a current convertible owner will trade for a stationwagon on his second trade?

b) What is the probability that a stationwagon owner will purchase a convertible within five trades?

c) What portion of the total market will each body style eventually capture if no changes are made?

d) Where would you concentrate your sales effort in order to assure long-run success for convertibles? Why?

7–19   A local stag movie is shown every 10 minutes. When each showing ends, all sweating students are discharged from the make-shift theater and a new batch is permitted to enter. Because of limited facilities the present batch size is only three students and waiting facilities outside of the theater are limited to five students. The cumulative distribution for number of arrivals in the 10 minute show interval is given by

$$
\begin{aligned}
G(x) = 0.10 & \quad x = 0 \\
0.20 & \quad x = 1 \\
0.40 & \quad x = 2 \\
0.60 & \quad x = 3 \\
0.80 & \quad x = 4 \\
0.90 & \quad x = 5 \\
0.95 & \quad x = 6 \\
0.98 & \quad x = 7 \\
0.99 & \quad x = 8 \\
1.00 & \quad x = 9
\end{aligned}
$$

The distribution in any interval is independent of all other intervals.

a) Assuming that the theater comes under police surveillance immediately after the 9 P.M. showing begins and that they find one student in the queue, what will be the probability distribution for the queue length immediately *prior to* the 9.20 P.M. showing?

b) Develop a steady-state probability distribution for line length immediately *following* the admission of each batch.

7–20   Professor Backward has recently perfected a learning device in which students are given a series of true-false questions directed toward discovering the content of the next Jeanne Dixon forecast. After each question the student is informed about the correctness of his response. The following data have been collected from pilot runs consisting of two-question tests with the outcome of question 1 known before question 2 is attempted:

Test Result	Number of Observations
Both answers correct	120
Both answers incorrect	60
First correct, second incorrect	180
First incorrect, second correct	140

Professor Backward believes that the reponses obtained from a more extensive series of questions will follow essentially this same pattern in which response to any upcoming question can be predicted in a probability sense from a knowledge of the very latest known response.

a) Using your knowledge of transform techniques, construct a model which will enable Professor Backward to predict the success or failure of a student on the last question of an *n* question test knowing only the outcome of the first question.

Evaluate for a student who has just missed the first question the probability of missing the 15th.

b) John is an old hand at taking exams from Professor Backward having suffered through several courses with him. This quarter he expects to receive the same old T–F exams. Without knowing John's initial response some quarters ago, what do you predict will be his score on 100 questions given under Backward's feedback system?

7–21 In our Nay Pom struggle it is often hard to identify the political beliefs of the troops. When we began, both North and South each had N troops and all were native to the region. Each month since the struggle began propaganda leaflets have been dropped on the last day of the month with the result being that one man from each side defects to the opposition. Defections occur at random, and past political belief has no influence on the probability of a successful appeal to a man. Each side thus maintains a force of N men even though their initial loyalties may be opposite to their present attachment. The southern commander has suddenly become quite interested in the origin of his troops. He defines his "state" E_j as meaning that he has j southern-born troops under his command.

a) Determine the monthly transition probabilities for state changes in the southern force.

b) What can you tell him about the distribution of possible states if this war continues indefinitely? Why?

c) Suppose that $N = 5$ divisions and each propaganda appeal changes an entire division. Determine the steady-state composition of the southern troops (if possible).

d) Losing a loyal division costs three pazoos and gaining one nets five pazoos. Calculate the southern commander's expected return over the first three months' operations. (At the end of three months he will defect for a price of 10 pazoos for each northern division he leaves in the South.)

CHAPTER 8

Economics of
Decision Making

NEARLY EVERY prescriptive model developed by an operations engineer uses money as the primary measure of performance. Decisions concerning production or purchase quantities in commercial enterprises are made such that they will maximize profits. Decisions concerning alternative means of performing a task are made such that they will minimize costs. In government operations the profit motive and pure cost considerations may be replaced by considerations of general welfare. However, even in that environment the time value of money is important. The purposes of this chapter are to discuss what factors should be considered when making investment decisions and to provide mathematical techniques to facilitate comparisons.

Production Levels and Profits

It is often important to functionally describe the amount of profit expected for any given level of production. This is true for a corporation taken as a whole as well as for individual products manufactured by a corporation. The question of most interest to the decision maker is " How much will we make if we sell x units of our product?" The following sections will explore idealized models designed to provide insight to that question.

Fixed and Variable Costs. The total cost of operating at any given level of production can be viewed as the sum of two components. These components are fixed costs and variable costs.

Fixed costs are those costs of doing business which remain nearly constant over a wide range of activity. Property taxes, interest on debts, and many overhead costs are examples of the type of cost included in this classification.

Variable costs are those costs which vary in some manner with the volume of production. In the simplest case they are assumed to vary directly with the number of units produced. Such things as direct labor, material, and power are normally considered to be variable costs. However, many costs related to production may be extremely difficult to classify as fixed or variable. For example, in an assembly operation a single foreman may be adequate to handle up to 15 assemblers. As long as production volume requires no more than 15 assemblers, his salary might properly be classed as a fixed cost. On the other hand, as soon as volume becomes great enough to warrant a second foreman, the cost element of supervision is no longer clearly a fixed cost. Neither is it a simple variable cost which varies linearly with volume. Reality lies somewhere between the two extremes. For analysis purposes we may want to consider supervision to be fixed, but only over a limited volume range.

Recognizing the potential pitfalls of this simple approach, let us suppose that cost of production can be related to volume by

$$C(x) = F + vx \qquad (8\text{--}1)$$

where

$C(x)$ = total cost to produce x units
F = fixed cost
v = variable cost per unit
x = units produced

The rate of change of cost with respect to volume is referred to as the marginal cost or incremental cost. For our simple model we have a marginal cost of

$$MC(x) = \frac{dC(x)}{dx} = v \qquad (8\text{--}2)$$

under the assumption that x can be treated as a continuous variable. If x is discrete, the marginal cost is obtained by taking differences.

$$MC(x) = C(x + 1) - C(x) = v \qquad (8\text{--}3)$$

In this case the marginal cost is the cost of producing one additional unit when production is at level x.

The Revenue Function. The revenue function for a firm is in its simplest form the product of number of units sold times price per unit. For most firms this will be a simple straight line over a considerable range of volume. That is,

$$R(x) = px \qquad (8\text{--}4)$$

where
$R(x)$ = total revenue when x units are sold
p = price per unit

In a manner analogous to the cost function, the rate of change of revenue with respect to volume is defined as the marginal revenue. For the simple linear function, marginal revenue reduces to

$$MR(x) = \frac{dR(x)}{dx} = p \qquad (8\text{-}5)$$

Break-Even Charts.   A break-even chart is created whenever we display both the total revenue and total cost functions on the same graph. This chart receives its name from the break-even point which occurs where the two curves cross. The break-even point is the zero profit level for production since revenues and cost are exactly equal. For the simple linear functions shown in Equations 8–1 and 8–4, any volume below the break-even point will lead to negative profits or losses. Any volume above the break-even point will lead to profits. The magnitude of profits or losses at any volume is depicted by the distance between the total revenue and total cost curves since

$$\text{Profit} = \text{Total Revenue} - \text{Total Cost}$$

$$= px - (F + vx) \qquad (8\text{-}6)$$

This information is depicted graphically in Figure 8–1.

FIGURE 8–1

A Break-Even Chart for Linear Functions

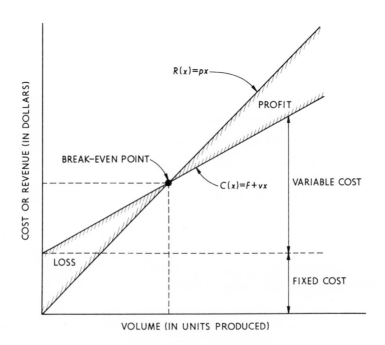

Figure 8–1 is obviously an idealized picture of how costs and revenues are related to change in volume. However, it may serve as a reasonable aid to decision making if one does not try to extrapolate results too far from current operating levels. Also, one must recognize that the data used to develop the cost and revenue functions may be highly inaccurate. For that reason any comments about the break-even point should be tempered by the realization that the indicated volume is not exactly correct but only in the neighborhood. With those reservations, the break-even point can be analytically developed by solving for the value of x at which profit is zero.

$$\text{Profit} = px - (F + vx) = 0$$

leads to

$$x = \frac{F}{p - v} \tag{8-7}$$

Since the denominator of this expression is the marginal profit on each unit sold, we can say that break even occurs at that volume for which marginal profits will recover the total fixed cost of operation.

Break-even charts are commonly used to show the relative effects of changes in the cost structure of a business. It can be used to answer such questions as how would the break-even point and profits shift if costs are reduced by y percent? Does it make any difference if the cost reduction occurs in fixed or variable costs? The following example will illustrate this use of the chart.

Example. An automobile dealer is considering accepting the franchise for a new compact car. The corporate marketing staff estimates that the dealers area has a potential market of 100 cars per year at an average retail price of $2,500 per car. The invoice price from the factory to the dealer is $1,850 per car. Based upon his experience with other car lines, the dealer estimates that it will cost him $350 per car for commissions, handling charges, financing, etc. Furthermore, he feels that taking this additional franchise will require an expenditure of approximately $1,000 per month over his current operations regardless of the number of units sold.

In terms of our previous notation, we can develop a break-even chart for annual operations from

$p = \$2,500$
$v = \$1,850 + \$350 = \$2,200$
$F = (\$1,000 \text{ per month})(12 \text{ months per year}) = \$12,000 \text{ per year}$

The appropriate curves are

$$R(x) = \$2,500x$$

and

$$C(x) = \$12,000 + \$2,200x$$

from which the break-even point may be determined as

$$x = \frac{F}{p - v} = \frac{\$12,000}{\$2,500 - \$2,200} = 40 \text{ cars}$$

If he sells more than 40 cars per year he can make a profit. Below 40 he will sustain a loss. The maximum potential annual profit for this car line is

Maximum profit $= R(100) - C(100) = \$250,000 - \$232,000 = \$18,000$

All of this information is depicted graphically in Figure 8–2(a).

Now suppose that another manufacturer offers a similar vehicle with the same potential market, selling price, invoice price, and sales expense. However, the second manufacturer's car is more compatible with the dealer's current operations. Because of this, the dealer feels that he can save $10,000 per year in fixed costs. The maximum profit potential for this franchise is then

Maximum profit $= \$250,000 - \$222,000 = \$28,000$

Furthermore, the break-even point has shifted to

$$x = \frac{\$2,000}{\$300} \approx 7 \text{ cars}$$

Under this arrangement, the dealer will begin to show a profit as soon as he has sold seven cars. This is only 17.5 percent of the volume necessary to achieve a profit under the first proposal.

Armed with this information, the dealer may attempt to receive some price concession from the first manufacturer. Suppose that this manufacturer agrees to discount his cars $100. At the maximum potential market of 100 vehicles, both franchises now offer a potential profit of $28,000 per year. However, note what happens to the break-even point under this agreement. The new break-even point is

$$x = \frac{\$12,000}{\$400} = 30 \text{ cars}$$

This new break-even point is only 75 percent as large as the original deal. However, it requires that over four times as many vehicles be sold, compared to the fixed cost reduction, before a profit is registered. The impact of these two alternatives is shown in Figure 8–2(b).

A simple break-even analysis of the type illustrated in this example does not offer an optimal decision. However, it does offer management a graphic picture of the effects of volume and cost changes. If management is optimistic and feels that the factory projections of 100 units per year can be exceeded, then they should obviously take the $100 discount per car rather than the $10,000 fixed cost reduction. On the other hand if they are conservative by nature, the reduction in fixed cost will be more attractive since it greatly reduces the volume necessary to register some profit.

FIGURE 8-2

Comparing Alternatives with Break-Even Analysis

a) Break-Even Chart for Original Offer

b) Effects of $10,000 Cost Savings

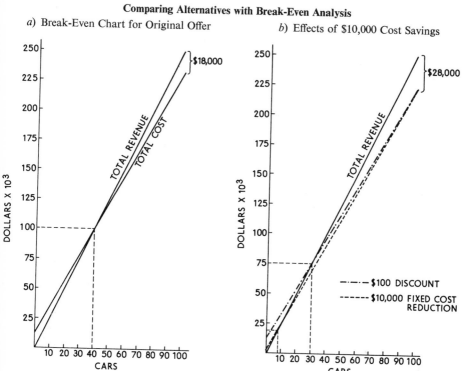

c) Profit Comparison

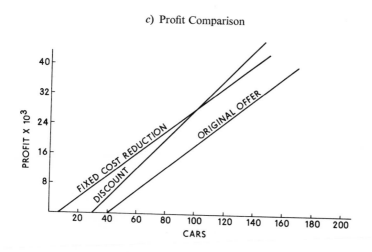

Figure 8–2(c) illustrates another type of break-even analysis. Here the profit equation for each of the three deals under consideration has been plotted. From the graph it is obvious that offers two and three are at every point superior to the original offer, one. The break-even volume between offers two and three occurs at 100 cars, as our previous discussion indicated. Below this point, offer two is preferred; above it, offer three is superior.

Break-Even Extensions.   Let us now explore some of the basic economic principles of production by introducing a further idealization of the process. Suppose that a firm can mathematically describe the relationship between price charged and the demand for their product. At low price levels one would expect demand to be high. Conversely, at high price levels one would expect demand to be low. If we write price as a function of demand (x), the simplest equation to capture such a relationship would be

$$p = a - bx \qquad (8\text{–}8)$$

If we use the simple straight line to represent the firm's demand curve, the total revenue function can be written as the quadratic

$$R(x) = px = (a - bx)x = ax - bx^2 \qquad (8\text{–}9)$$

This revenue function possesses a global maximum. Maximum revenue will be obtained at the volume for which marginal revenue is zero. That is

$$MR(x) = \frac{dR(x)}{dx} = a - 2bx = 0$$

from which

$$x = \frac{a}{2b} \qquad (8\text{–}10)$$

Here we are assuming that a and b are positive constants.

It is important to note, however, that maximizing revenue will not necessarily maximize profits. For the special case of a linear demand function, the profit Equation 8–6 becomes

$$\text{Profit} = R(x) - C(x) = ax - bx^2 - (F + vx) \qquad (8\text{–}11)$$

Taking derivatives we obtain a marginal profit expression of

$$\frac{dP}{dx} = a - 2bx - v \qquad (8\text{–}12)$$

To maximize profit, we can set $dP/dx = 0$ and solve for x. This gives

$$x = \frac{a - v}{2b} \qquad (8\text{–}13)$$

which is not generally equivalent to the point of maximum revenue. The only time they are equivalent is when the variable cost of production is zero.

The price which can be obtained for any given level of output is given by

Equation 8–8. Under optimum operating conditions, the price which should be charged is then

$$p = a - bx_0 = a - b\left(\frac{a-v}{2b}\right) = \frac{a+v}{2} \qquad (8-14)$$

Under the assumption of a linear demand function, combining the total revenue and total cost curves yields a modified version of the break-even chart. The form of this modified curve is noted in Figure 8–3. Several economic principles can be illustrated from such a chart. For example, as noted by many economics texts, at the maximum profit level for production, marginal revenue is equal to marginal cost. Equivalently, one might suggest that production be increased as long as incremental revenue exceeds incremental production cost and stop when the two are equal. DeGarmo suggests that such a rule is much more usable than our previously derived analytic expression for the point of maximum profit, since the factor "a" is seldom known with any degree of certainty.[1] Note also that there are two break-even points on the modified chart. The second point occurs because we eventually reach a volume which necessitates serious price concessions if the total production is to be sold.

FIGURE 8–3

Break-Even Analysis under Conditions of a Linear Demand Function

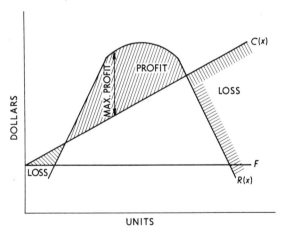

Following the discussion by Morris, we can use simple mathematical relationships to demonstrate other basic economic principles.[2] For example,

---

[1] E. Paul DeGarmo, *Engineering Economy* (4th ed.; New York: The Macmillan Co., 1967), p. 33.
[2] William T. Morris, *Engineering Economy* (Homewood, Ill.: Richard D. Irwin, Inc., 1960), pp. 23–30.

we can calculate the average cost per unit by dividing total cost by units sold.

$$\bar{C}(x) = \frac{C(x)}{x} = \frac{F + vx}{x} = \frac{F}{x} + v \qquad (8\text{-}15)$$

This is obviously a decreasing function of x. It suggests that the more we produce, the lower will be our cost per unit. This is consistent with the usual notions of the economies of mass production so important to our industrial development. However, it is obvious that such a process cannot be expanded to an infinitely large production rate in any given facility. As the limits of the existing physical plant are approached, overtime is necessary, quality may suffer, materials handling costs go up, etc. To capture that flavor, a more realistic cost expression might be of the form

$$C(x) = F + v_1 x + v_2 x^2 \qquad (8\text{-}16)$$

Average cost in this instance is not a monotonically decreasing function of volume but rather is a function with a minimum point.

$$\bar{C}(x) = \frac{F}{x} + v_1 + v_2 x \qquad (8\text{-}17)$$

The volume necessary for minimum average cost occurs where the derivative is zero, from which

$$x = \left(\frac{F}{v_2}\right)^{1/2} \qquad (8\text{-}18)$$

Beyond this value the average cost per unit begins to rise consistent with our notions of the "law of diminishing returns."

The forms of the various curves in the preceding analysis are obviously oversimplifications. They are of value only to illustrate the logic of some basic economic principles most often enunciated in more qualitative terms. As a practical matter the operations engineer must bear in mind the principles as he attempts to make recommendations over a much more narrow range of alternatives. He can rarely be more precise than the simple linear break-even analysis of the last section.

The Value of Money

When evaluating the economic worth of any long-range proposal, two factors must be considered. First, capital is productive. Second, the value of any sum of money is a function of when in time it will be available. The following sections will clarify these points.

Capital Productivity. The capital necessary to finance any enterprise may come from one of two general sources. Either it is borrowed or it is taken from capital already owned by the individual or corporation. Borrowing may occur in a variety of ways, among which are selling bonds and seeking loans from commercial banks. When funds are borrowed, the cost of obtaining this capital, consisting mostly of interest, is clearly an expense of the proposed project. When previously owned capital is used to finance a project, however, there is no interest expense in the usual sense of the word. The expense associated with the use of existing capital will be referred to as the *opportunity cost* of that capital.

The term opportunity cost is somewhat confusing. It is not really a cost at all but rather the profit which one normally expects to receive from the use of his capital. The idea behind an opportunity cost is that if we use our own capital to finance the proposed venture, we will forego the opportunity to use that capital for other purposes. The profit that we could earn if we used that capital for some other purpose, such as depositing it in a savings account, is charged as an expense to the proposed venture. The usual procedure is to include opportunity costs in a factor treated as an interest rate when evaluating the cost of a project.

The productivity of capital explains why one can often afford to borrow capital for a project even though he must repay both the borrowed capital and interest. It also explains why we must include an opportunity cost when evaluating projects to be funded from equity capital. Capital productivity means simply that the borrower can produce more income with capital than he could without it. The easiest way to illustrate this is to consider the possibility of purchasing or leasing an improved piece of equipment.

Consider the case of a stone-crushing contractor who currently receives a net income of $15,000 per year by operating his obsolete but functional equipment. He now has the opportunity to lease a new crusher for one year at a cost of $60,000 to be paid in advance. His banker has agreed to loan him the money for one year at 10 percent interest to be paid at maturity. With the addition of the new crusher the contractor expects to be able to gross $150,000 next year. His operating expenses are projected as $50,000. His total costs for the year will be

Crusher lease	$ 60,000
Interest	6,000
Operating expenses	50,000
	$116,000

The net gain for the year is

Income	$150,000
Expenses	116,000
Net earnings	$ 34,000

The contractor has increased his productivity for the year by $19,000 through the use of $60,000 of borrowed capital.

Determining an Interest Rate. The classical view of interest is that it represents the rent paid for the use of capital over some stipulated time period. The interest rate is the ratio of the amount of rent paid to the amount of money involved over a fixed time period. The period selected is usually one year. For example, if $80 is paid for the use of $1000 for one year, the interest rate is 8 percent. The $80 can be viewed as a profit to the lender and an expense to the borrower.

A person with money has several alternatives available for the potential use of his capital. One alternative is to lend it to a borrower who will repay the sum of money and interest on the sum at some future date. If he elects that alternative, he must consider several items in establishing an interest rate. Thuesen lists the most important components as (1) risk of loss, (2) administrative expenses, and (3) pure gain.[3]

The risk of loss is measured by the probability that the borrower will not repay the loan. The higher the earning potential and integrity of the borrower, the lower will be the risk of loss. The scaling of this component of interest is visible in the banking practice of giving loans to established businesses at the so-called prime rate while charging home buyers, investors, and others rates greater than prime. For example, if there are historically four chances in a hundred that a particular class of borrower will not repay a loan, the lender might make a charge of 4 percent of the sum to compensate for the risk of loss.

Administrative expenses are incurred in investigating the borrower, processing the loan, and collecting the loan. If this cost is $2 per $100 loan for one year, than a 2 percent administrative charge should be included in the interest rate.

The pure gain component represents the amount necessary to compensate the lender for being deprived of his capital for one year. By loaning it to the borrower he foregoes other uses for his capital. This pure gain might amount to $5 for a $100 loan. The sum of the three major components would then lead to 11 percent as a reasonable interest rate for the example discussed above.

Interest rates developed from the previous arguments may reflect the decision process from a lender's point of view and give some indication of what one can expect to pay for borrowed funds. However, for purposes of operations engineering analysis, a more appropriate measure is the anticipated rate of return on invested capital. Such a rate of return is often much larger than the interest rates associated with borrowing money. DeGarmo notes that the average rate of return for all manufacturing companies reporting to the Securities Exchange Commission during 1951–55 was 22.9 percent before taxes and 11 percent after taxes.[4] It seems reasonable to suppose that today's returns are even higher.

[3] H. G. Thuesen, *Engineering Economy* (2d ed.; Englewood Cliffs, N.J.: Prentice-Hall, Inc., 1957), pp. 37–38.

[4] DeGarmo, *op. cit.*, p. 203.

The rate of return to be used in operations engineering studies may be based upon the opportunity cost of some standard investment alternative, which must be foregone, or upon some minimum satisfactory return established by management policy. Once a particular rate of return has been accepted as standard, cost comparisons among alternatives using that rate will be valid regardless of the particular combinations of borrowed funds and equity capital used to finance the projects.[5]

Cash Flow Considerations. Money employed for productive purposes has a time value. This is evident from our previous discussion of the productivity of capital and the rental or interest one expects to pay for the use of capital. One thousand dollars which you cannot collect for two years is not worth as much as $1,000 in your hands today. The reason it is worth less is that a person possessing $1,000 today can hopefully put that sum to work so that by the end of two years he will have accumulated more than $1,000.

Now suppose that a slightly different set of alternatives is posed. Alternative A will provide $1,000 cash today. Alternative B will provide $1,200 cash two years from today. The question, of which alternative is to be preferred in this case hinges upon the rate of return which we normally expect to receive on our investments. In order to compare alternatives such as these, we need methods for moving money back and forth on the time axis so that each alternative is measured from a common bench mark. A variety of interest formulas are developed in the following sections to accomplish that purpose.

The cash flow pattern for a project is merely a time history of receipts and disbursements expected over the life of the project. If an interest rate is used, all of the time history of money movements into and out of the system can be reduced to an equivalent sum of money at the present time. This is referred to as a discounted cash flow. This is a common means of evaluating proposals in industry.

Interest Formulas

We will use a standard set of symbols to develop the formulas needed to shift money from point to point in time. Let

P = principal sum at the present time
S = sum n interest periods in the future
R = single amount in a series of n equal amounts received or disbursed at the end of each interest period
n = number for interest periods
i = interest rate of a given interest period (usually one year)
I = interest amount

Although we will use the symbol i to represent interest rate, the reader

[5] Eugene L. Grant and W. Grant Ireson, *Principles of Engineering Economy* (4th ed.; New York: Ronald Press, 1960), p. 81.

should bear in mind that this is often more properly an anticipated rate of return based upon opportunity costs.

Simple Interest.   Simple interest is charged on many classes of commercial loans. The interest or rent charged for the use of a principal sum is proportional to the duration of the loan. Under these conditions, money is earned only on the principal amount. Symbolically simple interest can be expressed as

$$I = inP \tag{8-19}$$

For example, consider a sum of $1,000 loaned for three years at 8 percent per annum. The interest earned is

$$I = (0.08)(3)(\$1,000) = \$240$$

The amount which the borrower must return to the lender at the end of three years is

$$S = P + I = \$1,000 + \$240 = \$1,240$$

Compound Interest.   Compound interest differs from simple interest in that money is earned on interest accumulated during previous periods. With compounding, one earns interest on the interest. Although it is common for savings institutions to compound interest every three months, most management decisions are based upon annual compounding. The term *compound amount* refers to the final amount of a sum on which interest has been compounded.

The effect of compounding can be illustrated by comparing two common savings account plans. Under plan A the depositor places a fixed sum of money P with a bank. The bank then agrees to send the depositor a check in the amount iP at the end of each interest period. At the end of the life of plan A, the depositor receives back his principal in full. Under plan B the interest on the principal is not paid directly to the depositor but rather is added to the account each period. The interest in period 1 is still iP. However, in period 2 the account has a new principal of $P + iP$ so that the interest becomes $i(i + 1)P$. If both plans are in effect for n interest periods, plan A will have returned a simple interest of niP while plan B will have returned

$$I = \sum_{k=1}^{n} i(1 + i)^{k-1}P \tag{8-20}$$

The interest formulas developed in the remainder of this chapter are all based upon compound interest. The notation used to designate the appropriate factors is due to Thuesen.[6]

Compounding a Single Payment.   A single payment which earns interest compounded at the end of each year over n years will grow in the following fashion:

---

[6] Thuesen, *op cit.*, p. 47.

Year	Start	Interest	Compound Amount at End of Year
1	P	iP	$(1+i)P$
2	$(1+i)P$	$i(1+i)P$	$(1+i)^2P$
3	$(1+i)^2P$	$i(1+i)^2P$	$(1+i)^3P$
n	$(1+i)^{n-1}P$	$i(1+i)^{n-1}P$	$(1+i)^nP$

The general equation to be used is

$$S = P(1 + i)^n \qquad (8\text{-}21)$$

The factor $(1+i)^n$ is given the name single-payment compound-amount factor. Symbolically we will use

$$SPi - n = (1 + i)^n \qquad (8\text{-}22)$$

This factor can be viewed as an operator which at our interest rate i, transforms an input P into an output S at some time n in the future. Values for this factor are tabulated in the Appendix.

An investment of \$1,000 for five years at 10 percent interest compounded annually would ultimately be worth

$$S = \$1,000(1 + 0.10)^5 = \$1,000(SP10\text{-}5)$$

$$= \$1,000(1.611) = \$1,611$$

One might say that if 10 percent interest is available, \$1,611 five years from now is equivalent to \$1,000 today. In a sense we have moved the \$1,000 investment along the time axis to establish its worth at a future date.

Discounting a Single Payment. A future sum can be equated to today's dollars by inverting the compounding operator. The resulting factor is called a single-payment present-worth factor. Since the discount calculation assumes that we have a known future sum S, the unknown present worth P can be obtained from Equation 8–21 as

$$P = S\left[\frac{1}{(1+i)^n}\right] \qquad (8\text{-}23)$$

The multiplier is given the symbol $PSi - n$. If not explicitly tabled, this factor can be calculated from the $SPi - n$ table since

$$PSi - n = \frac{1}{(1+i)^n} = \frac{1}{SPi - n} \qquad (8\text{-}24)$$

Suppose that we want to purchase a \$10,000 piece of equipment four years from now. The question is how much money should be deposited now at

8 percent compounded annually to finance this purchase. From Equation 8–23,

$$P = \$10,000 \left[\frac{1}{(1 + 0.08)^4} \right]$$

$$= \$10,000(PS8\text{--}4) = \frac{\$10,000}{SP8\text{--}4}$$

$$= \frac{\$10,000}{1.360} = \$7,350$$

Compounding Multiple Payments. Since we already know how to compound a single payment over any desired number of interest periods, it is a simple matter to extend this approach to a series of single payments. For mathematical simplicity let us suppose that R_j dollars are invested at the end of year j. The time series of payments would appear as follows:

The last payment in this series, R_n, is made at the termination of the program and has no opportunity to collect interest. Its compound amount at the end of period n is simply R_n. The payment made in period $n - 1$ can collect interest for one period, making its value at period n, iR_{n-1}. The payment R_{n-2} collects interest for two periods giving a compound amount of $(i + 1)^2 R_{n-2}$, and so forth. In general, R_{n-k} will yield a compound amount of

$$S_k = (1 + i)^k R_{n-k} \tag{8--25}$$

at the end of period n. The total compound amount for the series is

$$S = \sum_{k=0}^{n-1} (1 + i)^k R_{n-k}$$

$$= \sum_{k=0}^{n-1} (SPi - k) R_{n-k} \tag{8--26}$$

For the special case of $R_j = R$ for all j greater than zero, we can obtain a closed form solution to the sum indicated in Equation 8–26. From the sum calculus we know that[7]

$$\sum_{k=0}^{n-1} a^k = \frac{a^k}{a - 1} \bigg|_0^n = \frac{a^n - 1}{a - 1} \tag{8--27}$$

---

[7] See for example Kenneth S. Miller, *The Calculus of Finite Differences and Difference Equations* (New York: Henry Holt & Co., Inc.), p. 23.

If we define $a = (1 + i)$, our sum reduces to

$$S = R \sum_{k=0}^{n-1} (1 + i)^k = R\left(\frac{(1 + i)^n - 1}{(1 + i) - 1}\right)$$

$$= R\left(\frac{(1 + i)^n - 1}{i}\right) \tag{8-28}$$

The multiplier for R is given the name equal-payment series compound-amount factor. The symbol is

$$SRi - n = \left(\frac{(1 + i)^n - 1}{i}\right) \tag{8-29}$$

This factor is tabulated in the Appendix. It transforms a series of equal payments into an equivalent sum at a future date.

Suppose that $1,000 each year is invested at 6 percent for a period of 10 years. Assuming compound interest, these investments will accumulate to

$$S = \$1,000\left(\frac{(1.06)^{10} - 1}{0.06}\right)$$

$$= \$1,000(SR6\text{--}10)$$

$$= \$1,000(13.181) = \$13,181$$

The inverse problem is to determine the size of each payment in a series of equal payments such that their compound amounts will yield S at the end of n periods. From Equation 8–28 it is obvious that

$$R = S\left[\frac{i}{(1 + i)^n - 1}\right] \tag{8-30}$$

The multiplier for S is given the name equal-payment series sinking-fund factor expressed as

$$RSi - n = \left[\frac{i}{(1 + i)^n - 1}\right] \tag{8-31}$$

As an example, suppose that a certain piece of equipment must be replaced at the end of 10 years. The replacement cost is expected to be $15,000. Money placed in a sinking fund earns interest at 6 percent. The amount which should be placed in the sinking fund at the end of each year is

$$R = \$15,000\left[\frac{0.06}{(1.06)^{10} - 1}\right] = \$15,000(RS6\text{--}10)$$

$$= \frac{\$15,000}{SR6\text{--}10} = \frac{\$15,000}{13.181} = \$1,140$$

Discounting Multiple Payments. As with compounding, it is a simple matter to extend our knowledge of discounting single payments to solve the problem of discounting multiple payments. Each value R_j in a series of end-of-period payments can be equated to a present amount by the $PSi - n$ factor where R_j takes the role of S. The sum of all such discounted amounts is

$$P = \sum_{j=1}^{n} R_j (PSi - j)$$

$$= \sum_{j=1}^{n} R_j \left[\frac{1}{(1 + i)^j} \right] \tag{8-32}$$

When all end-of-period payments are identical, we can obtain a closed form expression for the indicated sum. From Equation 8–27 we know that

$$\sum_{k=1}^{n} a^k = \frac{a^k}{a - 1} \Big|_1^{n+1} = \frac{a^{n+1} - a}{a - 1}$$

If we define $a = 1/(1 + i)$, our sum reduces to

$$P = R \sum_{j=1}^{n} \left(\frac{1}{1 + i} \right)^j = R \left[\frac{(1/(1 + i)^{n+1} - (1/(1 + i))}{1/(1 + i) - 1} \right]$$

$$= R \left[\frac{(1 + i)^n - 1}{i(1 + i)^n} \right] \tag{8-33}$$

The multiplier for R is given the name equal-payment series present-worth factor. The symbol is

$$PRi - n = \left[\frac{(1 + i)^n - 1}{i(1 + i)^n} \right] \tag{8-34}$$

Values for this factor are tabulated in the Appendix.

As an example, suppose that we want to establish an annuity of $4,000 per year for a period of 20 years. Funds invested are expected to return 8 percent per year. A deposit of

$$P = \$4,000 \left[\frac{(1.08)^{20} - 1}{0.08(1.08)^{20}} \right] = \$4,000(PR8-20)$$

$$= \$4,000(9.818) = \$39,272$$

at the present time will provide such an annuity.

The inverse problem is to establish the size of the annuity which can be purchased for P dollars today. From Equation 8–34 we have

$$R = P \left[\frac{i(1 + i)^n}{(1 + i)^n - 1} \right] \tag{8-35}$$

The multiplier

$$RPi - n = \left[\frac{i(1 + i)^n}{(1 + i)^n - 1} \right] \qquad (8\text{-}36)$$

is called the equal-payment series capital-recovery factor. It provides a means of equating a present sum to a series of equal future payments.

For example, suppose that a firm has borrowed $100,000 at 8 percent which is to be repaid in equal installments over the next 20 years. The amount of each payment will be

$$R = \$100,000 \left[\frac{0.08(1.08)^{20}}{(1.08)^{20} - 1} \right] = \$100,000(RP8\text{-}20)$$

$$= \frac{\$100,000}{(PR8\text{-}20)} = \frac{\$100,000}{9.818}$$

$$= \$10,185$$

It is interesting to note that because of the 8 percent interest charge, the firm will have paid back over twice the value of the loan during the 20-year loan period. Similar calculations should be of interest to potential users of consumer credit where interest rates may be much larger than 8 percent.

Summary of Interest Formulas. In the previous sections we have developed six basic interest formulas. Each is designed to perform some particular movement of funds back and forth in time under compound interest conditions. The factors indicated are extensively tabled in a variety of publications. For that reason it is rarely necessary to perform the somewhat formidable appearing calculations indicated by the basic formulas.

We will use these equations extensively in developing common bases for comparison among different alternatives, each with a unique cash flow pattern. However, the reader should note that these same equations have wide application in a person's personal business. They can be used to analyze such everyday items as insurance programs, savings plans, mortgages, automobile purchases, and consumer loans. From the point of view of personal usefulness, these six interest formulas may well be the most important models presented in this text. A guide for using the formulas is presented in Table 8–1.

Depreciation Concepts

Engineers, managers, and accountants are all faced with the fact that most of the physical assets used to produce goods and services decrease in value over time. The loss in value over time is called depreciation. Difficulties arise because there may be several interpretations of the word value and because depreciation charges may be based upon several criteria.

TABLE 8-1

Interest Formulas

Given	Find	Formula	Factor Use
P	S	$S = P(1+i)^n$	$S = P(SPi - n)$
S	P	$P = \dfrac{S}{(1+i)^n}$	$P = S(PSi - n)$
R	S	$S = R\left[\dfrac{(1+i)^n - 1}{i}\right]$	$S = R(SRi - n)$
S	R	$R = S\left[\dfrac{i}{(1+i)^n - 1}\right]$	$R = S(RSi - n)$
R	P	$P = R\left[\dfrac{(1+i)^n - 1}{i(1+i)^n}\right]$	$P = R(PRi - n)$
P	R	$R = P\left[\dfrac{i(1+i)^n}{(1+i)^n - 1}\right]$	$R = P(RPi - n)$

Value and Time. In reality there are only two transactions of importance in the life of a depreciable asset. The first occurs when the asset is purchased. The second occurs when it is sold. The value of the asset at the time of purchase is well defined. It is worth the price the buyer is willing to pay for it, namely, the market value. This amount approximates the benefits the buyer thinks he can realize through ownership of the asset, with some profit included. Similarly, when the asset is liquidated a well-defined value is established. It is the amount of money which the owner can obtain for that asset on the open market. This is referred to as the salvage or resale value of the asset.

Between the time of purchase of an asset and the time of resale, both the accountant and the engineer may have occasion to forecast how its value is expected to change. Unfortunately the numbers developed by the accountant may not be satisfactory for use by the engineer. The book value specified by the accountant is constrained by Internal Revenue Service regulations and the necessity to use standardized methods for forecasting the consumption of assets. When comparing the alternative of retaining equipment already owned with the alternative of purchasing new equipment, however, this number is of little significance to the engineer. He must know what the asset is actually worth now, not what it was forecasted to be worth some years before.

The loss in value which occurs between initial purchase price and the current market price of an asset is the actual depreciation of that asset. The difference between purchase price and book value of an asset is merely the accountant's best guess, tempered by IRS (Internal Revenue Service) rulings, of how much that asset should have depreciated by that time.

Both the projected and the actual loss in value are some mix of physical and functional depreciation. *Physical depreciation* refers to the deterioration or wear and tear of an asset which reduces its ability to perform its intended service. *Functional depreciation*, on the other hand, is less well defined. It refers to the decrease in value caused by the change in demand for service. This includes loss in value because the product manufactured by a special piece of equipment is no longer in demand. It also includes relative loss in value caused by obsolescence.

A prime example of functional depreciation can be seen in the evolution of large scale digital computers. An IBM 704 may still be perfectly capable of performing the calculations for which it was designed. However, such machines depreciated rapidly due to the rapid technological changes incorporated into the IBM 709, 7090, 7094, and now System 370. The 704 has become obsolete and consequently has lost much of its value to functional depreciation.

Depreciation Models.   Depreciation is a legitimate cost of doing business. However, it differs from most costs in that it must always be paid in advance. The purpose of all commonly used accounting models of depreciation is to provide a means of recovering the capital used to prepay this cost. If depreciation is not charged against income, ultimately the capital of a firm will be depleted and the firm will have no funds for replacing assets as required.

Since profits are affected by the amount charged for depreciation, accurate annual profit figures depend upon accurate estimates of the useful life of assets and how they decline in value to the firm over their lives. Because the decline in value is very hard to forecast, the accountants usually employ one of several standard depreciation models. The reasons that market values are not used for annual depreciation calculations are that the bookkeeping difficulties would be too great and that the IRS will not permit it. We will discuss four commonly employed models which are acceptable for determining annual depreciation charges.

The *straight-line model* for *depreciation* is the easiest to employ. This model assumes that the value of an asset decreases at a constant rate over time. The depreciation charge each year, representing the amount of capital to be recovered is

$$D = \frac{P - L}{n} \qquad (8\text{-}37)$$

where P is the initial cost of the asset and L is the estimated salvage value after its n years of useful life. The amount still invested in the asset at the end of year j will be

$$P_j = P - j\left(\frac{P - L}{n}\right) \quad \text{for } j = 1, 2, \ldots, n \qquad (8\text{-}38)$$

As an example of the use of straight-line depreciation, suppose that an engine lathe is purchased at a cost of $12,000, has an estimated life of 10 years, and a salvage value of $2,000. The total depreciation over 10 years will be $10,000. The depreciation charge per year will be $1,000. The book value of the lathe after three years will be $9,000.

The *sinking fund depreciation* model can be used for assets whose value declines at an increasing rate. Here a fixed amount each year is assumed to be deposited in a real or imaginary sinking fund for the life of the asset. The size of the deposit is computed such that the amount paid to the fund, plus compound interest earned on deposits, will just equal the amount by which the asset is to be depreciated. The amount actually charged to depreciation in any given year is equal to the amount deposited plus the interest on the amount in the fund during the year. The size of the annual deposit can be determined by the use of the equal-payment series sinking fund factor as

$$A = (P - L)(RSi - n) \tag{8-39}$$

The depreciation charge for year j is

$$D_j = A + iA[SRi - (j - 1)] \quad \text{for } j = 1, 2, \ldots, n \tag{8-40}$$

The value of the asset at the end of year j is

$$P_j = P - \sum_{k=1}^{j} D_k \quad \text{for } j = 1, 2, \ldots, n \tag{8-41}$$

Using the data of the previous example and assuming an interest rate of 8 percent, the amount added to the sinking fund each year is

$$A = (\$12,000 - \$2,000)(RS8-10) = \$10,000(0.06903) = \$690.30$$

The amount charged to depreciation the first year is $690.30. However, depreciation for year 2 is the sum of the $690.30 deposit plus interest on the first-year deposit of (0.08)($690.30). That is,

$$D_2 = \$690.30 + \$55.22 = \$745.52$$

In year 3 the amount of depreciation is

$$D_3 = \$690.30 + 0.08(\$1,435.82) = \$805.17$$

Similar approximate calculations for the life of the asset are summarized in Table 8-2.

The *fixed percentage model* is used for assets whose values decrease at a decreasing rate. Each year a fixed percentage of the book value of the asset is charged for depreciation. If $p(100)$ is the percentage used, the book value at the end of year n will be given by

$$L = P(1 - p)^n \tag{8-42}$$

For a known service life n, salvage value L, and purchase price P, the proper

TABLE 8-2

Sinking Fund Depreciation

Year	Book Value at Beginning of Year	Depreciation	Size of Depreciation Fund—End of Year
1	$12,000.00	$ 690.30	$ 690.30
2	11,309.70	745.52	1,435.82
3	10,564.18	805.17	2,240.99
4	9.759.01	869.01	3,110.00
5	8,890.00	940.00	4,050.00
6	7,950.00	1,010.00	5,060.00
7	6,940.00	1,100.00	6,160.00
8	5,840.00	1,180.00	7,340.00
9	4,660.00	1,270.00	8,610.00
10	3,490.00	1,390.00	10,000.00
11	2,000.00		

value for p may be determined from

$$p = 1 - \left(\frac{L}{P}\right)^{1/n} \quad L > 0 \tag{8-43}$$

The amount of depreciation for any year j is given by

$$D_j = pP(1 - p)^{j-1} \quad \text{for } j = 1, 2, \ldots, n \tag{8-44}$$

This method is sometimes referred to as the double-declining balance method of depreciation. The expression arises from IRS rulings which limit the percentage factor p to be no more than twice the straight-line percent for similar assets. The advantage of this method is that heavy depreciation is taken early in the life of an asset. This permits extra cash to be retained for work at an early date and protects against obsolescence.

In the previous example, under the fixed percentage method, the fraction written off each year would be

$$p = 1 - \left(\frac{\$2000}{\$12,000}\right)^{1/10} = 0.164$$

Depreciation for the first year would be

$$D_1 = (0.164)(\$12,000) = \$1,968$$

For the second year it would be

$$D_2 = (0.164)(\$12,000)(0.836) = \$1,650$$

and so forth.

Sum-of-the-year's digits depreciation is another method which gives a fast write-off early in the life of an asset. A decreasing fraction of the amount to be depreciated is written off each year. The denominator of the fraction is the sum of the digits 1 through n, where n represents the expected life of the asset. The numerator for any year is the life remaining for the asset at the start of that year. Depreciation for year j is then

$$D_j = (P - L)\left(\frac{n - j + 1}{\sum_{k=1}^{n} k}\right) = (P - L)\left[\frac{(n - j + 1)2}{n(n + 1)}\right] \qquad (8\text{--}45)$$

For the numbers of our previous example, under sum-of-the-years' digits depreciation, depreciation for the first year would be

$$D_1 = (\$12,000 - \$2,000)\frac{(10)(2)}{110} = \$1,818$$

Second-year depreciation would be

$$D_2 = (\$10,000)\frac{(9)(2)}{110} = \$1,636$$

and so forth.

Return on Unrecovered Capital. The purpose of any depreciation scheme is to recover the capital invested in a productive asset. At a bare minimum, the asset must contribute that much to earnings in order to preserve the capital of an organization. However, in addition to recovering one's initial investment, normal expectations are to earn a return on capital invested. From a decision-making point of view, then, we are most often concerned with capital recovery plus return. Capital recovery represents depreciation. Return refers to expected earnings on unrecovered capital.

In the engine lathe example of the last section under straight-line depreciation, we expect to recover $1,000 of our capital during the first year. The capital invested during that time is $12,000. If we normally expect our investments to yield 15 percent, we would expect a first-year return of (0.15)($12,000), or $1,800. The amount of capital recovery plus return for the first year is then $2,800. For year 2 the investment is only $11,000 from which we expect a return of $1,650. Second-year capital recovery plus return is $2,650. Similar calculations can be made for each depreciation policy.

Fortunately, if we ignore the effects of income taxes, we can evaluate any number of alternatives, regardless of the depreciation scheme employed, by the same calculation. Fabrycky and Torgersen have shown that the equivalent annual amount for capital recovered plus return is

$$E = (P - L)(RPi - n) + Li \qquad (8\text{--}46)$$

regardless of the method of depreciation.[8] In this case all cash flows involving

[8] W. J. Fabrycky, and Paul E. Torgersen, *Operations Economy* (Englewood Cliffs, N.J.: Prentice-Hall, Inc., 1966), pp. 141–43.

the total amount of depreciation, the variable amount of unrecovered capital and returns on that amount have been reduced to an equivalent stream of equal payments of R each. The term Li represents the annual return expected on the L dollars which are tied up every year in the life of the asset.

The Sunk Cost Concept. There is no disagreement between traditional accounting procedures and engineering evaluation of assets not yet owned by the company. Each assigns its current worth as market value and attempts to forecast a useful life and salvage value. However, differences may arise when attempting to compare the alternative of retaining an asset not yet fully depreciated versus investing in new equipment. The divergence of opinion hinges on the sunk cost concept.

In replacement studies sunk cost refers to the difference between the unrecovered balance of an asset and what it would bring if sold on the open market at the time of the study. From a decision-making point of view, the book value of that asset is irrelevant. Only future incomes and expenditures are under control of management. Any errors in evaluating assets in the past are beyond control and should not influence future decisions. The engineering viewpoint is that an asset is worth only what it can bring on the open market, regardless of what the company books may say it is worth.

The temptation confronting an analyst is to charge the sunk cost to the cost of new equipment being considered. If, for example, a trade-in value of $2,000 is offered for a machine which carries a book value of $5,000, one might be tempted to add $3,000 to the cost of the new equipment. This is incorrect. Trading does not incur the $3,000 sunk cost but only reveals that amount. The cost has already occurred but never been acknowledged.

Comparing Alternatives

There are many different criteria one could apply in choosing among investment alternatives. In this section we will consider three major methods for evaluating proposals. Each of these considers cash flows to be deterministic, a time value for money, and known life for each asset. The methods are

1. Present worth.
2. Equivalent annual cost.
3. Annual rate of return.

In every case we will make the simplifying assumption that all receipts and disbursements occur at the end of a period. Since these data are only estimates of the future, the error introduced by lumping them at the year's end versus spreading them over each year will be negligible at normal rates of return.

Present-Worth Comparisons. The present-worth model in its simplest form requires that one determine the present worth of the total cash transaction series associated with competing investment alternatives. If net income is measured, one chooses the alternative with the largest present worth. If net costs are measured, one chooses the alternative with the smallest present worth. Present worth in each case is established by discounting all future cash flows to establish an equivalent sum of money expressed in current dollars.

Suppose, for example, that alternative A requires $10,000 initial investment, an annual operating expense of $2,000, and has a salvage value of $1,000 at the end of its 10-year life. Income produced is expected to be $4,000 per year. Alternative B requires $6,500 initial investment, $500 salvage, and $3,000 annual operating expense over a 10-year life. Income produced is expected to be $4,500 per year. The company normally expects 10 percent return on investments. The present-worth calculations are:

Alternative A:
Initial Investment	$= \$10,000.00$
Operating Expenses $= \$2,000(PR10-10) = \$2,000(6.144) =$	$12,288.00$
Salvage Value $= \$1,000(PS10-10) = \$1,000(0.3855)$ $=$	385.50
Income $= \$4,000(PR10-10) = \$4,000(6.144)$ $=$	$24,576.00$
Net Profit $=$ Total Income $-$ Total Expense	
$= \$24,576 + \$385.50 - \$12,288 - \$10,000$ $=$	$2,673.50$

Alternative B:
Initial Investment	$= \$\ 6,500.00$
Operating Expense $= \$3,000(PR10-10) = \$3,000(6.144) =$	$18,432.00$
Salvage Value $= \$500(PS10-10) = \$500(0.3855)$ $=$	192.75
Income $= \$4,500(PR10-10) = \$4,500(6.144)$ $=$	$27,648.00$
Net Profit $= \$27,648 + \$192.75 - \$6,500 - \$18,432$ $=$	$2,908.75$

Since the present worth of net profit is greater for alternative B, it is to be preferred to A.

Note the influence of the rate of return on this calculation. If we ignore the time value of money one might argue that alternative A earns a net profit of $2,000(10) - \$9,000 = \$11,000$ while alternative B earns $1,500(10) - \$6,000 = \$9,000$, in which case A would be preferred. However, this comparison overlooks the much higher initial investment of A, representing productive capital with an opportunity cost. When the opportunity cost is considered, the balance swings to B.

The present-worth comparison poses no difficulties as long as the time series involved are of equal length. However, if the life of the investments are different, we must alter the calculation slightly to obtain meaningful figures. It would not be realistic to compare the present worth of a 5-year investment program with one of 10 years, for example. What is normally done is to choose a planning horizon which is the least common multiple of the alternatives involved. Present-worth calculations are then performed for a series of identical investments covering the selected horizon.

As an example, suppose that alternative A requires the purchase of a

$10,000 machine with a life of five years, salvage value of $1,000, and an annual operating expense of $4,000. Alternative B requires a $20,000 investment with a life of 10 years, zero salvage value, and an annual operating expense of $3,500. Gross income per year for each alternative is identical. The company expects an 8 percent rate of return. The net cash flow diagram for these alternatives over a common 10-year horizon would be

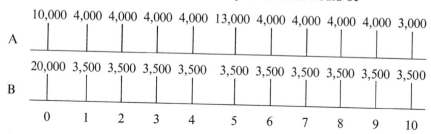

10,000 4,000 4,000 4,000 4,000 13,000 4,000 4,000 4,000 4,000 3,000

A

20,000 3,500 3,500 3,500 3,500   3,500 3,500 3,500 3,500 3,500 3,500

B

0   1   2   3   4   5   6   7   8   9   10

At zero interest rate, the total cost for 10 years under alternative A is $58,000 and for B is $55,000. With this comparison B should be selected. However, with the 8 percent rate of return, the present worth of net cost under each alternative is:

Alternative A:

Initial Investment	= $10,000.00
Operating Expense = $4,000($PR8$–10) = $4,000(6.710)	= 26,840.00
Second Investment = $10,000($PS8$–5) = $10,000(0.6806)	= 6,806.00
First Salvage = $1,000($PS8$–5) = $1,000(0.6806)	= 680.60
Second Salvage = $1,000($PS8$–10) = $1,000(0.4632)	= 463.20
Net Cost = Total Expense – Salvage	= $42,502.20

Alternative B:

Initial Investment	= $20,000.00
Operating Expense = $3,500($PR8$–10) = $3,500(6.710)	= 23,485.00
Total Net Cost	= $43,485.00

By the present-worth criterion, A is the preferred alternative.

Capitalized Amount. If a proposed investment has a very long life, say greater than 20 years, or if we expect to maintain a series of identical investments forever, a special kind of present-worth calculation called capitalized comparison may be employed. The capitalized amount can be viewed as the amount of dollars today which are equivalent to an infinite stream of equal annual flows.

Suppose, for example, that a company is considering the construction of a reservoir to supply their needs for cooling water. The reservoir, once created, will essentially last forever. Using their own supply instead of municipal water is expected to result in an operating savings of $20,000 per year. The company expects a return of 8 percent on investments. The reduction in operating cost will justify an investment of

$$\$20,000 \div 0.08 = \$250,000$$

in the reservoir. If it can be constructed for less than this amount, the reservoir project should be completed. If it costs more than this amount, the company should continue to purchase water. One implication of this calculation is that $250,000 invested at 8 percent will provide an annuity of $20,000 per year forever. That is the capitalized amount of the series of payments.

Equivalent Annual Costs. The equivalent annual cost method of comparison is similar to the present-worth comparison and will lead to the same conclusions. In this calculation all cash flows are reduced to a series of equal amounts occurring at the end of each year in the life of an asset. This technique does have an advantage in that persons normally tend to think in terms of annual amounts. To say that an alternative has a present worth of $3,000 carries less meaning than to say that it will yield $500 per year.

Consider the present-worth cost example of the last section. The equivalent annual cost of capital recovery plus return for the investment in alternative B is

$$E = (P - L)(RP8\text{--}10) + Li$$
$$= \$20,000(0.14903) + 0 = \$2,980.60$$

Annual operating expense is $3,500, making the total annual cost for alternative B

$$T_B = \text{Capital Recovery} + \text{Return} + \text{Operating Expense}$$
$$= \$2,980.60 + \$3,500 = \$6,480.60$$

The fact that this annual amount is equivalent to the present worth previously calculated can be shown by calculating the present worth of 10 equal payments of $6,480.60.

$$\text{P.W.} = \$6,480.60(PR8\text{--}10)$$
$$= \$6,480.60(6.710) = \$43,485$$

This equivalence suggests that an important way to establish equivalent annual costs, especially when expected expenditures may vary year to year, is to reduce the entire cash flow to a present amount, then reallocate it equally over the planning horizon. Applying this principle to alternative A, whose net present worth was calculated as $42,502.20, we can calculate the equivalent annual cost as

$$T_A = \$42,502.20(RP8\text{--}10) = \$42,502.20(0.14903) = \$6,334.10$$

Since $T_A < T_B$, alternative A, which involved purchasing two $10,000 machines with 5-year lives as opposed to one $20,000 machine with a 10-year life, is preferred. This is the same decision reached with the present-worth criterion.

So far we have assumed that the alternatives being considered have identical lives. We forced this to be true in the last example by considering a series of two 5-year periods for machine A and a single 10-year period for machine B. If we adopt the view that alternatives A and B could both provide the needed service indefinitely, then the annual cost criterion becomes especially applicable. Here we assume that we are comparing infinite sequences of identical machines. Under these conditions we only need to calculate the equivalent annual cost of the first machine in each sequence. For example, the equivalent annual cost for alternative A over its five-year life is

$$\text{Capital Recovery} + \text{Return} = (\$10,000 - \$1,000)(RP8\text{--}5) + \$1,000(0.08)$$

$$= \$9,000(0.25046) + \$80 = \$2,334.14$$

Annual Operating Expense $\qquad\qquad\qquad\qquad = \$4,000.00$

Total Annual Cost $\qquad\qquad\qquad\qquad\qquad\quad = \overline{\$6,334.14}$

Within the accuracy of the tables used, this number is the same as the $6,334.10 obtained by considering a series of two such machines. The same answer would be obtained for any number of identical machines.

For reasons of computational convenience and ease of communication with decision makers, the equivalent annual amount calculation is probably the best of the comparison methods, which consider the time value of money under deterministic conditions.

To further illustrate the use of equivalent annual costs, consider the following replacement decision for a company which normally expects a 10 percent rate of return. Machine A was purchased four years ago at a cost of $22,000. At that time it was expected to have a 10-year life with a salvage value of $2,000. Last year's operating expense for A was $4,000. Because of increased maintenance problems, this is expected to rise at an average of $400 per year. Machine B, which normally sells for $30,000, has been offered to the company for $18,000 plus their old machine A. Machine B has an expected life of 15 years, $5,000 salvage value, and will cost $3,000 per year to operate. Both machines can perform the task required equally well.

We could adopt one of several points of view in comparing these alternatives. We could compare costs (1) for infinite sequences of identical machines, (2) for the life of the existing equipment with no further value for machine B, or (3) for the life of the existing equipment with B to retain value at the end of the horizon. The first viewpoint is unacceptable since it is unlikely that we would replace our existing equipment at the end of its remaining life of six years with a second six-year machine of equivalent market value. The second viewpoint is acceptable for certain contract situations in which no further use for machine B is anticipated beyond the six-year horizon. However, for most organizations who expect to remain in business for an extended period of time, the third viewpoint is preferable. This is the one we will adopt.

Under straight-line depreciation, the book value for machine A is now $14,000. However, assuming that the trade-in offer is a realistic appraisal of current market value, the present worth of machine A should be placed at $12,000. The $2,000 difference in these values is a sunk cost and should not enter the analysis. To establish the equivalent annual cost for retaining machine A through the end of its useful life, we must first reduce the flow of operating expenses to present worth. We are forced to do this because the expenditures vary year to year.

1st year operating P.W. = $4,400($PS$10–1) = $4,400(0.9091) = $4,000

2d year operating P.W. = $4,800($PS$10–2) = $4,800(0.8264) =   3,967

3d year operating P.W. = $5,200($PS$10–3) = $5,200(0.7513) =   3,907

4th year operating P.W. = $5,600($PS$10–4) = $5,600(0.6830) =   3,825

5th year operating P.W. = $6,000($PS$10–5) = $6,000(0.6209) =   3,725

6th year operating P.W. = $6,400($PS$10–6) = $6,400(0.5645) =   3,613

P.W.O. = Total Present Worth of Operating Expenses = $23,037

Converting to an equivalent annual cost gives

$$E_o = (\text{P.W.O.})(RP10–6) = (\$23,037)(0.22961) = \$5,290$$

The equivalent annual cost of capital recovery plus return based upon the $2,000 salvage value is

$$E_c = (\$12,000 - \$2,000)(0.22961) + \$2,000(0.10) = \$2,496$$

The total equivalent annual cost for retaining machine A is

$$E_A = E_o + E_c = \$5,290 + \$2,496 = \$7,786 \text{ per year}$$

Similar calculations for B based upon a 15-year life give capital recovery plus return of

$$E_c = (\$30,000 - \$5,000)(RP10–15) + \$5,000(0.10)$$
$$= \$25,000(0.13147) + \$500 = \$3,787$$

The total equivalent annual cost is then

$$E_B = E_o + E_c = \$3,000 + \$3,787 = \$6,787$$

This shows that it will cost approximately $1,000 per year less over the next six years to purchase the new machine now. Note that the decision would be reversed if we assume that machine B is of no value, other than salvage, beyond six years. In that case $E_B = \$9,240$.

Rate of Return. In many investment decisions there is no well-defined set of alternatives of the type we have considered so far. The present worth and equivalent annual amount criteria used to choose among competing projects are not as meaningful for evaluating a single alternative. However, rate of return is a well-established measure of the worth of investments and can be applied whenever the alternatives to a proposal are believed to exist but are not specifically identified. If the calculated rate of return for an investment meets established norms for the company, then the investment should be made.

The rate-of-return model is not meaningful if only costs are involved. A positive rate of return implies that some income has been received. The effective rate of return for an investment is established by determining the interest rate at which receipts and disbursements are equivalent. This can be accomplished by examining either present worth or equivalent annual amount of the net cash flow.

Consider an investment with an original purchase price of $15,000, no salvage value, and an estimated life of 10 years. Operating expense is projected at $5,000 per year. Estimated annual production income from this equipment is $7,500. To establish the expected rate of return, we can solve the equation of equivalent annual amounts for the unknown interest rate i.

$$\text{Equivalent Annual Income} = \text{Equivalent Annual Expense}$$

or

$$\$7,500 = \$5,000 + \$15,000(RPi - 10)$$

from which

$$(RPi - 10) = 0.16667$$

From the tables we see that $RP10\text{--}10 = 0.16275$ and $RP12\text{--}10 = 0.17698$. This means that the rate of return on the proposed investment is somewhere between 10 and 12 percent. By linear interpolation

$$i = 10 + \left(\frac{0.16667 - 0.16275}{0.17698 - 0.16275}\right)2 = 10.55$$

If the company's rate of return on investments is less than 10.55 percent, this equipment should be purchased.

There are inconsistencies in this internal rate-of-return method as pointed out by Bernhard.[9] In some applications it is possible to obtain nonunique rates of return some of which are above the established norm or market rate and others which are below. This may arise, for example, when projected net flows may be positive or negative for any given year. This may place the company in a position of being a lender to the project during periods in which the unrecovered investment is positive and a borrower when it is negative. For the project to be desirable, one would like the rate-of-return i to be greater than the target r when functioning as a lender and less than r when functioning as a borrower. The alternating roles may produce more than one rate i which will satisfy the income and expense flow equality.

---

[9] Richard H. Bernhard, *Journal of Industrial Engineering*, Vol. XIII, No. 1 (January–February, 1962), pp. 19–27.

A second inconsistency arises in the possibility of calculating opposite rankings of projects when compared by present worth and by rate-of-return methods. The difficulty here stems from the inherent assumption that intermediate incremental returns from a project will be reinvested at the same rate of return which the project itself is earning. This is not consistent with the assumption that there exists a normal or market rate of return for alternatives.

Bernhard supports an average rate-of-return calculation as being the best way to circumvent the difficulties cited. In this procedure, a rate-of-return r is calculated as that rate of interest on the initial project investment P which would give the same total wealth at the end of n periods as would be given by the net annual incremental returns $Q_1, Q_2, \ldots, Q_n$. Here one assumes reinvestment of the Q_i amounts at the market rates $i_1, i_2, \ldots, i_n$ which may be different from year to year. Symbolically,

$$P(1 + r)^n = Q_1(1 + i_2)(1 + i_3) \cdots (1 + i_n)$$
$$+ Q_2(1 + i_3) \cdots (1 + i_n) + \cdots + Q_n \qquad (8\text{--}47)$$

from which

$$r = \left[\frac{Q_1(1 + i_2) \cdots (1 + i_n) + Q_2(1 + i_3) \cdots (1 + i_n) + \cdots + Q_n}{P} \right]^{1/n} - 1 \quad (8\text{--}48)$$

The average rate of return so calculated will be consistent with present-worth techniques.

The difficulties discussed for the internal rate-of-return method do not arise for the special case of constant incremental returns and interest rates over an infinite planning horizon. As the alternative under consideration moves farther from these assumptions the classical rate-of-return method becomes a progressively poorer technique for analysis. In the more general case the average rate of return may lead to a better decision rule.

The Effect of Taxes. The techniques for comparing alternatives discussed in the preceding sections have adopted a very simple view of taxes. The interest rate used can be interpreted as a before-taxes rate of return. In competitive enterprises it often is a very complex matter to predict the tax consequences of isolated decisions. This happens because the effects of that one decision may be impossible to isolate from the effects on taxes of other decisions made by the company. For that reason, many investment decisions are handled exactly as we have suggested. The effects of income taxes are merely reflected in the choice of interest rate.

As long as the alternatives are such that considering taxes has the effect of reducing all profits by approximately the same amount, taxes can be ignored in the analysis. There are some situations, however, in which after-tax profits to the firm are affected in identifiably different fashions by competing alternatives. In such instances, the payment of forecasted income and capital gains taxes, for example, can be treated as additional cash flows in the calculation of equivalent annual costs.

Tax laws and their effect on economic decisions are specialized topics of considerable scope. Most corporations retain experts in the field to keep abreast of the constant changes in tax rulings. We cannot hope to cope with all the intricacies of tax laws. However, we will attempt to show the influence that capital gains taxes and income taxes may have on certain types of decisions.

We have already mentioned that depreciation is a legitimate cost of doing business. Any expense charged to depreciation is written off against income and ultimately reduces the amount of income tax paid. However, at the time an asset is sold, its book value may be quite different from its sale value. In the event that it sells for more than its depreciated value and it has been held over six months, a capital gains tax must be paid on the difference. For our purposes, we will consider that tax to be 25 percent of the net gain. Land and inventories are two productive assets which present tax laws do not permit to be depreciated. Since real estate has in general risen in price over the past few years, it is common to receive capital gains on land.

To illustrate the influence of capital gains and income taxes, consider the decision of retaining an existing warehouse versus selling that property and renting space in a commercial warehouse. The present warehouse was purchased 15 years ago for $90,000. For tax purposes that price was divided into $60,000 for the building and $30,000 for the land. The building is being totally depreciated by the straight-line method over a 40-year life. The warehouse property can be sold now for a net price of $120,000. The company expects to need warehouse space in this location for 10 more years. They estimate that the property can be sold for $100,000 at that time. Based on past records, it costs $6,600 per year for operation and maintenance and $3,000 per year for property taxes and insurance.

Comparable commercial warehouse space is available in the area for a 10-year contract price of $18,000 per year. Total annual operating expense for this facility is estimated to be $4,000. The company normally expects a minimum before-tax rate of return of 10 percent for this class of investment. The income tax rate is 50 percent and capital gains rate is 25 percent.

Before taxes, the annual costs would be calculated as follows:

A—Keep Present Warehouse:

Capital Recovery = ($120,000 − $100,000)($RP$10–10) + $100,000(0.10)
  = ($20,000)(0.16275) + $10,000 = $13,255
Other Expenses = $6,600 + $3,000   =   9,600

Total Annual Cost   = $22,855

B—Sell Warehouse and Rent:

Annual Rent   = $18,000
Other Expenses   =   4,000

Total Annual Cost   = $22,000

Since $22,000 < $22,855, the decision without tax considerations should be to sell and rent.

If we consider the effect of taxes, several other items must be accounted for in the total cash flow. First, if the existing warehouse is sold an immediate capital gain is incurred. The book value of the property is $67,500 as established by 15 years at $1,500 per year for building depreciation. The $30,000 investment in land is nondepreciable. The amount of capital gain is then the difference between the sales price of $120,000 and the book value, that is $52,500. The tax outlay of ($52,500)(0.25) = $13,125 reduces the effective after-tax value of the warehouse to $106,875. Second, the sale price of the warehouse at the end of 10 years must be similarly adjusted for capital gains taxes. The gain at that time is expected to be

$$\$100,000 - [\$90,000 - 25(\$1,500)] = \$47,500$$

which will incur a capital gains tax of $11,875. The effective salvage price is then $88,125.

The annual taxes on ordinary income will be different under these two alternatives. If the present warehouse is retained, gross income will be reduced for tax purposes by the sum of the annual depreciation charge of $1,500 and other expenses of $9,600. This amounts to $11,100. On the other hand, if warehouse space is rented, the entire cost of $22,000 per year may be charged against current income. Retaining the warehouse will therefore reflect $10,900 per year more taxable income than renting. At the 50 percent tax rate, the cost in added income taxes would be $5,450 per year.

The after-tax cost of retaining the warehouse compared to renting is based upon a 5 percent rate of return. Therefore

$$
\begin{aligned}
\text{Capital Recovery} &= (\$106,875 - \$88,125)(RP5\text{–}10) + \$88,125(0.05) \\
&= (\$18,750)(0.12950) + \$3,606 = \$\ 6,036
\end{aligned}
$$

Operating Expenses	$= \quad 9,600$
Added Income Tax over Rental	$= \quad 5,450$
Total Annual Cost	$= \$21,086$

The comparable annual cost of rental remains at $22,000. Since $22,000 > $21,086, the net effect of capital gains and income taxes has been to reverse the decision. In this instance the warehouse should be retained.

Note that the annual costs compared on an after-tax basis are relative costs. The annual difference of $914 between them is a more meaningful measure of the advantage of owning versus renting.

Continuous Discounting. Throughout this chapter we have based our calculations on discrete time periods. All cash flows have been assumed to occur at the end of an interest period and compounding occurred one period at a time. For reasons of mathematical convenience in certain kinds of replacement studies, it is desirable to consider continuous discounting. The continuous approximation to the single-payment compound-amount factor can be developed by considering each year to be divided into m separate periods. The continuous approximation is then obtained from the limit as m approaches infinity. That is,

$$(SPi - n) \approx \lim_{m \to \infty} \left(1 + \frac{i}{m}\right)^{mn} = e^{in} \qquad (8\text{-}49)$$

In like manner, the continuous approximation to the single-payment present-worth factor is

$$(PSi - n) \approx \lim_{m \to \infty} \left[\frac{1}{(1 + i/m)^{mn}}\right] = e^{-in} \qquad (8\text{-}50)$$

These factors are especially helpful when we can express operating costs as a continuous function of time. Let $R(t)$ represent operating cost at time t expressed as an annual rate. Under continuous discounting the present worth of operating expense over time T would be

$$P.W. = \int_0^T R(t)e^{-it}\,dt \qquad (8\text{-}51)$$

This expression can be differentiated by the usual methods of calculus. Such capability eases the difficulty of optimizing replacement intervals in some equipment studies. In addition, Equation 8-51 can be evaluated with fewer computational steps than discrete discounting under conditions of varying annual expenditures.

Suppose, for example, that the productivity of a certain piece of equipment is essentially constant at $20,000 per year. The rate of operating expenditure increases linearly with age. The increase in rate is $2,000 per year. The nominal rate of return is 10 percent. Beginning with a new machine, the present worth of operating profit over a life of five years is

$$P(T) = \int_0^T R(t)e^{-it}\,dt$$

$$= \int_0^5 (\$20,000 - \$2,000t)e^{-0.1t}\,dt$$

$$= \$200,000(1 - e^{-0.5} - 1 + 1.5e^{-0.5})$$

$$= \$200,000(0.30327) = \$60,654$$

A comparable calculation using discrete discounting would require bringing each year's expense back to present worth individually, then summing. The results would then be subtracted from the present worth of a series of five equal payments of $20,000 each.

Economic Life

In the process of comparing alternatives by the techniques introduced so far in this chapter, the number of years life for each asset must be specified. There is some danger of confusing such concepts as physical life, accounting life, service life, and economic life. For purposes of analysis, it is the economic life, which may or may not be synonymous with one or more of the other concepts, which is important. The economic life period for a piece of equipment should not be established by an arbitrary decree but rather should be the subject of a thorough analysis on the part of the operations engineer. For our purposes, economic life is the period that an asset spends on its intended service prior to being liquidated or moved to a secondary task. An incorrect specification of the life period can change the decision.

For example, suppose that management arbitrarily specifies a four-year recovery period for all equipment and a minimum rate of return of 10 percent. A machine with a purchase cost of $20,000, annual operating costs of $6,000, and no salvage value is being considered to perform a task currently subcontracted for $11,000 per year. A careful prediction of the economic life of the machine is 10 years. Under the four-year recovery period, the equivalent annual costs are:

Machine cost per year = $20,000(RP10–4) + $6,000 = $12,309
Subcontract cost per year = $11,000

Under the four-year life assumption, subcontracting is preferred. However, under the more accurate 10-year economic life the machine costs are:

Machine cost per year = $20,000(RP10–10) + $6,000 = $9,255

The apparent annual advantage of $1,309 for subcontracting is seen to be more properly a $1,745 advantage for the decision to purchase the machine. If we accumulate the effect of this decision over the 10-year life of the machine and assume that the $5,000 per year difference in operating expenses can be invested at 10 percent, the total cost to the company for enforcing a poor estimate of economic life will amount to $27,805. Obviously the question of economic life should not be taken lightly. For a thorough development of the concepts which follow, the interested reader is referred to the excellent discussion by Taylor.[10]

Classifying Equipment. The economic life of different types of equipment may be influenced by a variety of factors. However, the analyst may be assisted in developing better predictions for a particular piece of equipment if he can identify the particular major factors which are most likely to cause its economic demise. The classification schemes which follow are based upon

---

[10] George A. Taylor, *Managerial and Engineering Economy* (Princeton, N.J.: D. Van Nostrand Co., Inc., 1964), chap. x.

different views of the possible timing of the primary factors of deterioration and obsolescence.

Deterioration can manifest itself in the form of gradually increased cost of maintenance and operation or in the form of sudden catastrophic failure. An automobile is an example of a piece of equipment which may have its economic life determined by increased maintenance and repair costs. As it ages, its life can be prolonged but only by the investment of increasingly large sums of money. At some point in time it becomes more economical to replace it rather than repair it. That defines its economic life. On the other hand, some items such as light bulbs and electron tubes commonly exhibit sudden failure in which deterioration is latent until the equipment ceases to function. In this case economic life and physical life coincide. No amount of maintenance and repair can extend their life once failure occurs.

Similar extremes exist for the obsolescence factor. A technological breakthrough may occur which will render some equipment economically obsolete overnight. This phenomenon is often observed with military weapon systems. The life period of a weapon system is established by the sudden appearance of a superior model which makes all existing models uneconomical for their intended purpose. Similar events occur with commercial equipment. The advent of jet aircraft, for example, rendered propeller driven aircraft obsolete for both commercial air carrier and military use in many applications. Other equipment may obsolesce because of a steady emergence of improved machines. Digital computers offer an illustration of this type of obsolescence. The moves from IBM 704 to 7090 to 7094 to System 360 represent a progression of technological improvements. The IBM 704, therefore, became more obsolete with each new generation of computers but did not succumb to the sudden obsolescence experienced by propeller driven fighter aircraft.

By considering different combinations of deterioration and obsolescence the following classification scheme is suggested to assist in the prediction of economic life:

1. Sudden failure.
2. Instant obsolescence.
3. Progressive deterioration.
4. Deterioration and obsolescence.

Sudden Failure. Determination of the economic life of equipment in this class can be made by a statistical study of failure rates of similar equipment under similar conditions. In the simplest case one assumes that obsolescence is completely ruled out and that even though maintenance and repair costs may exist, they have no effect on prolonging the life of the equipment.

The problem of selection of alternatives in this case then reduces to one of forecasting. The information desired is the probability distribution of item lives. From the distribution, statements about expected life, the probability that life will fall in a specified range, etc., can be developed.

In addition to initial selection of equipment of this class, one is often faced with the prospect of developing replacement policies. If we assume that all items which fail will be replaced by a new item of the same class, the problem is to plan replacement of items which have not failed. Replacement of a used but still functioning item of the sudden failure class can be justified only if the cost of replacement after failure is greater than the cost of replacement before failure and if the new item reduces the probability of future failure. The conditional probability of failure in the interval $(t, t + \Delta t)$ may be constant, an increasing function of t, or a decreasing function of t. Constant probability of failure is associated with items that fail from random causes, such as shock, which are unrelated to age. An increasing probability of failure is the most prevalent pattern. Decreasing probability of failure may be exhibited by some items with high initial mortality. This sometimes happens with complex systems which must be "shaken down" before one has confidence in their ability to continue functioning. After the initial decline, however, most real systems will then exhibit an increasing failure rate with age.

Instant Obsolescence. Equipment in this class is assumed to be just as efficient and reliable at the time it is displaced as it was when it was first put in service. New chemical processes, new machining methods, and new information systems may render old equipment suddenly obsolete. The demise of economic usefulness in this case is nearly as abrupt as for items that fail. The impending technological breakthrough is not preceded by annual obsolesence of the type experienced by model changes in essentially similar equipment.

The prediction of economic life for equipment of this class is extremely difficult. One must rely on past patterns of similar items to make estimates of the future. The whole problem is related to an emerging study area known as technological forecasting.[11] However, these tools do not yet appear to be well developed enough to be of immediate use to the operations engineer. At the present time, the pragmatic engineer must often simply rely on persons working closely with the process to provide the forecasts.

Progressive Deterioration. Some pieces of equipment do not become obsolete but rather have their economic life limited by mounting annual maintenance and repair costs. Past maintenance and repair records for similar equipment can be used to compute the economic life for items of this class. The various forecasting techniques of Chapter 7 provide potential methods for establishing projected expense patterns. Once these patterns are available, the equivalent annual cost over a variety of assumed lives should be calculated. The life with the minimum annual cost should be the one selected as the economic life of the equipment in making selection or replacement studies. The assumption here, of course, is that we could obtain a

---

[11] See for example James R. Bright, *Technological Forecasting for Industry and Government* (Englewood Cliffs, N.J.: Prentice-Hall, Inc., 1968).

continuous stream of like equipment. In some cases it may be convenient to use the continuous discounting procedure of Equation 8–51 to facilitate this calculation.

Suppose, for example, that one machine under consideration has an initial cost of $10,000, zero salvage value, a projected annual operating expense of $1,000, and maintenance expense which increases at a rate of $1,600 per year. The company uses a nominal interest rate of 10 percent. The equivalent annual costs for various assumed life periods are shown in Table 8–3.

TABLE 8–3

Equivalent Annual Costs for an Item with Progressive Deterioration

Life	Capital Recovery	Equivalent Annual Operating and Maintenance Expense	Total Annual Cost
0	$10,000	$ 0	
1	11,000	2,600	$13,600
2	5,762	3,368	9,130
3	4,021	4,096	8,117
4	3,155	4,816	7,971
5	2,638	5,504	8,142
6	2,230	6,016	8,246

From the values in the table, the apparent economic life of this asset is four years. This is the number which should be used to compare the worth of this alternative against other options. Such a calculation is preferable to accepting by fiat an arbitrary life of say six years which might be based on accounting considerations.

An alternative method of calculation to determine the economic life of progressive deterioration items is to calculate the present worth of an infinite stream of identical items, with periodic renewals every n years, using continuous discounting. The resulting equation can then be differentiated to determine a minimum cost life. A complete discussion of this and other more advanced techniques is contained in the book by Jorgenson et al.[12] If we assume that the annual operating and expense rate function is $d(t)$ and that a new machine is purchased every n years, the discounted cost for one cycle is

$$C(n) = P + \int_0^n d(t)e^{-it}\, dt \qquad (8\text{–}52)$$

Let $P(n)$ represent the present worth of an infinite number of such cycles. After the first cycle has been completed at $t = n$, the investment process continues from the same initial condition as at $t = 0$. Starting at $t = n$, the

---

[12] D. W. Jorgenson, J. J. McCall, and R. Radner, *Optimal Replacement Policy* (Chicago: Rand McNally & Co., 1967).

present worth is $P(n)$ just as it was at $t = 0$. Discounting this quantity from $t = 0$ gives the net present worth over the interval (n, ∞), which added to the present worth over $(0, n)$, gives

$$P(n) = P + \int_0^n e^{-it} d(t)\, dt + e^{-in}P(n) \qquad (8\text{--}53)$$

Solving this equation for $P(n)$, we have

$$P(n) = \frac{[P + \int_0^n e^{-it} d(t)\, dt]}{(1 - e^{-in})} \qquad (8\text{--}54)$$

This is the quantity to be optimized by setting $dP(n)/dn = 0$.

Deterioration and Obsolescence. Obsolescence costs depend upon unequal life periods and therefore arise almost exclusively in replacement situations. Gradual obsolescence usually manifests itself in the form of reduced operating costs to perform the same functions with each new model of a piece of equipment.

Suppose, for example, that new machines appear annually with operating costs c dollars less per year than the previous model. However, maintenance costs on all models increase at a constant slope of m dollars per year, starting with the date of purchase. The decision involves timing of replacements such that the reduced operating costs because of model improvements are reflected in the total cost equation. Assuming a constant purchase price of P dollars, the pattern of expenses for a four-year replacement cycle would appear as shown in Table 8–4. The optimal decision would be determined by comparing

TABLE 8–4

Year	Purchase Cost	Operating Cost	Maintenance Cost
1	P	K	m
2		K	$2m$
3		K	$3m$
4		K	$4m$
5	P	$K - 4c$	m
6		$K - 4c$	$2m$
7		$K - 4c$	$3m$
8		$K - 4c$	$4m$
9	P	$K - 8c$	m
$\vdots$	$\vdots$	$\vdots$	$\vdots$

the present worth of this stream with the present worth of five-year, six-year, etc., replacement policies. Obsolescence then appears as a comparative cost between the alternative policies.

Synopsis. Prediction of an economic life period cannot usually be accomplished by the simple application of a formula. The classification schemes suggested in previous paragraphs are offered as idealized models to help the analyst sharpen his predictions rather than as cures for all prediction problems. It would be rare indeed if a particular piece of equipment fit exactly into any one of the patterns discussed. More realistically, any combination of deterioration and obsolescence may be acting at any one time. For example, a gradually deteriorating machine might be displaced by sudden obsolescence prior to the optimum life established by its maintenance pattern.

For the most part, estimates of economic life based upon gradual or sudden deterioration seem more amenable to quantitative analysis than those based upon obsolescence. Until technological forecasting becomes a more mature technique, the operations engineer will probably rely upon subjective estimates for obsolescence effects.

Accounting for Risk and Uncertainty

Every calculation performed so far in this chapter has been based on the assumption of a certain future. There has been no question raised concerning the need for alternative investments in the face of several possible future events. In this practice of decision making under assumed certainty, we merely calculate total income or expenditure for our feasible alternatives and choose the one with the largest profit or smallest cost. Only one future is considered.

In some decision situations it may be necessary to evaluate each of the alternative investments under several possible futures. If the decision maker can estimate the probabilities of each of the possible futures, he is said to be making a decision under risk. In that event he may choose the alternative which maximizes his expected annual profit or present worth. If the probabilities of the future events cannot be estimated, he is said to be making a decision under uncertainty. In this instance he may elect to choose the alternative which maximizes his minimum profit or apply one of the other principles from decision theory.

Conceptually we can use the present worth and equivalent annual cost calculations to fill the cells of a decision matrix. Each row represents the worth of one alternative under a number of possible futures. Each column represents the worth of all alternatives under one possible future. When the construction of such an array is feasible, the decision maker can use any number of principles of choice for decisions under risk or uncertainty. Many of the models of this text assume decision making under risk, although the decision matrix is rarely explicitly defined. For a complete discussion of decision theory and its ramifications, the interested reader should consult Morris.[13]

---

[13] William T. Morris, *The Analysis of Management Decisions* (Homewood, Ill.: Richard D. Irwin, Inc., 1964).

For the remainder of this chapter we will assume that the analyst has available some type of probability information about future events. These data will often be subjective probabilities gleaned from conversation with decision makers. The use of probability information, even though it may be highly subjective, will provide management with a range of possible outcomes and the likelihood of achieving different goals under each investment alternative. This is a decided departure from the deterministic view which is fostered by the classical discounted cash flow methods of our earlier discussions.

The use of probability information about future events supplements rather than replaces the more traditional analysis. Indeed, when one uses the present worth, equivalent annual cost, and rate of return criteria as normally formulated, the decision is really being made on the basis of expected values. A single cost, a single interest rate, a single life, etc., are specified and used in the calculations with sometimes unwarranted precision. For the most part, any uncertainty the decision maker may have about future events is accommodated by specifying a large interest rate to cover less than desirable returns which may accrue from an investment alternative.

What we are now suggesting is that the decision maker be asked to specify not only an expected value for each of the factors in the investment decision but also a range of values for each of the factors. If the decision maker is sufficiently knowledgeable about probability theory we might even ask that he specify the form of the probability distribution and provide an estimate of correlation among random variables. Otherwise we might simply assign a value of six standard deviations to his estimates of range and assume that all random variables are normally distributed over that range or possibly beta distributed in cases where the estimate of expected value does not fall at mid-range. This information can be used to obtain expected values of each of the classical criteria exactly as suggested earlier in this chapter. However, with the probability estimates we can now supplement this information with quantitative estimates of the risk involved with an investment alternative.

This approach is sometimes called *risk analysis*. Its value as a decision aid hinges on the often observed preference of decision makers for a reasonably safe investment with a modest expected rate of return over a much more risky investment with a somewhat higher expected rate of return. This preference is especially evident when the risky investment is so large that failure to meet expected performance would significantly affect the financial position of the corporation. Our purpose is to highlight the risks involved.

Risky Investments.   As suggested by Hillier, we will first treat net cash flows as random variables.[14] The net cash flow in year j is simply income minus expense for that year. Let C_j be the net cash flow for year j and assume

---

[14] Frederick S. Hillier, "The Derivation of Probabilistic Information for the Evaluation of Risky Investments," *Management Science*, April, 1963, pp. 443–57.

a fixed rate of interest i over the n-year economic life of an investment alternative. The present worth, P, as previously defined is:

$$P = \sum_{j=0}^{n} \frac{C_j}{(1 + i)^j} \qquad (8\text{-}55)$$

A more general form of P could also be developed by specifying different values of i for each of the n periods without increasing the computational difficulty. However, to be consistent with most actual applications, we will use uniform values of i.

In this context, P is a random variable consisting of a sum of n random variables, C_j, each multiplied by a constant of the form $(1 + i)^{-j}$. Applying the results of Equations 3–77 and 3–78 of Chapter 3, it follows that

$$E(P) = \sum_{j=0}^{n} \frac{\mu_j}{(1 + i)^j} \qquad (8\text{-}56)$$

and

$$\sigma_P^2 = \sum_{j=0}^{n} \frac{\sigma_j^2}{(1 + i)^{2j}} + 2 \sum_{j=0}^{n-1} \sum_{k=j+1}^{n} \frac{\sigma_{jk}}{(1 + i)^{j+k}} \qquad (8\text{-}57)$$

where μ_j, σ_j^2, and σ_{jk} represent the mean, variance, and covariance respectively, of the random variables $\{C_j\}$. This can also be written as a function of correlation coefficients among variables by recalling that $\sigma_{jk} = r_{jk}\sigma_j\sigma_k$.

Hillier argues that it may be unrealistic to expect investment analysts to develop reliable estimates for covariances.[15] For that reason, he suggests that the net cash flow in any year be divided into those portions which are reasonably independent from year to year and those that are closely related. That is,

$$C_j = X_j + Y_j^{(1)} + Y_j^{(2)} + \cdots + Y_j^{(m)} \qquad (8\text{-}58)$$

where the X_j values are mutually independent but $Y_0^{(k)}$, $Y_1^{(k)}$, ..., $Y_n^{(k)}$, are perfectly correlated for $k = 1, 2, \ldots, m$. Perfect correlation implies that if $Y_r^{(k)}$ takes on a value $\mu_r^{(y)} + t\sigma_r^{(y)}$ then $Y_j^{(k)}$ must take a value $\mu_j^{(y)} + t\sigma_j^{(y)}$ for $j = 0, 1, \ldots, n$. Under conditions of perfect correlation, $(r_{jk} = 1)$, it follows that

$$\sigma_{Y(k)}^2 = \sum_j \sum_k \left[\frac{\sigma_{jk}^{(y)}}{(1 + i)^{j+k}} \right]$$

$$= \sum_j \sum_k \left[\frac{r_{jk}\sigma_k^{(y)}\sigma_j^{(y)}}{(1 + i)^{j+k}} \right]$$

$$= \sum_j \sum_k \left[\frac{\sigma_k^{(y)}\sigma_j^{(y)}}{(1 + i)^{j+k}} \right] \qquad (8\text{-}59)$$

---

[15] *Ibid.*, p. 449.

where $\sigma_j^{(y)}$ refers to the random variable $Y_j^{(k)}$. Alternatively, we can write the standard deviation as

$$\sigma_{Y(k)} = \sum_{j=0}^{n} \frac{\sigma_j^{(y)}}{(1 + i)^j} \tag{8-60}$$

The model then suggested by Hillier is

$$E(P) = \sum_{j=0}^{n} \frac{\mu_j}{(1 + i)^j} = \sum_{j=0}^{n} \frac{E(X_j) + \sum_{k=1}^{m} E(Y_j^{(k)})}{(1 + i)^j} \tag{8-61}$$

and

$$\sigma_P^2 = \sum_{j=0}^{n} \frac{\text{Var}(X_j)}{(1 + i)^{2j}} + \sum_{k=1}^{m} \left[\sum_{j=0}^{n} \left(\frac{\sqrt{\text{Var}(Y_j^{(k)})}}{(1 + i)^j} \right) \right] \tag{8-62}$$

Equations 8–61 and 8–62 can be viewed as special cases of 8–56 and 8–57 where part of the variables carry correlation coefficients zero and the remainder have correlation coefficients of unity.

Since we are usually considering the combination of a large number of random variables which are either identically distributed or uniformly bounded, we may use the central limit theorem to argue that P is normally distributed with mean and variance as calculated above. This is absolutely correct only if the C_j variables are mutually independent. However, we will adopt the view that the normal distribution is a reasonable approximation for our purposes. If we are not willing to make that assumption, Equations 8–56 and 8–57 still give the proper values for mean and variance, which could be used to make weak probability statements employing the Tchebycheff inequality.

Now that we have a method for developing the distribution of present worth P, it is a simple matter to extend this result to the development of a distribution for equivalent annual cost (or profit). From Equation 8–35 we know that a present worth P can be converted to an equivalent annual amount by multiplying by the $(RPi - n)$ factor. In symbols that gives

$$R = P \left[\frac{i(1 + i)^n}{(1 + i)^n - 1} \right] = \sum_{j=1}^{n} \left[\frac{C_j}{(1 + i)^j} \right] RPi - n \tag{8-63}$$

For a fixed interest rate i and investment period n, it follows that the random variable R is simply the random variable P multiplied by a constant. If we are willing to assume that P is normally distributed, then R will be normally distributed with

$$E(R) = (RPi - n)E(P) \tag{8-64}$$

and

$$\sigma_R^2 = (RPi - n)^2 \sigma_p^2 \tag{8-65}$$

Let us ignore for now the reservations against using the internal rate-of-return method for evaluating proposed investments. The internal rate-of-return r may then be defined as that value of i for which $P = 0$. When ranking investment alternatives the highest priority is given to those investments with the highest values of r. The cumulative distribution for r can be estimated from the probability distribution of P for various values of i. Since P represents the present worth of net cash flows for a fixed value of i, it follows that the event $P < 0$ is equivalent to the event $r < i$. In other words a negative net present worth implies that the project is not returning the desired interest rate i. In equation form we have

$$\text{Prob.}\{r < 1\} = \text{Prob.}\{P < 0 \,|\, i\} \qquad (8\text{--}66)$$

The cumulative distribution of r is then developed by merely repeating the calculation of $\text{Prob.}\{P < 0 \,|\, i\}$ for as many i values as desired.

Example. A flight school operator is considering the alternatives of purchasing a utility category training aircraft (U) versus purchasing an acrobatic version of the same aircraft (A). Having been in the flight training business for a number of years, the operator has reason to believe that income and expense from a utility category aircraft will be nearly independent from year to year. Although he does not have sufficient data to project complete probability distributions, he has provided us with his best guesses about the expected values and possible ranges of the pertinent variables of the problem. These include initial purchase price and salvage value at the end of a projected five-year life as well as annual net cash flow estimates. These data are summarized in Table 8–5.

TABLE 8–5

Estimated Net Cash Flows for a Utility Model Aircraft

Year	Source of Flow	Symbol	Expected Value	Range	Standard Deviation
0	Purchase	C_0	− $12,000	$10,500–13,500	$500
1	Income-expense	C_1	+ 2,200	2,050–2,350	50
2	Income-expense	C_2	+ 2,200	1,900–2,500	100
3	Income-expense	C_3	+ 2,200	1,900–2,500	100
4	Income-expense	C_4	+ 2,000	1,700–2,300	100
5	Income-expense	$C_5^{(1)}$	+ 1,000	700–1,300	100
5	Salvage	$C_5^{(2)}$	+ 6,000	4,800–7,200	400

Investment in the acrobatic aircraft (A) is a more risky but promising investment. The acrobatic aircraft is also expected to have a life of five years. The operator feels that maintenance costs will be nearly independent year to year with this aircraft. However, since his school has never offered an acrobatic course before there is some uncertainty regarding the demand for time in such an aircraft. It is felt that if the reception of the acrobatic airplane exceeds expectations for the first year or two, it will exceed expectations thereafter and vice versa. For that reason it will be assumed that the net cash flow from sale of flight time for each of the five years will be perfectly correlated. The data for alternative A are summarized in Table 8–6.

TABLE 8–6

Estimated Net Cash Flows for an Acrobatic Model Aircraft

Year	Source of Flow	Symbol	Expected Value	Range	Standard Deviation
0	Purchase	X_0	− $14,000	$13,100–14,900	$300
1	Operating expense	X_1	− 10,000	9,100–10,900	300
2	Operating expense	X_2	− 10,000	9,100–10,900	300
3	Operating expense	X_3	− 11,000	10,100–11,900	300
4	Operating expense	X_4	− 12,000	10,800–13,200	400
5	Operating expense	$X_5^{(1)}$	− 12,000	10,800–13,200	400
1	Income	$Y_1^{(1)}$	+ 12,000	9,000–15,000	1,000
2	Income	$Y_2^{(1)}$	+ 13,000	10,000–16,000	1,000
3	Income	$Y_3^{(1)}$	+ 13,000	10,300–15,700	900
4	Income	$Y_4^{(1)}$	+ 14,000	11,600–16,400	800
5	Income	$Y_5^{(1)}$	+ 13,000	10,900–15,100	700
5	Salvage	$X_5^{(2)}$	+ 7,500	6,000–9,000	500

For investment in the utility model U, Equations 8–56 and 8–57 indicate that for an interest rate of 10 percent,

$$E(P) = \sum_{j=0}^{5} \frac{\mu_j}{(1.1)^j} = -12,000 + \cdots + \frac{1000}{(1.1)^5} + \frac{6000}{(1.1)^5} \approx -\$810$$

$$\sigma_p^2 = \sum_{j=0}^{5} \frac{\sigma_j^2}{(1.1)^{2j}} = (500)^2 + \cdots + \frac{(100)^2}{(1.1)^{10}} + \frac{(400)^2}{(1.1)^{10}} \approx 334,741$$

Furthermore, the probability that return will be less than 10 percent is

$$\text{Prob.}(r < 10\%) = \text{Prob.}(P < 0 \mid i = 10\%) \approx 0.92$$

In similar fashion, investment in the acrobatic model A, yields from Equations 8–61 and 8–62

$$E(P) = \sum_{j=0}^{5} \frac{E(X_j) + E(Y_j^{(1)})}{(1.1)^j} = -14,000 + \frac{1000}{1.1} + \cdots + \frac{8500}{(1.1)^5} \approx -\$1540$$

$$\sigma_P^2 = \sum_{j=0}^{5} \frac{\text{Var}(X_j)}{(1.1)^{2j}} + \left[\sum_{j=0}^{5} \left(\frac{\sqrt{\text{Var}(Y_j^{(1)})}}{(1.1)^j} \right) \right]^2$$

$$= 90,000 + \cdots + \frac{41,000}{(1.1)^{10}} + \left(\frac{1000}{1.1} + \cdots + \frac{700}{(1.1)^5} \right)^2 \approx 11,631,930$$

Again assuming normality, the probability that return will be less than 10 percent is

$$\text{Prob.} (r < 10\%) = \text{Prob.}(P < 0 \mid i = 10\%) \approx 0.67$$

It is interesting to note that on the basis of the expected present worth of net cash flows, the utility aircraft is preferred over the acrobatic aircraft, even though neither of them will achieve the nominal rate of return of 10 percent. If they had achieved that rate, their expected present worth would have been zero. On the other hand if one aspires to have a reasonable chance of achieving the nominal 10 percent rate of return, then the acrobatic aircraft is to be preferred. It has roughly a 33 percent chance of returning 10 percent on the investment while the utility aircraft has only an 8 percent chance. Other calculations at different nominal interest rates could be performed to give the operator a complete picture of the risks of each alternative.

Total Risk Analysis. The techniques of the previous section can be extended to more complex capital investment decisions. Unfortunately, however, when a large number of random variables enter the model, it becomes extremely difficult to achieve an analytic solution with a high degree of realism. At that point simulation techniques may be employed to develop measures of risk.

Before turning to a discussion of risk analysis by simulation, it should be noted that some extensions have been made to the analytical methods discussed by Hillier. For example, Kaplan and Barish treat the investment problem with rate-of-return i as a random variable.[16]

Hertz describes a simulation program in which nine input factors for the capital investment decision are introduced as random variables.[17] We will have much more to say about simulation later in this text, but for the moment let us say that simulation is a sampling experiment. In simulation, individual values for each random variable are selected from their indicated populations and combined in the manner indicated by the investment model. A large number of such experiments are run to obtain an empirical estimate for the distribution of measures such as present worth and internal rate of return.

The factors considered by Hertz as being typical of those which must be analyzed to determine the attractiveness of a proposed capital facilities investment are:

1. Market size.
2. Selling prices.
3. Market growth rate.
4. Share of the market.
5. Investment required.

---

[16] S. Kaplan, and N. Barish, "Decision Making Allowing for Uncertainty of Future Investment Opportunities," *Management Science*, June, 1967, pp. B-569–77.

[17] David B. Hertz, "Risk Analysis in Capital Investment," *Harvard Business Review*, Vol. XLII (1964), pp. 95–106.

6. Residual value of investment.
7. Operating costs.
8. Fixed costs.
9. Useful life of facilities.

Management is asked for estimates of the probability distributions for each of these random variables. A computer is then used to carry out the trials for the simulation method. The rate-of-return probabilities are developed from the relative frequency with which values appear in the simulation runs. This information can be displayed graphically to assist in understanding of the risk of each alternative.

Simulations such as this have the advantage of being able to treat problems of much broader scope than those for which we have developed analytic solutions. However, the goals are exactly the same. They are used to produce valuable information about the sensitivity of possible outcomes to the variability of input factors and to develop measures of the likelihood of achieving various possible rates of return.

SELECTED BIBLIOGRAPHY

DeGarmo, E. Paul. *Engineering Economy*. 4th ed. New York: The Macmillan Co., 1967.

Fabrycky. W. J., and Torgersen, Paul E. *Operations Economy*, chaps. vi and vii. Englewood Cliffs, N.J.: Prentice-Hall, Inc., 1966.

Grant, Eugene L., and Ireson, W. Grant. *Principles of Engineering Economy*. 4th ed. New York: Ronald Press, 1960.

Jorgenson, D. W.; McCall, J. J.; and Radner, R. *Optimal Replacement Policy*. Chicago: Rand McNally & Co., 1967.

Morris, William T. *The Analysis of Management Decisions*. Homewood, Ill.: Richard D. Irwin, Inc., 1964.

――――. *The Capacity Decision System*. Homewood, Ill.: Richard D. Irwin, Inc., 1967.

Taylor, George A. *Managerial and Engineering Economy*. Princeton, N.J.: D. Van Nostrand Co., Inc., 1964.

Thuesen, H. G., and Fabrycky, W. J. *Engineering Economy*. 3d ed. Englewood Cliffs, N.J.: Prentice-Hall, Inc., 1964.

PROBLEMS

8-1 A small rubber company is considering the manufacture of rubber baby buggy bumpers. Being in a highly competitive market, they have concluded that the sales price for each set of bumpers must be $25 as dictated by market conditions. The production engineering department feels that no more than 800 sets per month can be manufactured due to space limitations. The cost accounting department has provided the following cost figures:

Fixed cost chargeable to this operation = $3,000 per month

Labor charges = $10 per set of bumpers

Because of a complex interaction with other items which may be manufactured on the same machines, machine operating expenses (M) are estimated to be related to the production quantity (X) by

$$M = 0.00005X^3 - 0.03X^2$$

a) Write equations and draw graphs for total revenue, total cost, and total profit.

b) Compute the marginal revenue, marginal cost, average revenue, and average cost functions. Graph these functions.

c) (1) Derive the number of sets which should be manufactured each month to (*i*) maximize profit, (*ii*) maximize revenue, (*iii*) break even.

(2) Show these points on the graphs developed in parts (*a*) and (*b*) above.

(3) Compare profits at the maximum profit and maximum revenue points.

8-2 The Student Glorification Company is considering the manufacture of an Instructor Persuader. A market survey has revealed that expected demand (D) is related to sales price (P) in the following manner:

$$D = 500 - 5P$$

To produce these units will require physical facilities with the following estimated costs:

Heat and light   = \$500
Property taxes   = \$1,500
Interest on loans = \$2,000

A vendor has agreed to supply material whose price is related to the units demanded as follows:

$$M = 0.00046D^3$$

Labor expense is given as \$10 per unit produced.

a) Write an equation and draw a graph (on the same axes) for each of the following:

(1) Marginal revenue   (3) Average revenue
(2) Marginal cost   (4) Average cost

Indicate the equilibrium point or point of maximum profit on the figure.

b) Show analytically how many units should be manufactured to maximize total revenue. Prove that this is the point of maximum revenue.

c) Show analytically how many units should be manufactured to minimize total cost. Prove that this is the point of minimum cost.

d) Show analytically how many are needed to maximize profits. What will be the sales price of these units? What is the maximum profit?

8-3 Thanks to the work of some off-hour IE students, the local bar has determined that demand (D) in kegs for their suds is related to price (P) charged per keg in the following manner:

$$D = \frac{10 - P}{0.05}$$

Variable cost is related to quantity consumed by

$$V.C. = 0.95D^2 - 45D$$

A fixed cost of $250 is incurred each evening the bar is open.

a) Calculate the quantity consumed each evening which will permit the bar to break even.

b) Calculate the price which should be charged to produce maximum profits.

c) Calculate the demand quantity at which the bar should close down for the evening. Explain why it should close at this point.

8-4   Ignoring complications posed by the Internal Revenue Service, you wish to determine the correct annual write-off for a recently purchased machine using a "fixed percent of declining balance" depreciation method. The machine was purchased new at a cost of $10,000. Barring IRS interference it is estimated to have a salvage value of $81 four years from now. What percent should you write off each year to reach this salvage value in the time specified? Show all calculations.

8-5   Ignoring complications posed by the Internal Revenue Service, you wish to determine the correct annual write-off for a recently purchased still using a "*fixed-percent of a declining balance*" depreciation method. The still was purchased new from Moonshiner's Specialties at a cost of $100,000. Barring IRS interference, it is expected to have a salvage value of $1,024 five years from now. What percent should you write off each year to reach this salvage value in the time specified? Show *all* calculations.

8-6   Machine A was purchased four years ago for $1,200 and had an estimated life of 10 years with an estimated salvage value of $200. Today machine A can be sold to a used machinery dealer for $300.

a) What is the present book value of machine A—

(1)   Under straight-line depreciation?

(2)   Under double-declining balance depreciation?

(3)   Under sum-of-the-years'-digits depreciation?

b) Set up an equation to calculate the equivalent annual cost of retaining machine A for the *rest* of its estimated life assuming an interest rate of 5 percent. (Plug the correct numbers into the equation but do not solve.)

8-7   *Develop* an expression for effective annual interest rate, given a published rate of *i* per year which is to be compounded *K* times each year.

8-8   A year ago the president of the local Funboy Club purchased a new Gord for $3,400 to squire the bunnies around town. At that time the Gord had an estimated life of six years and a salvage value of $400. Its operating cost is $3,200 per year including the stock of booze in the backseat bar. At the end of the first year a salesman offers the president a new Blunderbird for $4,600. This car has an estimated life of five years, a salvage value of $600, and owing to reduced bar space, an operating cost of only $2,200. The salesman offers to allow $1,400 for the Gord on the purchase of the Blunderbird. Funboy uses 8 percent in all interest calculations.

a) What is the present book value of the Gord—
(1) Under straight-line depreciation?
(2) Under sum-of-the-years'-digits depreciation?

b) Calculate the proper percentage to use in a fixed-percent-of-declining-balance formula for the new Blunderbird. What will be its book value one year from now?

c) Compare the equivalent annual costs for the two vehicles as calculated from the present point in time. Which auto should the president have?

8–9   A company currently has a three-year-old Clip-Twister Mark I which they carry on their books at $30,000. They have a buyer for this machine who will give them $40,000. If they sell it, they will purchase the Mark II model for $70,000. The Mark I should last another four years if they spend $1,000 on it at the end of each three-month period. At that time it will be worth $5,000. The Mark II should last 10 years with a routine expense every six months of $500 plus an additional overhaul charge of $1,000 at the end of each year. The Mark II also has an expected salvage value of $5,000. The company seeks to receive a return of 16 percent per year on their cash. They are in the 50 percent income tax bracket.

a) What is the present value of money exchanges implied by each of the alternatives?

b) Should the company buy the new machine? (Show all calculations.)

8–10   Five years ago Joe College purchased a new Rolled Joyce with powerless steering for $8,000. It was depreciated by straight-line depreciation based on an eight-year life. The current bluebook price for Joe's Rolled is $2,000. A replacement Rolled to do the same work is priced at $9,000, but since today's coeds are more demanding the proper car to buy costs $10,000.

Over the past five years Joe has put his depreciation cash to work in a special account as it became available and has managed to earn a pre-tax profit of 10 percent per year on his investment. (Joe's primary business is selling peanuts to Zoo patrons.) Income taxes have amounted to 40 percent of all profits each year.

a) How much extra money beyond those funds tagged for depreciation will Joe have to find now in order to replace his Rolled Joyce with the new $10,000 vehicle?

b) Assume that Joe is now $1,000 short. What amount of extra sales of peanuts each year would it have taken to provide an adequate sinking fund for this extra amount of money if he gets a pre-tax profit of 20 percent of the sales price on these nuts. (Assume tax rate of 40 percent.)

8–11   N. O. Dumbell desires to purchase a new car every X years. A local investment opportunity provides i percent interest compounded monthly. Develop for Dumbell an analytic expression for the amount of money (R) he should invest at the end of each month in order to be able to purchase an auto costing S dollars X years hence. Show *all* steps in the calculation.

8–12   Two years ago the president of the local gin mill purchased an automatic martini mixer for $1,300. At that time the mixer had an estimated life of six years and a salvage value of $100. Its operating costs have averaged $150 per month during the past two years and management foresees no change in this figure. Today a salesman has offered an improved model of the mixer with an attached olive stuffer for the full price of $1,800. An annual operating cost of $1,200 is predicted for this machine over its estimated lifespan of three years with no salvage value. The salesman has agreed to allow $600 trade-in if we purchase his new machine. Management feels that all investments should yield 10 percent interest.

a) What is the present book value of our current mixer—
(1)   Under sum-of-the-years'-digits depreciation?
(2)   Under double-declining balance depreciation?

b) Assume that the gin mill has used straight-line depreciation methods. Based on an equivalent annual cost calculation, show which mixer management should have.

c) As an alternative financing plan the salesman has offered the company monthly payments based on bank rate interest of 6 percent per annum.
(1)   What effective interest is being charged?
(2)   What will be the monthly payment if the loan is set up for two years with interest being charged only on the unpaid balance?

8–13   Two years ago an automatic martini mixer was purchased for $1,500. At that time it was estimated to have a life of six years and a salvage value of $300. Operating costs have run $150 per month, and management foresees no change in this figure. Today an improved model with an automatic olive stuffer is available for $2,000. An annual operating cost of $1,200 is predicted for this machine over its estimated life-span of three years with no salvage value. The old machine will bring $800 on trade-in. Management feels 10 percent is a fair return on investment.

a) What is the current book value of the old mixer—
(1)   Under sum-of-the-years'-digits depreciation?
(2)   Under double-declining balance depreciation?

b) Assume that straight-line depreciation has been used. Based on an equivalent annual cost calculation, show which mixer management should have. Show all calculations.

8–14   The "marginal contribution" of a product is estimated to be 30 percent of the sales dollar. The fixed costs associated with its manufacture are $5,000,000.
a) What dollar volume of sales is necessary to break even?
b) What is the profit for sales of $20,000,000?

8–15   A company is considering the purchase of a new executive lap warmer. The new warmer lists for $2,000 and can be purchased in a variety of ways:
a) $2,000 cash in 90 days with the old warmer being sold outside.
b) $1,500 cash plus the old warmer as trade-in today.
c) $300 per quarter for two years with the old warmer being retained.
The old warmer carries a book value of $800 and can be sold to a scrap dealer for $480. Assume that the company considers 16 percent per year to be a fair rate of return and that the old warmer will be worth $50 at the end of its three-year life and the new will be worth $100 at the end of its five-year life. Calculate an equivalent annual cost for owning the new warmer under each of the purchase plans described above.

8–16   The operator of a fleet of cars is faced with the decision of leasing his vehicles or purchasing them outright. He can lease each of the desired cars for $100 per month payable on the last day of the month. The lease contract covers two years. The lease price covers all maintenance, but his insurance premium is $150 per six months with the first premium due on the date the lease is signed. He can purchase the same vehicle outright for $3,000. Under this plan his insurance premmium will be $200 per year with the first payment due at the time of purchase. It is estimated that the rate of maintenance expense will be a continuous function of time described by $5e^{2t}$ where t represents time measured in years since new. If he purchases his vehicles he plans to replace them at the end of three years. He estimates that they will be worth $1,200 at that time.

   a) Assuming that our executive values money at 24 percent for lease payments and at 12 percent per year nominal rate for all other expenses, calculate the present worth of each of the above alternatives.

   b) Which alternative is to be preferred? Why?

   c) Assuming that the supplier of the above lease vehicles experiences a maintenance cost rate function of the form $M(t) = 200$, an interest rate of 10 percent and a purchase cost of $2,500, at what point in time will he " break even " in terms of present worth? (For computational convenience, you may assume that his lease income comes in at a constant rate throughout the year.)

   d) Suppose that IRS imposes a six-year life on these vehicles and that the company uses sum-of-the-years'-digits depreciation method. What will be the book value at the time of sale of the purchased vehicles (three years)?

8–17   The Alaskan Fried Whale franchise and equipment can be purchased for $100,000. The seller agrees to buy back the used equipment at the end of the 10-year franchise agreement for $10,000. The estimated sales income from this franchise is $58,270 per year. Operating expense is expected to be $40,000 per year. Calculate the internal rate of return for the purchaser of the franchise.

8–18   Sam is considering the purchase of a delivery truck which he will then lease to a local merchant. The truck will cost $8,000 and is expected to be worthless after five years. Sam estimates the following income and expense schedules:

Year	Gross Receipts	Operating Expense
1	4,000	$2,000
2	4,000	2,200
3	4,000	2,800
4	4,000	3,500
5	4,000	3,900

Sam is considered to be a good customer by the local bank and normally invests his funds in deposit certificates currently yielding 6 percent. However with the inflationary spiral, he expects that in another two years he can receive 8 percent for his money.

a) From the information given, calculate the average rate of return for the delivery truck.

b) Compare this result with the internal rate of return based upon average net profit.

8–19 A machine currently under consideration has an initial cost of $20,000 and zero salvage value. Operating expense is estimated to be $2,000 per year. Maintenance expense increases at a rate of $3,000 per year. The company expects a nominal rate of return of 12 percent on investments. Determine the economic life of this machine.

8–20 An automobile dealer is considering entering the leasing business. When a new vehicle is leased to a customer, the customer agrees to pay $100 per month for three years. The dealer can only estimate maintenance costs by providing a range for each item. Routine preventive maintenance is felt to be independent year to year, but major drive-train repairs are felt to be highly correlated. The data he is willing to provide are:

Year	Preventive Maintenance	Drive-Train Repairs
1	120–300	0–180
2	250–490	60–300
3	300–540	150–450

A new car costs the dealer $2,400 and will be sold for $800 at the end of three years. He would like to receive a return of 15 percent on his investment.

a) Calculate the mean and variance for the present worth of such a lease agreement.

b) Estimate the probability that his return will exceed 15 percent.

8–21 The following data are available for cost elements for operating machines A and B valued at $1,000 each:

Year	A—Mean	A—Variance	B—Mean	B—Variance
1	1,000	4,900	1,200	4,900
2	1,200	6,400	1,200	4,900
3	1,500	10,000	1,200	6,400
4			1,200	6,400
5			1,200	10,000

A has a three-year life and B has a five-year life. Both have zero salvage value. A nominal interest of 12 percent is used.

a) Assuming independence, calculate the mean and variance for the equivalent annual cost of operating each machine.

b) From the results of part (*a*), calculate the probability that the annual cost of operating A will exceed the cost of operating B.

c) Repeat the calculations of parts (*a*) and (*b*) under the assumption that the correlation coefficients between any two years operating expenses for machine A is 0.5.

d) Suppose that costs for A are perfectly correlated, costs for B are uncorrelated, and both machines are to be leased. The receipts from each machine are $1,500 per year. Calculate the mean and variance for total present worth.

CHAPTER 9

Statistical Quality Control

THE PURPOSE of this chapter is to introduce some basic concepts from the area of statistical quality control (SQC). There is an extensive literature in the field with handbook-type equations, tables, and graphs for a wide variety of quality control situations. These tools are readily available to the interested reader.

It is not the intent of this chapter to reproduce handbook information but rather to develop an appreciation for how quality control plans are conceived from basic statistical and economic considerations. In this manner the reader will hopefully be better prepared to intelligently employ the widely distributed handbook information as well as alter and design control plans tailored to his own peculiar working situation.

The Quality Control Problem

It is sometimes said that one cannot inspect quality into a finished product. The implication of such a statement is that many different people, making a variety of decisions, influence the quality of an end product. The engineer influences quality by specifying tolerances, material to be used, and the manufacturing process. Management influences quality by policy decisions relative to quality level, incentives offered to workers, and desired product characteristics. Workmen influence quality by the pride they take in their work and the degree to which they accept responsibility for the quality of their own work. Finally, the inspection department influences quality by enforcing the quality standards specified by management and engineering.

An exhaustive treatise on quality control would require that we investigate all such influences on the quality of an end product. An initial division for such a study might be the creation versus the measurement of quality. The creation of quality involves process capability studies, human motivation, and market potential. These considerations often lead to unquantifiable results which must be resolved by subjective management judgment. The measurement of quality, on the other hand, is a well-defined problem which often deals in hard, impersonal numbers. This is the area of immediate concern to us. How can we establish inspection plans to ensure that desired quality standards are being achieved? Since statistical techniques are widely used, this area receives the title statistical quality control.

Functions of SQC. For our purposes, the subject of statistical quality control will be divided into two major subtopics. The first concerns the design of acceptance sampling plans. The second concerns the design of control charts to monitor continuous production processes. Both cases are merely special applications of the elementary statistical techniques introduced in Chapter 4. All acceptance sampling plans and control charts can be viewed as hypothesis tests designed to test the hypothesis that the process is operating at a specified quality level. Although we will discuss such tests in the context of a production operation, it will soon become apparent that they are very general and can be applied to many problems other than the manufacture and purchase of physical goods.

All manufacturing processes involve some inherent random variation. For example, an automatic screw machine is incapable of turning pins which are exactly 0.5000 inches in diameter. One may measure 0.5001, the next 0.4998, etc., while the process is completely in control in the sense that it is performing within the limits of its capabilities. If this machine is incapable of holding diameters closer than ± 0.0005 inches, we may find individual pins measuring anywhere in the interval 0.4995 to 0.5005 when the tools are set for a target of 0.5000 inches. The quality control problem begins with the assumption that there is an inherent variation in output. The problem is to decide whether observed process variation represents a change in the process or is merely a part of the natural variability of the output.

Acceptance sampling plans are used by both producers and consumers of manufactured goods. A producer uses such plans to insure that his customers are receiving the quality of goods specified before a lot is shipped. A consumer uses acceptance sampling plans to gain assurance that lots of material received meet the quality level desired. This prevents the investment of labor and additional material in goods of unacceptable quality. In addition, sampling inspection may offer comparisons among alternative sources of supply, grading of material for different applications, etc.

Samples drawn from a continuous production process perform similar functions to acceptance sampling plans. They flag changes in process output quality so that they may be corrected. This prevents additional investment in subsequent operations for goods that are already defective, as well as complying with announced specifications for the product. In addition to immediate process control, control chart procedures may be used to augment incentive pay plans for workers by making them aware that quality of output is monitored and providing initiation of penalties for faulty output. Control charts can also be used to detect trends and process adjustment procedures, as well as to provide guidelines for product specifications by establishing quality obtainable from existing processes.

Role of Statistics.   The primary reason for using sampling procedures in quality control is economy. One hopes to achieve specified quality assurance without the necessity of 100 percent inspection. In addition there may be applications in which inspection destroys the item as in certain yield strength tests and hardness tests. In such situations 100 percent inspection is obviously impossible. The decision on whether or not a lot meets specifications must of necessity be made from sample data. Finally, one might argue that inspection quality on a small sample is much higher than it would be for 100 percent inspection for reasons of monotony and fatigue. Most of our previous discussion relative to hypothesis tests in general is applicable to the design of SQC procedures.

Once the sampling procedures have been specified, the conduct of an SQC system is one of management by exception. Sample data can be collected and tabulated by relatively unskilled personnel. The production system or purchasing procedure is not touched unless the sample data indicate that a change from hypothesized conditions may have taken place. At that point more skilled persons may be notified to adjust the process in production operations or instructions for 100 percent inspection given in receiving operations.

The design of a control procedure requires the specification of sample size, sample frequency, and control limits. The particular numbers selected represent compromises among desired quality consistency, cost of inspection, cost of missing quality shifts, and cost of citing nonexistent shifts in the process.

Acceptance Sampling Plans

Acceptance sampling plans are usually described by professional jargon of practitioners in the field. However, the construction of a sampling plan and its execution are merely practical applications of the hypothesis testing procedures discussed in Chapter 4. For that reason we will devote most of our example computations to the normal and Poisson distributions. The jargon and basic concepts introduced can then be easily extended to situations requiring less tractable distributions, such as the hypergeometric and binomial.

Single Sampling Plans.   The simplest inspection plans to design are those involving attribute inspection of a single sample drawn from a lot of size N. The plan is specified by sample size n and acceptance number c. Each item in the sample is inspected and classified as good or bad. If the number of bad items exceeds c, the lot is rejected. Otherwise it is accepted. Rejecting the lot usually means one of two things. It is either returned to the supplier or 100 percent inspection is instituted on the remaining items in the lot. An intermediate form of decision requiring that additional samples be taken may also be considered. The implications of each of these decisions on ultimate lot quality can be determined from the mathematical characteristics of the inspection plan.

Since every item can be classed as either good or bad, a potential model to employ for describing the population is the binomial distribution. This view is absolutely correct as long as we consider the lots of N items to be drawn at random from a theoretically infinite process. The random samples of size n drawn in turn from each lot of size N are then equivalent to drawing random samples of size n directly from the process. This permits us to ignore the lot size N in our calculations.

On the other hand, one may want to view an isolated lot as a one-of-a-kind situation. The sampling plan then establishes the proportion of lots that would be accepted in an infinite series of identical lots by the rationale of confidence interval calculations previously discussed. In this situation we are sampling from a finite universe N rather than the infinite universe implied by the continuous process.

The sampling problem here can be viewed as drawing a sample from a population of N elements containing m defective and $N - m$ nondefective items. We seek the probability $p(x \mid n)$ that a sample of n elements selected at random from this population will contain exactly x defective items. The sample will contain x defective and $n - x$ nondefective items. The defective ones can be selected in $\binom{m}{x}$ different ways. The nondefective ones can be selected in $\binom{N - m}{n - x}$ ways. Since any choice of x defective items can be combined with any choice of nondefective items, the total number of ways to draw such a sample is $\binom{N - m}{n - x}\binom{m}{x}$. The relative frequency of drawing this sample is obtained by dividing by the total number of ways a sample of size n can be drawn from the population of N items.

The appropriate model for this population is the hypergeometric distribution given by

$$p(x \mid n) = \frac{\binom{N - m}{n - x}\binom{m}{x}}{\binom{N}{n}} \tag{9-1}$$

The interpretation in our sampling context is that $p(x \mid n)$ is the probability of obtaining x defective items in a random sample of n taken without replacement from a population of N items containing m defective items. The differences between the finite and infinite population viewpoints are discussed at length by Duncan.[1]

As the lot size N becomes large relative to the sample size n, the hypergeometric distribution approaches the binomial. For that reason we will confine our discussion to the binomial and its approximations. When more exact methods are required, the reader is urged to consult one of the textbooks listed at the end of this chapter which are devoted entirely to quality control.

Obtaining the Sample. Acceptance sampling plans can be used to screen purchased material or to screen in-process lots of material produced within a plant. In both cases, the first task is to define the lot. Bowker and Lieberman caution that all parts in a lot should have been produced under essentially the same conditions.[2] This means that we must take care to see that parts purchased from different suppliers or made on different machines are not mixed into one lot, whenever practical. The discrimination power of the sampling plan depends upon variation from lot to lot and should not be compromised by mixing different lots.

In addition to carefully defining the content of individual lots, we must observe sound sampling procedures in choosing the n items to be inspected. This means that the sample must be drawn from the lot in a random manner such that each item in the lot has an equal chance of being selected. The safest policy is to select the sample by choosing items in an order determined from a table of random numbers. The folly of yielding to the temptation to inspect the first 10 items in a production lot of 100 pistons, for example, should be obvious. If the tooling failed midway in the production of the lot, our sample might show zero defective items when in fact the lot could contain as much as 90 percent defective items.

Producer and Consumer Risks. A common method of designing sampling plans is to specify the risks of Type I and Type II errors exactly as we did in hypothesis testing. These errors are specified relative to a null hypothesis H_0 and an alternative hypothesis H_1. The risk of a Type I error is defined as the probability that the null hypothesis will be rejected when it is in fact true. The risk of a Type II error is defined as the probability that the null hypothesis will be accepted when the alternative hypothesis is in fact true, i.e., the risk of accepting a false hypothesis.

In a sampling procedure, we are essentially estimating the fraction defective in the lot. If d defective items are found in a sample of size n, our estimate of lot fraction defective is $p = d/n$. Sampling inspection can then be viewed as testing the hypothesis that $p \le p_g$ against the alternative that $p > p_g$ where p_g represents the dividing fraction between good and bad lots.

[1] Acheson J. Duncan, *Quality Control and Industrial Statistics* (3d ed.; Richard D. Irwin, Inc., 1965), pp. 147–53.

[2] Albert H. Bowker, and Gerald J. Lieberman, *Engineering Statistics* (Englewood Cliffs, N.J.: Prentice-Hall, Inc., 1959), p. 403.

The quality control literature has attached special names to the different levels and risks. The following four definitions are common:

AQL = acceptable quality level. This is the quality level of the supplier's process which is considered good. It characterizes the performance capability of the production process. The sampling plan should yield a high probability of accepting lots of this quality or better.

α = producer's risk. This is the probability of rejecting lots of AQL and is equivalent to the risk of a Type I error. With frequency α a producer whose process is running satisfactorily will have his lots rejected.

LTPD = lot tolerance percent defective. This is considered to be a very poor quality level. The sampling plan should yield a low probability of accepting lots of this quality or poorer.

β = consumer's risk. This is the probability of accepting lots of LTPD quality level and is equivalent to the risk of a Type II error. With frequency β a consumer will accept lots which come from a process running at LTPD level.

Historically, the risk levels were commonly set at $\alpha = 0.05$ and $\beta = 0.10$. More recently, the users of statistical quality control have become more knowledgeable about general hypothesis testing techniques and been much more flexible in the risk levels specified. For a general discussion of Type I and II errors the reader should refer to Chapter 4.

The four quantities specified above can be used to obtain a pair of simultaneous equations in the unknown design parameters c and n. Assuming a large lot size N, we have the following equations to be approximately satisfied:

$$P(d \leq c \mid \text{AQL}) = \sum_{d=0}^{c} \binom{n}{d}(\text{AQL})^d (1 - \text{AQL})^{n-d} = 1 - \alpha \qquad (9\text{--}2)$$

and

$$P(d \leq c \mid \text{LTPD}) = \sum_{d=0}^{c} \binom{n}{d}(\text{LTPD})^d (1 - \text{LTPD})^{n-d} = \beta \qquad (9\text{--}3)$$

When the sample size is also relatively large, we can use the Poisson approximation to the binomial. The equations then become

$$P(d \leq c \mid \text{AQL}) = \sum_{d=0}^{c} \frac{[(\text{AQL})(n)]^d e^{-(\text{AQL})(n)}}{d!} = 1 - \alpha \qquad (9\text{--}4)$$

and

$$P(d \leq c \mid \text{LTPD}) = \sum_{d=0}^{c} \frac{[(\text{LTPD})(n)]^d e^{-(\text{LTPD})(n)}}{d!} = \beta \qquad (9\text{--}5)$$

Since both the binomial and Poisson are discrete distributions, it is obvious that the specified α and β will in most instances be only approximately met.

Because the actual α and β for the end plan both will differ from specifications, it becomes a management decision to determine which risk level will be held most closely. There are extensive tables and graphs available in the literature which can be used to solve the somewhat awkward Equations 9–4 and 9–5. Basically they involve trial-and-error solutions effected with the cumulative Poisson tables. Our approach will be to seek analytic approximations which can be solved without trial and error, while recognizing that solutions so obtained may not come as close to specifications as those obtained by extensive trial-and-error calculations.

For purposes of illustration, we will go one step further in approximation by using the normal approximation to the binomial. The normal approximation will have a mean of np and a variance of npq. The specification equations to be satisfied are then of the form

$$p(x \le c \mid p) = \int_{-\infty}^{c} (2\pi npq)^{-1/2} \exp\left[\frac{-(x - np)^2}{2npq}\right] dx \qquad (9\text{–}6)$$

The parameters c and n are determined from the expression for the standard normal deviate. Critical z values are selected from the cumulative normal tables to correspond with the specified α and β. The transformation

$$z_{\text{CRIT}} = \frac{x - \mu}{\sigma}$$

leads to the pair of equations

$$z_{(1-\alpha)} = \frac{c - (\text{AQL})(n)}{[(\text{AQL})(1 - \text{AQL})(n)]^{1/2}} \qquad (9\text{–}7)$$

and

$$z_{\beta} = \frac{c - (\text{LTPD})(n)}{[(\text{LTPD})(1 - \text{LTPD})(n)]^{1/2}} \qquad (9\text{–}8)$$

which can be solved for c and n.

For example suppose that we must design a plan to meet the following specifications:

$$\text{AQL} = 0.02 \qquad \alpha = 0.05$$

$$\text{LTPD} = 0.06 \qquad \beta = 0.10$$

The probability statements to be satisfied are

$$p(d \le c \mid p = 0.02) = 0.95 \qquad \text{for AQL}$$

and

$$p(d \le c \mid p = 0.06) = 0.10 \qquad \text{for LTPD quality}$$

From the cumulative normal we have set the set of equations

$$z_{0.95} = 1.65 = \frac{c - (0.02)n}{[(0.02)(0.98)(n)]^{1/2}}$$

table

p 444 stat bk.

$$z_{0.10} = -1.28 = \frac{c - (0.06)n}{[(0.06)(0.94)(n)]^{1/2}}$$

the simultaneous solution of which yields approximately

$$n = 180 \qquad c = 6.7$$

Since n and c must both be integers, let us fix n at 180 and examine the trade-off between $c = 6$ and $c = 7$ relative to the desired risk levels. Although the normal approximation has been adequate to obtain a solution somewhere in the neighborhood of the one called for by specification, it is desirable to perform the final screening by using the more nearly correct Poisson distribution. For $c = 6$, from the Poisson approximation, the producer and consumer risks are

$$\alpha = \sum_{x=7}^{\infty} \left[\frac{(3.6)^x e^{-3.6}}{x!} \right] = 0.0733$$

$$\beta = \sum_{x=0}^{6} \left[\frac{(10.8)^x e^{-10.8}}{x!} \right] = 0.0890$$

For $c = 7$, the risks are

$$\alpha = \sum_{x=8}^{\infty} \left[\frac{(3.6)^x e^{-3.6}}{x!} \right] = 0.0308$$

$$\beta = \sum_{x=0}^{7} \left[\frac{(10.8)^x e^{-10.8}}{x!} \right] = 0.1586$$

If we offer no latitude in the choice of n, it appears that $c = 6$ comes closest to fitting the plan specifications, although neither α nor β is exactly the number requested.

The calculation procedure outlined above is illustrated graphically in Figure 9–1. Any number of defects falling to the right of c will cause the lot to be

FIGURE 9–1

Producer and Consumer Risks for a Single Sample Acceptance Sampling Plan

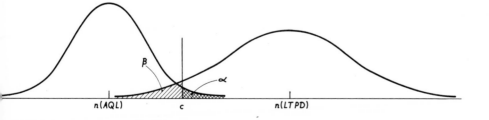

rejected. Any number to the left will cause the lot to be accepted. The two distributions with means $n(AQL)$ and $n(LTPD)$ both have some area on each side of c. The producer and consumer risks are equal to the indicated shaded areas.

Justification for Normality. The use of the normal approximation to a known binomial distribution can be justified on the basis of the central limit theorem. Recall earlier in this chapter that we compared the single sampling plan with its acceptance number to a hypothesis test on p, the population fraction defective. The sample estimate for p, d/n, can be viewed as an estimate for the mean of a Bernoulli distribution. The Bernoulli distribution is given by

$$f(x) = p^x(1 - p)^{1-x} \qquad x = 0, 1 \qquad (9\text{--}9)$$

This distribution has mean and variance of

$$E(x) = p$$

$$\text{Var}(x) = p(1 - p)$$

The sample estimates for p, say $\bar{p}$, are then by the central limit theorem normally distributed with

$$E(\bar{p}) = p$$

$$\text{Var}(\bar{p}) = \frac{p(1 - p)}{n}$$

However, since our critical number c can be related to fraction defective M by $M = c/n$, we can express a test on $\bar{p}$ in terms of the standard normal deviate as

$$z = \frac{M - p}{[p(1 - p)/n]^{1/2}}$$

$$= \frac{c/n - p}{[p(1 - p)/n]^{1/2}} = \frac{c - np}{[np(1 - p)]^{1/2}}$$

This is exactly the statistic we employed in Equations 9–7 and 9–8.

The Operating Characteristic Curve. In the previous section we developed single sample acceptance sampling plans by specifying two pairs of numbers. We gave these numbers special names, i.e., AQL, α, LTPD, and β. In reality they are nothing more than two points on an operating characteristic or OC curve. The entire curve specifies the discriminating power of an acceptance sampling plan. The fraction defective of the lot being sampled appears on the abscissa. The ordinate shows the probability that a lot will be accepted.

The ideal sampling plan would be one which would distinguish between good and bad lots with probability one. The OC curve for such a plan would be z shaped. Every lot with less than p_g percent defective, where p_g is the dividing line between good and bad lots, would be accepted with probability one, while those lots with greater than p_g percent defective would be accepted with probability zero. There is one plan with such an OC curve. Assuming that the inspection process is totally effective, one hundred percent inspection produces the ideal z-shaped OC curve. As sample size is reduced from total lot size for a fixed acceptance number, the OC curve retreats further from the ideal z shape. The spread between AQL and LTPD quality levels reflects the economic necessity of sampling inspection. With one hundred percent inspection both AQL and LTPD become the same number p_g, the dividing line between good and bad lots.

To plot the OC curve for a given plan, one needs only to consider the probability that the random variable d will take on a value less than or equal to the acceptance number c, under the assumption of a particular population fraction defective. Let $L(p)$ be the probability of accepting a lot containing fraction defective p. Then

$$L(p) = P(d = 0) + P(d = 1) + \cdots + P(d = c)$$

where $P(d = i)$ is the probability of i defectives in a sample of n. Using the binomial distribution

$$L(p) = \sum_{d=0}^{c} \binom{n}{d} p^d(1 - p)^{n-d} \qquad (9\text{--}10)$$

The Poisson approximation is

$$L(p) = \sum_{d=0}^{c} \frac{(np)^d e^{-np}}{d!} \qquad (9\text{--}11)$$

The most accurate normal approximation for use in this context is

$$L(p) = \int_{-\infty}^{c+1/2} (2\pi)^{-1/2}[np(1 - p)]^{-1/2} \exp\left[\frac{-(x - np)^2}{2np(1 - p)}\right] dx \qquad (9\text{--}12)$$

Adding 1/2 to the upper limit in the normal approximation increases the accuracy somewhat since the continuous normal is being used to approximate the discrete binomial. The probability of finding exactly c defects, for example, can be best written as

$$P(c) = \binom{n}{c} p^c(1 - p)^{n-c} \approx \int_{c-1/2}^{c+1/2} [2\pi np(1 - p)]^{-1/2} \exp\left[\frac{-(x - np)^2}{2np(1 - p)}\right] dx$$

The probability that $x = c$ in both the binomial and the normal can be related to the area under a curve in the interval $(c - \frac{1}{2}, c + \frac{1}{2})$. The use of 1/2 in the limits could also be extended to our previously introduced sample size calculations at some expense in computational ease.

Consider, for example, the probability of accepting a lot whose incoming quality is 10 per cent defective, using a sample of size $n = 20$ and an acceptance number of $c = 2$. From the binomial distribution

$$L(0.10) = \sum_{d=0}^{2} \binom{20}{d}(0.10)^d(0.90)^{20-d} = 0.6779$$

using the Poisson approximation with $\mu = np = 2.0$

$$L(0.10) = 0.6767$$

which is in close agreement with the binomial. Using the normal approximation with $\mu = 2.0$, $\sigma^2 = 1.8$

$$L(0.10) = \int_{-\infty}^{2.5} N(2.0, 1.34) = 0.6453$$

which is not quite as accurate, but still a reasonably close approximation.

With these calculations one could construct a table of $L(p)$ for all values of p of interest for a given sampling plan. A plot of these values gives the OC curve. Figure 9–2 shows the shape of the OC curves for various sampling plans with a fixed acceptance number $c = 2$ but different sample sizes n. Figure 9–3 shows the shapes obtained for fixed sample size $n = 50$ but various acceptance numbers c. Such curves permit management to compare the merits of alternative sampling plans over a wide range of possible population parameters.

Average Outgoing Quality.   The average outgoing quality (AOQ) is an important measure of performance for an inspection plan. AOQ refers to the quality level of lots after they have been inspected. The implication is that the lots have been altered by the inspection process. This happens in two principal ways. Either all defective units are discarded as discovered and those

FIGURE 9–2

OC Curves for Fixed Acceptance Number

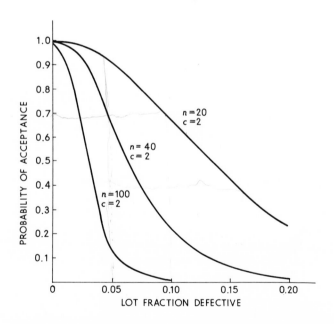

LOT FRACTION DEFECTIVE

FIGURE 9-3

OC Curves for Fixed Sample Size

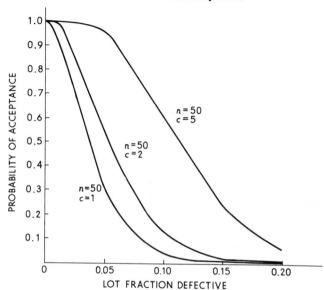

lots which are rejected are inspected 100 percent, or all defective units are replaced or repaired so that the outgoing lot size remains constant. If rejected lots are merely sent back to a supplier, then of course the inspection plan does not affect the quality level of lots submitted for inspection.

Conceptually, we can view AOQ as

$$AOQ = \frac{\text{Average number of defective units after inspection}}{\text{Total units per lot}}$$

Assuming that all lots rejected are subjected to 100 percent inspection, the numerator in this expression refers to the average number of defective items in lots which the plan accepts. If the lot has a fraction defective p, the $(N - n)$ units which are not subject to inspection will yield an average of $p(N - n)$ defective units. The probability of accepting lots of p quality level is $L(p)$, as determined from the OC curve. The average number of defective units per lot which get by an inspection plan is then

$$\text{Average} = L(p)p(N - n)$$

If defective units are discarded but not replaced, the average number of units per lot after inspection is

$$\text{Lot} = N - np - [1 - L(p)]p(N - n)$$

If defective units are replaced by good units, the lot size remains constant at N. In that event

$$AOQ = \frac{L(p)p(N - n)}{N} \qquad (9\text{--}13)$$

Without replacement of defective items

$$AOQ = \frac{L(p)p(N - n)}{N - np - [1 - L(p)]p(N - n)} \qquad (9\text{--}14)$$

One could plot the AOQ curve for any particular inspection plan by evaluating AOQ for various values of incoming lot quality p. The resulting figure looks like Figure 9–4. This curve is approximately correct for a sampling plan in which $n = 20$, $c = 2$, $N = 1,000$. Note that the AOQ calculation is particularly simple when sample size n is small compared to lot size N, as it is in this case. For numbers of this magnitude

$$AOQ = \frac{L(p)p(N - n)}{N} \approx L(p)p \qquad (9\text{--}15)$$

Using Equation 9–15, the AOQ curve can be approximated by multiplying the ordinant of the OC curve by its corresponding abscissa.

FIGURE 9–4

Average Outgoing Quality for a Sampling Inspection
Plan with $n = 20$, $c = 2$, $N = 1,000$

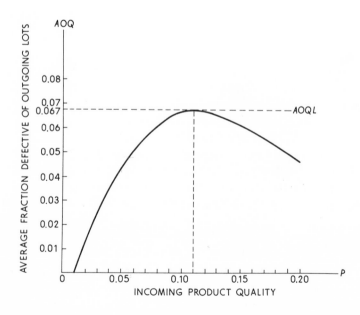

Note that the AOQ curve achieves a maximum at $p = 0.067$. This value of p is known as the average outgoing quality limit (AOQL). The existence of such a limit provides an alternative means of measuring the effectiveness of a sampling plan. Theoretically plans can be designed which provide assurance that average outgoing quality will not be worse than some specified limit. Although not often used by practitioners of SQC, it is interesting to note that the character of such rectifying sampling procedures can be determined analytically. The reason that the AOC curve does reach a maximum is that an increased fraction defective in the incoming lot triggers more and more rejections and subsequent 100 percent inspections. After AOQL quality is reached, enough lots are totally inspected, with all bad units being replaced, that the actual lot quality of goods passing through the system increases.

Using the Poisson approximation, an analytic expression for AOQL can be obtained from the derivative of AOQ. That is,

$$
\begin{aligned}
\frac{dAOQ}{dp} &= \left(\frac{N-n}{N}\right)\frac{d}{dp}\left[p\sum_{x=0}^{c}\frac{(np)^{x}e^{-np}}{x!}\right] \\
&= \frac{N-n}{N}\left[\sum_{x=0}^{c}\frac{(np)^{x}e^{-np}}{x!} + p\left(\sum_{x=0}^{c}nx\frac{(np)^{x-1}e^{-np}}{x!} - \sum_{x=0}^{c}n\frac{(np)^{x}e^{-np}}{x!}\right)\right] \\
&= \frac{N-n}{N}\left[\sum_{x=0}^{c}\frac{(np)^{x}e^{-np}}{x!} + np\left(\sum_{x=0}^{c}\frac{(np)^{x-1}e^{-np}}{(x-1)!} - \sum_{x=0}^{c}\frac{(np)^{x}e^{-np}}{x!}\right)\right] \\
&= \frac{N-n}{N}\left[\sum_{x=0}^{c}\frac{(np)^{x}e^{-np}}{x!} - \frac{np(np)^{c}e^{-np}}{c!}\right] = 0
\end{aligned}
$$

from which

$$
\sum_{x=0}^{c}\frac{(np)^{x}e^{-np}}{x!} = \frac{(c+1)(np)^{c+1}e^{-np}}{(c+1)!} \qquad (9\text{--}16)
$$

The AOQL is that value of AOQ determined by the p for which Equation 9–16 holds. Equation 9–16 can be solved by scanning the Poisson tables. Although this particular model is not widely used, these calculations should offer some insight into the ways in which special sampling plans can be analyzed. However, a more conventional approach is to employ one of the sets of sampling tables which are available.[3]

Multiple and Sequential Sampling. Multiple sampling provides for a range of uncertainty in the decision-making process. In double sampling, for example, a sample of n_1 items is drawn from the lot. If there are no more than c_1 defective items in that sample, the lot is accepted. If there are between $c_1 + 1$ and c_2 defective items a second sample of n_2 is drawn. If the number of defective items in the combined sample of $n_1 + n_2$ exceeds c_2 the lot is rejected.

---

[3] See for example, Harold F. Dodge, and Harry G. Romig, *Sampling Inspection Tables* (New York: John Wiley & Sons, Inc., 1944).

By this technique, very good lots would be accepted and very poor ones would be rejected on the first sample. Lots of intermediate quality would be given a "second chance" by the additional sample, which may provide a decided psychological advantage for some users. Such plans also have the advantage of requiring fewer average total inspections than corresponding single sample plans for any specified quality protection, but require a higher maximum amount of inspection. The potential for a high maximum amount of inspection is indicative of the primary defect of multiple and sequential sampling plans. They may require an excessive amount of administrative burden in the sense that it is extremely difficult to predict the inspection load from day to day. In addition, such plans are harder for relatively unskilled inspectors to use in that they require more thought to execute than do single sampling plans. Because of the difficulties of administration these plans have not met with wide industrial acceptance.

The OC curve for a double sampling plan can be constructed by enumerating the total number of ways that a lot may be accepted.

$$L(p) = P(d_1 \leq c_1 \mid p) + P(d_1 + d_2 \leq c_2 \mid c_1 < d_1 \leq c_2; p)$$

As noted by Bowker and Lieberman,[4] this can be written as

$$L(p) = \sum_{d_1=0}^{c_1} \binom{n_1}{d_1} p^{d_1}(1-p)^{n_1-d_1}$$

$$+ \sum_{d_1=c_1+1}^{c_2} \sum_{d_2=0}^{c_2-d_1} \binom{n_1}{d_1} p^{d_1}(1-p)^{n_1-d_1} \binom{n_2}{d_2} p^{d_2}(1-p)^{n_2-d_2} \qquad (9\text{-}17)$$

Higher order multiple sampling is carried out in similar fashion by specifying further sets of acceptance numbers and sample sizes. The decision to accept or reject at each sample is based upon the cumulative number of defects in all samples to date.

Item by item sequential sampling provides the possibility of even greater reduction in costs. Basically sequential sampling requires that a control band be established as a function of items inspected. If the number of defects falls below the lower limit at any time, the lot is accepted. If it falls above the upper limit the lot is rejected. Between the limits no decision is made about acceptance and another item is inspected. The concept is based upon the notion of a "random walk" from probability theory. The interested reader is urged to consult one of the SQC references listed at the end of the chapter for possible extensions of the concepts of multiple and sequential sampling.

Military Sampling Plans. Standard military sampling procedures have been developed for use by the Department of Defense. Originally issued during World War II, these procedures have undergone several modifications. Mil. Std. 105D, issued in 1963, is discussed by Duncan.[5] These plans are

---

[4] Bowker and Lieberman, *op. cit.*, p. 414.
[5] Duncan, *op. cit.*, chap. x.

currently the most widely used in industry. Their popularity in part stems from the fact that OC curves have been constructed for a large number of potential plans. Single sample plans, for instance, can be designed simply by scanning the curves until one which passes near the desired specification points is located. The sample size and acceptance number are then predetermined with no calculation required by the analyst.

The purpose of the sampling scheme is to constrain suppliers of military items to produce products which are at least as good as AQL quality. The particular number selected for AQL is determined by a high level conference between a supplier and the military agency. Three general inspection levels plus four special levels, relating lot size to sample size, are available. Level II denotes normal discrimination, Level I less discrimination, and Level III more discrimination. Levels are selected on the basis of product type. Inexpensive items might require a low level, while expensive items would require a high level.

Once AQL, inspection level, and lot size have been established, Mil. Std. 105D tables are used to obtain a normal sampling plan. If this plan rejects two out of five consecutive lots, it is concluded that AQL quality is not being maintained. Mil. Std. 105D then requires that a tightened inspection plan be instituted. Normal inspection is restored only when five consecutive lots are accepted on original inspection. The procedure also permits reduced inspection providing that several rather stringent conditions are met. Tables for normal, tightened, and reduced inspection plans are provided for single, double, and multiple sampling.

Cost Considerations. It is a simple matter to calculate an expected cost for a particular sampling plan, given a known lot fraction defective. The cost components are the cost of inspecting each item and the cost incurred by undetected defective items. We will denote these as

k_1 = cost per unit for inspection

k_2 = cost per defective unit which goes undetected

Under the assumption of 100 percent inspection of rejected lots, the average number of units inspected per lot is given by

$$U = n + [1 - L(p)](N - n) \qquad (9\text{–}18)$$

The average number of defective units which escape detection is

$$D = L(p)p(N - n) \qquad (9\text{–}19)$$

The total expected cost for any particular lot fraction defective p is then

$$K(p) = k_1[n + (1 - L(p))(N - n)] + k_2 L(p)p(N - n) \qquad (9\text{–}20)$$

where $L(p)$ is the probability of accepting lots of quality p.

The expression for $K(p)$ assumes that n and c have been specified so as to satisfy some criterion such as meeting given AQL, α, LTPD, β specifications.

Obviously any number of plans could be compared by this calculation, but determination of an optimum plan requires some prior knowledge of the distribution of p values. If one is willing to assume a distribution for incoming fraction defective, say $f(p)$, then the weighted cost becomes

$$K = \sum_p K(p)f(p) = k_1\left[N - (N - n) \sum_p L(p)f(p)\right] + k_2(N - n) \sum_p pL(p)f(p)$$

$$(9\text{--}21)$$

Fetter has developed a computer program which searches for the minimum cost plan once the system designer has determined the prior distribution $f(p)$.[6]

Some information concerning optimal plans can be obtained by examining the extreme cases of 100 percent inspection and no inspection. If no units are inspected, the expected cost per lot is

$$K_0 = k_2N \sum_p pf(p) \qquad (9\text{--}22)$$

If 100 percent inspection is followed, the cost per lot is

$$K_{100} = k_1 N \qquad (9\text{--}23)$$

The optimum plan will obviously fall somewhere between these extremes.

Table 9–1 and Figure 9–5 illustrate the cost behavior for several sampling

TABLE 9–1

Cost Behavior for Sampling Plans on Lots of 200

			$K(p)$		
p	$n = 200$	$n = 0$	$n = 20, c = 2$	$n = 40, c = 2$	$n = 50, c = 5$
0.01	$1,000	$ 80	$ 173	$ 271	$ 325
0.05	1,000	400	503	676	641
0.10	1,000	800	879	961	1,000
0.15	1,000	1,200	1,076	1,010	1,090
0.20	1,000	1,600	1,128	1,006	1,051

plans involving lots of 200. The cost of inspection is assumed to be $k_1 = \$5$ per unit and the cost of passing a defective unit is assumed to be $k_2 = \$40$ per unit. For the data given and the plans examined it appears that no inspection is the best policy as long as the lot fraction defective is less than 0.125. Above this point, which is the break-even point between 100 percent and no inspection, other plans become more economical. Performance

---

[6] Robert B. Fetter, *The Quality Control System* (Homewood, Ill.: Richard D. Irwin, Inc., 1967), pp. 29–32 and Appendix II.

FIGURE 9-5

Cost of Inspection Plans for Lot Size 200, $k_1 = \$5$, $k_2 = \$40$.

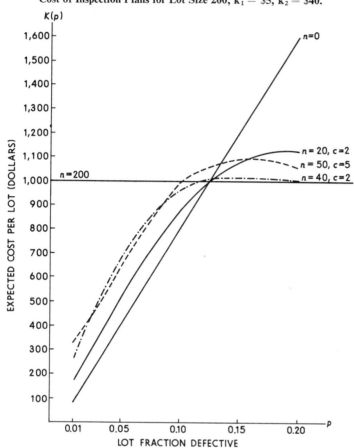

curves such as this permit management to balance economic objectives with subjective estimates of process capability without forcing the development of a prior distribution $f(p)$. Performance over the entire range of p may be more meaningful than a single expected value developed from the sometimes ill-defined function $f(p)$.

Sampling Plans for Variables. So far everything we have discussed has pertained to attribute inspection. Every item in a lot is classed as good or bad in attribute inspection. This type of inspection is required when we are examining a product for blemishes, for example. It either has or does not have a blemish. We may also use attribute sampling for inspection involving a continuous variable. For example, we might use a snap gage to classify pistons as good or bad depending upon whether or not they meet specification limits on diameter. When we use go, no-go inspection of this type, however, we are ignoring information contained in the sample. In the case of piston inspection we could obtain more information by using micrometers, for example, than we get from a snap gage. When the quality characteristic is measured on a continuous scale and the outcome of the sampling procedure is a function of such measurements, one is said to be using sampling inspection by variables.

Since inspection by variables makes greater use of the information contained in the sample than does attribute sampling, it follows that variables plans can provide the same protection with smaller sample sizes. The economy of potentially smaller sample sizes must, however, be balanced against the increased cost of inspection per item usually encountered with variables inspection.

The statistic used in variables inspection is the sample mean $\bar{x}$. The assumption is often made that the process is producing units with a known variance but with a mean that may shift from lot to lot. The inspection plan specifies a critical number M and a sample size n. The number M corresponds to the ratio c/n used in attribute sampling. It is an estimate of lot fraction defective based upon the probability that the sample mean will fall outside certain rejection limits. The sampling procedure requires that we measure each of the n items in the sample and compute the sample mean $\bar{x}$. If $\bar{x}$ is less than the critical value $\bar{x}_c$, the lot is rejected; otherwise it is accepted. The critical mean, $\bar{x}_c$, is related to M by

$$P\left(z < \frac{\bar{x}_c - \mu}{\sigma/\sqrt{n}}\right) = M \qquad (9\text{--}24)$$

Here we are employing a one-sided test under the assumption that our only concern is for a downward shift in the mean. Two-sided tests will be discussed later.

Suppose, for example, that we are running a tensile test in which 18,000 psi is the minimum acceptable tensile strength for a serviceable unit. Furthermore the process used to manufacture these items usually operates with a mean of 20,000 psi and $\sigma = 970$. The distribution for tensile strength is assumed to be normal. With these specifications, the lot fraction defective we would expect to see produced is

$$\text{AQL} = P(x < 18{,}000 \,|\, \mu = 20{,}000; \, \sigma = 970)$$

$$= P\left(z < \frac{18{,}000 - 20{,}000}{970}\right)$$

$$= P(z < -2.054) = 0.02$$

That is, the AQL level specifies the fraction of items produced which will be bad even though the process is operating at its normal level. In general terms

$$AQL = P(x < x_L \mid \mu, \sigma) \qquad (9\text{–}25)$$

where x_L represents the specification limit.

Now if the mean of the process were to shift down by e, the number of defective units in the lot would go up. Defining the percent defective separating good from bad lots as LTPD, we have

$$LTPD = P(x < x_L \mid \mu - e, \sigma) \qquad (9\text{–}26)$$

Suppose for example that we want LTPD = 0.06, then

$$P\left[z < \frac{18{,}000 - (20{,}000 - e)}{970} \right] = 0.06$$

from which

$$z = -1.555 = \frac{-2000 + e}{970}$$

and

$$e = 492$$

This tells us that if the mean shifts to $\mu = 19{,}508$ we can expect to find 6 percent of the units in the lot which will fail to meet specifications.

We could design a sampling plan for specified risks α and β in which every item tested would simply be classed as good or bad depending upon whether or not its tensile strength exceeded 18,000 psi. However, such a plan would essentially be an attribute inspection plan which ignores valuable information present in the sample for estimating the true process mean. This plan was developed in our first example for attribute plans where we found $c = 6$ and $n = 180$ met the qualifications for a plan with AQL = 0.02, LTPD = 0.06, $\alpha = 0.0733$, $\beta = 0.0890$.

Let us now examine how we might design a variables inspection plan to meet these sample specifications. From the central limit theorem we know that samples of size n drawn from a population with mean μ and standard deviation σ will be normally distributed with mean μ and standard deviation $\sigma/\sqrt{n}$. It follows, therefore, that we want to establish a critical $\bar{x}$ value, say $\bar{x}_c$, and sample size n such that

$$P(\bar{x} < \bar{x}_c \mid \mu_{AQL}, \sigma) = \alpha \qquad (9\text{–}27)$$

and

$$P(\bar{x} < \bar{x}_c \mid \mu_{LTPD}, \sigma) = 1 - \beta \qquad (9\text{–}28)$$

where μ_{AQL} is the process mean used to establish AQL and μ_{LTPD} is the process mean which will yield LTPD.

Converting to the standard normal deviate, we must solve the two equations

$$z_\alpha = \frac{\bar{x}_c - \mu_{AQL}}{\sigma/\sqrt{n}} \qquad (9\text{--}29)$$

$$z_{1-\beta} = \frac{\bar{x}_c - \mu_{LTPD}}{\sigma/\sqrt{n}} \qquad (9\text{--}30)$$

for the unknowns $\bar{x}_c$ and n. For the particular example under consideration these become

$$-1.451 = \frac{(\bar{x}_c - 20{,}000)\sqrt{n}}{970}$$

and

$$1.341 = \frac{(\bar{x}_c - 19{,}508)\sqrt{n}}{970}$$

from which

$$\bar{x}_c \approx 19{,}744 \text{ psi}$$

$$n \approx 30$$

These results indicate that we should take a sample of 30 units. If the average tensile strength exceeds $\bar{x} = 19{,}744$, the lot should be accepted. Otherwise it should be rejected.

Note that the sample size for the variables inspection plan is only one sixth as large as the sample necessary for an attributes plan with the same protection level. In cases such as the tensile test, if each item must be measured on a continuous scale to class it as good or bad, the variables plan is obviously superior. However, if we could substitute a simpler test, such as loading each unit to exactly 18,000 psi and observing whether or not failure occurs, the cost of testing might offset the advantage of sample size.

In the event that both upper and lower specification limits are required, the calculation becomes more tedious but follows the same basic logic. Now a range of $\bar{x}$ values which are acceptable must be established.

As with attribute plans, a variables sampling plan can be specified by its OC curve. The calculation of the OC curve proceeds exactly as before. Again we have designed a plan by specifying two points on that curve.

When the variance of the population is unknown, the calculations for a variables sampling plan become much more difficult. The reader interested in this extension should consult a text such as Duncan.[7]

---

[7] Duncan, op. cit.

Control Chart Design

So far, our discussion has been limited to statistical decisions involving whether or not to accept a given lot of material. Management was assumed to have no control over the process which produced the lot. Now we will turn our attention to the control of continuous processes in which the indication of an out-of-control condition signals some action on the part of management to bring the process back in control. For example, in a machining operation, tool wear might lead to the production of a large number of shafts which are larger than specifications call for. The purpose of the control chart is to signal the point at which the number of defective units is large enough to indicate that the process, in this case metal cutting, has changed sufficiently to warrant attention.

The basic assumption behind the use of control charts is that there are two basic causes of variation in quality. The first source of variation is pure chance. With the advent of statistics it has been recognized that very few processes are capable of producing exactly the same item each time. In the case of machining a shaft, for example, a particular engine lathe and operator may be capable of holding tolerances no closer than ± 0.002 inches. This says that even though the nominal size is 1.000 inch, the diameter of any shaft actually produced will be a random variable falling somewhere between 0.998 and 1.002 inches. Such variation is attributed to chance and can only be reduced by refining the process. In this instance, shafts of 0.998 inches in no way indicate that the machining process has changed from its nominal capability of 1.000 inch.

The second source of variation is related to assignable causes. Assignable causes, such as tool wear, different operators, change of material, etc., produce relatively large variations. When such large variations occur, it is the purpose of the control chart to flag the process change for management attention. A control chart consists of a set of limits within which some statistic, such as a sample mean, would be expected to fall if only chance variation were present. Values of the statistic falling outside these limits are treated as potential indicators of changes in the basic process. When the process produces points which fall outside these limits it is said to be out of control. The limits are set to reflect a small probability that when in control, the process would produce points beyond those limits. When the statistic falls outside the limits a search for assignable causes is initiated.

The complete specification for a control chart requires that one establish—

1. Sample size.
2. Sample frequency.
3. Control limits.

The particular numbers chosen for these parameters are functions of—

1. Process capability.
2. Cost of inspection.
3. Cost of missing a shift in the process.

As with acceptance sampling plans, control charts require that samples be as homogeneous as possible. They are intended to identify assignable causes in output variation and should not be compromised by mixing distinct groups. For example, samples which overlap two shifts might obscure distinct differences in performance between shifts. Similarly, two assembly operators producing the same item should be separated for purposes of sampling. In both examples there are strong candidates for assignable causes if samples falling beyond the control limits are taken from a distinct shift or operator. An out-of-control condition may not even show up on a combined sample, and if it does, the assignable cause may be impossible to identify. Control charts are graphic aids for testing hypotheses and as such should follow all the basic rules of good statistical procedures.

There are potentially many different kinds of control charts, one for each statistic we might use to describe the performance of a process. However, in keeping with our previous discussion of acceptance sampling plans, we will concern ourselves with a single chart to control fraction defective and a pair of charts to control variables. The chart for fraction defective is called a p-chart. The most commonly used pair for variables are the $\bar{x}$-chart and R-chart. These will be discussed at length in the following sections.

The p-Chart.   The p-chart shows how the fraction defective of a process varies from sample to sample. If the sample size n is constant, the chart consists of a central line p' representing the process fraction defective, which occurs when the process is under control, an upper control limit (UCL), and a lower control limit (LCL). It is common practice to set these limits at

$$UCL = p' + 3\sigma_{p'} \qquad (9\text{-}31)$$

$$LCL = p' - 3\sigma_{p'} \qquad (9\text{-}32)$$

where

$$\sigma_{p'} = \left[\frac{p'(1 - p')}{n}\right]^{1/2}$$

The use of three-sigma limits is not mandatory. They are merely a convenient means of identifying the range for most sample values obtained from a process operating at p' level. The chance of sample fraction defective falling outside these limits when the process is in fact operating at p' level is approximately 0.001. We could, however, design the control limits by using the Type I and Type II error considerations employed in acceptance sampling.

Constructing the p-Chart for a Fixed Sample Size.   For the moment, let us suppose that we are attempting to control the output from a stamping operation. A random sample of 25 units is taken from each shift's production. Preliminary data for five days' production (15 shifts) reveal the following rejection record:

Shift	Rejects	Shift	Rejects	Shift	Rejects
1	8	6	2	11	4
2	13	7	1	12	3
3	10	8	4	13	3
4	5	9	11	14	7
5	14	10	1	15	6

The first step is to establish whether or not the process is in control, i.e., to determine whether or not the observed points could reasonably be assumed to come from the same population. A preliminary estimate of p is obtained from

$$\bar{p} = \frac{\sum_i x_i}{nN} \tag{9–33}$$

where N represents the number of samples (n units per sample) drawn. For the data of this problem

$$\bar{p} = \frac{92}{(25)(15)} = 0.245$$

from which

$$\sigma_p = \left[\frac{\bar{p}(1 - \bar{p})}{n} \right]^{1/2}$$

$$= \left[\frac{(0.245)(0.755)}{25} \right]^{1/2} \approx 0.086$$

The limits are then calculated as

$$\text{UCL} = 0.245 + 3(0.086) = 0.503$$

and

$$\text{LCL} = 0.245 - 3(0.086) = -0.013$$

Since the negative fraction defective, which is a consequence of the normal approximation here, is obviously meaningless, the lower limit is set at zero. Figure 9–6 shows the data plotted on the resulting preliminary chart.

From the preliminary chart it appears that the fraction defective for the second and fifth samples are out of control. These data were taken from the same shift on two different days. Suppose that an investigation reveals that

FIGURE 9–6

Establishing a p-Chart

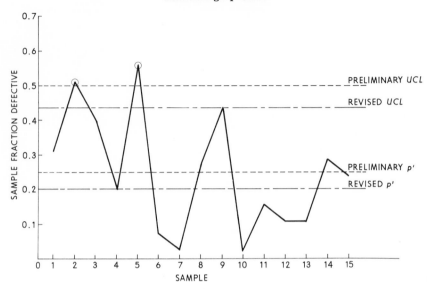

the regular operator on that shift was absent on those days and that a temporary operator was used. This is an assignable cause which may explain the unusually large fraction defective found in those samples. The normal fraction defective would then be better estimated by ignoring these atypical data points. By eliminating samples two and five, the revised estimates are

$$\bar{p} = \frac{65}{(25)(13)} = 0.20$$

$$\mathrm{UCL} = 0.20 + 3\left[\frac{(0.2)(0.8)}{25}\right]^{1/2} = 0.44$$

$$\mathrm{LCL} = 0.20 - 0.24 \approx 0$$

Since the remaining 13 data points fall within the revised limits, we may accept $\bar{p} = 0.20$ as the fraction defective produced when the process is in control. As future samples are taken they would be plotted on the revised chart. Those samples showing p values above UCL would be signals for management to investigate the process to see if there might be an assignable cause for the observed variation. If a number of points begin to fall outside the limits with no apparent assignable causes, or if there seems to be a general drift of points falling to one side of p', then another study may be in order to refine the estimate of p'. Otherwise, we may be using a false indication of control. There are quantitative ways to estimate when the control position has shifted, which are related to the theory of runs. For a discussion of these techniques, the reader is urged to consult Duncan.[8]

OC Curves for p-Charts. Plotting a point on a p-chart is analogous to testing an hypothesis about the true operating level of a process. As such, there exist the same possibilities for Type I and Type II errors discussed in Chapter 4 and again with acceptance sampling plans. The operating characteristic curve for a p-chart is calculated from

$$P(\text{acceptance} \mid p) = P\left(\text{LCL} \le \frac{d}{n} \le \text{UCL} \mid p\right) \qquad (9\text{--}34)$$

where d/n is the sample fraction defective and p is the lot fraction defective. For any given alternative hypothesis, say p_A, Equation 9–34 represents the probability of a Type II error.

The OC curve can be developed from the normal approximation, by

$$P(\text{acceptance} \mid p) = P\left(z \le \frac{\text{UCL} - p}{[p(1 - p)/n]^{1/2}}\right) - P\left(z \le \frac{\text{LCL} - p}{[p(1 - p)/n]^{1/2}}\right)$$
$$(9\text{--}35)$$

This approximation is generally valid if $p' \ge 0.10$ and $p'n \ge 5$. Otherwise, we must use the Poisson approximation or the binomial distribution in exactly the same manner as with acceptance sampling plans.

Points on the OC curve can be used to establish control limits and sample sizes for p-charts exactly as we used them to establish acceptance numbers and sample sizes in acceptance sampling plans. For example, suppose that known capability of a process is p', the sample size is predetermined at n, and we want the risk of an unwarranted investigation to be less than α. (Here α provides an alternative to the arbitrary three-sigma limits often used.) If we only require one-sided control, UCL is determined from

$$P\left(\frac{d}{n} \ge \text{UCL} \mid p'\right) = \alpha \qquad (9\text{--}36)$$

For example, suppose that we want an upper control limit for a process with $p' = 0.2$, $n = 25$, and $\alpha = 0.10$. Equation 9–36 can then be approximated by

$$P\left(z \ge \frac{\text{UCL} - 0.2}{[(0.2)(0.8)/25]^{1/2}}\right) = 0.10$$

from which

$$z_U = 1.282 = \frac{\text{UCL} - 0.2}{0.08}$$

and

$$\text{UCL} = 0.30256$$

---

[8] Duncan, *op. cit.*, pp. 132–37 and 352–57.

This control limit is obviously much tighter than the one developed for three-sigma variation shown in Figure 9–6.

To carry this example one step farther, suppose that n is also to be determined and that we want to catch a positive shift of Δp with probability $(1 - \beta)$. We now have a second equation to be solved together with 9–36:

$$P\left(\frac{d}{n} \geq \text{UCL} \mid p' + \Delta p\right) = 1 - \beta \qquad (9\text{–}37)$$

In our numerical example, suppose that $p = 0.2$ and $(1 - \beta) = 0.95$, then the normal approximations for Equations 9–36 and 9–37 lead to

$$z_U = 1.282 = \frac{(\text{UCL} - 0.2)\sqrt{n}}{\sqrt{0.16}}$$

$$z_L = -1.645 = \frac{(\text{UCL} - 0.4)\sqrt{n}}{\sqrt{0.24}}$$

After rounding, the approximate solution becomes

$$\text{UCL} = 0.278$$

and

$$n = 43$$

These are the same calculations performed for acceptance sampling plan design.

The x̄-Chart. The x̄-chart performs the same function for process control as did our sampling plans for variables used in acceptance sampling. The x̄-chart shows variation in averages of samples. It contains a center line, representing the normal process average, and an upper and lower control limit. It is common practice to use three-sigma limits, but there is no reason why other values might not be more reasonable for particular applications.

The design of the x̄-chart is based upon the central limit theorem. The assumption is made that averages of samples of size n will be normally distributed with mean equal to the population mean and variance equal to the population variance divided by sample size. The problems of estimating population mean and variance are the same statistical estimation problems discussed elsewhere in this text. However, since the same problem arises repeatedly in SQC work, the basic data necessary to establish the standard three-sigma limits for x̄-charts, as well as σ-charts and R-charts, have been tabulated in handbook form. One version of this information is shown in Table 9–2. The uses of the factors listed in the table are explained below.

In the simplest situation one might assume that the process capability has been previously established. If it is reasonable to suppose that during some test period the data collected were generated by a constant cause system,

TABLE 9-2

Factors Useful in the Construction of Control Charts

Number of Observations in Sample, N	Chart for Averages		Chart for Standard Deviations					Chart for Ranges						
	Factors for Control Limits		Factors for Central Line		Factors for Control Limits				Factors for Central Line		Factors for Control Limits				
	A	A_1	A_2	c_2	$1/c_2$	B_1	B_2	B_3	B_4	d_2	$1/d_2$	d_3	D_1	D_2	D_3	D_4
2........	2.121	3.760	1.880	0.5642	1.7725	0	1.843	0	3.267	1.128	0.8865	0.853	0	3.686	0	3.267
3........	1.732	2.394	1.023	0.7236	1.3820	0	1.858	0	2.568	1.693	0.5907	0.888	0	4.358	0	2.575
4........	1.500	1.880	0.729	0.7979	1.2533	0	1.808	0	2.266	2.059	0.4857	0.880	0	4.698	0	2.282
5........	1.342	1.596	0.577	0.8407	1.1894	0	1.756	0	2.089	2.326	0.4299	0.864	0	4.918	0	2.115
6......	1.225	1.410	0.483	0.8686	1.1512	0.026	1.711	0.030	1.970	2.534	0.3946	0.848	0	5.078	0	2.004
7..... ..	1.134	1.277	0.419	0.8882	1.1259	0.105	1.672	0.118	1.882	2.704	0.3698	0.833	0.205	5.203	0.076	1.924
8........	1.061	1.175	0.373	0.9027	1.1078	0.167	1.638	0.185	1.815	2.847	0.3512	0.820	0.387	5.307	0.136	1.864
9...	1.000	1.094	0.337	0.9139	1.0942	0.219	1.609	0.239	1.761	2.970	0.3367	0.808	0.546	5.394	0.184	1.816
10	0.949	1.028	0.308	0.9227	1.0837	0.262	1.584	0.284	1.716	3.078	0.3249	0.797	0.687	5.469	0.223	1.777
11........	0.905	0.973	0.285	0.9300	1.0753	0.299	1.561	0.321	1.679	3.173	0.3152	0.787	0.812	5.534	0.256	1.744
12........	0.866	0.925	0.266	0.9359	1.0684	0.331	1.541	0.354	1.646	3.258	0.3069	0.778	0.924	5.592	0.284	1.716
13........	0.832	0.884	0.249	0.9410	1.0627	0.359	1.523	0.382	1.618	3.336	0.2998	0.770	1.026	5.646	0.308	1.692
14........	0.802	0.848	0.235	0.9453	1.0579	0.384	1.507	0.406	1.594	3.407	0.2935	0.762	1.121	5.693	0.329	1.671
15........	0.775	0.816	0.223	0.9490	1.0537	0.406	1.492	0.428	1.572	3.472	0.2880	0.755	1.207	5.737	0.348	1.652
16........	0.750	0.788	0.212	0.9523	1.0501	0.427	1.478	0.448	1.552	3.532	0.2831	0.749	1.285	5.779	0.364	1.636
17........	0.728	0.762	0.203	0.9551	1.0470	0.445	1.465	0.466	1.534	3.588	0.2787	0.743	1.359	5.817	0.379	1.621
18........	0.707	0.738	0.194	0.9576	1.0442	0.461	1.454	0.482	1.518	3.640	0.2747	0.738	1.426	5.854	0.392	1.608
19........	0.688	0.717	0.187	0.9599	1.0418	0.477	1.443	0.497	1.503	3.689	0.2711	0.733	1.490	5.888	0.404	1.596
20........	0.671	0.697	0.180	0.9619	1.0396	0.491	1.433	0.510	1.490	3.735	0.2677	0.729	1.548	5.922	0.414	1.586
21........	0.655	0.679	0.173	0.9638	1.0376	0.504	1.424	0.523	1.477	3.778	0.2647	0.724	1.606	5.950	0.425	1.575
22........	0.640	0.662	0.167	0.9655	1.0358	0.516	1.415	0.534	1.466	3.819	0.2618	0.720	1.659	5.979	0.434	1.566
23........	0.626	0.647	0.162	0.9670	1.0342	0.527	1.407	0.545	1.455	3.858	0.2592	0.716	1.710	6.006	0.443	1.557
24........	0.612	0.632	0.157	0.9684	1.0327	0.538	1.399	0.555	1.445	3.895	0.2567	0.712	1.759	6.031	0.452	1.548
25.	0.600	0.619	0.153	0.9696	1.0313	0.548	1.392	0.565	1.435	3.931	0.2544	0.709	1.804	6.058	0.459	1.541
Over 25........	$\dfrac{3}{\sqrt{n}}$	$\dfrac{3}{\sqrt{n}}$	....	....	....	*	**	*	**	....	....	....	....	....	....	....

$$*1 - \frac{3}{\sqrt{2n}} \qquad\qquad **1 + \frac{3}{\sqrt{2n}}$$

Reproduced with permission from Table B2 of the *A.S.T.M. Manual on Quality Control of Materials*, 1951, p. 115.

we might estimate the mean and standard deviation of the process as

$$\bar{x} = \frac{\sum_{i=1}^{n} x_i}{n} \tag{9-38}$$

$$s_x = \left[\frac{\sum_{i=1}^{n} (x_i - \bar{x})^2}{n}\right]^{1/2} \tag{9-39}$$

If further testing of the data by means of a chi-square test, or the like, reveals that the normal distribution is a reasonable model to describe the process capability, we can establish appropriate probability intervals for the output of the process. For example, if we find $\bar{x} = 2.500$ and $s_x = 0.002$, we would expect 90 percent of the product produced by this equipment to fall in a range determined by

$$P(\bar{x} - ks_x < x < \bar{x} + ks_x) = 0.90$$

From the tables for the normal density we find $k = 1.645$. Thus our 90 percent capability interval is

$$P[2.500 - 1.645(0.002) < x < 2.500 + 1.645(0.002)] = 0.90$$

or

$$P(2.4967 < x < 2.5033) = 0.90$$

We must take care to distinguish such capability limits, or specification limits, from control limits to be used on the $\bar{x}$-chart. Limits on the $\bar{x}$-chart represent critical numbers to be used in testing an hypothesis relative to the mean operating level of the process. Suppose, for example, we wanted a two-tailed test for the null hypothesis that $\mu = 2.500$ with the risk of a Type I error set at $\alpha = 0.10$. The critical numbers for such a test would be

$$\text{UCL} = \mu + 1.645\sigma_{\bar{x}}$$
$$\text{LCL} = \mu - 1.645\sigma_{\bar{x}}$$

Using the previously developed sample standard deviation and assuming that future tests will involve samples of 25, we have

$$\text{UCL} = 2.500 + \frac{1.645(0.002)}{\sqrt{25}} = 2.5006$$

$$\text{LCL} = 2.500 - \frac{1.645(0.002)}{\sqrt{25}} = 2.4993$$

Note that the control limits are much narrower than the capability limits. The capability limits tell us that 90 percent of the items produced when the process is in control will fall in the interval $2.4967 < x < 2.5033$. The upper and lower control limits (UCL and LCL), on the other hand, have nothing to do with the bad parts produced. These numbers merely establish the frequency with which we may search for changes in the process when none exist. The difference between these limits stems from the difference between σ_x and $\sigma_{\bar{x}}$, the latter being the smaller of the two. For the special case of $n = 1$, the control and capability limits would coincide.

When the operating level of a process can be changed by a simple machine adjustment or the like, it is common practice to design control charts on the basis of specified values for process mean and variance. When this is done, a process may exhibit lack of control in the sense of producing sample means which fall outside the established limits, even though it may be in perfectly good statistical control. For example, if an $\bar{x}$-chart is designed on the basis of a target mean of 3.000 inches, a process operating in control with a mean of 2.750 inches would show up on the specified chart as being out of control. The interpretation in this context is that there is an assignable cause, such as machine setting, which is preventing the process from operating at its target level. Hopefully, investigation of statistical control capability will lead to intelligent assignment of process specifications.

When we have no prior information about the process standard deviation, it can be estimated from sample data. As Fetter points out, it is better to estimate the standard deviation by averaging a number of independent estimates of this statistic.[9] If we pool all observations we lose the ability to detect changes in the mean among our component samples. The strategy is to calculate a mean and standard deviation for each of several samples of size n by

$$\bar{x}_i = \frac{\sum_{j=1}^{n} x_{ij}}{n} \tag{9-40}$$

$$s_i = \left[\left(\frac{\sum_{j=1}^{n} x_{ij}^2 - n\bar{x}_i^2}{n} \right) \right]^{1/2} \tag{9-41}$$

If we have N such samples, the estimates for the corresponding population parameters would be

$$\bar{\bar{x}} = \frac{\sum_{i=1}^{N} \bar{x}_i}{N} \tag{9-42}$$

$$s_x = \frac{\sum_{i=1}^{N} s_i}{N} \tag{9-43}$$

The statistic s_x shown in Equation 9–43 is not an unbiased estimate for the population standard deviation. To correct the biased nature of this estimate, a quantity c_2 can be determined such that

$$E\left(\frac{s_x}{c_2}\right) = \sigma_x \tag{9-44}$$

The value of c_2 for various values of n is shown in Table 9–2. From the table, it is obvious that effect of c_2 becomes negligible as n becomes large. For $n > 25$, c_2 is approximately equal to one. The factor c_2 has been combined with $\sqrt{n}$ to obtain the A_1 factor shown in Table 9–2. Here

$$A_1 = \frac{3}{c_2\sqrt{n}} \tag{9-45}$$

in keeping with the usual three-sigma limit practice. The three-sigma control limits for an $\bar{x}$-chart can be expressed as

$$\bar{\bar{x}} \pm 3s_{\bar{x}} = \bar{\bar{x}} \pm \frac{3s_x}{c_2\sqrt{n}} = \bar{\bar{x}} \pm A_1 s_x \tag{9-46}$$

As an alternative to calculating sample standard deviations, it is possible to calculate the range R. Although this statistic is not as efficient, it is easier to calculate than s_x. The range (R) of a sample is simply the difference

[9] Fetter, *op. cit.*, p. 49.

between the largest and smallest values in the sample. The average of the ranges of N separate samples is given by

$$\bar{R} = \frac{\sum_{i=1}^{N} R_i}{N} \qquad (9\text{-}47)$$

An unbiased estimate of the population standard deviation can be obtained from

$$s_x = \frac{\bar{R}}{d_2} \qquad (9\text{-}48)$$

When the factor d_2 is combined with the square root of sample size, another standard multiplier for estimating three-sigma limits is obtained as

$$A_2 = \frac{3}{d_2 \sqrt{n}} \qquad (9\text{-}49)$$

The factors d_2 and A_2 are tabulated in Table 9–2. We now have a third alternative method for establishing three-sigma limits for an $\bar{x}$-chart as

$$\bar{x} \pm 3 s_{\bar{x}} = \bar{x} \pm \frac{3\bar{R}}{d_2 \sqrt{n}} = \bar{x} \pm A_2 \bar{R} \qquad (9\text{-}50)$$

The manner in which an $\bar{x}$-chart functions is illustrated graphically by Figure 9–7. The normal operation is depicted by curve a. If the process mean shifts, the distribution of $\bar{x}$ values may appear as curve b. The area of (b) falling above the UCL indicates the probability that a shift of the mean to this new level will be detected on a single sample. Curves c and d indicate the effect of changes in process variation. Even though the chance of finding $\bar{x}$ values beyond limits increases slightly when process variability increases, this is not an efficient way to detect such a change. For that reason it is common to use either a σ-chart or an R-chart in parallel with the $\bar{x}$-chart to catch variability shifts.

R-Charts and σ-Charts. The particular values of R or σ calculated for individual samples are themselves random variables with well defined distributions. The same strategy used to identify shifts in the process mean can be used to identify shifts in the process standard deviation and range. Control charts for σ and R are based upon a central value and limits established from estimates of σ_σ and σ_R. The probability distributions for both σ and R are related to the chi-square distribution. Since nearly all of the chi-square distribution is contained within its mean plus or minus three standard deviations, it is common practice to use three-sigma limits for control chart purposes.

The standard limits for an R-chart when the population variance is unknown are given by

$$\text{UCL}_R = \bar{R} + 3\sigma_R = D_4 \bar{R} \qquad (9\text{-}51)$$

$$\text{LCL}_R = \bar{R} - 3\sigma_R = D_3 \bar{R} \qquad (9\text{-}52)$$

FIGURE 9-7

Changes in Process Capability

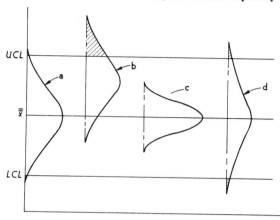

a = normal capability
b = shifted mean
c = reduced variance
d = increased variance

When the population standard deviation is known to be σ_x, the limits become

$$\text{UCL}_R = d_2 \sigma + 3\sigma_R = D_2 \sigma \qquad (9\text{-}53)$$

$$\text{LCL}_R = d_2 \sigma - 3\sigma_R = D_1 \sigma \qquad (9\text{-}54)$$

The factors d_i and D_i contained in Table 9-2 have been developed to correct the biased nature of sample estimates of R.

Sigma charts are developed in similar fashion. When sample data are used to estimate σ, the limits are

$$\text{UCL}_\sigma = s_x + 3\sigma_\sigma = B_4 s_x \qquad (9\text{-}55)$$

$$\text{LCL}_\sigma = s_x - 3\sigma_\sigma = B_3 s_x \qquad (9\text{-}56)$$

If the normal population standard deviation, σ_x, is known, the limits for sample standard deviation become

$$\text{UCL}_\sigma = c_2 \sigma_x + 3\sigma_\sigma = B_2 \sigma_x \qquad (9\text{-}57)$$

$$\text{LCL}_\sigma = c_2 \sigma_x - 3\sigma_\sigma = B_1 \sigma_x \qquad (9\text{-}58)$$

The B_i and c_i factors are shown in Table 9-2.

An OC Curve for the $\bar{x}$-Chart. As with all other techniques for hypothesis testing, we can associate risks of Type I and Type II errors with an $\bar{x}$-chart. This means that we can construct an OC curve for each $\bar{x}$-chart we design. The ordinants on the OC curve represent the probability of finding a sample mean which will fall within the specified control limits for various hypothesized values of the population mean. Mathematically this can be expressed as

$$P(\text{accept} \,|\, \mu) = P(\text{LCL} \leq \bar{x} \leq \text{UCL}) = \int_{\text{LCL}}^{\text{UCL}} f(\bar{x} \,|\, \mu) \, d\bar{x} \qquad (9\text{-}59)$$

where $f(\bar{x} \mid \mu)$ is the normal density with mean μ and variance σ^2/n. Although the general OC curve is a function of shifts in both mean and variance, we will assume for purposes of illustration that the variance of the process remains constant even though the mean may shift.

This suggests another way to design an $\bar{x}$-chart. We can specify acceptable risks for Type I and Type II errors then use two points on the OC curve to develop values for sample size and control limits. Suppose, for example, that we want to catch a shift of e in the process mean. When a shift of e has occurred, we want the probability of missing the shift to be no more than β. Furthermore, if no shift occurs, we want to limit the risk of falsely identifying a shift to α. The probability statements to be satisfied are then

$$P(\bar{x} \geq \text{UCL} \mid \mu = \mu_0) = \frac{\alpha}{2} \qquad (9\text{-}60)$$

$$P(\bar{x} \geq \text{UCL} \mid \mu = \mu_0 + e) = (1 - \beta) \qquad (9\text{-}61)$$

Here we are assuming that when a positive shift occurs, the α risk is split evenly between a pair of symmetric control limits and that the probability of $\bar{x}$ falling below LCL is negligible. This is the same procedure used to design hypothesis tests on the mean discussed in Chapter 4.

Suppose, for example, that we must design an $\bar{x}$-chart for a process with an in-control capability of $\mu_0 = 1.0000$ and $\sigma = 0.0020$. We are willing to tolerate $\alpha = 0.05$ and want the risk of a Type II error when $\mu_1 = 1.0004$ to be $\beta = 0.10$. Using the standard normal deviate, the equations to be satisfied are

$$z_{0.975} = \frac{\text{UCL} - 1.0000}{0.0020/\sqrt{n}} = 1.960$$

$$z_{0.90} = \frac{\text{UCL} - 1.0004}{0.0020/\sqrt{n}} = 1.282$$

Solving these equations simultaneously yields approximately

$$\text{UCL} = 1.00115 \qquad n = 12$$

As with our design of acceptance sampling plans, the α and β can rarely be met exactly because of the integer requirement on n. For this particular chart with $\bar{x} = 1.0000$, $\text{UCL} = 1.00115$, $\text{LCL} = 0.99885$, and $n = 12$, the exact α and β are

$$\alpha = \int_{\text{UCL}}^{\infty} N\left(1.0000; \frac{0.0020}{\sqrt{n}}\right) + \int_{-\infty}^{\text{LCL}} N\left(1.000; \frac{0.0020}{\sqrt{n}}\right) = 0.0466$$

$$\beta = \int_{-\infty}^{\text{UCL}} N\left(1.0004; \frac{0.0020}{\sqrt{n}}\right) = 0.0968$$

By rounding to the nearest percent, these risks do meet the specifications.

Economic Implications. So far, our discussion of control charts has followed the same reasoning as most introductory quality control texts. We have discussed ways to select a sample size and a critical range such that certain specified risks of Type I and Type II errors are satisfied. The problem of how frequently a sample should be taken has been ignored. This is consistent with common industrial practice which requires that the specified sample be taken " each hour." However, a more logical approach to the problem is to select sample frequency such that some total cost function is minimized.

Knappenberger and Grandage have developed a technique to search for minimum cost quality control tests based upon a Markov analysis.[10] They assume that the process parameter μ is a continuous random variable which can be approximated by a series of discrete values. One value, μ_0, is associated with the process in control and the remaining values imply that the process is out of control. The analysis technique involves describing a transition matrix for states of the system (values of μ_i) based upon a priori distribution parameters. This is used to develop a steady-state probability vector as a function of the number of units produced between samples. The resulting probability statements are used to establish an expected cost expression of the form

$$E(c) = E(c_1) + E(c_2) + E(c_3) \qquad (9\text{--}62)$$

where $E(c_1)$ is the expected cost per unit for carrying out the test procedure, $E(c_2)$ is the expected cost per unit of investigating an out-of-control condition, and $E(c_3)$ is the expected cost per unit associated with the production of defective units.

The solution to this equation is accomplished by a two-step numerical procedure. First, the expected cost is computed for a wide variety of sample sizes, units between samples, and control limits for the desired values of the a priori distribution parameters. These establish preliminary estimates of the optimal quality control test parameters. Stage two then uses the preliminary estimates as a starting point for a search routine designed to locate the desired values to any desired accuracy. A digital computer is required for solution.

Fetter has also developed a cost expression for sampling plans.[11] Rather than develop a probability vector to describe the state of the system, he relies exclusively on expected value arguments. Our cost model follows Fetter's approach.

Recall from our earlier discussion that the complete specification of a control plan involves a statement of the frequency with which samples are to be taken. For our purposes we will assume that the control limits and

[10] H. Allen Knappenberger, and A. H. E. Grandage, " Minimum Cost Quality Control Tests," *AIIE Transactions*, Vol. I, No. 1 (March, 1969), pp. 24–32.
[11] Fetter, *op. cit.*, pp. 67–70.

sample size have been established on the basis of certain noncost considerations. The frequency decision will be made to minimize cost given prior specifications for sample size and control limits. The economics of changing all three specification elements will be left to search routines described by the previously mentioned authors.

Consider a process which operates in only two states. The mean when the process is in control is μ_0 and when it is out of control it shifts to μ_1. We will assume that the variance remains unchanged at σ^2. Tolerance limits have been established at $\mu_0 \pm T$. Any items falling outside these limits are considered bad. A bad item which goes undetected incurs a penalty cost of C_3 dollars. Control limits for means of samples of size n have been established at $\mu_0 \pm L$. When a sample mean falls outside these limits, even though the process is in control, an investigation costing C_2 dollars is initiated. When the process is actually out of control, an investigation is fruitful and no penalty cost is incurred. Sample inspection costs $C_0 + C_1 n$. Production rate is R units per hour. It has been estimated that the process mean will shift on the average of once every h hours. Samples are to be taken every t hours.

There are three major sources of hourly cost for this system. They are the cost of inspection (S), cost of investigation (I), and the cost of defective units produced (D). Sampling frequency must be selected such that their total is minimized. The decision variable is t, the time between samples.

Normal inspection costs per hour can be obtained by multiplying the cost per inspection by number of inspections per hour. In symbols this can be expressed as

$$S = (C_0 + C_1 n)\left(\frac{1}{t}\right) \tag{9-63}$$

If the process is in control at the time of sample inspection, there is still a probability α that the sample mean will fall beyond the control limits and trigger an unwarranted investigation. From our previous discussion, α is the risk of a Type I error. That is,

$$\alpha = \int_{\mu_0 + L}^{\infty} N\left(\mu_0, \frac{\sigma}{\sqrt{n}}\right) + \int_{-\infty}^{\mu_0 - L} N\left(\mu_0, \frac{\sigma}{\sqrt{n}}\right) \tag{9-64}$$

The expected cost of unwarranted investigations per hour is then the expected cost per inspection times inspections per hour.

$$I = (\alpha C_2)\left(\frac{1}{t}\right) \tag{9-65}$$

Under normal operating conditions, the expected number of defective units per hour being produced is Rp_1 where

$$p_1 = \int_{\mu_0 + T}^{\infty} f(x \mid \mu_0, \sigma)\, dx + \int_{-\infty}^{\mu_0 - T} f(x \mid \mu_0, \sigma)\, dx \tag{9-66}$$

and $f(x)$ represents the probability density function for individual items.

When the mean shifts to μ_1, the number of defective units per hour changes to Rp_2 where

$$p_2 = \int_{\mu_0+T}^{\infty} f(x \mid \mu_1, \sigma)\, dx + \int_{-\infty}^{\mu_0-T} f(x \mid \mu_1, \sigma)\, dx \qquad (9\text{--}67)$$

Each hour that such a shift goes undetected will then incur a penalty cost of

$$C_3 R(p_2 - p_1) \qquad (9\text{--}68)$$

The probability that a shift will go undetected at the time of an inspection is β where

$$\beta = \int_{\mu_0-L}^{\mu_0+L} N\left(\mu_1, \frac{\sigma}{\sqrt{n}}\right) \qquad (9\text{--}69)$$

The number of inspections which must be performed before a shift will be detected is of course a random variable which may range from 1 to ∞. However, it can be shown that the expected number of inspections until detection is given by

$$E(\text{inspections}) = \frac{1}{1 - \beta} \qquad (9\text{--}70)$$

Using Fetter's argument, we will assume that the probability of a change in a time interval is proportional to the length of the interval. In the context of inspection intervals, we then expect that on the average one half an inspection interval will occur in the new state before the system is sampled. This means that even though the system is out of control for the first time at sample j, it will on the average only have been out of control for one half of the last inspection interval rather than for the entire interval. The total expected production time in the out-of-control state before detection is then

$$E(\text{time out of control}) = \left[\frac{1}{(1 - \beta)} - 0.5\right] t \qquad (9\text{--}71)$$

Now, since the expected time between process shifts is h hours, the average number of shifts per hour will be $1/h$. The total cost per hour incurred because of undetected shifts is then

$$\text{Cost} = C_3 R(p_2 - p_1) \left[\frac{1}{(1 - \beta)} - 0.5\right] \frac{t}{h} \qquad (9\text{--}72)$$

The total hourly cost is the sum of Equations 9–63, 9–65 and 9–72. That is,

$$K = \frac{(C_0 + C_1 n + \alpha C_2)}{t} + C_3 R(p_2 - p_1) \left[\frac{1}{(1 - \beta)} - 0.5\right] \frac{t}{h} \qquad (9\text{--}73)$$

For fixed sample size and control limits Equation 9–73 can be written in simplified form as

$$K = \frac{A}{t} + Bt \qquad (9\text{--}74)$$

where the constants A and B are given by

$$A = C_0 + C_1 n + \alpha C_2$$

and

$$B = C_3 R(p_2 - p_1)\frac{1/(1-\beta) - 0.5}{h}$$

Taking derivatives with respect to t and equating to zero we have

$$\frac{dK}{dt} = \frac{-A}{t^2} + B$$

from which

$$t = \sqrt{\frac{A}{B}} \tag{9-75}$$

This value of t is then the minimum cost inspection interval for a plan with specified sample size, control limits, and out-of-control state.

Example. Consider the special case of a cereal package line which produces 1,000 packages per hour at a nominal mean package weight of 16 ounces and has a variance of 0.09. Packages are defective if they do not fall in the range of ($15.25 < x < 16.75$). The failure of a critical item in the equipment causes the mean to shift to 16.5 ounces. The mean time between failures for this item is 25 hours. Based upon Type I and Type II risk considerations, a control plan with $n = 4$, UCL = 16.45, and LCL = 15.55 has been selected. Each package inspected costs \$0.50. Setup for inspection costs \$5, and an unwarranted investigation costs \$12. Any bad packages which escape detection cost the company \$2. The problem is to find the optimum inspection interval.

In our previous notation we have

$$
\begin{array}{lll}
C_0 = \$5 & R = 1,000 & n = 4 \\
C_1 = \$0.5 & h = 25 & \\
C_2 = \$12 & T = 0.75 & \\
C_3 = \$2 & L = 0.45 &
\end{array}
$$

From the normal tables:

$$\alpha = 2\left[1 - F\left(\frac{16.45 - 16}{0.3/\sqrt{4}}\right)\right] = 0.0026$$

$$\beta \approx F\left[\frac{16.45 - 16.50}{0.15}\right] = 0.3694$$

$$p_1 = 2F\left[\frac{15.25 - 16}{0.3}\right] = 0.0124$$

$$p_2 = F\left[\frac{15.25 - 16.50}{0.3}\right] + \left[1 - F\left(\frac{16.75 - 16.50}{0.3}\right)\right] = 0.2025$$

These data give values to the constants A and B of

$$A = \$5 + \$0.5(4) + 0.0026(\$12) = \$7.03$$

$$B = \$2(1,000)(0.2025 - 0.0124) \frac{[1/(1 - 0.3694) - 0.5]}{25} = \$16.50$$

The optimal inspection period is then

$$t = \sqrt{\frac{7.03}{16.50}} = 0.652 \text{ hours}$$

or approximately 39 minutes. The average hourly cost of this policy is approximately

$$K = \frac{\$7.03}{0.652} + \$16.50(0.652) = \$21.54 \text{ per hour}$$

A similar calculation could be made for different sample sizes and control limits to determine a global optimum.

Cumulative Sum Charts.   An alternative to the traditional $\bar{x}$-chart designs discussed so far is the cumulative sum chart.[12] In some cases it is possible for the mean of a process to change and still get long runs of sample means which fall within the control limits of the traditional $\bar{x}$-chart. In the past rules have been devised to test the length of runs on either side of the target mean to help detect such a shift. The cumulative sum chart attacks this problem in a different manner. It is based on the premise that even though a small change in the process may go undetected for a large number of samples, the difference between each sample mean and expected mean cumulated over several samples will give more rapid detection of the change.

The procedure involves calculating

$$x_m = \frac{\sum_{i=1}^{m} (\bar{x}_i - \bar{x})}{s_{\bar{x}}} \tag{9–76}$$

where

x_m = cumulative sum of deviations
$\bar{x}_i$ = sample mean
$\bar{x}$ = expected mean
$s_{\bar{x}}$ = standard deviation of means of samples of size n

In some applications it is not necessary to convert to sigma units by dividing by the standard deviation of the sample means. The limits are established on the basis of a standard expected change in the process and the probability

---

[12] See for example, Duncan, *op. cit.*, chap. xxii; or Fetter, *op. cit.*, pp. 94–97.

FIGURE 9–8

Cumulative Sum Control Chart

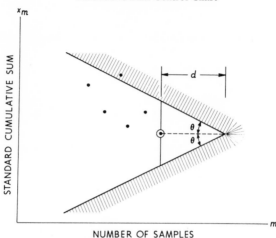

NUMBER OF SAMPLES

of an error of the first kind. The result is a v-mask which moves with time to show the increase in limits as observations are moved further back from the present.

The parameters of the v-mask are the angle θ and the lead-distance d as noted in Figure 9–8. The point "0" is placed over the last plotted point on the cumulative sum chart. If any points fall in the shaded region, the process is out of control. The covered point in Figure 9–8 indicates a downward shift in the process mean. As noted by Fetter,[13] it has been shown that the values for θ and d can be approximated by

$$\tan \theta = \frac{1}{2}\delta \qquad (9\text{–}77)$$

$$d \approx -2\delta^{-2}\ln \alpha \qquad (9\text{–}78)$$

where

δ = standard expected change in the process measured in sigma units
α = probability of an error of the first kind

Initial experience seems to indicate that this technique may be more effective for control than the standard $\bar{x}$-chart for small values of α. However, it is more expensive to design and administer. Further details for developing cumulative sum charts are left to texts specializing in quality control.

---

[13] Fetter, *op. cit.*, p. 96.

SELECTED BIBLIOGRAPHY

BOWKER, ALBERT H., AND LIEBERMAN, GERALD L. *Engineering Statistics.* Englewood Cliffs, N.J.: Prentice-Hall, Inc., 1959.

COWDEN, D. J. *Statistical Methods in Quality Control.* Englewood Cliffs, N.J.: Prentice-Hall, Inc., 1957.

DUNCAN, A. J. *Quality Control and Industrial Statistics.* 3d ed. Homewood, Ill.: Richard D. Irwin, Inc., 1965.

FETTER, ROBERT B. *The Quality Control System.* Homewood, Ill.: Richard D. Irwin, Inc., 1967.

KNAPPENBERGER, H. ALLEN, AND GRANDAGE, A. H. E. "Minimum Cost Quality Control Tests," *AIIE Transactions*, Vol. 1, No. 1 (March, 1969), pp. 24–32.

PROBLEMS

9–1 A sampling plan is to have the following requirements:

a) A single sample will be taken.

b) The plan will accept at least 90 percent of the time material which is 5 percent defective.

c) The plan will not accept more than 5 percent of the time material which is 10 percent defective.

i) Indicate the values for α, β, AQL, and LTPD.

ii) Design a sampling plan which meets these specifications.

iii) Draw the OC curve associated with this plan and indicate the location of α, β, AQL, and LTPD.

9–2 Design a single sample fraction-defective attribute sampling plan with the following characteristics:

$$0.10 = \text{AQL}$$
$$0.20 = \text{LTPD}$$
$$0.0668 = \alpha$$
$$0.0062 = \beta$$

The normal approximation may be used.

9–3 The Cold Hands Company provides ice cubes for I.E. parties. The 602 class feels that an acceptable quality level is an average of 200 cracked cubes in every bag of 2,000. The producers' risk has been set at 0.05. Because of the cool nature of the inspection task, the sample size has been predetermined at 100 cubes from each bag of 2,000.

a) Calculate an acceptance number.

b) If cubes are being provided of the indicated AQL quality, what is the average outgoing quality assuming $c = 10$ is used? (All cracked cubes found during inspection are replaced with good cubes.)

c) Using the data from part (*b*) of this question, what is the implied risk of a Type I error?

9-4   The Shady Fence Company purchases hubcaps by the carload from a local group of teen-agers. The company wishes to establish a single sample acceptance sampling plan in which 50 hubcaps for each carload will be inspected. Purchasing has decided that an acceptable quality level (AQL) is 2 percent defectives, and they want to limit the risk of rejecting lots of this quality to 0.0228. The normal approximation may be used.

a) What should be the acceptance number for such a plan?

b) If the lot-tolerance-percent-defective for this plan is 10 percent, what is the risk of a Type II error?

c) If the true percent defective of the hubcap stealing process is 4 percent, what will be the average outgoing quality (AOQ)? (Assume 100 percent inspection of defective lots with lot size = 500.)

9-5   The Atrophied Grape Company manufactures raisins from the rejects of a local winery. They have worked closely with the winery to develop a single sample acceptance sampling plan for their grapes. They purchase grapes from the winery by the carload, each car containing 800 crates. One half of the crates are inspected before shipment at the winery, and any rotten ones are replaced with good crates. Recent experience on the part of Atrophied suggests that on the average, 5 percent of every lot they receive is no good. The winery recently spot checked 700 crates before inspection and found 560 of them to be good. On the basis of the information given:

a) What proportion of the lots are being rejected at the winery?

b) What is the "acceptance number" of their sampling plan?

9-6   A producer of sharpened pencils sells pencils in lots of 600 each to a local department store. A pencil is defective if the point is broken. The producer believes that an acceptable number of defective pencils in a lot should be 12. As long as he is producing at this quality or better he wants to be 90 percent confident that the lot will be accepted. The department store believes that lots with more than 60 defective items should be rejected with probability 0.95.

a) Using the normal approximation, design a single sample acceptance sampling plan to satisfy these requirements.

b) What will be the average outgoing quality of lots produced when the system is operating at a 4 percent defective level under the assumption that any bad items found during inspection will be replaced with good ones?

9-7   The Bargain Annex is attempting to evaluate their pottery inspection plan. The present policy is to inspect 100 vases from each lot of 1,000 which are received from their supplier. If two or less broken ones are found, the lot is accepted. If over two are found the shipment is 100 percent inspected. The inspector is arguing that he can do the job more economically by inspecting only 50 vases per lot with an acceptance number of one. The cost accountant estimates that it costs $1.50 per unit to inspect a vase. When a broken vase goes undetected it may cost the store up to $10 for handling the resulting customer complaint.

a) Draw the OC curve for each of the plans under consideration.

b) A good guess at the relative frequencies for lot fraction defective is felt to be

p	$f(p)$
0.02	0.2
0.04	0.3
0.06	0.4
0.10	0.1

With this information, calculate the expected cost for each plan.

9–8 The minimum acceptable load which must be sustained by a certain class of passenger car tire is 2,000 pounds. From past experience with the manufacturer, the testing laboratory estimates the variance of this tire's load carrying capability at 40,000. The distribution for strength among tires is assumed to be normal. Under standard conditions, this manufacturer is capable of producing lots with a mean strength of 2,400 pounds. When the mean shifts to 2,200 pounds, the Sawbuck stores would like to see the laboratory reject the lot. Two methods of testing are available. One tests each tire in the sample until it fails and records the exact failure point. The second merely loads each tire in the sample to 2,000 pounds and records whether or not failure occurs.

a) Establish the AQL and LTPD quantities for this testing situation.

b) Current techniques call for the second method with a sample of 50 and acceptance number of 2. Calculate the risks of Type I and Type II errors under this plan.

c) Design a variables sampling plan which would meet the same specification as the current attribute plan.

d) It costs $4 per tire to test by the present method. Determine the range of testing costs under the variables plan for which variables sampling is preferred.

9–9 The Cold Hands Company would like to make use of control charts for their ice-making machines. When the machine is running correctly they expect an average of 10 percent defective cubes. They wish to establish a fraction defective chart with symmetrical control limits. They want the risk of stopping the machine when it is really functioning normally to be limited to 0.05. However, if the percent of defective cubes should reach 0.15, they want to stop the process with probability 0.90. Determine the control limits and sample size to be taken from each hour's production. (Use the normal approximation.)

9–10 Samples of size 25 are to be drawn from each hour's production of an automatic screw machine operation. Past experience indicates that the variance of diameters produced on this machine seldom changes, remaining at approximately 0.000004 square inch. The target diameter is 3.000 inches. Management wants a control chart which will catch a positive shift in the process mean of 0.004 inch at least 90 percent of the time. Similarly they want to catch a negative shift of 0.006 inch at least 95 percent of the time. Design an $\bar{x}$ chart which will satisfy these needs.

9–11 A machine is producing parts with a target mean diameter of 1.000 inches. The variance of the process is estimated to be 0.000036 square inch. Since tool wear is the most prevalent source of error, management desires to establish an upper control limit for the mean of a fixed sample size to be taken from each hour's production. No lower control limit is necessary. When the process is really running at the target mean they want to provide no adjustment with probability 0.9332. When the process mean shifts to 1.005, they wish to catch such a shift with probability 0.9772. Specify a control limit and sample size for an $\bar{x}$ chart to meet the above conditions.

9–12 The Honesty Hurts Corporation is seeking to establish a control chart for their cookie packing operation. They define a " max-pack " as one weighing 18 ounces, i.e., any packages over 18 ounces are no good. They aren't worried about underpacking. It has been established that the cookie packers prepare packages with weight following the Poisson distribution with mean usually equal to 16 ounces. The company feels that this weight is an acceptable target for the process mean.

a) Establish an $\bar{x}$ chart for this operation such that the probability of a Type I error is 0.0035 and the risk of missing a shift to max-pack quality or worse is 0.2420.

b) What proportion of the cookie packages produced will be " bad " by management's definition?

9–13 A shaft turning operation has been controlled by means of an $\bar{x}$ chart with mean 4.000, UCL $= 4.008$, LCL $= 3.992$. An examination of data taken from this operation reveals that in 100 samples of size 50, later proven to have been taken while the process mean was in fact 4.000 inches, the operation was halted four times because the sample mean was over 4.008 inches and five times because it was less than 3.992 inches. An additional 50 samples were taken with the mean deliberately set at an " unacceptable " level of 4.009 inches. In this case four sample means fell inside the control limits. On the basis of these data, calculate an empirical estimate for producer's and consumer's risks.

9–14 A machine is producing parts which are called " good " if their diameters are in the range 0.991 to 1.009. You want to set up a control chart for the output of the process. Assume that the process normally operates with a mean of 1.000 inch and variance 0.000036 square inch. You have decided on symmetrical limits and want the probability of making a change in the process when the mean is really 1.000 to be 0.0456. Management has already decreed that the size of each sample will be 4.

a) What are the control limits?

b) If the process is in control, i.e., $\mu = 1.000$, what percentage of parts will be bad?

9–15 Company management wants an $\bar{x}$ chart which will signal a lathe turning operation out of control when it really isn't no more than 2.28 percent of the time. The machine tool manufacturer has assured management that this lathe is capable of holding the desired size of 1.000 inch with a variance among individual pieces of 0.000004 square inch. Because of the nature of the product, management is concerned most when the target diameter shifts in a positive direction. They want a chart which will miss a positive shift of 0.004 inch in the process mean no more than 6.68 percent of the time. Specify a one-sided (upper only) control limit and a sample size which will meet the required conditions.

9-16 A shaft turning operation has been controlled by means of an $\bar{x}$ chart with a mean 1.000, UCL = 1.005, and LCL = 0.995 inches. An examination of data taken from this operation reveals that in 100 samples of size 50, later proven to have been taken while the process mean was in fact 1.000 inches, the operation was halted three times because the sample mean was greater than UCL and four times because it was less than LCL. An additional 50 samples were taken with the process mean deliberately set at 1.003 inches, a value sufficiently distant from 1.000 inches to mark unacceptable performance from the customers' point of view. In this case 46 of the sample means fell outside the UCL and 4 fell within the limits. On the basis of these data calculate an empirical estimate for producer's risk and consumer's risk.

9-17 A machine tool manufacturer has assured the Watch Fob Corporation that their lathes are capable of holding the "Big Ben Fob" dimension to 1.000 inch with a variance of 0.000004 square inch. Management wants an $\bar{x}$ chart which will signal this turning operation out of control when it really is in control no more than 4.56 percent of the time. Because of the nature of the product, management is concerned when the target diameter shifts in either direction. They want a chart which will miss a shift of 0.004 inch in the process mean no more than 13.36 percent of the time. Specify the proper symmetrical control limits and sample size which will meet the required conditions.

9-18 An automatic screw machine produces 150 units per hour with a normal mean diameter of 1.300 inches and a standard deviation of 0.002. The failure of a cutting tool causes the mean to shift to 1.305. The mean time between failures for this tool is 10 hours. Current inspection plans call for selecting five units from each hour's production to determine a mean to be plotted on a chart with an upper control limit of 1.303 and a lower limit of 1.297. Setup for inspection costs $6 and an unwarranted search for cause costs $18. Any defective units escaping detection cost the company $3. Find the optimum inspection interval for the specified limits and sample size. Compare the costs of the optimal plan with current practice.

CHAPTER 10

Deterministic Inventory Models

PHRASED in the simplest terms, inventory control consists of determining when and how much to order for every item purchased or manufactured by a company. The illusion of simplicity is soon shattered if one examines the factors involved in making such decisions. It is the purpose of this chapter to examine some of these factors and to indicate how they may be accounted for in simple deterministic models for single item inventories stocked at one location.

The Inventory Problem

As a referent, let us consider a firm which manufactures ashtrays from hot rolled steel stock. Looking at the product involved, one could immediately construct a list of raw materials required by the actual manufacturing process. Let us first consider the basic raw material, hot rolled steel stock. What influences the decisions of when and how much of this stock to order?

When to Order. When to order is certainly influenced by existing stock levels. If one hopes to maintain continuous production he must have a continuous supply of raw material. This requires only that replenishments arrive by the time existing stock levels reach zero. A snap judgment at this point might lead to a policy of ordering when stock is exhausted. This is generally unsatisfactory since very few suppliers will provide zero lead time. Lead time then becomes another factor to consider in the determination of when to order. Lead time may vary among suppliers so that we must also consider which suppliers or combination of suppliers we will patronize. Closely related to the lead time and present inventory level of rolled steel is the rate at which this inventory is being depleted. This depletion rate is a function of current production schedules which are in turn functions of forecasted future demand and existing orders. Since there is probably a cost associated with being unable to supply customer demands, a cost of shortage must also be considered. Obviously the "when to order" question can be rather formidable so let us now turn our attention to the question of the "how much to order."

How Much to Order. How much to order is intimately related to all of the factors previously mentioned plus a number of purely economic considerations. To begin with, placing an order costs money. This cost is made up of accounting and handling charges such as paper work expenses, shipping charges, materials handling charges, and data processing charges. When the item is manufactured in-plant, the order cost would include machine setup charges. The obvious solution to reduce unit order cost is to order in very large quantities. This may be an expensive solution if one considers charges such as the cost of capital invested in idle inventories, the cost of providing warehouse space for such inventories, and property taxes. Lumping all such expenses under "carrying charges" does not reduce the number of forces impinging upon our basic decision. The price paid for the stock also influences the how much decision. There may be price breaks available for large quantity purchases. Different suppliers may have different price schedules. The amount of capital available may be limited. Fortunately, over limited ranges of the decision variables many of the carrying charges are proportional to the price of the item.

Successful inventory management for just this one item involves an extensive list of considerations only hinted at in the previous paragraphs. Figure 10-1 summarizes the major points to be considered. If the organization exists for economic purposes, it is the goal of the inventory manager to make the decisions of when and how much to order in such a manner that costs are minimized while at the same time balancing many intangible factors for which dollar figures cannot be obtained.

So far nothing has been said about the large variety of items controlled by such a company. In addition to steel stock, paints, cleaners, tooling, cartons, and labels may be directly involved in the manufacture of our simple ashtray. These items must also be stocked and the interaction among them considered. For example, they all compete for space and dollars; they all have unique price, lead time, and demand characteristics; and they all are available in a variety of forms. A question might be raised concerning the form in which to stock items. Should they all be stocked as raw material or should in-process banks and finished goods inventories be established? If so in what proportions?

A similar set of problems could be posed for routine office supply items, janitorial supplies, and maintenance items. Multiply these considerations several thousand times over and one can begin to appreciate the magnitude

FIGURE 10–1

The Inventory Problem

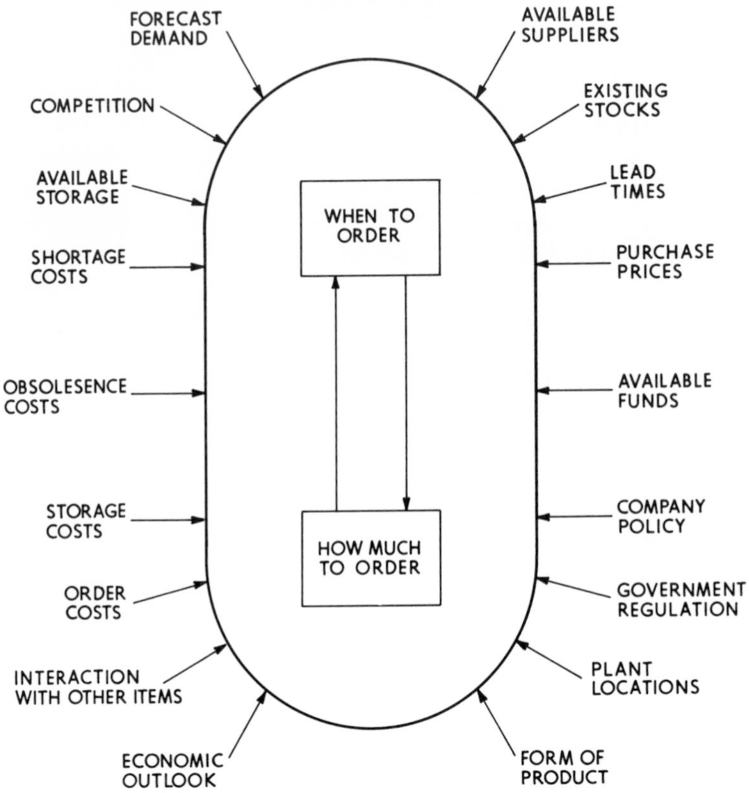

FORECAST
DEMAND

AVAILABLE
SUPPLIERS

COMPETITION

EXISTING
STOCKS

AVAILABLE
STORAGE

LEAD
TIMES

WHEN TO
ORDER

SHORTAGE
COSTS

PURCHASE
PRICES

OBSOLESENCE
COSTS

AVAILABLE
FUNDS

STORAGE
COSTS

COMPANY
POLICY

HOW MUCH
TO ORDER

ORDER
COSTS

GOVERNMENT
REGULATION

INTERACTION
WITH OTHER ITEMS

PLANT
LOCATIONS

ECONOMIC
OUTLOOK

FORM OF
PRODUCT

of the problem facing the managements of large corporations when they attempt to answer the questions of when and how much to order.

The Role of Inventories

If controlling inventories is such a complicated business, why bother to keep them? In some custom industries no inventory may be a plausible solution, particularly for finished goods inventories. For example, a home-building contractor may never reach the point where he stocks finished homes but rather he builds strictly to customer order. His product is characterized by high unit costs, considerable variation among units, relatively low demand, and reasonably patient customers. However, even a building contractor may sometimes find it to be to his advantage to stock raw materials which are common to all homes.

Buffering. For other companies involved in more or less continuous purchase, production, and sale of a reasonably standard product, inventories provide several useful functions. In a general sense they may be viewed as buffers between subsystems. For example, raw material inventories serve as a buffer between suppliers and the manufacturer. Fluctuations in stock delivery time, breakdowns in supplier operations, and price variations can be smoothed by the inventory buffer before they can cause undesirable fluctuations in a plant's ability to produce. In-process inventories provide similar damping capability for fluctuations between subsystems within a plant. Finished goods inventories provide the buffer between the producer and the customer. Variations in daily demand can be absorbed by the inventories without causing customer dissatisfaction and without introducing undesirable perturbations in production schedules. The buffer function of inventories is essentially that of smoothing operations.

Quantification. In addition to the desirable buffering properties of inventories, it is in many cases much cheaper to operate with them than without them. Intelligent selection of inventory policies involves the best possible tradeoffs among order costs, purchase costs, and carrying costs. These tradeoffs do not necessarily lead to a policy of purchase only to firm orders.

Attempts to provide quantitative assistance to inventory managers date back to the early 1900's, but it has only been in recent years that mathematical methods of inventory control have gained wide acceptance. Much of the work in this area has been developed in the fields of industrial engineering and operations research. The successful application of mathematical techniques for inventory control depends upon the ability of the analyst to construct realistic models and the ability of the manager to understand their power and limitations. Both abilities are of fairly recent origin.

In spite of the formidable appearance of many current journal articles on the topic, one's abilities to find optimum solutions to very complex inventory problems are still rather limited. The aim of all inventory models is to extend decision-making abilities by providing mathematical insights into the behavior of relatively simple systems. Such quantitative tools serve to strengthen rather than replace the traditional skills of management. When the system becomes too complex to handle by analytical means, large-scale simulation studies are often used to seek a means of improving existing operations.

It is the purpose of the remainder of this chapter and the next to introduce a few of the techniques of the inventory model builder. The goal is to develop an understanding of how inventory systems operate and the capability on the part of the reader to analyze new and more complex systems as they arise in day-to-day business operations.

Modeling Approach

The purpose of a mathematical model of an inventory system is to provide a logical representation of that system. The resemblance of model behavior to system behavior can be improved upon only by increasingly complex and expensive models. A rough guide to the relative expense of developing and manipulating classes of inventory models is shown in Figure 10–2. The higher the isomorphism with the real system, the greater the expense. The most successful applications of inventory modeling have been with single-item deterministic and probabilistic models. In this text we will limit our discussion to those types.

Single-Item Deterministic Models. In order to demonstrate basic modeling techniques and to highlight fundamental concepts of inventory control, let us begin by analyzing a class of single-item deterministic models. These models are valuable from a conceptual point of view, although their immediate applicability to existing systems is limited.

In a deterministic model it is assumed that the values of all parameters of the system are known absolutely at every point in time. There is no question of uncertainty about next week's demand or the amount of lead time necessary to produce an item. One has perfect knowledge of their values. In addition to this perfect knowledge over time, it will often be assumed that the values do not change from period to period. Demand occurs at a constant rate over time, the production function is the same every time it is called upon and lead time is constant (i.e., lead time in December is identical with lead time in July).

FIGURE 10–2

Study of Inventory Systems

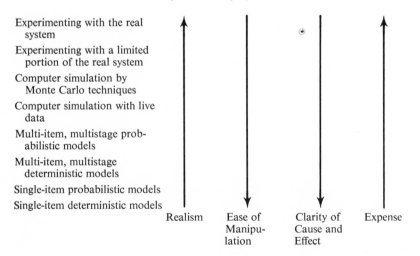

Descriptive Models. If one desires a purely descriptive model for inventory level, $L(t)$, at any time t after observations have begun, it could be obtained by merely summing the effects of all inputs, $p(i)$, and outputs, $o(i)$, up to time (t). If time of input and output is viewed as a discrete variable, as might occur if one had only daily sales and daily production figures, inventory level at time (t) would be

$$L(t) = L(0) + \sum_{i=1}^{t} p(i) - \sum_{i=1}^{t} o(i)$$

$$= L(0) + \sum_{i=1}^{t} [p(i) - o(i)] \qquad (10-1)$$

where $L(0)$ represents the initial inventory level. The time increment Δt, in this case is one day. Under very general conditions if we consider the limit as $\Delta t \to 0$ the above summation can be replaced by an integral. A continuous approximation to this model is then

$$L(t) = L(0) + \int_{0}^{t} [p(\tau) - o(\tau)] \, d\tau \qquad (10-2)$$

In this instance $p(t)$ and $o(t)$ may be viewed as instantaneous production rates which may or may not vary over time.

Such a descriptive representation may be useful to study fluctuations in inventory over time once a production schedule and demand schedule are known, but it does little to answer the basic questions of when and how much to order. Management can usually influence the production rate $p(t)$ but may find the demand function $o(t)$ to be completely beyond their control. The problem then is to define some measure of effectiveness for inventory performance which will permit management to make an intelligent choice for the production function $p(t)$. Note that even though $p(t)$ has been called a production function it is equally valid to view it as a time history of purchases when the item in question is obtained from outside vendors. An obvious measure of effectiveness is the annual variable cost incurred by the inventory system. By applying this measure the influence of different production schedules may be evaluated. In addition it is often possible to determine an optimum schedule for the abstracted system—optimum in the sense of minimum annual variable cost.

The General Model for No Shortages

Since we are concerned in this chapter with deterministic systems it is possible to specify with complete assurance that shortages will not occur if that is the policy desired. To do so requires only that a new order of stock arrive at the instant existing stock levels reach zero. This avoids all questions of lost sales and back orders expense. If in addition it is assumed that the unit purchase price of the item in question is independent of order quantity, the only variable cost terms involved will be the cost of placing an order and the cost of carrying an item in stock. Although we will treat these costs as given parameters of the system, it is well to remember that the estimation of each of these cost figures may itself be a sizable research task.

A plot of inventory level as a function of time for such simple deterministic systems would appear as one of the graphs shown in Figure 10–3. Graph (*a*) of that figure represents the classical fixed order quantity system in which a fixed quantity Q is ordered at a time that will insure its arrival at the instant existing stocks are exhausted. In this instance all Q units are delivered at once as would be the case for many items purchased from outside vendors.

Graph (*b*) of Figure 10–3 illustrates an idealized version of a production system in which items are produced at a constant rate simultaneously with inventory withdrawals. Here it is assumed that the production rate is greater

FIGURE 10–3
Deterministic Inventory Systems

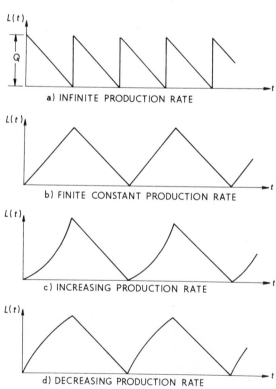

a) INFINITE PRODUCTION RATE

b) FINITE CONSTANT PRODUCTION RATE

c) INCREASING PRODUCTION RATE

d) DECREASING PRODUCTION RATE

than the withdrawal rate so that only intermittent production is necessary. This graph could represent inventory levels for an item produced in one's own plant. Order costs for this system would be in the nature of setup costs incurred when a job shop switches from one product to another.

Other variations in production rates are useful to gain more realistic pictures of actual production capabilities. For example, each time a new order is received by the producing department there may be some relearning that takes place. Production rate the first day is not as great as production rate the 10th day. Graph (c) of Figure 10–3 illustrates this type of system. It is also possible to have production systems, such as those found in certain chemical processes, in which production rate begins quite high and tapers off over time. This is represented by graph (d) of Figure 10–3. Other systems may be more closely approximated by some combination of these production functions. In each instance graphed it has been assumed that demand rate is constant over time. This is not an essential assumption, however, inasmuch as one could also construct time varying demand rates. Models for a wide variety of deterministic production and demand patterns are developed by Naddor.[1]

Annual Cost.   Rather than employing purely geometric arguments often advanced for the simple fixed-order quantity model, let us adhere to the more general approach suggested by Hadley and Whitin.[2] They have shown that average annual cost may be obtained for a great number of models by calculating the average cost per cycle and multiplying by the average number cycles per year.

The following notation will be used:

C = purchase price per unit, assumed constant in this problem
A = cost of placing an order
I = inventory carrying charge expressed as an annual rate per dollar invested
Q = order quantity per cycle
$o(t)$ = demand rate as a function of time
$p(t)$ = production rate as a function of time
T = cycle time

The first component of average cycle cost is the cost of placing an order. This has already been expressed as the fixed amount A. Here it is assumed that the cost of ordering 5 pieces is the same as that incurred when ordering 500. Note that this is strictly a data processing and materials handling cost. It does not include the price which must be paid for the items.

The second component of average cycle cost is the cost of carrying the inventory for one cycle. Consider the cost of carrying a fixed amount of

[1] Eliezer Naddor, *Inventory Systems* (New York: John Wiley & Sons, Inc., 1966).
[2] G. Hadley, and T. M. Whitin, *Analysis of Inventory Systems* (Englewood Cliffs, N.J.: Prentice-Hall, Inc., 1963).

stock L for a time Δt. The carrying cost is proportional to the product of the amount of money invested and the amount of time involved. The proportionality constant is I. The cost of carrying L units of stock for Δt would then be

$$\text{COST} = ICL\,\Delta t \qquad (10\text{–}3)$$

Consider the graph of one cycle of an inventory system to be made up of a series of rectangles of height $L(i)$ and width Δt. It is apparent that total carrying cost per cycle is equal to the area under the curve times the product IC. This concept is illustrated in Figure 10–4.

It is now a simple matter to develop a mathematical expression for carrying cost per cycle. All that is necessary is to mathematically define the inventory curve over one cycle, integrate to establish the area under the inventory curve, and multiply by the product of unit cost times carrying charge. In general, for the case of continuous variables with initial inventory zero and no shortages allowed, the inventory curve may be defined in terms of production rate and demand rate as

$$L(t) = \int_0^t [p(\tau) - o(\tau)]\,d\tau \qquad (10\text{–}4)$$

The area under this curve for one cycle of length T is given by

$$\int_0^T L(t)\,dt = \int_0^T \int_0^t [p(\tau) - o(\tau)]\,d\tau\,dt \qquad (10\text{–}5)$$

Total carrying cost per cycle is IC times this quantity. The complete expression for total variable cost per cycle may now be written as

$$\text{CYCLE COST} = A + IC \int_0^T \int_0^t [p(\tau) - o(\tau)]\,d\tau\,dt \qquad (10\text{–}6)$$

FIGURE 10–4
The Area under the Inventory Curve

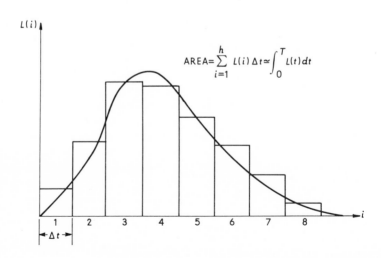

This expression is easily converted to average annual cost by multiplying by the average number of cycles per year. The number of cycles in a year depends upon the total annual demand and the number of units ordered each cycle. If the time scale used in expressions developed so far is expressed in years, the total annual demand will be

$$\text{ANNUAL DEMAND} = \int_0^1 o(t)\, dt \qquad (10\text{–}7)$$

From this point it is obvious that the average number of cycles per year is given by

$$\text{CYCLES} = \frac{\text{annual demand}}{\text{order quantity/cycle}}$$

$$= \frac{\int_0^1 o(t)\, dt}{Q} \qquad (10\text{–}8)$$

We are now in a position to write the complete expression for average annual cost as

$$K = \left[A + IC \int_0^T \int_0^t (p(\tau) - o(\tau))\, d\tau\, dt \right] \left[\frac{\int_0^1 o(t)\, dt}{Q} \right] \qquad (10\text{–}9)$$

This model is general enough to encompass all of the cases enumerated in Figure 10–3 and indeed most deterministic systems in which no shortages are allowed. Although it may appear rather unwieldly in its present form, it will be seen to reduce to comparatively simple expressions when specific cases of production and demand rates are considered. In most of the simpler models discussed here the basic decision variable under control by management is the order quantity Q. All other parameters are given or can be functionally related to Q. Although the models which follow can be derived by simple geometric arguments, it is this author's contention that the general form of Equation 10-9 is valuable for conceptualizing a wide range of inventory production problems. Some function forms which do not easily yield to geometric arguments will be introduced in problems at the end of the chapter.

The Infinite Production Rate Model

The infinite production rate model is appropriate for purchased items. Graphs of inventory level over time for such systems look like Figure 10–3(a) as long as shortages are not permitted. Let us assume that demand rate for the purchased item in question is constant at λ units per year. Using the notation developed in the previous section, the demand function would be a continuous function

$$o(t) = \lambda \qquad (10\text{–}10)$$

The production function would be a series of impulses occurring every T time units. When viewed as a continuous function, the instantaneous production rate would be infinite at the point of the pulse. However when viewed a discrete function of time such pulses can be represented as

$$p(t) = \begin{cases} Q & t = 0, T, 2T, \ldots, nT, \ldots \\ 0 & \text{elsewhere} \end{cases} \tag{10-11}$$

In this instance we are treating production rate as a discrete function and demand rate as a continuous function of time. The general expression for inventory level must then be modified as follows

$$L(t) = \int_0^t p(\tau) - o(\tau)\, d\tau \rightarrow \sum_{\tau=0}^t p(\tau) - \int_0^t o(\tau)\, d\tau \tag{10-12}$$

which within the limits of one cycle ($0 \leq t < T$) becomes

$$L(t) = Q - \int_0^t o(\tau)\, d\tau$$

$$= Q - \int_0^t \lambda\, d\tau$$

$$= Q - \lambda t \tag{10-13}$$

Since demand rate has been given as units per year the total annual demand is obviously

$$\int_0^1 o(\tau)\, d\tau = \int_0^1 \lambda\, d\tau = \lambda \tag{10-14}$$

We are now in a position to develop the complete expression for average annual cost as

$$K = \left[A + IC \int_0^T (Q - \lambda t)\, dt \right] \left[\frac{\lambda}{Q} \right]$$

$$= \frac{\lambda A}{Q} + IC \left(QT - \frac{\lambda T^2}{2} \right)\left(\frac{\lambda}{Q} \right) \tag{10-15}$$

This expression can be further simplified by recognizing that the cycle time T is fixed by the order quantity Q and demand rate λ. This variable T is simply the time necessary to exhaust the initial inventory of Q units, namely,

$$T = \frac{Q}{\lambda} \tag{10-16}$$

Combining the Equations 10–15 and 10–16 and collecting terms leads to

$$K = \frac{\lambda A}{Q} + \frac{ICQ}{2} \tag{10-17}$$

This equation could have been developed directly from simple geometric arguments. Since the inventory level varies between Q and zero in straight-line fashion, the average number of units on hand is $Q/2$. Carrying charges for the year are then simply the carrying charge per unit, IC, times the average inventory. Order costs are developed exactly as before by multiplying the cost per order times the number of orders placed per year. For this very special case the geometric arguments appear so simple that one might question the wisdom of the more general approach suggested. The reader should bear in mind, however, that such geometric arguments may not work as one considers more complex systems, whereas the general approach advocated in this text will solve a very large class of inventory problems. Our goal is to develop general model formulating capability rather than to survey a large number of unique formulations for specific situations.

Model Properties. The expression for average annual cost given above is a strictly convex function of the decision variable Q and as such possesses a unique minimum. The optimum value of Q may be ascertained by employing the usual methods of basic calculus to identify relative minima. Setting the first derivative of K with respect to Q equal to zero gives

$$\frac{dK}{dQ} = -\frac{\lambda A}{Q^2} + \frac{IC}{2} = 0$$

from which the optimum value of Q is

$$Q_0 = \left(\frac{2\lambda A}{IC}\right)^{1/2} \tag{10-18}$$

This is the standard economic lot size formula found in most texts which discuss inventories. The fact that Q_0 does represent a minimum point on K may be verified by evaluating d^2K/dQ^2 which is seen to be greater than zero for any positive Q.

The square root relationship between order quantity and the other variables is the single most important result from the analysis of deterministic systems. This same form appears in all of the standard inventory models. Its interpretation leads to some important principles of inventory control, namely that order quantity should be proportional to the square root of demand rate and inversely proportional to the square root of the value of the item being stored. This tells us that demand should increase by a factor of four before order quantity is doubled. It also indicates that order quantities for \$4 items should be only one half as large as for \$1 items.

The value of K at the minimum point may be developed by substituting the expression for Q_0 in place of the variable Q in the original cost equation. This reveals a minimum cost expression of

$$K_0 = (2\lambda AIC)^{1/2} \tag{10-19}$$

The behavior of this simple model in the neighborhood of the optimum solution gives one courage to apply it to many situations for which this representation is a gross approximation. For example, consider an item with a purchase price of $C = \$10$, order cost $A = \$25$, carrying charge $I = 0.20$, and annual demand rate $\lambda = 400$. From our previous calculations, the optimum order quantity should be 100 units which will incur an average annual variable cost of $200. However, this model is not very sensitive to the value of Q selected. Figure 10–5 illustrates the cost behavior for varying values of Q. The curve is rather flat for some distance on either side of the optimum order quantity Q_0.

Examination of Figure 10–5 reveals that doubling the optimum order quantity from 100 to 200 causes only a 25 percent increase in annual variable costs. Cutting the optimum order quantity in half also leads to a 25 percent increase in annual expense. This sensitivity of cost to order quantity may be expressed in general terms as

$$\frac{K}{K_0} = \frac{1}{2}\left(\frac{Q_0}{Q} + \frac{Q}{Q_0}\right) \qquad (10\text{–}20)$$

FIGURE 10–5

Cost Behavior of the Infinite Production Rate Model

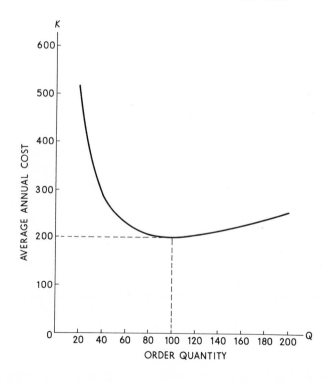

General expressions for the sensitivity of annual costs to variations in system parameters may also be desirable. For example, since the order cost A includes a large number of data which may be of questionable accuracy, the gain possible by improving the estimate of A is of interest. Let B represent an estimate of the actual order cost A. Let K be the actual annual cost incurred by ordering in off-optimum lots of size Q, Q having been determined by assuming an order cost B. Then

$$K = \frac{\lambda A}{(2\lambda B/IC)^{1/2}} + \left(\frac{IC}{2}\right)\left(\frac{2\lambda B}{IC}\right)^{1/2} \tag{10-21}$$

which may be compared with the optimum cost $K_0 = (2\lambda AIC)^{1/2}$.
The ratio of K to K_0 reveals

$$\frac{K}{K_0} = \frac{1}{2}\left[\left(\frac{A}{B}\right)^{1/2} + \left(\frac{B}{A}\right)^{1/2}\right] \tag{10-22}$$

Suppose that our estimate of A had been \$100 instead of the actual expense of \$25 in the previous example. The resulting operating expense would have been increased only 25 percent over optimum even though the order cost estimate was in error by a factor of four.

Sensitivity can also be measured by $\partial K/\partial A$, $\partial K/\partial C$, and $\partial K/\partial \lambda$. The resulting derivatives measure the change in annual cost caused by a unit change in the parameters A, C, and λ. Sensitivity analyses such as these reveal when only order of magnitude estimates of system parameters and decision variables are necessary to achieve near optimal solutions. They also indicate the amount of money management can afford to allocate to improving the estimates of parameters. In addition they show which variables exercise the most influence on system behavior.

In the simple system being discussed here, it is apparent that a large number of combinations of decision variable and parameter values will give near optimal solutions. For this reason we may use the model in many situations in which we recognize that it is less than a perfect description. The gains in cost reduction may simply not be worth the additional expense necessary to obtain more accurate models.

Reorder Points for Infinite Production Rate Models. Model developments so far have centered on how much to order. Nothing has been said about the equally vital question of when to order. The answer to this question for the infinite production rate model takes a particularly simple form.

An operating system can be viewed as having two inventory levels. One level is the apparent inventory which is physically present in the plant. This is the inventory level we have used to develop our model for average annual variable cost. A second level reflects the total inventory commitments for the item in question. At any point in time a company has available for planning purposes not only the stock on hand but also the stock currently on order from suppliers. Let us call the sum of these inventories the effective inventory. Effective inventory, $E(t)$, at any time t is then expressed as

$$E(t) = L(t) + D(t) \qquad (10\text{-}23)$$

where $D(t)$ represents the number of units on order not yet delivered and $L(t)$ has the usual meaning of on-hand inventory. The relationships among these quantities are shown in Figure 10-6.

In the system currently under consideration, no shortages are permitted. If one considers only the effective inventory level, this means that an order for replenishment stock must be placed when $E(t)$ contains just enough stock to operate the system over the lead time necessary to receive an order. Since we are considering a deterministic system, let us treat the lead time as a constant d. This implies that regardless of when an order is placed, d time units will elapse before that particular order becomes a part of the on-hand inventory.

Using the notation previously developed, the above statements require that an order be placed when $E(t)$ reaches the critical level E_c

$$E_c = \int_0^d o(\tau)\, d\tau \qquad (10\text{-}24)$$

FIGURE 10-6

Inventory Patterns

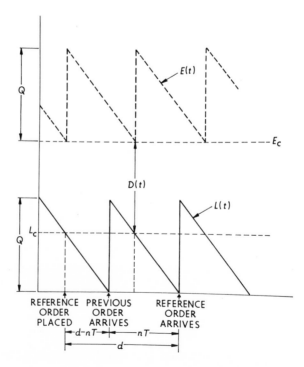

In effect, E_c is the lead time demand for the system. For the infinite production rate model, E_c reduces to λd.

Particularly if the reorder decision is to be made by a tag system, it is often more convenient to express it in terms of on-hand inventories. Since we know that an order must be placed when on-hand plus on-order equals lead time demand, all that is necessary is to determine the number of units already on order but not yet delivered. Anything already on order will arrive before the order now being placed since we have assumed that all orders have a constant lead time d. The number of orders outstanding, n, is then equal to the number of complete cycles contained in one lead time or

$$n = \text{int}\left(\frac{d}{T}\right) \qquad (10\text{–}25)$$

where int is read as "the integer portion of" and T is the length of one cycle. Since each order contains Q units, the critical level for on-hand inventory, L_c, may now be written as

$$L_c = E_c - nQ \qquad (10\text{–}26)$$

which reduces to $\lambda d - nQ$ for the infinite production rate model. L_c is the quantity in the bin at the time an order is placed. It represents the trigger point for systems in which orders are placed on the basis of inventory physically available rather than total commitment.

Example. As an example of how these expressions might be applied, consider a system for which annual demand is 400 units, lead time is 0.3 years, and the optimum order quantity has been determined to be 100 units. In terms of effective inventory an order should be placed when $E(t)$ reaches

$$E_c = \lambda d = (400)(0.3) = 120 \text{ units}$$

In terms of the apparent inventory, the corresponding physical stock level at the time an order is placed will be

$$L_c = E_c - nQ = 120 - \text{int}\left(\frac{d\lambda}{Q}\right)Q$$

$$= 120 - (1)(100) = 20$$

Finite Production Rates

The method of attack illustrated for the infinite production rate case applies equally well to finite production rates. Let us consider the simplest case in which production occurs at a constant rate, P, over time. Obviously for the system to operate with a positive inventory level P must be greater than λ, the annual demand rate. This problem arises in production operations when one has manufacturing capabilities which exceed the demand for a particular item. The production line might operate for three days on ashtrays and five days on paperweights. During the three days on ashtrays enough will be manufactured to supply the system until the next production cycle begins. However, demand is continuous and stock is being depleted even while the production portion of the inventory cycle is occurring. Management must balance the cost of changeover or setup against the cost of carrying finished goods inventories. Inventory behavior for this system is depicted by Figure 10–3(b).

Consider first the production function $p(\tau)$. Since production rate exceeds demand rate, production will only occur over a portion of the total inventory cycle. Let t_p represent the time during which production takes place and t_d represent the time during which demand is satisfied from existing stocks. Figure 10–7 illustrates the parameters necessary to describe one cycle of this system. Note that the maximum inventory level achieved is no longer equal to the order quantity Q. This occurs because part of the order Q is being used as it is manufactured and the entire quantity does not reach the bins at one time. From Figure 10–7 it is obvious that the production function may be defined as

$$p(t) = \begin{cases} P & 0 \le t \le t_p \\ 0 & t_p < t < T \end{cases} \qquad (10\text{--}27)$$

The Cost Equation.   Examination of the carrying cost term of our general model shown in Equation 10–9 reveals

$$IC \int_0^T \int_0^t [p(\tau) - o(\tau)] \, d\tau \, dt = IC \left\{ \int_0^{t_p} \int_0^t (P - \lambda) \, d\tau \, dt + \int_0^{t_d} \left(L_{\max} - \int_0^t \lambda \, d\tau \right) dt \right\}$$

$$= IC \left\{ \int_0^{t_p} (Pt - \lambda t) \, dt + \int_0^{t_d} [(P - \lambda)t_p - \lambda t] \, dt \right\}$$

$$= IC \left\{ \frac{(P - \lambda)t_p^2}{2} + (P - \lambda)t_p t_d - \frac{\lambda t_d^2}{2} \right\} \qquad (10\text{--}28)$$

This expression may be written as a function of the decision variable Q by recognizing that the time necessary to produce Q units, t_p, is equal to the number to be produced divided by the rate at which they are produced, i.e.,

$$t_p = \frac{Q}{P} \qquad (10\text{--}29)$$

The time during which no production occurs, t_d, is given by the difference between total cycle time and production time, i.e.,

$$t_d = T - t_p = \frac{Q}{\lambda} - \frac{Q}{P} = \left(\frac{Q}{\lambda}\right)\left(\frac{P - \lambda}{P}\right) \qquad (10\text{--}30)$$

The setup cost is assumed fixed at A dollars per cycle. The number of

FIGURE 10-7

Finite Production Rate Cycle

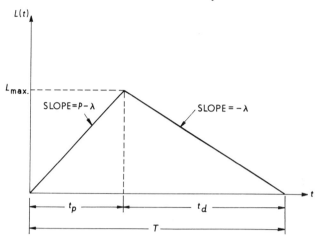

cycles per year is given as before by

$$\left(\frac{1}{Q}\right) \int_0^1 o(\tau) \, d\tau = \left(\frac{1}{Q}\right) \int_0^1 \lambda \, d\tau = \frac{\lambda}{Q} \tag{10-31}$$

Substituting the above items into our general inventory model and simplifying gives

$$K = \frac{\lambda A}{Q} + \left(\frac{ICQ}{2}\right)\left(\frac{P - \lambda}{P}\right) \tag{10-32}$$

Note that this model looks quite similar to the one developed for infinite production rates. They differ only by the factor $(P - \lambda)/P$ in the carrying cost terms.

It is also possible to develop this model from purely geometric arguments. However, it remains the premise of this author that the goal of the reader is to gain facility in inventory model building, hence we continue to follow the more powerful method for illustrative purposes even though it may appear to be somewhat circuitous in the more simple cases.

From the cost Equation 10-32 it is now a simple matter to develop an expression for the optimum order quantity by taking derivatives, i.e.,

$$\frac{dK}{dQ} = \frac{-\lambda A}{Q^2} + \left(\frac{IC}{2}\right)\left(\frac{P - \lambda}{P}\right) = 0$$

from which

$$Q_0 = \left[\left(\frac{2\lambda A}{IC}\right)\left(\frac{P}{P - \lambda}\right)\right]^{1/2} \tag{10-33}$$

It is of interest to note that we could have developed the infinite production rate model by limit arguments on the finite production rate model. The limit of K as P approaches infinity is

$$\lim_{P \to \infty} \left[\frac{\lambda A}{Q} + \left(\frac{ICQ}{2} \right)\left(1 - \frac{\lambda}{P} \right) \right] = \frac{\lambda A}{Q} + \frac{ICQ}{2}$$

which agrees with Equation 10–17. Similarly, the order quantity is given by

$$\lim_{P \to \infty} \left[\left(\frac{2\lambda A}{IC} \right)\left(\frac{1}{(1 - \lambda/P)} \right) \right]^{1/2} = \left(\frac{2\lambda A}{IC} \right)^{1/2}$$

Sensitivity analyses of the type suggested for the infinite production rate model follow in straightforward fashion and are left as exercises for the reader.

Reorder Points for Finite Production Rate Model.   Developing an answer to the question of when to reorder is not quite as straightforward as it was for the infinite production rate model. In terms of the effective inventory level the answer is the same, that is, reorder when $E(t) = \lambda d$. The graph of effective inventory as a function of time looks the same for both systems. Establishing reorder points in terms of on-hand inventory requires more thought, however, since it is possible to place another order during the production portion of the cycle. In this instance the number of units outstanding includes not only the whole orders not yet delivered, but also the unfinished portion of the current order. Figure 10–8 depicts the two possible cases for determining reorder points.

Case 1 behaves exactly as the infinite production rate model. The parameter n represents the number of whole cycles contained in one lead time d and is calculated by Equation 10–25. Case 1 applies whenever $d - nT$ is less than the pure demand portion of the cycle, t_d. In this instance the new order is being placed during the nonproductive portion of the cycle. The on-hand inventory at the time of reordering must be sufficient to cover all demands until the next production cycle begins. Under our usual assumptions of deterministic parameters the reorder point is

$$L_c = (d - nT)(\lambda) = \lambda d - nQ \tag{10–34}$$

Case 2 arises when $(d - nT) > t_d$. In this instance a new order is being placed at a time when the facilities are engaged in producing a previously requested order. The on-hand inventory plus the amount still to be produced on the order currently in process must be sufficient to cover all demands occurring before the next production cycle begins. As shown in Figure 10–8 the amount of time remaining in the current production cycle is $(d - nT) - t_d$. Replacing t_d with $T - t_p$ gives $t_p - [T - (d - nT)]$. The amount of material that can be produced in that time is $P[t_p - ((n + 1)T - d)]$. The total amount of material that is needed before the next production cycle begins is $\lambda(d - nT)$.

FIGURE 10–8

Reorder Points for Finite Production Models

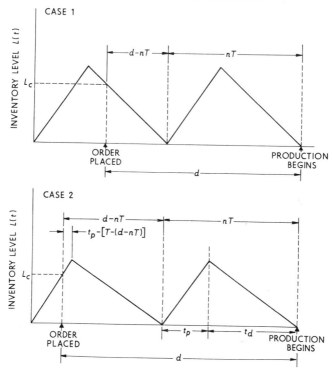

Combining these expressions, the reorder point in terms of on-hand inventory is given by

$$L_c = \lambda(d - nT) - P[t_p - ((n + 1)T - d)] \tag{10–35}$$

which may be rewritten as a function of Q as

$$L_c = \lambda d - Pd + (n + 1)Q\left(\frac{P}{\lambda} - 1\right) \tag{10–36}$$

Example. A company manufactures both ashtrays and paperweights utilizing the same facilities. Ashtrays can be produced at a rate of 5,000 per month for $1.50 each. The annual demand rate is 20,000. Setup costs for a production run of ashtrays are estimated to be $300. The company follows a policy of no stockouts and believes that a fair carrying rate is 30 percent. Paper work and scheduling delays are such that it requires four weeks from receipt of an order until production can begin on that order. From Equation 10–33 the optimal lot size is

$$Q_0 = \left\{ \left[\frac{2(20,000)(300)}{(0.30)(1.50)} \right] \left[\frac{5000(12)}{5000(12) - 20,000} \right] \right\}^{1/2}$$

$$= \left[\frac{(12)(10^6)(1.5)}{0.45} \right]^{1/2} = 6,320 \qquad (10\text{--}37)$$

This lot size is over 22 percent greater than the optimal lot size obtained for the same system under conditions of infinite production rate. The total cycle time is Q_0/λ or 0.316 years. From Equation 10–25 the number of orders outstanding is

$$n = \text{int} \left[\frac{(4/52)}{(0.316)} \right] = \text{int}[0.244] = 0 \qquad (10\text{--}38)$$

The quantity $d - nT$ is then simply d or 0.077 years. Since production time is Q_0/P or 0.105 years the pure demand portion of the cycle is

$$t_d = T - t_p = 0.316 - 0.105 = 0.211 \text{ years} \qquad (10\text{--}39)$$

Obviously $d - nT$ is less than t_d, therefore case 1 is used to determine the reorder point in terms of on-hand inventory, i.e.,

$$L_c = \lambda d - nQ = (20,000)(0.077) = 1,540 \qquad (10\text{--}40)$$

If the lead time for this system was 16 weeks instead of 4, then $(d - nT)$ would be 0.308 years which is greater than the time $t_d = 0.211$ years. In this instance case 2 applies and from Equation 10–36 the reorder point in terms of on-hand inventory would be

$$L_c = (20,000)(0.308) - (5,000)(12)(0.308) + (6,320)(3 - 1) = 320 \qquad (10\text{--}41)$$

Note that this reorder point of 320 units is conditional upon being in the production portion of the cycle. The reorder rule would be "when the on-hand inventory reaches 320 units *and* the production system is currently operating, place a new order."

Shortage Models

In the models we have developed so far, it has been assumed that the system will never run out of stock. Since we are here concerned with deterministic systems it is possible to specify quite rigorously that stock-outs never occur. We know exactly when current stock will be exhausted and can plan to have new stock arrive at the instant stock levels reach zero. In the event that customers are impatient to the point of refusing to wait for new stock to arrive, the models developed so far are obviously optimal. That is to say that for deterministic systems it is never optimal to permit shortages if those shortages lead to lost sales. In the probabilistic models developed in the next chapter this will not be true.

In many inventory systems it is not true that failure to have supplies immediately available will lead to lost sales. Customers may be willing to wait for some time for the goods to be delivered. In this case unsatisfied demands are treated as back orders and appropriate costs for this condition must be determined. The estimation of the cost of shortage is one of the most difficult tasks facing the inventory model builder. Obviously if there is no penalty for being short, the system should operate on a build-to-order basis and carry no inventories. Most companies do carry inventories, however, so they must place some value on shortages. When we study probabilistic models it will be possible to introduce means of imputing a cost of shortage when management will not or cannot provide dollar estimates for this expense. For the time being let us assume that dollar estimates for shortages are available and proceed with the analysis.

A graphic description for a simple back-orders model is contained in Figure 10–9. Note that another basic decision variable has been added to the model. Now we must choose not only when and how much to order, but also the number of shortages to be permitted each cycle. In order to obtain mathematically tractable solutions let us assume that shortages incur a fixed cost, B, for every unit back ordered and a variable cost, b, which is proportional to the amount of time stock is back ordered. The cost B represents the loss of goodwill and the fixed accounting expense incurred when an item is back ordered. The cost b is analogous to the carrying charge IC for inventories. Customers become increasingly displeased as the time to

FIGURE 10–9

Back-Orders Case

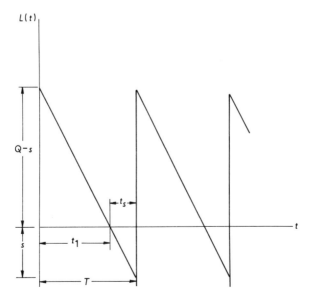

delivery is extended, additional bookkeeping and expediting charges are incurred, and available income from sales is postponed. The basic decision is then one of balancing the cost of carrying inventories against the cost of carrying back orders.

Let the total number of shortages in one cycle be given by s. Applying the same techniques used to determine carrying cost in 10–6, the total back-order cost per cycle for the infinite production rate model is

$$\text{Back order cost} = Bs - b \int_0^{t_s} \int_0^t p(\tau) - 0(\tau)\, d\tau\, dt$$

$$= Bs + b \int_0^{t_s} \lambda t\, dt$$

$$= Bs + \frac{b\lambda t_s^2}{2} \tag{10-42}$$

Notice that the minus sign was introduced on the second term to compensate for the fact that the area under the back-orders portion of the curve would appear as a negative term in our general model. Since the time in back-order status, t_s, is related to total back orders incurred and demand rate by

$$t_s = \frac{s}{\lambda} \tag{10-43}$$

the entire back-order cost per cycle may be rewritten as

$$Bs + \frac{bs^2}{2\lambda} \tag{10-44}$$

For this model the initial inventory for a cycle is not zero as we assumed in our earlier calculations but is $-s$, the number of shortages incurred. The general expression for inventory level over time is then

$$L(t) = -s + \int_0^t p(\tau) - o(\tau)\, d\tau$$

$$= Q - s - \lambda t \qquad 0 \le t \le T \tag{10-45}$$

The carrying charges apply only for the time t_i during which the inventory level is positive. With these modifications the general model 10–9 leads us to an annual variable cost of

$$K = \frac{[A + IC \int_0^{t_i}(Q - s - \lambda t)\, dt + Bs + bs^2/2\lambda]\lambda}{Q} \tag{10-46}$$

The time t_i is total cycle time less shortage time or

$$t_i = T - t_s = \frac{Q - s}{\lambda} \tag{10-47}$$

The complete cost expression then reduces to

$$K = \frac{\lambda A}{Q} + \frac{IC(Q - s)^2}{2Q} + \frac{\lambda Bs + bs^2/2}{Q} \qquad (10\text{-}48)$$

In order for the choice of Q and s to be optimal for this system, the differential calculus requires that

$$\frac{\partial K}{\partial Q} = \frac{\partial K}{\partial s} = 0 \qquad (10\text{-}49)$$

Applying this to 10–48 gives

$$s_0 = (b + IC)^{-1}\left[-B\lambda + \left((2\lambda AIC)\left(1 + \frac{IC}{b}\right) - \frac{IC(B\lambda)^2}{b}\right)^{1/2}\right] \qquad (10\text{-}50)$$

and

$$Q_0 = \left[\frac{(b + IC)}{b}\right]^{1/2}\left[\frac{2\lambda A}{IC} - \frac{(B\lambda)^2}{IC(b + IC)}\right]^{1/2} \qquad (10\text{-}51)$$

for $b \neq 0$.

Note that Equations 10–50 and 10–51 apply only when $b \neq 0$. When $b = 0$ the optimal solution lies on the boundary, and if the system should be operated at all, $s = 0$ will give the minimum cost configuration. When $B = 0$, Equations 10–50 and 10–51 may be modified in straightforward fashion. If the value for s computed from Equation 10–50 is less than zero then the optimum solution is $s_0 = 0$. An excellent discussion of these various cases is contained in Hadley and Whitin.[3]

If we consider the inventory level $L(t)$ as a function defined for both positive and negative inventories the calculation of a reorder point proceeds exactly as before. Stock needed at the reorder point is equal to the total lead time demand less the shortages permitted, minus the number of units already on order but not delivered. In this instance a negative value for $L(t)$ indicates a back-order condition. It is possible for the reorder point L_c to have a negative value which implies that a new order should be placed when the number of back orders equals $-L_c$. The calculation is

$$L_c = \lambda d - s_0 - nQ_0 \qquad (10\text{-}52)$$

Example. A manufacturer uses 3/8 inch titanium fasteners to assemble his product. Demand is such that he needs 4,000 boxes per year. Each box costs $40, and the company imposes a carrying charge of $0.20 per year for every dollar invested in inventories. It cost $25 to place an order which will require three months for delivery. Each box short causes production delays estimated at $0.30, and each day a box remains on shortage costs an additional $0.10.

---

[3] *Ibid.*, pp. 44–46.

Converting the given data into our standard terms gives:

$\lambda = 4{,}000$ boxes per year $b = \$36.50$ per box per year
$A = \$25$ per order $I = 0.20$
$C = \$40$ per box $d = 0.25$ years
$B = \$0.30$ per box

From Equations 10–50 and 10–51, $s_0 = 1.8$ and $Q_0 = 160$ which implies that an order for 160 units should be placed every 0.04 years or approximately every two weeks. The number of orders outstanding at reorder time would be

$$n = \text{int}\left(\frac{d}{T}\right) = \text{int}\left(\frac{0.25}{0.04}\right) = 6$$

From (10–52) the reorder point is

$$L_c = d - nQ_0 - s_0 = 1{,}000 - 960 - 1.8 = 38.2 \text{ boxes}$$

Model Extensions

From this brief introduction it is easy to see how the basic formulation we have developed can be extended to a large number of special cases. We have already mentioned the possibility of employing different time functions to describe production and demand rates. In addition we can consider such things as price breaks, constrained solutions, order costs which are functions of order quantity, and many others. Some of these considerations will be taken up in the problems at the end of the chapter. For detailed discussions of these and other extensions the reader may refer to the references listed.

The point is that virtually an infinite number of special cases of deterministic models can be studied. It is the belief of this author, however, that a thorough understanding of the general model building approach suggested in this chapter will enable the reader to cope with such special cases as they arise. In addition he will be much better prepared than he would be with a large catalog of specific plug-in type formulas.

SELECTED BIBLIOGRAPHY

BUFFA, ELWOOD S. *Production-Inventory Systems: Planning and Control.* Homewood, Ill.: Richard D. Irwin, Inc., 1968.
HADLEY, G AND WHITIN, T. M. *Analysis of Inventory Systems.* Englewood Cliffs, N. J.: Prentice-Hall, Inc., 1963.
MAGEE, JOHN F., AND BOODMAN, DAVID M. *Production Planning and Inventory Control.* 2d ed. New York: McGraw-Hill Book Co., Inc., 1967.
NADDOR, ELIEZER. *Inventory Systems.* New York: John Wiley & Sons, Inc., 1966.
PLOSSL, G. W., AND WIGHT, O. W. *Production and Inventory Control.* Englewood Cliffs, N. J.: Prentice-Hall, Inc., 1967.
PRICHARD, JAMES W., AND EAGLE, ROBERT H. *Modern Inventory Management.* New York: John Wiley & Sons, Inc., 1965.

PROBLEMS

10–1 The Villified Oil Company sells 600 quarts of oil per month. The unit cost of a quart of oil to the company is $0.40, and the cost of placing an order is $10. The company uses a carrying charge of $I = 0.22$. Assume that demand is continuous and deterministic. No stock-outs are allowed.

a) Determine the optimal order quantity.

b) Determine the minimum average annual variable cost.

c) Determine the time between orders.

d) If procurement lead time is one month, what is the reorder point based on the on-hand inventory?

10–2 The refinery supplying Villified Oil experiences a constant demand rate of 10,000 barrels per month. When they are producing this particular grade, their production rate is 16,000 barrels per month. The cost of setup for a production run is $1,200. The cost of storing one barrel of oil for one month is estimated to be $3. The lead time necessary to initiate a production run is two weeks. The company does not tolerate shortages.

a) Calculate the optimal order quantity.

b) Determine the maximum inventory level.

c) Calculate the reorder point in terms of on-hand inventory.

d) Determine the average annual variable cost.

e) Determine the sensitivity of this solution to estimates of the monthly carrying cost.

10–3 Consider a deterministic inventory model in which the cost of placing an order is $50, the carrying charge is $I = 0.25$, the item is valued at $400, and annual demand is 100 units. Each unit back ordered costs the company $9. Determine the optimal operating policy. Show all calculations.

10–4 *Part I.* A user of a small centrifugal pump purchases 1/4 h.p. electrical motors from a wholesaler for $35 each. He uses 1,200 of these motors annually. The wholesaler can provide delivery in two months. The ordering and handling costs associated with each order amount to $15, and storage and capital costs amount to $5 annually for each motor.

a) Determine the economic order quantity.

b) Determine the minimum annual variable cost.

c) Determine the reorder point.

Part II. Suppose that management requires that stock never reaches zero. They always want at least three units on hand. How will this change your answers to Part I?

10–5 Management policy of your company is to never run out of stock. You have been asked to carry out an analysis of one item to evaluate this policy. Demand is deterministic and constant over time at 900 units per year. Unit cost is $50 independent of quantity ordered. Cost of placing an order is $5, and carrying charge is $I = 0.25$. Units could be back ordered at a cost of $0.20 per unit per week.

a) Calculate the optimal operating doctrine under the assumption that no stock-outs are allowed.

b) What is the dollar loss per year caused by the no stock-out policy?

10–6   The "Pained Pharmacy" used a policy of ordering tranquilizers and pep pills at the same time. The characteristics of these items are tranquilizers: $\lambda = 6,000$ boxes per year, $C = \$10$, $A = \$3$, $I = 0.30$; pep pills: $\lambda = 900$ boxes per year, $C = \$2$, $A = \$3$, $I = 0.30$. Management policy permits no stockouts. Calculate the best policy (time between orders) for ordering these two items if both must be ordered at the same time. What are the average annual costs of this policy? Calculate the additional savings to be obtained by establishing a different ordering policy for each of the items.

10–7   Consider an inventory system which bases carrying cost on the expected maximum amount of inventory space needed, the carrying cost per space per year being D dollars. Any demands occurring when the system is out of stock are lost. The ordering and lost sales information follow the usual notation. Modify the basic operating cost equation and resulting reorder-point, reorder-quantity expressions to describe the system.

10–8   Consider an inventory control system in which demands are deterministic with a constant rate λ, carrying charges $= I$, cost per unit $= C$, order cost $= A$. In addition suppose that management insists that on-hand inventory must never fall below a predetermined level s, $(s > 0)$.

a) Develop an equation describing the *total* annual cost (both fixed and variable) for operating the system described when the order quantity is Q.

b) Develop an expression for the optimum order quantity, Q^*.

c) Develop an expression for the reorder point, in terms of on-hand inventory when a fixed lead time is known.

d) Express the optimal time between orders as a function of λ, I, C, A, and s.

10–9   A local maintenance facility uses 500 screwdrivers per month. The unit cost of a screwdriver to the facility is $0.50, and the cost of placing an order is estimated to be $8. Lead time for receiving an order is one month. The facility employs a carrying charge of $I = \$0.20/\$1$ year. For purposes of maintaining an emergency stock management insists that stock levels never fall below 50.

a) Determine the optimum *time* between orders.

b) Determine the level of on-hand inventory at which orders must be placed.

c) Determine the total annual cost of operating this system.

10–10   Consider an inventory system in which units are demanded one at a time and with a constant time between demands of t years. The item is so expensive that management wishes to account for the integrality of demand e.g., our old method of taking derivatives with respect to Q will not work. In this system the inventory level ranges from a maximum of $(Q - 1)$ units to zero. No stock-outs are permitted. Let $t =$ time between demands (deterministic), $A =$ order cost, $I =$ carrying charge in dollars per dollar per year, $C =$ cost per unit, $Q =$ order quantity.

a) Write an equation for total variable annual cost $K(Q)$.

b) Develop an expression for finding the optimum order quantity Q^*. (Hint: Because K is convex, the optimum Q is the largest Q such that $\Delta K(Q) = K(Q) - K(Q-1) < 0$.)

10-11   Consider an inventory system in which the cost of placing an order is $20, the cost of storing one unit for one year is $80, and the annual demand rate is 200. Whenever a customer is required to back order, an estimated penalty of $4 is incurred.

a) Determine an optimum stocking policy, i.e., select a Q^* and s^*. Is your solution unique?

b) Suppose that management has decreed that the order quantity will be 50. How many back orders should they incur each cycle?

c) Suppose that the estimate for back-order cost is found to be 10 cents too high. How will your answer to part (*a*) change?

10-12   A local military supply agency stocks three models of landing lights. Management has placed a restriction on the minimum number of lights they will carry in stock. Their policy states that the minimum level for *total* landing light stocks will be M. Demand is believed to be deterministic with time between demands of 0.005, 0.020, and 0.025 years for the different types. The symbols I, C_j, and A carry their usual meaning. Ignore the possibility of scheduling orders such that all items never reach their minimum levels simultaneously.

a) Assuming continuous approximations to demand, formulate an expression for total average annual costs.

b) Develop an expression for the optimum order quantities Q_j.

c) What are the minimum inventory levels for each item *j* under the constrained condition assuming the following data: $C_1 = \$300$, $C_2 = \$250$, $C_3 = \$350$, $A = \$50$, $I = 0.20$, $M = 10$.

10-13   An employer of Longshoremen on the Gulf of Acaba hires workers by the day. Each day he must pay all workers their wage earned that day. (From an analyst's point of view this may be treated as a constant flow of cash since the work force is relatively stable.) A U.N. analyst, until recently stationed in the area, had determined that the employer should maintain a wage fund by transferring a fixed sum of money from his Swiss bank accounts to the company safe 12 times per year. The paper work necesssary to accomplish a transfer of funds costs $150. Any funds in the safe earn no interest but those funds in the Swiss banks earn 5 percent. Assuming that the U.N. analyst has established an optimum size of cash transfer, calculate the total annual wages paid to Longshoremen.

10-14   Consider the problem faced by a user of a certain nonferrous metal which currently sells for $1.12 per pound. On May 1st a price increase of 8 cents per pound will go into effect. He uses five tons of this metal per year at a constant rate, tolerates no shortages, incurs an order cost of $20 per order, and has an annual carrying charge of 20 cents per dollar in inventory. His current ordering policy will cause him to reach zero inventory on April 30.

a) Construct a general model to assist in the decision of whether or not a large pre-increase purchase is warranted. (Use the usual symbols, not numbers.) State all assumptions.

b) For the data given in this problem, determine the optimum pre-increase purchase quantity and the long-range policy.

10–15 The Melt-No-More Ice Company stocks blocks of ice each of which occupies five square feet of floor space. Available freezer space is limited to 800 square feet. The appropriate data on these blocks are $\lambda = 1{,}000$ blocks per year, $A = \$10$, $C = \$2$, $I = 0.25$.

  a) What is the optimum order quantity for this constrained problem?

  b) How much would the first additional square foot of storage space be worth?

  c) How much would 100 additional square feet of storage space be worth?

10–16 Consider an inventory system in which orders are delivered in two parts. Immediately upon placing an order, 20 percent of the order quantity will be delivered; 80 percent of the order quantity is delivered five days later. There is never more than one order outstanding at any one time. Annual demand is given by the constant λ, the cost of placing an order is A, order quantity is Q, and the daily cost of storing one unit is S dollars. No shortages are permitted. (Consider a year to be made up of 250 days.)

  a) Develop an expression for the average annual cost of operating this system.

  b) Determine the optimum order quantity Q and reorder point r in terms of on hand inventory.

  c) Compare your results with a system which delivers all orders with a five-day delay, i.e., what are the relative sizes of order quantities and reorder points?

10–17 A drug is produced by chemical reaction at a rate of $50e^{0.2t}$ pounds per day. The production time required for the reaction is 10 days. Demand for the product varies over each production cycle and is estimated to be at the rate $(10 + 10 \sin \pi t)$ where t is measured in time from start of the latest production cycle. Inventory carrying charges are estimated to be $0.30 per pound per day. Back-order costs are estimated to be $1.40 per pound back ordered. The cost of setup for a production run is $150.

  a) Determine an equation for inventory level as a function of time. What is the cycle time?

  b) Determine the optimum ordering policy.

  c) Determine the total average annual cost based upon 365 days per year.

10–18 The Bearded Fringe Company manufactures protest signs for student demonstrations. Local agitators purchase such signs at a constant rate λ per year. Because of the learning process necessary for changeover to a new sign configuration, B.F. Company experiences an instantaneous production rate which is thought to be functionally related to time by

$$P(t) = \psi e^{\psi t}$$

Here time is measured from the point of initiation of each order of size Q. The cost of setup for an order of " Ban the Draft " signs is estimated to be

$$A + \alpha Q^2$$

Back orders are not permitted. Carrying charges for finished signs are B dollars per sign per year.

  a) What assumptions must be made about the relative magnitudes of ψ and λ?

  b) Sketch and label the behavior of two cycles of this system.

c) How long is the production portion of the cycle?

d) What is the maximum inventory level achieved?

e) Develop an expression for average annual cost using the symbols mentioned above. Show all calculations.

The following identities from basic algebra may be of some help:

$$\log_b(b^x) = x \qquad b^{\log_b x} = x$$

10–19 A local soap plant operates a process in which the production rate varies as a function of time since the latest start-up. This function is given by

$$p(t) = 5t \qquad \text{(measured in tons per day)}$$

Management policy has decreed that at no time will the inventory level fall below 40 tons. In addition it has been decided that because of other processes using the same equipment, the soap process will be initiated once every 100 working days. Demand for the product is essentially constant at 2.5 tons per working day whether or not the process is currently running. It costs the company $3 per working day to store one ton of soap and $400 to set up the process for a run. Soap is valued at $2,000 per ton. There are 250 working days per year.

a) Determine the production order quantity.

b) Develop an equation for inventory level as a function of time since the last setup.

c) Determine the maximum inventory level ever reached.

d) Determine the total annual cost of operating this system.

10–20 The manager of a computer installation has arranged with a supplier of data processing cards to always receive shipments of Q boxes of cards on the first of each month. Because of the monthly reporting cycle at this installation, the work load is high at the first of the month and tapers off as the month progresses. The cumulative demand for boxes of cards up to time t after the first of each month is estimated to be

$$D(t) = 600\sqrt{\frac{t}{30}} \qquad 0 \le t \le 30$$

where 30 is the assumed number of days per month. Each box of cards costs $5, and the cost of placing an order is $50. Carrying cost per day is proportional to inventory level (L) (where L is measured in boxes) and is estimated to be $C_1(L) = 0.30\,L$, $L \ge 0$. Back-order cost per day is estimated to be

$$C_2(L) = 0.20L^2 \qquad L < 0$$

a) If management follows a policy of no stock-outs, what is the optimum order quantity each month?

b) Assuming back orders are permitted, develop an expression for total variable monthly costs as a function of the total number of back orders, s. (To save time, leave in integral form with s as the only unknown.)

10–21 Consider an inventory system in which the rate of production varies over time. Each time the processing of a new order begins, the initial production rate is 50 per month. Seven weeks after production begins the rate is increased to 60 per month and can remain there indefinitely. The inventory carrying charge is $10 per unit per year. Setup cost for a new run is $25. Demand is constant at 400 units per year. No shortages are permitted.

a) Develop an expression for total variable annual cost of operation. (Use symbols and an accompanying diagram.)

b) Determine the optimum order quantity, Q.

10–22 In our later-day moonshining operation, the efficient " shiner " purchases his barrels from a middle man. Our shiner depends upon his girlfriend to make out the purchase orders, stack the barrels, and keep the books. Her salary is $2,600 per year. He figures that any money wrapped up in barrels costs him 30 cents on the dollar per year. In order to avoid suspicion on the part of IRS, he figures that no more than six orders for barrels can be made in one year. The demand for 20-gallon barrels is 1,000 per year; and for 10-gallon barrels, 3,000 per year. A 10-gallon barrel costs $12 regardless of order quantity and a 20-gallon barrel costs $20 if ordered in lots of 500 or more. If less than 500 are purchased, they cost $25 each. Lead time is fixed at four weeks for each type. No shortages are allowed.

a) If there are *no constraint* and *no price breaks*, what are the optimum order quantities for each size?

b) Determine the optimum order quantities for the constrained, pricebreak problem posed. Show all calculations.

CHAPTER 11

Probabilistic Inventory Models

IN THE PRECEDING chapter models were developed in which it was assumed that all parameters of the system were known with absolute certainty. This is obviously a gross approximation for nearly all realistic inventory problems. One seldom knows exactly what demands will occur next week or exactly how long it will take to receive an order. Indeed there may even be some doubt about the deterministic nature of the various cost estimates used in evaluating inventory performance. The best description of the system in the face of such uncertainties is one utilizing probability functions to describe the various system parameters.

It is the purpose of this chapter to illustrate how probabilistic models may be constructed. These models will be limited to single-item, single-stage inventories in which demand and lead time are expressed as random variables. Three major classes of such models will be considered:

1. Single-order models.
2. Fixed-reorder-point models.
3. Fixed-review-period models.

Single-Order Models

The single-order model applies to situations sometimes referred to as the "Christmas tree" problem. Such inventories are characterized by their nonrepeating nature. Only one purchase of Christmas trees is made by a seller to last him for the season. If he purchases too few trees he incurs a cost in the form of lost profit on customers turned away plus a potential goodwill cost. If he purchases too many trees, they must be disposed of at a loss at the end of the season. The problem is to determine the amount to be purchased in the face of uncertain demand such that some criterion function is satisfied. A commonly accepted practice is to maximize expected profit.

Developing a Criterion Function. The following symbols will be used for the single-order models:

S = sales price per unit
C = cost per unit
B = goodwill cost incurred when a customer is denied service
V = salvage value of items on hand at the end of the sales period
$f(x)$ = probability distribution for sales during the sales period (may be continuous or discrete)
Q = purchase quantity

To assist in developing an expression for expected profit, it is helpful to first define profit as a function of the random variable x, representing the number of units demanded during the sales period. In general terms profit may be defined as:

Sales Income + Salvage Income − Purchase Expense − Lost Sales Expense

The expression for each of these terms varies as different ranges of x are considered. For example, if the number of units demanded, x, is less than the order quantity Q, the sales income will be Sx. On the other hand, if x exceeds Q, sales income will be limited by the total units available to SQ. Table 11–1

TABLE 11–1

Terms of the Profit Equation

Range	Sales Income	Salvage Income	Lost Sales Expense	Purchase Expense
$0 \leq x \leq Q$	Sx	$V(Q-x)$	0	CQ
$Q < x < \infty$	SQ	0	$B(x-Q)$	CQ

shows the appropriate expressions for each of the income and expense terms for different ranges of x.

Each of the entries in the above table may be described as a function of the random variable x. The total profit equation written as a function of x may be viewed as a sum of functions of the random variable x. Since the expected value of a sum is simply the sum of expected values, total expected profit may be written as

$$E(\text{profit}) = E(\text{sales}) + E(\text{salvage}) - E(\text{lost sales}) - E(\text{purchase}) \qquad (11–1)$$

However, the expected value of a function of the random variable x, say $g(x)$, is

$$E[g(x)] = \int_{-\infty}^{\infty} g(x)f(x)\, dx \qquad (11\text{–}2)$$

where $f(x)$ is the probability density of x. This assumes $f(x)$ is continuous. The corresponding discrete term is $\sum_{x=-\infty}^{\infty} g(x)f(x)$. Utilizing this information for each expression in Table 11–1, it is obvious that

$$E(\text{sales}) = \int_{-\infty}^{\infty} g(x)f(x)\, dx = S\int_{0}^{Q} x f(x)\, dx + SQ\int_{Q}^{\infty} f(x)\, dx \qquad (11\text{–}3)$$

$$E(\text{salvage}) = \int_{-\infty}^{\infty} g(x)\,f(x)\, dx = \int_{0}^{Q} V(Q-x)\,f(x)\, dx \qquad (11\text{–}4)$$

$$E(\text{lost sales}) = \int_{-\infty}^{\infty} g(x)\,f(x)\, dx = \int_{Q}^{\infty} B(x-Q)\,f(x)\, dx \qquad (11\text{–}5)$$

$$E(\text{purchase}) = \int_{-\infty}^{\infty} g(x)\,f(x)\, dx = \int_{0}^{\infty} CQ\,f(x)\, dx = CQ \qquad (11\text{–}6)$$

Combining Equations 11–3, 11–4, 11–5, and 11–6 gives

$$E(\text{profit}) = S\int_{0}^{Q} x f(x)\, dx + SQ\int_{Q}^{\infty} f(x)\, dx + \int_{0}^{Q} V(Q-x)\,f(x)\, dx$$

$$- \int_{Q}^{\infty} B(x-Q)\,f(x)\, dx - CQ \qquad (11\text{–}7)$$

An alternative criterion is expected penalty cost. The loss incurred when a unit is scrapped is the difference between its purchase price and its salvage price, i.e., $C - V$. The loss incurred when a demand cannot be satisfied is the sum of lost profit, $S - C$, and goodwill cost, B, i.e., $S - C + B$. Utilizing those terms in an expected value expression gives

$$E(\text{penalty}) = \int_{0}^{Q} (C-V)(Q-x)\,f(x)\, dx + \int_{Q}^{\infty} (S-C+B)(x-Q)\,f(x)\, dx$$

$$(11\text{–}8)$$

Optimum Solutions. The decision variable in Equations 11–7 and 11–8 is the purchase quantity Q. If one wishes to maximize expected profit or minimize expected penalty cost and the function $f(x)$ is continuous, the usual methods of calculus may be employed. In this model, as well as many other inventory models, one often is faced with taking derivatives under an integral sign. The general rule is that if the function $F(Q)$ is of the form

$$F(Q) = \int_{a(Q)}^{b(Q)} f(x, Q)\, dx \qquad (11\text{–}9)$$

then

$$\frac{df}{dQ} = \int_{a(Q)}^{b(Q)} \frac{\partial f}{\partial Q} \, dx + f(b, Q) \frac{db}{dQ} - f(a, Q) \frac{da}{dQ} \qquad (11\text{–}10)$$

Applying rule 11–10 to our expression for expected cost gives

$$\frac{dE(\text{cost})}{dQ} = (C - V)\left[\int_0^Q f(x) \, dx + 0 - 0\right] + (S - C + B)\left[\int_Q^\infty -f(x) \, dx + 0 - 0\right]$$

$$= (C - V)\left[1 - \int_Q^\infty f(x) \, dx\right] - (S - C + B)\int_Q^\infty f(x) \, dx \qquad (11\text{–}11)$$

Setting the derivative equal to zero leads to

$$\int_Q^\infty f(x) \, dx = \frac{C - V}{(C - V) + (S - C + B)} \qquad (11\text{–}12)$$

Since the expected cost function is generally strictly convex, the solution to Equation 11–12 gives necessary and sufficient conditions for establishing the minimum cost solution. Solving this equation for the optimum Q may be difficult in general terms but straightforward for particular numerical problems. Verbally this expression says that the optimum purchase quantity Q_0 is that value of Q for which the complementary cumulative distribution of demand equals the ratio of overage cost per unit to the sum of overage plus shortage cost per unit.

In the event that the random variable x has a discrete distribution, the integrals in the cost expression 11–8 will be replaced by sums and the minimum point will be determined by taking differences. In order for $K(Q_0)$ to be a minimum point it is necessary that

$$K(Q_0) - K(Q_0 - 1) < 0 \qquad (11\text{–}13)$$

and

$$K(Q_0 + 1) - K(Q_0) \geq 0 \qquad (11\text{–}14)$$

Since $K(Q)$ is in general strictly convex, the minimum point can be found from only one of the above differences. Defining $K(Q) - K(Q - 1)$ as $\Delta K(Q)$, the optimal value of Q is the largest Q such that

$$\Delta K(Q) = K(Q) - K(Q - 1) < 0$$

Applying this to our modified penalty cost expression gives

$$\Delta K(Q) = \left[\sum_{x=0}^Q (C - V)(Q - x)f(x) + \sum_{x=Q}^\infty (S - C + B)(x - Q)f(x)\right]$$

$$- \left[\sum_{x=0}^{Q-1} (C - V)(Q - 1 - x)f(x)\right.$$

$$\left. + \sum_{x=Q-1}^\infty (S - C + B)(x - Q + 1)f(x)\right] < 0 \quad (11\text{–}15)$$

from which

$$\sum_{x=Q}^{\infty} f(x) > \frac{C - V}{(C - V) + (S - C + B)} \qquad (11\text{--}16)$$

The optimum solution then is to choose the largest value of Q for which the sum of the probability distribution from Q to infinity exceeds the ratio of overage to overage plus shortage costs.

The same results are obtained if one seeks to maximize expected profit. The proof that maximizing expected profit and minimizing expected penalty costs lead to the same results is left as an exercise for the reader. For a more complete discussion of this model the reader is referred to Hadley and Whitin.[1]

A Probability Distribution for Penalty Costs

Often a manager may be in such a position that safety of capital or risk of penalty is of prime interest to him. In that case he may require additional information relative to the risk he is incurring by pursuing a given policy. For example, even if the manager purchases the optimum order quantity indicated by the solution to Equation 11–12, there is still a certain probability that he will lose money by this policy. It is the purpose of this section to develop techniques for finding a distribution for profit or penalty cost as a function of the purchase quantity Q. The method used is one developed by Sullivan.[2]

The Cost Equation. Consider the penalty cost associated with operating the system for a given purchase quantity as a function of the number of units demanded, x. If the number of units demanded is exactly equal to the purchase quantity Q, every unit will be sold, profit will be maximized, and no shortage or overage cost will be incurred. If the number of units demanded is less than the purchase quantity, a penalty of $(C - V)(Q - x)$ is incurred for scrap loss. If the number of units demanded is greater than the purchase quantity, a penalty of $(S - C + B)(x - Q)$ is incurred for goodwill and profit loss.

The information in the preceding paragraph is summarized in Figure 11–1. Obviously the penalty cost equation consists of two straight-line elements with a minimum at $x = Q$.

$$\text{Penalty cost} = K(Q, x) = \begin{cases} (C - V)(Q - x) & 0 \le x \le Q \\ (S - C + B)(x - Q) & Q < x \end{cases} \qquad (11\text{--}17)$$

where K is itself a random variable defined in terms of the random variable x.

---

[1] G. Hadley, and T. M. Whitin, *Analysis of Inventory Systems* (Englewood Cliffs, N.J.: Prentice-Hall, Inc., 1963), chap. vi.

[2] Richard L. Sullivan, unpublished notes, General Motors Research Laboratories, 1959.

FIGURE 11-1

Penalty Cost versus Demand

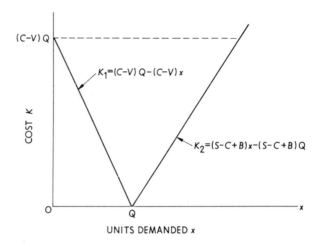

It is well to note that the cost K is not a realized cost in the sense used by an accountant. It measures the difference between the net income that would be realized if exactly x units were sold, $[(S - C)x]$, and the profit from such sale where profit is given by Table 11-1. When $x > Q$ obviously only Q units can be sold and the above cost equation becomes artificial in the sense that it includes a cost of "lost opportunity" for profit on the unstocked items.

The Probability Distribution.   From Figure 11-1 it is apparent that in the range $0 < K < (C - V)Q$ the same cost can be obtained from either of the straight-line segments K_1 or K_2. For $K > (C - V)Q$ only that segment defined for $x > Q$ is needed. This implies that a penalty cost greater than some amount P will be incurred if K_1 is greater than P or if K_2 is greater than P when $0 < P < (C - V)Q$. These events are mutually exclusive and collectively exhaustive. When $P > (C - V)Q$ the only possible penalty cost greater than P is incurred when K_2 is greater than P. Expressed in cumulative probability terms the random variable K is related to the random variables K_1 and K_2 by

$$Pr(K \geq P) = \begin{cases} Pr(K_1 \geq P) + Pr(K_2 \geq P) & 0 \leq P < (C - V)Q \\ Pr(K_2 \geq P) & P \geq (C - V)Q \end{cases} \quad (11\text{-}18)$$

Each of the arguments K_i is a simple function of the random variable x. This permits us to rewrite the components of the above probability statement in terms of the cumulative distribution of x, say $F(x)$, as follows:

$$Pr(K_1 \geq P) = Pr[(C - V)(Q - x) \geq P]$$

$$= Pr\left[x \leq \left(Q - \frac{P}{C - V}\right)\right]$$

$$= F\left[Q - \frac{P}{C - V}\right] \qquad (11\text{--}19)$$

and

$$Pr(K_2 \geq P) = Pr[(S - C + B)(x - Q) \geq P]$$

$$= Pr\left[x \geq \left(Q + \frac{P}{S - C + B}\right)\right]$$

$$= 1 - F\left[Q + \frac{P}{S - C + B}\right] \qquad (11\text{--}20)$$

If we now define the cumulative distribution of penalty cost for a given purchase quantity Q as $G(K, Q)$ and make use of the fact that $Pr(K < a) = 1 - Pr(K \geq a)$ we have

$$G(K, Q) = \begin{cases} F\left[Q + \dfrac{K}{S - C + B}\right] - F\left[Q - \dfrac{K}{C - V}\right] & 0 \leq K < (C - V)Q \\[2em] F\left[Q + \dfrac{K}{S - C + B}\right] & K \geq (C - V)Q \end{cases}$$

$$(11\text{--}21)$$

The cumulative distribution for profit is developed in similar fashion. If the density function is desired when $F(x)$ is a properly defined continuous function, it may be obtained by differentiating $G(K, Q)$ with respect to K over the appropriate range of values. These matters are left as exercises for the reader.

With a probability function for profit or penalty cost now available, criteria other than expected values may be used in decision making. For example it is now possible to choose an order quantity such that the probability of a penalty cost less than K is known. Similarly it is possible to determine the distribution for penalty costs when a policy minimizing expected costs is to be followed.

Example. Consider a department store which must stock bathing suits for the summer season. A particular model suit costs the company $5 and normally sells for $9. Any suits left at the end of the season are discounted to $3 each to clear the shelves. Management estimates that a goodwill cost of $2 is incurred when they are unable to supply the suit a customer desires. Historical data from past years indicate that sales for the season are approximately normally distributed with mean 400 and standard deviation 100.

Using our notation the parameters are then

$$C = \$5; \ V = \$3; \ S = \$9; \ B = \$2; \ f(x) = N(\mu = 400, \ \sigma = 100)$$

From Equation 11–12, if one wishes to maximize profit or minimize penalty costs, suits should be ordered in an amount Q such that

$$\int_{Q}^{\infty} f(x)\,dx = \frac{C - V}{(C - V) + (S - C + B)} = \frac{2}{2 + 6} = 0.25$$

From the cumulative probability table in the Appendix one must find now the value for z, the standard normal deviate, such that

$$1 - F(z) = 0.25$$

or

$$F(z) = 0.75$$

From the tables, $z = 0.6745$. However, we know that to convert our distribution for demand into standard unit normal terms requires that

$$z = \frac{Q - \mu}{\sigma}$$

Using the numbers we have developed

$$0.6745 = \frac{Q - 400}{100}$$

from which $Q_0 \approx 467$.

Applying Equation 11–8 leads to an expected value for penalty cost of

$$\int_{0}^{Q} (C - V)(Q - x)f(x)\,dx + \int_{Q}^{\infty} (S - C + B)(x - Q)f(x)\,dx$$

$$= \int_{0}^{467} (\$2)(467 - x)f(x)\,dx + \int_{467}^{\infty} (\$6)(x - 467)f(x)\,dx$$

$$\approx \$260$$

Similarly one may apply Equation 11–7 to determine that the expected value of profit is

$$S \int_{0}^{Q} xf(x)\,dx + SQ \int_{Q}^{\infty} f(x)\,dx + \int_{0}^{Q} V(Q - x)f(x)\,dx$$

$$- \int_{Q}^{\infty} B(x - Q)f(x)\,dx - CQ$$

$$= (S - V)\mu - (C - V)Q - (S + B - V)\int_{Q}^{\infty} (x - Q)f(x)\,dx$$

$$= (\$6)(400) - (\$2)(467) - (\$8)\int_{467}^{\infty} (x - 467)f(x)\,dx$$

$$\approx \$1,340$$

Hadley and Whitin have developed an extensive list of identities to facilitate calculations such as these.[3]

Note that the expected penalty costs plus expected profit is equal to the expected net income if all customers could obtain service. That is,

$$\text{Expected net income} = E[(S - C)x] = (S - C)\mu = \$1,600$$

and

$$E(\text{penalty cost}) + E(\text{profit}) = \$260 + \$1,340 = \$1,600$$

In order to more accurately assess the risks involved in the policy of minimizing expected penalty costs, we may now calculate the cumulative distribution for costs. For example, to determine the probability that a penalty or regret of less than $100 will be incurred if we order 467 suits, we have from Equation 11–21,

$$G(100, 467) = F\left[467 + \frac{100}{9 - 5 + 2}\right] - F\left[467 - \frac{100}{5-3}\right]$$

$$= F(484) - F(417)$$

where $F(x)$ is the cumulative distribution for demand. Since our demand distribution is normal with mean 400 and standard deviation 100, this statement may be converted into standard unit normal terms by substituting

$$z = \frac{x - \mu}{\sigma}$$

or

$$G(100, 467) = F_z\left(\frac{484-400}{100}\right) - F_z\left(\frac{417-400}{100}\right)$$

$$= F_z(0.84) - F_z(0.17)$$

$$= 0.7995 - 0.5675$$

$$= 0.2320$$

reading from the normal tables.

The above development leads to the conclusion that if one orders 467 suits, there is approximately a 23 percent chance that a penalty cost of less than $100 will be incurred. Similar calculations can be carried out for other critical cost figures. A summary of such points is contained in Table 11–2 and Figure 11–2. Note that with the given order quantity the chance is 98 percent that the penalty incurred will be less than $900.

With these tools it is now possible to investigate in detail the profit and penalty risk for any given order quantity. Each new value of Q generates a

---

[3] Hadley and Whitin, op. cit., pp. 441–47.

TABLE 11–2

Cumulative Distribution for Penalty Costs When
$Q = 467$ and Demand is $N(\mu = 400, \sigma = 100)$

K	Probability That Cost < K
0	0
100	0.2320
200	0.4936
300	0.6868
400	0.8181
500	0.9025
600	0.9426
700	0.9650
800	0.9768
900	0.9849
1,000	0.9904

new distribution. By changing the Q value from that necessary to maximize expected profit, one might pull the 98 percent level of risk down to $600, for example. This alternative might be more attractive to the cautious manager than one which minimizes expected penalty but exposes him to higher potential risks.

FIGURE 11–2

Cumulative Distribution for Penalty Costs

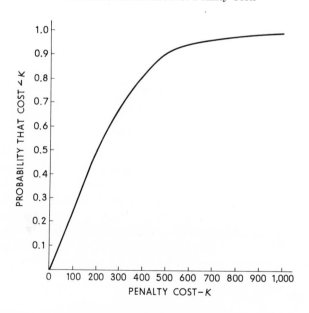

Fixed-Reorder-Point Models

The next class of models to be considered is the probabilistic analogue of the simple economic lot size formulations considered in the earlier chapter on deterministic models. Recall that for deterministic models we discussed order policies for a product which was sold continuously over time. This differs from the single-order model of the last section in which orders are placed only once. Now we place orders whenever our stock reaches a critical level, the goal being to minimize expected annual variable cost. The models of this section differ from the deterministic models in that demand is no longer assumed to be known with certainty. It is now considered to be a random variable which is known only in a probabilistic sense. For our immediate purposes we will consider only those systems with a fixed lead time, known demand distribution, and instantaneous production capability. Such systems appear in many situations in which supplies are purchased from outside vendors.

Modeling Strategy. The basic modeling technique is the same as that introduced for deterministic models, namely, find an expected cost per cycle and multiply by the average number of cycles per year. We will begin by examining a system in which back orders are permitted, i.e., all demands will be satisfied sometime. A typical graph of inventory fluctuations over time might appear as Figure 11–3. We will employ the same notation as before.

$L(t)$ = net inventory level as a function of time
L_c = reorder point in terms of net inventory
A = cost of placing an order
C = purchase price per unit
I = carrying charge per dollar per year
λ = average annual demand
d = lead time
$f(x \mid d)$ = conditional distribution for demand given a lead time of d
B = cost of a back order

To facilitate the calculations the only back-order cost considered will be a fixed cost for every unit that goes short. We will not consider a cost proportional to the time a unit is back ordered. In addition we are considering a fixed lead time, although later we will introduce techniques to handle lead time as a random variable. Furthermore we will initially consider a transactions reporting scheme in which inventories are reviewed after each unit is sold. The policy we are about to develop is a fixed-reorder-point, reorder-quantity policy. Each time the inventory level reaches a critical amount L_c an order for a fixed amount Q is placed. Such a policy is optimal only when transactions reporting is used. When inventory status is reviewed at discrete points in time, an (s, S) policy is optimal. Here an order is placed only if

FIGURE 11–3

Inventory Fluctuations

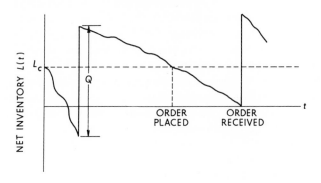

inventory level is below s. The amount ordered is sufficient to take the level to S. The (L_c, Q) policy is a special case of (s, S) in which $L_c = s$, $Q + L_c = S$ and review occurs after every transaction. An intermediate policy, discussed later, orders at every review period an amount sufficient to reach a target $M = S$ regardless of the amount on hand.

From the appearance of the graph we can readily develop an approximate model for this system. Note that a cycle can be defined as the time between receipt of two consecutive orders. Cycle time is a random variable which depends upon the number of units demanded over time, itself a random variable. The net inventory, defined as on hand less back orders, fluctuates between some minimum level W and a maximum of $Q + W$ each cycle. Under the assumption that there is never more than one order outstanding, the random variable W is simply the difference between the units on hand when an order is placed, L_c, and the units demanded while that order is being delivered, x.

$$W = L_c - x \qquad (11–22)$$

The expected value of W is

$$E(W) = E(L_c - x) = \int_0^\infty (L_c - x)f(x \mid d)\, dx$$

$$= L_c - \mu \qquad (11–23)$$

where $\mu = $ mean lead time demand. If we assume that the mean rate of demand is constant, the expected value of net inventory decreases in straight-line fashion between $Q + W$ and W during one cycle. It now may be argued that the average amount of stock in net inventory throughout the year is simply the arithmetic average of expected maximum and expected minimum or

$$\bar{L} = \frac{(Q + L_c - \mu) + (L_c - \mu)}{2}$$

$$= \frac{Q}{2} + L_c - \mu \qquad (11\text{–}24)$$

Inventory carrying costs are based upon on-hand inventory. Equation 11–24 gives a means of calculating net inventory. The assumption is usually made that back orders are relatively small, and for purposes of calculating carrying costs, net inventory is a sufficiently accurate estimate of on-hand inventory. Since the cost of carrying one unit in stock for one year is IC, the expected annual carrying cost is given by

$$C_1 = IC\left(\frac{Q}{2} + L_c - \mu\right) \qquad (11\text{–}25)$$

Back-order costs per cycle are based upon the total number of customers denied immediate service. Service is denied only when demand during the lead time exceeds the number of units on hand when an order is placed. Let W^1 represent the total number of back orders in a cycle, then

$$W^1 = \begin{cases} 0 & 0 \leq x \leq L_c \\ x - L_c & x > L_c \end{cases} \qquad (11\text{–}26)$$

The expected number of back orders per cycle is

$$E(W^1) = \int_{L_c}^{\infty} (x - L_c)f(x\,|\,d)\,dx \qquad (11\text{–}27)$$

The average number of cycles per year is still λ/Q. We can therefore calculate the expected annual back-order cost as

$$C_2 = \frac{\lambda B}{Q} \int_{L_c}^{\infty} (x - L_c)f(x\,|\,d)\,dx \qquad (11\text{–}28)$$

The annual cost of placing orders is calculated exactly as it was for deterministic models. Each order costs A dollars, and on the average λ/Q orders are placed each year. Thus,

$$C_3 = \frac{\lambda A}{Q} \qquad (11\text{–}29)$$

Combining the cost expressions 11–25, 11–28, and 11–29 gives

$$E(\text{annual variable cost}) = \frac{\lambda A}{Q} + IC\left(\frac{Q}{2} + L_c - \mu\right)$$

$$+ \frac{\lambda B}{Q} \int_{L_c}^{\infty} (x - L_c)f(x\,|\,d)\,dx \qquad (11\text{–}30)$$

For a fixed lead time d or for a variable lead time with which the marginal distribution for lead time demand can be calculated, this expression may be rewritten as

$$E(\text{cost}) = \frac{\lambda A}{Q} + IC\left(\frac{Q}{2} + L_c - \mu\right) + \frac{\lambda B}{Q}\left[\int_{L_c}^{\infty} xh(x)\,dx - L_c\hat{H}(L_c)\right] \quad (11\text{--}31)$$

where $h(x)$ is the marginal distribution for lead time demand and $\hat{H}(x)$ is the complementary cumulative. The decision variable L_c can be interpreted as the reorder point in terms of inventory position for those cases in which more than one order is outstanding.

With a basic understanding of how this model is constructed it is a simple matter to develop similar expressions for systems with discrete demands, lost sales, and other variations. Hadley and Whitin have excellent discussions about this model and its extensions.[4]

Determining the Optimum.   There are now two decision variables whose values must be determined. In this case the reorder quantity Q and reorder point L_c must both be selected by management. Assuming that the goal is to minimize expected annual variable costs, the usual methods of calculus may be applied to Equation 11–31.

$$\frac{\partial K}{\partial Q} = \frac{\lambda A}{Q^2} + \frac{IC}{2} - \frac{\lambda B}{Q^2}\left[\int_{L_c}^{\infty} xh(x)\,dx - L_c\hat{H}(L_c)\right] = 0$$

$$\frac{\partial K}{\partial L_c} = IC + \frac{\lambda B}{Q}[-L_ch(L_c) - \hat{H}(L_c) + L_ch(L_c)] = 0 \quad (11\text{--}32)$$

from which

$$Q = \sqrt{\frac{2\lambda\left[A + B\left(\int_{L_c}^{\infty} xh(x)\,dx - L_c\hat{H}(L_c)\right)\right]}{IC}} \quad (11\text{--}33)$$

and

$$\hat{H}(L_c) = \frac{QIC}{B\lambda} \quad (11\text{--}34)$$

These equations are not easy to solve simultaneously. The usual procedure is to employ numerical techniques to reach the solution. Hadley and Whitin offer an iterative scheme which permits the solution to be obtained in straightforward fashion.[5] The key to their technique is the relative shapes of the curves described by Equations 11–33 and 11–34. A typical set of curves is shown in Figure 11–4.

---

[4] *Ibid.*, chap. iv.
[5] *Ibid.*, p. 169.

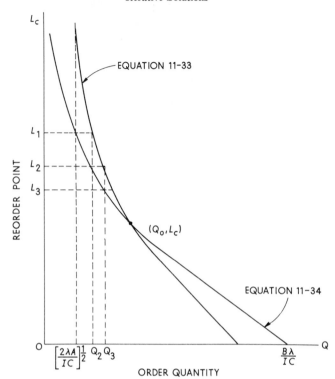

FIGURE 11-4
Iterative Solutions

Note that from Equation 11–33, Q will never be less than Q_0 determined in the previous chapter on deterministic models, i.e.,

$$Q > \sqrt{\frac{2\lambda A}{IC}}$$

for all values of L. Q is asymptotic to this value, however, as L_c approaches infinity.

From Equation 11–34 it is seen that as Q approaches zero, L_c must approach infinity. When L_c approaches zero, Q approaches $B\lambda/IC$. The point at which the curves described by Equations 11–33 and 11–34 cross gives the optimum reorder point. Note that it is possible for this solution to give nonsense answers since the model is an approximate one. For example if $QIC/B\lambda > 1$ the model is not appropriate as it would be impossible for the complementary cumulative distribution to exceed one. This anomaly arises because we ignored the influence of back orders when calculating carrying costs. Such an approximation is warranted only when back orders are expensive relative to carrying charges. For low back-order costs this model is inappropriate.

The recommended solution procedure, which is shown graphically in Figure 11–4, is as follows:

1. Calculate as a first estimate for Q_0

$$Q_1 = \left(\frac{2\lambda A}{IC}\right)^{1/2}$$

2. Use the latest estimate for Q_0 in Equation 11–34 to calculate an estimate for L_c, i.e.,

$$\hat{H}(L_1) = \frac{Q_1 IC}{B\lambda}$$

3. Use the new value for L_c in Equation 11–33 to calculate a revised estimate for Q, i.e.,

$$Q_2 = \left[\frac{2\lambda\left[A + B(\int_{L_c}^{\infty} xh(x)\,dx - L_c\hat{H}(L_c))\right]}{IC}\right]^{1/2}$$

4. Repeat steps 2 and 3 until the change occurring between successive estimates of the decision variables becomes negligible.

Example. A factory warehouse provides a special chrome wheel for auto supply houses. The cost of changing the electrolyte in the plating tanks and processing the paper work to produce an order of wheels is estimated to be $100. The wheels are valued at $25 each. Management feels that the extra paper work involved and the loss in goodwill amount to $50 for each wheel back ordered. An annual carrying charge of $I = 0.20$ is used throughout the company. Because of the scheduling conflicts with other products, the lead time for an order of wheels averages three months. Past data indicate that demand during lead time is approximately uniformly distributed in the interval (0, 250) with a mean of 125 wheels.

Since the average demand for a three-month period is 125 wheels, the average annual demand rate will be $(12/3)(125) = 500$ wheels. The lead time demand distribution is given by

$$h(x) = \begin{cases} \dfrac{1}{250} & 0 \le x \le 250 \\ 0 & \text{elsewhere} \end{cases}$$

Converting to our usual notation, the problem's remaining parameters are

$$\lambda = 500$$
$$A = \$100$$
$$I = 0.20$$
$$C = \$25$$
$$B = \$50$$

Applying the iterative technique, the solution proceeds as follows:

1. The first estimate for Q_0 is

$$Q_1 = \left(\frac{2\lambda A}{IC}\right)^{1/2} = \left(\frac{100,000}{5}\right)^{1/2} = 141$$

2. Using 141 as an estimate for Q_0, the first estimate for L_c is obtained from

$$\hat{H}(L_1) = \frac{Q_1 IC}{B\lambda} = \frac{141(5)}{25,000} = 0.0282$$

where

$$\hat{H}(L_1) = \int_{L_1}^{\infty} h(x)\, dx = \int_{L_1}^{250} \frac{1}{250}\, dx$$

$$= \left.\frac{x}{250}\right|_{L_1}^{250} = 1 - \frac{L_1}{250}$$

Solving for L_1 gives:

$$L_1 = (1 - 0.0282)(250) = 243$$

3. The estimate of $L_c = 243$ is now used to revise the estimate for Q_0 by

$$Q_2 = \left\{\frac{2\lambda\left[A + B\left(\int_{L_c}^{\infty} xh(x)\, dx - L_c\hat{H}(L_c)\right)\right]}{IC}\right\}^{1/2}$$

But

$$\int_{L_c}^{\infty} xh(x)\, dx = \left.\frac{x^2}{2(250)}\right|_{243}^{250} = 7$$

and

$$L_c\hat{H}(L_c) = (243)(0.0282) \approx 6.86$$

therefore

$$Q_2 = [200(100 + 50(7 - 6.86))]^{1/2} \simeq 146$$

4. This new estimate of $Q_0 = 146$ is then used to revise the estimate of L_c by

$$\hat{H}(L_2) = (146)(5)/25,000 \simeq 0.0292$$

from which L_c is still approximately 243.

5. Since there was no change in two successive estimates of L_c, the optimum solution occurs when $Q_0 = 146$ and $L_c = 243$. The total expected annual variable cost incurred by ordering 146 wheels each time the inventory position reaches 243 units is from Equation 11–27:

$$K = \frac{\lambda A}{Q} + IC\left[\frac{Q}{2} + L_c - \mu\right] + \frac{\lambda B}{Q}\left[\int_{L_c}^{\infty} xh(x)\, dx - L_c \hat{H}(L_c)\right]$$

$$= \frac{50,000}{146} + 5(73 + 243 - 125) + \left(\frac{25,000}{146}\right)(0.14)$$

$$= 342 + 955 + 24 = \$1,321$$

It is instructive to compare this cost with the average annual cost that would be incurred if a deterministic model of this system was used. From the chapter on deterministic models it is noted that

$$Q_0 = \left(\frac{2\lambda A}{IC}\right)^{1/2} = 141$$

and

$$K_0 = (2\lambda A IC)^{1/2} = (500,000)^{1/2} = \$707$$

The difference between the cost in the probabilistic model and the cost in the deterministic model, using the same average values, is sometimes called an average annual cost of uncertainty. In this case the cost of uncertainty is

$$\$1,321 - \$707 = \$614$$

This implies that a maximum savings of $614 is possible if all uncertainties relative to lead time and demand variables are eliminated. If the cost of eliminating the uncertainty in the system exceeds $614 per year, one is obviously better off to tolerate the random nature of the system.

Another interesting comparison can be made between the expected annual cost incurred by following the optimal policy and the expected annual cost that would be incurred if one ignored the probabilistic nature of the system when determining the lot size and reorder point. Under the deterministic approximation, the lot size has previously been calculated as $Q_0 = 141$. The reorder point is given by

$$L_c = \mu = 125$$

Such a calculation might be performed by analysts who are familiar with the classical economic lot size formula but lack understanding of the probabilistic nature of the system. The expected cost they would incur by following such a policy is given by Equation 11–31 since they have not eliminated uncertainty but only ignored it. Thus

$$K = \frac{\lambda A}{Q} + IC\left(\frac{Q}{2} + L_c - \mu\right) + \frac{\lambda B}{Q}\left[\int_{L_c}^{\infty} xh(x)\, dx - L_c \hat{H}(L_c)\right]$$

$$= \frac{50,000}{141} + 5(70.5 + 125 - 125) + \frac{25,000}{141}\left[\int_{125}^{250} \frac{x}{250}\, dx - 125(0.5)\right]$$

$$= 354 + 352 + 177(94 - 62) = \$6,376$$

The difference ($6,376 − $1,320 = $4,056) might be termed a cost of ignorance. This is the expected annual penalty incurred by using a deterministic approximation for a system which has certain well-defined probabilistic features. With the expected costs of the deterministic approximation exceeding the expected costs of the optimal probabilistic model by a ratio of 4.8 to 1 in this case, the analyst is well advised to use the most complete representation possible.

Fixed-Review-Period Models

The model developed in the previous section is applicable only when one has immediate knowledge of changes in the system. The decision maker knows immediately when the reorder point has been crossed and can initiate a new order. A system with these properties is sometimes referred to as a "transactions reporting" system. With the advent of modern data processing equipment such a model may be a fair representation of many inventory situations. However, in most plants a more common procedure is to review inventory levels at certain fixed points in time and to order enough stock to bring the inventory level up to the desired target level. Between orders, stock status is unknown. This procedure may also be representative of plants possessing electronic data processing equipment. Even in these operations it is customary to accumulate sales data for some period of time, perhaps only a day, before updating master inventory records.

Although it is obvious that many variations of such operating systems exist in practice, we will limit ourselves to the simplest case. We will assume that the inventory is reviewed every T time units and at the time of review enough stock is ordered to bring the inventory position to some desired target level M. Back orders are permitted, and it will be assumed that an arriving order is always sufficient to relieve any existing back orders. To further simplify the calculations we will initially assume that lead time is fixed and only one order is outstanding at any time. Permitting d to become a random variable is conceptually easy if one ignores the possibility of orders crossing. Permitting an arbitrary number of outstanding orders does not change the resulting equations. Such considerations are discussed at length in Hadley and Whitin.[6]

In the fixed-reorder-point model, the order quantity was constant and the cycle time varied. In the fixed-review-period model the order quantity is a random variable depending upon demand but the cycle time is fixed. Management may have selected a review period based upon total data processing work load or other considerations. In that case the optimum target level M_0 is easily calculated. In other instances both review period and target level may be manipulated to obtain an optimum solution. Such solutions again require numerical techniques similar to those introduced in the last section.

---

[6] *Ibid.*, chap. v.

Modeling Strategy.   Let us redefine the symbols to be used in this model:

A = cost of placing an order plus cost of review
C = unit cost of the item
I = carrying charge
λ = mean annual demand
μ = mean lead time demand
d = lead time
$f(x \mid t)$ = probability of x demands in time t
M = target level for inventory position
$L(t)$ = net inventory level
$E(t)$ = inventory position level
T = review period
B = unit back-order cost

Figure 11–5 shows the fluctuations in expected value of net inventory and inventory position over time. (Note that this straight-line graph represents averages. A true time-varying plot of net inventory would consist of wavy lines without the fixed height sawtooth pattern shown here.) At the time inventory is reviewed and an order placed, inventory position (net inventory plus on order) will reach the target M. Since we are initially assuming that only one order is outstanding, it is obvious that the expected value of net inventory immediately after the arrival of a procurement is the target M less the expected demands occurring during the lead time, i.e., $M - \mu$. (This holds for an arbitrary number of outstanding orders as long as they are not permitted to cross.) Consider a cycle to be the time between arrivals

FIGURE 11–5
Expected Inventory Fluctuations

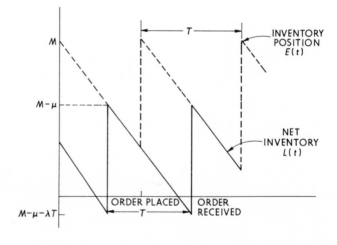

of successive procurements. The expected net inventory immediately prior to the arrival of a procurement will be the maximum expected net inventory less the demands occurring during the cycle, i.e., $M - \mu - \lambda T$. On the average, then, net inventory fluctuates between $M - \mu$ and $M - \mu - \lambda T$.

Note how this system differs from the fixed-reorder-point system. In the fixed-reorder-point model we were concerned with "lead time demand" since that determined whether or not our protection was adequate. In the fixed-review-period model, however, the target M must cover our inventory demands for a lead time plus a review period. This occurs because a subsequent purchase cannot be made for another T time units regardless of stock position in the intervening interval.

The average number of units contained in net inventory is calculated exactly as it was in the fixed-reorder-point model. Assuming that the average demand rate over time is constant, average net inventory is

$$\bar{L} = \frac{L_{max} + L_{min}}{2}$$

$$= \frac{(M - \mu) + (M - \mu - \lambda T)}{2}$$

$$= M - \mu - \frac{\lambda T}{2} \tag{11-35}$$

Assuming that back orders have a negligible influence on carrying cost, the average number of units on hand is approximately equal to $\bar{L}$. Annual carrying costs may then be approximated by

$$C_1 = IC\left(M - \mu - \frac{\lambda T}{2}\right) \tag{11-36}$$

Back orders occur in a cycle whenever the number of units demanded during the lead time plus one review period exceed the target level M. If we let w^1 represent the number of back orders in a cycle, then

$$w^1 = \begin{cases} 0 & x \leq M \\ x - M & x > M \end{cases} \tag{11-37}$$

where x is the number of units demanded in $(t, t + d + T)$. The expected number of back orders per cycle is

$$E(w^1) = \int_M^\infty (x - M)f(x \mid d + T)\, dx \tag{11-38}$$

where $f(x \mid d + T)$ is the distribution for demand over $d + T$ time units. The average number of cycles per year is simply the inverse of the cycle time or $1/T$, and the cost per back order is B. Combining these terms gives an average annual back-order cost of

$$C_2 = \frac{B}{T} \int_M^\infty (x - M) f(x \mid d + T)\, dx \qquad (11\text{-}39)$$

As before the annual ordering cost is obtained by multiplying cost per cycle times cycles per year or

$$C_3 = A\left(\frac{1}{T}\right) = \frac{A}{T} \qquad (11\text{-}40)$$

Combining Equations 11–36, 11–39, and 11–40 leads to the total expected annual variable cost expression

$$K = \frac{A}{T} + IC\left(M - \mu - \frac{\lambda T}{2}\right) + \frac{B}{T} \int_M^\infty (x - M) f(x \mid d + T)\, dx \qquad (11\text{-}41)$$

Determining an Optimum Solution. A solution is easily obtained when the review period T has been fixed by management. In this instance Equation 11–41 is a function of the single decision variable M. Expected annual cost can be minimized for a fixed T by setting the derivative dK/dM to zero and solving for M.

$$\frac{dK}{dM} = IC + \frac{B}{T}\left[-\int_M^\infty f(x \mid d + T)\, dx + 0 - 0 \right] = 0 \qquad (11\text{-}42)$$

from which

$$\int_M^\infty f(x \mid d + T)\, dx = \frac{ICT}{B} \qquad (11\text{-}43)$$

Equation 11–43 suggests that the optimum value of M occurs where the complementary cumulative distribution of demand over the period $(0, d + T)$ is equal to ICT/B.

If the decision maker has complete freedom in selecting a value of T as well as a value of M, then one may treat K as a function of M and T. Setting $\partial K/\partial M$ and $\partial K/\partial T$ equal to zero will in theory lead to a global minimum for expected annual variable costs. However, the resulting equations must be solved numerically employing Newton's method or some similar technique. It is often more expedient to simply calculate the optimum value of M for various fixed values of T, plot the resulting conditional optimum costs, and select the minimum of the points plotted.

To assist in numerical calculations of this type it is useful to represent the basic cost equation as a function of well-tabulated values of the demand distribution. Two distributions commonly encountered in inventory systems are the normal and the Poisson. For the normal distribution Hadley and Whitin[7] have shown that

$$\int_M^\infty xh(x)\,dx = \sigma\phi\left(\frac{M-\mu}{\sigma}\right) + \mu\Phi\left(\frac{M-\mu}{\sigma}\right) \qquad (11\text{–}44)$$

where $h(x)$ is the normal density with mean μ and variance σ^2 and

$$\phi(z) = \frac{1}{\sqrt{2\pi}}\,e^{-z^2/2}$$

$$\Phi(z) = \int_z^\infty \phi(x)\,dx$$

Similarly for the Poisson distribution they have shown that

$$\sum_{j=M}^\infty jp(j) = \mu P(M-1) \qquad (11\text{–}45)$$

where

$$p(j) = \frac{\mu^j}{j!}\,e^{-\mu}$$

and

$$P(x) = \sum_{j=x}^\infty p(j)$$

These identities are particularly useful for the models of this chapter since they all contain terms of the type

$$\int_N^\infty xf(x)\,dx$$

or

$$\sum_{x=N}^\infty xf(x)$$

and the density and complementary cumulative functions for the normal and Poisson are well tabulated.

Applying Equation 11–44 to the expression for expected annual cost when demand is normally distributed gives

$$K = \frac{A}{T} + IC\left[M - \mu - \frac{\lambda T}{2}\right] + \frac{B}{T}\left[\sigma\phi\left(\frac{M-\mu_1}{\sigma}\right) - (M-\mu_1)\Phi\left(\frac{M-\mu_1}{\sigma}\right)\right] \qquad (11\text{–}46)$$

where μ_1 and σ are the mean and standard deviation of demand over $(0, d+T)$. This expression is easily tabulated for various values of T and M

[7] *Ibid.*, p. 167.

since the integration problem has been reduced to a simple table look-up.

Example. Consider an automotive supply house which must stock alternators for the new Gord 8. Each alternator costs the supply house $50. The cost of conducting a review of alternator inventory status is estimated to be $20. An additional $20 in paper work is necessary to place an order to the factory. The extra paper work incurred when an alternator must be back ordered is estimated to be $30. The goodwill cost associated with a back order is $70. The company uses an inventory carrying charge of $10 per alternator per year in stock. Lead time is approximately one week. An examination of demand indicates that demand over time for the range of t likely to be considered can be approximated by a normal density with mean $1,000t$ and variance $1,600t^2$. Current management policy is to place an order every 10 weeks. The problem is to determine the optimum target level for this policy and to examine the effects of different order periods.

Using the standard notation of this chapter, A is made up of $20 in review costs plus $20 in paper work and B is made up of $30 in paperwork plus $70 in goodwill cost. The remainder of the parameters are obvious:

$$IC = \$10 \qquad \lambda = 1,000 \text{ per year}$$
$$A = \$40 \qquad d = 0.02 \text{ years}$$
$$B = \$100 \qquad f(x) = N(\mu = 1,000t, \sigma = 40t)$$

From Equation 11–46 the expected annual cost for a system with order period T, target level M, and the parameters indicated above is

$$K \doteq \frac{40}{T} + 10[M - 20 - 500T] + \left(\frac{100}{T}\right)$$

$$\times \left\{ 40(0.02 + T)\phi\left[\frac{M - 1,000(0.02 + T)}{40(0.02 + T)}\right]\right.$$

$$\left. - [M - 1,000(0.02 + T)]\Phi\left[\frac{M - 1,000(0.02 + T)}{40(0.02 + T)}\right]\right\}$$

From Equation 11–43 and the properties of the normal distribution, the optimum target level M for a given T occurs where

$$\Phi\left[\frac{M - 1,000(0.02 + T)}{40(0.02 + T)}\right] = \frac{ICT}{B} = 0.1T$$

Since the given review period of 10 weeks is approximately 0.20 years, the optimum value for the unit normal deviate (z) occurs where

$$\Phi(z) = \int_z^\infty N(0, 1)\, dx = 0.1T = 0.02$$

From tables for the cumulative normal distribution this implies that $z = 2.054$ from which

$$M = \sigma z + \mu = 40(0.02 + 0.2)(2.054) + 1,000(0.02 + 0.2)$$
$$= 238 \text{ alternators}$$

FIGURE 11–6

Minimum Annual Cost versus Review Period

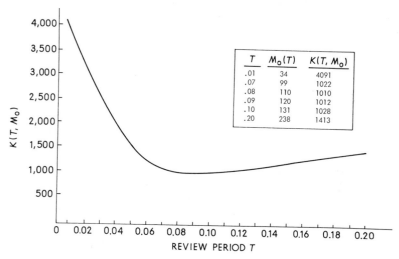

T	$M_0(T)$	$K(T, M_0)$
.01	34	4091
.07	99	1022
.08	110	1010
.09	120	1012
.10	131	1028
.20	238	1413

The expected annual variable cost associated with a policy of ordering enough stock to bring the alternator inventory to 238 units every 10 weeks is from Equation 11–46,

$$K = \frac{40}{0.2} + 10(238 - 120) + 500[8.8(0.0484) - 18(0.020)]$$

$$= \$1,413$$

This is the minimum expected annual cost given that a review period of 10 weeks is used. Similar calculations have been carried out for review periods of 0.01, 0.07, 0.08, 0.09, and 0.10 years. The minimum expected cost for each of these review periods is plotted in Figure 11–6.

Note that among the values tabulated, the optimum fixed review period policy appears to be to order up to 110 units every 0.08 years. This gives an expected cost of \$1,010 per year. Note also the shape of the curve in the region of the optimum. As was the case with the deterministic models, the expected annual variable cost function is relatively flat in the region of the optimum.

It makes very little difference whether the order period is 0.07, 0.08, 0.09, or 0.10 years as long as the optimum target is used for the period selected. Note also that the curve rises much more sharply for review periods which are shorter than the optimum than it does for more lengthy periods.

Combined Models

The basic modeling strategy for single-stage, single-item inventory systems has been introduced in the previous sections. We have discussed single-order models, fixed-reorder-point models, and fixed-review-period models. In each case a rather restrictive set of assumptions such as infinite production rate and customer willingness to back order were made. Let us now examine methods for relaxing these assumptions and making our basic models more general. The primary goal is to extend the reader's ability to construct and adapt mathematical models of physical systems. Since our purpose is not to develop an extensive handbook of off-the-shelf models, we will limit our illustrations to two major extensions of the fixed-reorder-point model. Extensions of the other models are left as exercises for the reader.

Back Orders and Lost Sales. In many inventory systems one cannot expect customers to wait for items which are currently out of stock. Some or all of the customers may seek alternate sources of supply if denied immediate service. In such instances the pure back-order models of the previous sections are not applicable. Let us now consider how one might modify the fixed-reorder-point model to account for possible lost sales.

Suppose that we can identify a fraction f of our total demands, occurring when the system is out of stock, which can be back ordered. The remaining portion $(1 - f)$ represents lost sales. Further suppose that each lost sale represents a cost to the system of D dollars which is different than the cost of a back order B. The remaining symbols carry the same meanings as in Equation 11–31.

From Equation 11–27 it is evident that the expected number of demands per cycle occurring when the system is out of stock is the number we previously considered as back orders. That is,

$$\bar{n}(L_c) = \int_{L_c}^{\infty} (x - L_c)h(x)\,dx \tag{11–47}$$

where $h(x)$ is the lead time demand distribution and L_c is the reorder point. Now rather than all such demands being back ordered, only a portion f goes into back-order status; the remaining portion $(1 - f)$ is lost to the system. It follows that the expected cost of back orders plus the expected cost of lost sales per cycle is

$$B(f)[\bar{n}(L_c)] + D(1 - f)[\bar{n}(L_c)] = [Bf + D(1 - f)]\left[\int_{L_c}^{\infty} (x - L_c)h(x)\,dx\right] \tag{11–48}$$

The carrying cost term must also be modified since only a fraction f of the demands occurring after net inventory reaches zero will remain for service. From Equation 11–22, the random variable W representing net inventory at the time of order arrival now becomes

$$W_m = \begin{cases} L_c - x & \text{for } L_c - x \geq 0 \\ f(L_c - x) & \text{for } L_c - x < 0 \end{cases} \tag{11-49}$$

The expected value of W_m is

$$E(W_m) = \int_0^{L_c} (L_c - x)h(x)\,dx + \int_{L_c}^{\infty} f(L_c - x)h(x)\,dx$$

$$= L_c - \mu + (1 - f)\int_{L_c}^{\infty} (x - L_c)h(x)\,dx \tag{11-50}$$

This expression is intuitively appealing since expected inventory depletion over the lead time is total expected lead time demand, μ, less demands lost, $(1 - f)[\bar{n}(L_c)]$. Units available at the time of ordering, L_c, less the expected inventory depletion over the lead time then gives $E(W_m)$.

Again employing the argument that average amount of stock in net inventory throughout the year is simply the arithmetic average of expected maximum and expected minimum we have

$$\bar{L} = \frac{(Q + L_c - \mu + (1 - f)\bar{n}(L_c)) + (L_c - \mu + (1 - f)\bar{n}(L_c))}{2}$$

$$= \frac{Q}{2} + L_c - \mu + (1 - f)\bar{n}(L_c)$$

Expected annual carrying cost is IC times this quantity.

The expected number of cycles per year is no longer exactly λ/Q. That does not account for the average length of time per cycle for which the system is out of stock and losing sales. However, in most realistic systems this length of time is a very small portion of the total cycle. Since it also complicates the analysis, we will assume that the portion of cycle time out of stock is negligible and go with the approximation that the number of cycles per year equals λ/Q. We are now in a position to construct our total average annual variable cost expression by using cost per cycle times cycles per year. That is,

$$K = \frac{\lambda A}{Q} + IC\left[\frac{Q}{2} + L_c - \mu + (1 - f)\bar{n}(L_c)\right] + \frac{\lambda\bar{n}(L_c)}{Q}[Bf + D(1 - f)] \tag{11-52}$$

which by rearranging terms becomes

$$K = \frac{\lambda A}{Q} + IC\left[\frac{Q}{2} + L_c - \mu\right]$$

$$+ \left[\frac{\lambda(Bf + D(1 - f))}{Q} + IC(1 - f)\right]\int_{L_c}^{\infty}(x - L_c)h(x)\,dx \tag{11-53}$$

The optimum solution for this convex function is obtained as usual by solving $\partial K/\partial Q = \partial K/\partial L_c = 0$. The solution leads to the pair of equations

$$Q = \left\{ \frac{2\lambda[A + \bar{n}(L_c)(Bf + D(1 - f))]}{IC} \right\}^{1/2} \tag{11-54}$$

and

$$\hat{H}(L_c) = \frac{QIC}{\lambda(Bf + D(1 - f)) + QIC(1 - f)} \tag{11-55}$$

Optimum values for Q and L_c are most easily determined by the iterative technique outlined on page 428, substituting Equations 11-54 and 11-55 for 11-33 and 11-34.

Note that our general model 11-53 reduces to the pure back-orders case of Equation 11-31 when we let $f = 1$. Similarly we have the solution for the pure lost sales case by using $f = 0$. Any intermediate value of f may be used as appropriate for the system being analyzed.

Finite Production Rates. The development of the last section still retains the flavor of a procurement system in which all inventory replenishments occur in batch fashion. Let us now examine a means of approximating a production type system in which production occurs at a constant rate p. This model is the probabilistic version of the deterministic finite production rate model of Chapter 10.

Let us assume that during shortage conditions new customers are served before back orders. Further suppose that production rate p is sufficiently higher than the expected demand rate λ to permit all demands occurring while production is taking place to be satisfied from the current production. The expected number of units added to net inventory during the production portion of the cycle is the order quantity Q less the number of demands occurring while the order is in production. Time to produce an order is

$$t_p = \frac{Q}{p}$$

It therefore follows that the expected net addition to inventory during t_p is

$$\text{Net} = Q - \lambda t_p = Q - \frac{\lambda Q}{p}$$

$$= \frac{Q(p - \lambda)}{p} \tag{11-56}$$

Expected maximum inventory is this net addition plus expected minimum inventory. Expected minimum inventory is given by Equation 11-50. This holds since total demands and the fraction back ordered during the period between starting successive production runs are unaffected by production rate.

Since we are representing average inventory as the arithmetic average of the expected maximum and expected minimum, it follows that average annual carrying costs are

$$C_1 = IC\left[Q\frac{(p-\lambda)}{2p} + L_c - \mu + (1-f)\bar{n}(L_c)\right] \qquad (11\text{-}57)$$

The average annual costs of back orders, lost sales, and placing orders are unchanged from Equation 11–53. This gives a total average annual variable cost of

$$K = \frac{\lambda A}{Q} + IC\left[Q\frac{(p-\lambda)}{2p} + L_c - \mu\right]$$

$$+ \left[IC(1-f) + \frac{\lambda}{Q}(Bf + D(1-f))\right]\int_{L_c}^{\infty}(x - L_c)h(x)\,dx \qquad (11\text{-}58)$$

The solution of $\partial K/\partial Q = \partial K/\partial L_c = 0$ yields

$$Q = \left[\frac{2p\lambda[A + \bar{n}(L_c)(Bf + D(1-f))]}{IC(p-\lambda)}\right]^{1/2} \qquad (11\text{-}59)$$

and

$$\hat{H}(L_c) = \frac{QIC}{\lambda[Bf + (D + QIC)(1-f)]} \qquad (11\text{-}60)$$

where $\bar{n}(L_c)$ is the expected number of demands occurring while the system is out of stock. These are also most easily solved by the iterative technique.

Note that the model represented by Equations 11–58, 11–59, and 11–60 encompasses all of the cases for fixed-reorder-point, reorder-quantity systems discussed in this chapter. It is an approximate model for systems with a constant production rate, stochastic demands, and a mixture of lost sales and back orders. The usual purchase or infinite production rate model can be obtained by taking the limit as p approaches infinity. Pure back order or pure lost sales models are obtained by letting f equal one or zero. Combinations of these characteristics are obtained in obvious fashion.

Demand Distributions

In all of our inventory work to date we have employed probability distributions for demand as though they were given parameters of the system. This ignores one of the major tasks of the inventory system analyst, namely, what probability function best fits the demand for a given product?

Empirical Data.   The solutions to models presented in this chapter make no assumptions about the particular form of the demand distributions employed. For that reason it may be possible to use empirical data to achieve a solution providing such data exist. The pitfalls encountered in developing empirical curves are many. We will enumerate a few of the more common ones.

First, it is well to remember that shipping data for a product are that and nothing more. Shipments do not represent a good demand history. There may be a considerable time lag between receipt of an order and shipment of the product. The size of the shipment may depend more upon the availability of supplies than on true customer demand. Finally, a demand may be delayed until several items being shipped to a single customer can be consolidated into one order.

A second difficulty occurs in obtaining a sufficiently large sample. In those systems using a single-order model, there may be no historical data for demand and estimates must be made on the basis of similar experiences and outside events. In those systems requiring lead time demand distributions, it may be impossible to secure all combinations of lead times and demands. Even the lead time distribution itself may be difficult to obtain. Often the best you can do is to obtain an estimate of the maximum and minimum lead times.

A third difficulty related to sample size is the fact that the tail of the distribution may not be accurately represented by empirical data. Often in inventory models only the tail of the distribution is important and most empirical curves do not contain enough data to depict it accurately.

Known Probability Distributions. In some systems it may be possible to obtain data for number of days in a lead time, number of customers per day, number of units demanded per customer, etc. The data for each of these random variables may then be checked against known analytic functions by means of a chi-square goodness-of-fit test or other statistical techniques. In other systems we may have strong a priori reasons for believing that certain of these events will conform to known probability distributions. In either case it may be possible to develop analytic approximations for the distributions in question without knowing what the composite lead time demand distribution may look like. At that point we may call upon our knowledge of transform techniques for establishing the distributions of sums of random variables.

Single-Period Distributions. In many applications involving the single-period model, the number of days in the planning horizon is known with certainty. For example, a passenger ship about to sail from San Francisco to Honolulu can be expected to require a fixed number of days to make the trip. A single-period inventory model might be used to determine the stores of perishable fruit to be served on board. From past experience it may be possible to determine that the daily consumption per passenger is distributed by $f(x)$. Furthermore it is known that there are n passengers on board and that the trip will require d days.

Total demand per day is the sum of n independent random variables x_i each distributed by $f(x_i)$.

$$\text{Daily demand} = x_1 + x_2 + \cdots + x_n \tag{11-61}$$

The probability distribution $g(y)$ for daily demand y is the n-fold convolution of $f(x)$. Since the convolution operation reduces to a simple multiplication of transforms, we have the transform of the daily demand distribution given by

$$T[g(y)] = [T(f(x))]^n \qquad (11\text{-}62)$$

Total demand for the trip is the sum of d independent random variables y_i each distributed by $g(y_i)$. Here y_i represents total consumption for day i.

$$\text{Trip demand} = t = y_1 + y_2 + \cdots + y_d \qquad (11\text{-}63)$$

The transform of the probability distribution $h(t)$ representing total trip demand is then

$$T[h(t)] = [T(g(y))]^d = [T(f(x))]^{nd} \quad \ldots\ldots\ldots \quad (11\text{-}64)$$

The distribution can be obtained by inverting $T[h(t)]$. If inversion is impossible it can be approximated by determining an appropriate number of moments which can be used to establish the parameters of some general class of distribution such as the gamma.

Example. Suppose that daily consumption of lemons per passenger never exceeds four and can be approximated by a binomial distribution with parameter $p = 0.2$. That is,

$$f(x) = \frac{4!}{x!(4-x)!}(0.2)^x(0.8)^{4-x} \qquad 0 \le x \le 4$$

Since this is a discrete distribution, let us use the geometric transform as defined in Chapter 5, then

$$T[f(x)] = \sum_{x=0}^{\infty} z^x f(x) = \sum_{x=0}^{4} \frac{4!}{x!(4-x)!}(0.2z)^x(0.8)^{4-x}$$

This sum represents the terms of a binomial expansion of $(0.2z + 0.8)$, therefore the closed form is

$$T[f(x)] = (0.2z + 0.8)^4$$

Further suppose that there are 80 passengers on board and that passage will take five days. The transform for total trip demand is then

$$T[h(t)] = [T(f(x))]^{nd} = \{[0.2z + 0.8]^4\}^{(80)(5)}$$

$$= [0.2z + 0.8]^{1,600}$$

The transform $T[h(t)]$ is obviously the transform of another binomial distribution with parameters $n = 1,600$ and $p = 0.2$. Due to the large size of n a normal approximation can be used with

$$\text{Mean} = np = 320$$
$$\text{Variance} = np(1 - p) = 256$$

therefore

$$h(t) \approx N(\mu = 320, \sigma^2 = 256)$$

Distributions for Fixed-Reorder-Point Models. The most common complication for fixed-reorder-point systems which will run continuously is the determination of the lead time demand distribution when lead time is a random variable.

In the event that lead time is fixed at d days and daily demand is distributed by $f(x)$, lead time demand is the sum of d independent random variables x_i.

$$\text{Lead time demand} = y = x_1 + x_2 + \cdots + x_d \qquad (11\text{--}65)$$

and the transform of the distribution of y for a fixed d is

$$T[h(y \,|\, d)] = [T(f(x))]^d \qquad (11\text{--}66)$$

If we now permit d to become a discrete random variable distributed by $g(d)$, the sum in Equation 11–65 becomes a random sum of random variables. The transform in Equation 11–66 is a conditional transform. To obtain the unconditional transform of the lead time demand distribution, $h(y)$, we must weight the transform $T[h(y \,|\, d)]$ by $g(d)$ and sum over all d. The transform sought is then

$$T[h(y)] = \sum_{d=0}^{\infty} T[h(y \,|\, d)]g(d)$$

$$= \sum_{d=0}^{\infty} T[f(x)]^d g(d) \qquad (11\text{--}67)$$

Equation 11–67 holds regardless of whether x is a continuous or discrete random variable. However, if x and d are both discrete the geometric transform of $h(y)$ can be expressed by the nested function developed in Chapter 6. That is,

$$T[h(y)] = T_g[T(f(x))] \qquad (11\text{--}68)$$

where the argument z in the transform of $g(d)$ is replaced by the transform $T[f(x)]$.

Example. Suppose that daily demand for solvent in the vapor degreaser of a specialty paint shop can be approximated by an exponential distribution with a mean of 20 gallons per day. Further suppose that a limited history for lead time to obtain fresh solvent reveals lead time of three, four, and five days observed eight, seven, and five times, respectively. The necessary distributions are then

$$f(x) = 0.05 \, e^{-0.05x}$$

$$g(d) = \begin{cases} 0.40 & d = 3 \\ 0.35 & d = 4 \\ 0.25 & d = 5 \end{cases}$$

The Laplace transform of $f(x)$ is

$$\mathscr{L}[f(x)] = \int_0^\infty e^{-sx} f(x)\, dx = \frac{0.05}{(0.05 + s)}$$

The transform for lead time demand is

$$\mathscr{L}[h(y)] = \sum_{d=0}^\infty [\mathscr{L}(f(x)]^d g(d)$$

$$= 0.40 \left[\frac{0.05}{(0.05 + s)} \right]^3 + 0.35 \left[\frac{0.05}{(0.05 + s)} \right]^4 + 0.25 \left[\frac{0.05}{(0.05 + s)} \right]^5$$

which is the transform of a weighted sum of gamma distributions.

Distributions for Fixed-Review-Period Models.   Recall from our discussion of fixed-review-period models that it is not the lead time demand distribution which is of interest but rather the demand over lead time plus one review period. Total demand of interest can be expressed as the sum of two independent random variables y_d and y_t representing demand over the lead time and demand over a review period. That is,

$$y = y_d + y_t \tag{11–69}$$

If the transform of the distributions of each of these variables is known, the transform of the distribution of y is simply their product by virtue of the convolution property.

The transform of the distribution for y_d can be obtained in the manner of Equation 11–67. That is,

$$T[h_d(y_d)] = \sum_{d=0}^\infty T[f(x)]^d g(d) \tag{11–70}$$

where $f(x)$ is the distribution for daily demand and $g(d)$ is the distribution for days in a lead time. The variable y_t is a fixed sum of T random variables each distributed by $f(x)$. That is, demand over a review period equals demand on day one, plus demand on day two, etc., up to the number of days T in the period. The transform of the distribution for y_t must then be

$$T[h_t(y_t)] = [T(f(x))]^T \tag{11–71}$$

The total transform for the distribution of demand during lead time plus one review period is

$$T[h(y)] = T[h_d(y_d)] T[h_t(y_t)]$$

$$= \sum_{d=0}^\infty T[f(x)]^{d+T} g(d) \tag{11–72}$$

Extensions

The models presented in this chapter together with the previously developed deterministic models have done little more than introduce the subject of mathematical models for inventory control. The operations research, management science, and industrial engineering literature of recent years contain many variations of the single-item, single-stage models introduced here as well as much more complex representations.

There are a number of extensions for the basic models of this text which the reader should be in a position to easily understand. For example, price breaks which are functions of the amount purchased at one time add computational difficulty in determining optimum solutions but the basic models remain unchanged. The same statement can be made for problems in which several commodities interact in the sense that the order quantities may be constrained by lack of funds or floor space. Lagrange multipliers are used to develop solutions for these problems but the basic cost equations remain unchanged.

Very little has been said in this chapter about the forecasting problem, although some discussion is available in Chapter 7. The models presented have assumed that demand is either constant over time or that the probability distribution of demand is known and constant over time. The first assumption is obviously naive and is justifiable for computational convenience only when a gross approximation is all that is necessary. Before a probability distribution for demand can be determined a large data analysis study is usually required. Many items have no time invariant demand properties. Demand may experience seasonal fluctuations, long-term trends, and response to external and internal policy decisions. Here the whole idea of time series analysis may be called upon to make the models more representative of the true inventory problem. Texts such as Brown, *Smoothing, Forecasting and Prediction of Discrete Time Series*, are devoted to analyzing this problem area.[8] The demand problem may also be complicated by inventories that are perishable over time or that are partially interchangeable with other products.

Inventory problems are further complicated when they are considered in the context of a large factory-warehouse-retailer system. In such multi-echelon systems decisions must be made concerning the amount to stock at each level, the form to stock (i.e., raw materials, subassemblies, etc.), and the interaction with other products. Demand predictions are complicated by the delays built in between system levels. For example, retail demand is reflected back to the warehouses only when the retail stock reaches a critical level and is further distorted at the factory by the individual warehouse policies. When the production and inventory problems are considered

---

[8] Robert G. Brown, *Smoothing, Forecasting and Prediction of Discrete Time Series* (Englewood Cliffs, N.J.: Prentice-Hall, Inc., 1963).

together in this fashion, control theory concepts may be employed to aid understanding of the system. Often the problem is simply too complex to be solved by the usual analytic techniques and large-scale simulation is used to improve operating policies.

From the above comments it is obvious why this text makes no attempt to provide a complete exposition of inventory control techniques. To do so would require many volumes of much more sophisticated material than has been introduced here. Although mathematical methods for inventory control is probably one of the most thoroughly researched topics in operations research, there are more problems yet to be solved than have so far yielded to analysis. The purpose of this chapter has been to provide the reader with some flavor of the inventory problem. The hope is that the techniques introduced will permit him to further his own education through self-study of the more advanced literature.

Before leaving this topic it is well to note that despite the shortcomings of the simple models introduced in this text, they often represent a considerable increase in sophistication over control techniques in active use by many companies. At the present time the simple approximate models are the most usable as control tools. The more sophisticated models are so far principally used as research tools.

SELECTED BIBLIOGRAPHY

BROWN, ROBERT G. *Smoothing, Forecasting and Prediction of Discrete Time Series.* Englewood Cliffs, N. J.: Prentice-Hall, Inc., 1963.

BUCHAN, JOSEPH, AND KOENIGSBERG, ERNEST. *Scientific Inventory Management.* Englewood Cliffs, N. J.: Prentice-Hall, Inc., 1963.

HADLEY, G., AND WHITIN, T. M. *Analysis of Inventory Systems.* Englewood Cliffs, N. J.: Prentice-Hall, Inc., 1963.

HANSSMANN, FRED. *Operations Research in Production and Inventory Control.* New York: John Wiley & Sons, Inc., 1962.

HOLT, CHARLES C.; MODIGLIANI, FRANCO; MUTH, JOHN F.; AND SIMON, HERBERT, A. *Planning Production, Inventories and Work Force.* Englewood Cliffs, N. J.: Prentice-Hall, Inc., 1960.

NADDOR, ELIEZER. *Inventory Systems.* New York: John Wiley & Sons, Inc., 1966.

PROBLEMS

11-1   The concessionaire at the local football stadium is faced with the decision of how many cups of hot chocolate to prepare before a football game. It costs 3 cents a cup to manufacture and is sold for 15 cents a cup. Past experience indicates that 38,000 cups are enough to prevent any shortage, and this is the number prepared each game. However, all left-over chocolate is disposed of at a complete loss. A study of past sales records indicates that demand per game is distributed in the following manner:

Thousands of cups	27	28	29	30	31	32	33	34	35
Relative frequency	0.07	0.12	0.20	0.25	0.15	0.10	0.05	0.05	0.01

a) How many cups (to the nearest thousand) should be prepared each game to maximize expected profit?

b) How much are they losing on their present policy?

11–2   Consider the advertising problem faced by a dealer who begins the month with an existing inventory of goods (*L*). These items sell for *S* dollars, cost the dealer *C* dollars, and incur a storage charge of *I* dollars per item if unsold at the end of the month. A goodwill cost of *R* dollars is incurred each time a customer demand cannot be satisfied. Monthly demand follows a Poisson distribution whose mean *M* can be controlled by advertising.

a) Develop a model for dealer profit for the month.

b) Determine the optimum demand level.

c) Explain how one might use the results of this model to establish policies for changing the level of advertising expenditure each month.

11–3   The (*S*, *s*) policy or two-bin inventory policy has had extensive use in industry.

a) Explain how this policy operates.

b) Under what conditions is an (*S*, *s*) policy optimal?

c) Can this policy be used for multiperiod dynamic systems? Explain.

d) Consider the terminal-buy decision faced by an automobile parts dealer. The hood ornament now in use will become obsolete in three months. Any stock on hand at that time will be assessed a carrying charge of $5 per unit. Demands occurring when the dealer's supply is exhausted are satisfied by obtaining stock from a competitor at $15 each. At the time of the buy decision, they can be obtained for $12 each. Demand is estimated to be uniformly distributed between 2,000 and 4,000. Placing an order will cost $100. Stock on hand at the time of the decision is *x*. Determine the optimal policy for this terminal buy.

11–4   The financial committee of Generous Motors is about to submit a special bond offering to the public. The size of the offering must be determined. The bond revenues are earmarked for a set of projects whose total cost is known only in a probability sense. The corporate analysts estimate this demand to be normal with a mean of $36 million and standard deviation of 3 million. All bonds will be redeemed at the end of one year and pay the purchaser 7 percent. Average corporate return on investment is 24 percent. Corporate policy dictates that all projects be funded up to the point that only 20 percent of the bond revenues remain. Thereafter, all requests for funds are automatically reduced by 30 percent. The portions of any projects receiving less than 100 percent funding must wait one year for a new issue and will require bonds paying 8 percent. Ignore the effects of income tax and base all calculations on a one-year planning horizon.

a) Develop a model to reflect corporate profit as a function of issue size. Leave in profit equation integral form. Do not try to optimize.

b) What size should the issue be if the policy on partial fulfillment of requests is removed?

11–5   Construct a model to represent the following situation: A manufacturer of men's shaving lotion is about to purchase his last batch of olive oil for a product due to be phased out. His cost of the oil is C_1 dollars per gallon. When used in his shaving lotion, the cost of manufacture adds an additional C_2 dollars per gallon. As a shaving lotion it sells for S dollars per gallon. As a raw product it can be salvaged for V_1 dollars per gallon, but as a finished product anything left at phase out must be disposed of at a cost to the manufacturer of V_2 dollars per gallon. Terminal demand (x) for the product is best described by the probability density function $f(x)\,dx$. One half of the customers are willing to wait for the product to be manufactured to order if not immediately available in finished form. All others are lost if they cannot receive goods from finished inventory.

a) Develop a criterion function. (Let $Q_1 =$ finished product to be stored and $Q_2 =$ raw material to be stored.)

b) Suppose that management has already fixed the amount of finished product to be stored at Q_1. Develop an equation, the solution of which will give raw material to be stored in excess of that already committed to finished goods.

11–6 Tri Tu Chetime is a blackmarket dealer in a small hamlet in South We-et-napalm. He has heard rumors that a large U.S. offensive is scheduled to end in his village. He is interested in selling Rot Saki to the G.I.s at $5 per bottle. Each bottle costs him $1, and he knows that any bottles left after the soldiers depart may be sold to the resident VC at $0.50 per bottle. Tri fears that if he runs out of saki, the soldiers will be unhappy and will trample his rice paddies. He estimates this cost at $10 per bottle. His local advisor for Advanced Inventory Decisions (AID) has estimated that G.I. demand will be normally distributed with a mean of 900 bottles and variance of 9×10^4.

a) How many bottles should Tri purchase?

b) Suppose Tri was unable to specify a goodwill cost but wanted to be 90 percent confident that his rice paddies would not be trampled. How many bottles should he order?

c) What is the imputed cost of goodwill, exclusive of lost profit implied by the strategy in part (*b*)?

11–7 The local medicine man is about to load his wagon with an inventory of nostrums in preparation for his trip to OSU. Each unit of LSD powder he sells will net him a profit of $5. Any LSD left at the end of the trip is disposed of by paying 30 cents a unit for the local janitor to flush it down the drain. He also stocks glue rags which net him a profit of $3 for each unit sold. Model airplane builders will take any rags left at the end of his trip for 50 cents over his cost. He refuses to disclose his cost of glue rags to the analyst but does admit that he inherited the LSD from a recently busted friend at essentially zero cost. The demand for glue rags is uniform in the interval $100 \le x_g \le 200$. It has been estimated that the probability density for LSD is $f(x_L) = (e^{-0.01x})/100$.

Since he will visit only once, he feels his goodwill cost is negligible.

a) Assuming that his wagon has unlimited capacity, how much of each nostrum should he stock to maximize profit?

b) Suppose that LSD requires 6 cubic inches per unit for storage, glue rags require 8 cubic inches per unit, and his wagon only has a 10 feet $\times$ 10 feet $\times$ 10 feet compartment. What is the new optimum solution?

11-8 A retailer sells a perishable health food, Yuk. He receives fresh Yuk each day. Every bale of Yuk he purchases but does not sell must be disposed of at a net loss of $10 per bale. Each bale he sells yields a $15 profit. The retailer defines service as the percent of customers each day who ask for an item and obtain it. He estimates that it costs him $5 for every percent below 98 percent service that he gives. His demand for early October as reflected from his sales tape was:

10/1.....10 bales	10/7 .....12 bales
10/2..... 6 bales	10/8 ..... 8 bales
10/3..... 6 bales	10/9 ..... 5 bales
10/4.....13 bales	10/10..... 4 bales
10/5..... 5 bales	10/11..... 6 bales
10/6.....12 bales	10/12..... 9 bales

a) Develop a criterion function for this operation. State all assumptions.

b) How much should he stock each day for the period of 10/13 through 10/18 and why?

c) Comment on the data given and outline a procedure for validating your model.

11-9 An army procurement office is buying an experimental military tank. Spare parts such as treads are most easily made when the tank is built. They are expensive to obtain later. The manufacturer will provide spare treads at a cost of $4,000 each when procured at the time the tank is constructed and $16,000 each if procured later. Any treads left at the end of the test period can be sold as surplus for $500 each. Past experience on other tanks has indicated that the number of treads worn out is related to the length of test period in the following fashion:

Demand X	Test Period t	Number of Observations
0	1 month	5
1	1 month	10
2	1 month	10
0	2 months	4
1	2 months	20
2	2 months	10
3	2 months	6
1	3 months	1
2	3 months	3
3	3 months	4
4	3 months	2

The test period is variable and may be distributed as

$$f(t) = \begin{cases} 0.3 & t = 1 \text{ month} \\ 0.5 & t = 2 \text{ months} \\ 0.2 & t = 3 \text{ months} \\ 0 & \text{elsewhere} \end{cases}$$

From the available information, how many spares for the item under consideration should be purchased when the tank is built? What is the expected cost of such a policy?

11–10 Harry's Market specializes in two-pound porterhouse steaks which are limited to one per customer. Harry estimates that he sells an average of five per day and agrees that the Poisson distribution is a close approximation for the distribution of daily sales. Each steak sells for $5.10, which includes a 70 percent mark-up over Harry's cost. Order costs are $1, carrying charges are $I = 0.20$, and a lost sale is estimated to cost $20. Procurement lead time is four days with probability 0.7, two days with probability 0.2 or one day. Harry uses a fixed-reorder-point system and is open seven days per week.

a) Set up an expression for Harry's average annual variable cost using the quantities given above. (Do not solve.)

b) Suppose Harry changes his purchase limit from one to two steaks per customer and that each customer will want two with probability 0.7. Find the probability generating function for lead time demand.

11–11 A project officer is buying an experimental weapon system. Spare parts such as gear reduction units are most easily manufactured at the time of manufacture of the prototype. They are expensive to obtain later. The manufacturer will provide spare reduction units at a cost of $5,000 each when procured at the time the prototype is constructed and $15,000 each if procured later. Any unused units left at the end of the test period can be sold as surplus for $1,000. Past experience on other systems has indicated that the number of reduction units failing is related to the length of test period in the following fashion:

Demand	Test Period t	Number of Observations
0	1 month	10
1	1 month	10
2	1 month	5
0	2 months	4
1	2 months	10
2	2 months	20
3	2 months	6
1	3 months	1
2	3 months	4
3	3 months	3
4	3 months	2

The test period is variable and may be distributed as

$$f(t) = \begin{cases} 0.5 & t = 1 \text{ month} \\ 0.3 & t = 2 \text{ months} \\ 0.2 & t = 3 \text{ months} \\ 0 & \text{elsewhere} \end{cases}$$

From the available information, how many spares for the item in question should be purchased when the weapon system is built? What is the expected cost of such a policy?

11–12   An appliance dealer has adopted a fixed-reorder-point, reorder-quantity inventory system for his stock of color TV's. His present policy is to order Q sets from the factory whenever his inventory position reaches 100. Since he is the only dealer in town, all customers are willing to back order but at a penalty of $20 each. The only demand data available are the first two moments about zero for weekly demand. They are first moment, 25; second moment, 650. There are five days in each sales week and 50 sales weeks per year. Lead time is four weeks. Placing an order costs $40, and carrying one set for one year costs $100.

Assuming that the reorder point is beyond your control, what is the optimal reorder quantity?

11–13   Based upon the demand data given in Problem 11–12, estimate the mean and variance of sales days between placement of orders if the appliance dealer orders 75 sets every time his inventory position reaches 100. Explain all calculations.

11–14   A local drugstore manager is required by company policy to order his speciality item, Vunder Bar Soap, every four months. Each bar of soap costs the store $2. The act of taking inventory in preparation for ordering costs $10. Paper work to place the order amounts to $3. The store loses $15 every time a customer enters the store and finds the shelves empty. (Due to an offensive personal problem, Vunder Bar cannot be back ordered.) Procurement lead time is either two or three months with the relative frequency of two months being 0.8. Demand for the product is estimated to be Poisson distributed with a mean of 15 bars per month. An inventory carrying charge of $I = 0.20$ is used.

a) Modify the appropriate cost equation to fit this situation.

b) Find the optimum target level for inventory position at the time an order is placed.

c) Find the expected number of lost sales per year under your suggested policy.

d) Indicate briefly how you would find an optimal review period if given that latitude.

11–15   Consider an item for which demand can be treated as deterministic, the demand being $\lambda = 260$ units per year. The items' cost is $20 per unit, and the system employs a carrying charge of $I = 0.30$. The cost of placing an order is $60. The procurement lead time is not a constant. It is always either 6 weeks or 12 weeks, the probability that it is 6 weeks being 0.2. All demands occurring when the system is out of stock are back ordered, but management refuses to estimate a cost for back orders. Instead, they want a system which will limit the probability of being out of stock to no more than one third. Inventory is controlled using a fixed-re-order-point, reorder-quantity system. Use the approximate model in answering the following questions:

a) Develop an expression for the criterion function to be optimized.

b) Treating Q as continuous and L_c as discrete, calculate Q_0 and L_c.

c) What is the imputed cost of a shortage?

11-16 A local shoe store has determined that 0.8 of their customers will go to a competitor in the event that they are unable to satisfy a demand from existing stocks. The others are willing to back order items. The cost of a back order is π, the shoe in question costs C, the cost of placing an order is A, and a carrying charge of I is used. Lead time demand is distributed by $h(x)$, and the annual demand rate is λ. Management has been unable to estimate the cost of a shortage but does feel that the probability of being out of stock should be less than 0.05.

a) Develop an average annual cost equation for this situation.

b) Establish a means of optimizing the reorder point and reorder quantity within the constraints of the system.

11-17 Consider an item for which demand can be treated as deterministic, the demand rate being $\lambda = 520$ units per year. The item's cost is $10 per unit, and the system employs a carrying charge of $I = 0.20$. The cost of placing an order is $50. The procurement lead time is not a constant. It is always either four weeks or eight weeks, the probability that it is eight weeks being 0.6. All demands occurring when the system is out of stock are back ordered, the cost being $150 per back order. The inventory is controlled using a fixed-reorder-point system.

a) Develop an expression for expected annual variable cost, using standard symbols rather than numerical quantities.

b) What is the mean lead time demand?

c) Treat Q as continuous and L_c discrete. Calculate Q_0 and L_c.

11-18 Data obtained in studying an inventory system indicate that demand may be influenced by lead time necessary to receive an order. Lead time has been found to be either one or three weeks, the probability of three weeks being 0.4. A frequency count of demands occurring during several observations of each lead time period is given below:

Lead Time $= 1$ Week		Lead Time $= 3$ Weeks	
Demands (x)	Observed Frequency	Demands (x)	Observed Frequency
0	1	0	0
1	2	1	1
2	2	2	5
3	4	3	4
4	1	4	4
		5	3
		6	3

a) What is the marginal distribution for lead time demand?

b) What is the mean lead time demand?

c) If a reorder point of $L_c = 3$ is chosen, what is the expected number of back orders per cycle?

11–19   A destroyer captain is preparing his stores of depth charges for an upcoming submarine patrol. The number of subs encountered is a random variable with distribution $h(x)$. The number of charges required to destroy each sub is a random variable with distribution $g(y)$. Any charges remaining after the patrol must be hauled back to port with a net delay of four days per charge in the destroyer's total mission. If any charges are needed but unavailable, the mission is delayed by six days per charge. Determine the optimum number of charges to be carried for the special case of $h(x) = C_x^2 (0.6)^x (0.4)^{2-x}$ and

$$g(y) = \begin{cases} 0.6 & y = 1 \\ 0.4 & y = 2 \end{cases}$$

11–20   Consider the fixed-review-period model. Suppose that daily demand can be approximated by an exponential distribution with a mean of 20 per day. Furthermore, we have a limited history of delivery times which reveals lead times of three, four, and five days observed eight, seven, and five times, respectively. The review period is five days.

a) Develop an appropriate transform for demand during a review period and identify the resulting probability distribution.

b) Develop an appropriate transform for the function $f(x \mid d + T)$ necessary to use the information of this problem in the model.

c) Find the mean and variance of $f(x \mid d + T)$.

11–21   Consider an inventory problem in which the number of days in a lead time, the number of customers per day and number of units requested per customer are all random variables. The distributions are as follows:

Lead time: $f(n) = \begin{cases} 0.4 & n = 2 \text{ days} \\ 0.6 & n = 4 \text{ days} \end{cases}$
(n = No. of days in a lead time)

Customers per day: $g(c) = \dfrac{5^c e^{-5}}{c!}$
(c = No. of customers in a day)

Items demanded per customer: $h(x) = C_x^4 0.3^x 0.7^{4-x} \qquad 0 \le x \le 4$
(x = No. of items requested per customer)

Consider all days, all customers, and all lead times to be independent. The probability generating function for the Poisson distribution is $e^{-\mu(1-s)}$ where μ is the mean of the distribution and s is the transformation variable.

a) Develop a probability generating function for each of the following:
(1) $f(n)$
(2) $h(x)$
(3) The distribution for number of items sold in a day.
(4) The marginal distribution for lead time demand.

b) Calculate the mean and variance for lead time demand.

11–22   An extensive study by the I.E. Department has revealed that the daily demand for boxes of sheet-metal screws can be described by a probability generating function of the form

$$G(s) = e^{-14}e^{14s}$$

A study of supplies reveals that lead time for fulfilling orders has the following probability distribution:

τ = Lead Time (Days)	$h(\tau)$
2	0.1
4	0.7
6	0.2

a) Develop a probability generating function for lead time demand.
b) From the above generating function, determine mean lead time demand.
c) What is the variance of lead time demand?

11-23 Consider a probabilistic extension to the simple finite production rate model. Let lead time demand be a continuous random variable, uniformly distributed in the interval $[a, b]$. Production rate is a constant (when producing) ψ. Setup time for a production run is two weeks and costs A dollars. Inventory carrying cost is $3 per item per year. A back-order cost of $10 is incurred for every unit the system is unable to immediately supply. A fixed-reorder-point system is to be designed. An operating year is assumed to be 50 weeks.

a) Determine the average annual demand as a function of the parameters given.

b) Develop an expected annual variable cost in terms of the parameters given, i.e., $K = f(a, b, \psi, Q, r)$. An approximate model will be sufficient. Carry out all integrations.

11-24 Sexy Sue stocks favors for her customers on a fixed-review-period basis. She places an order each Monday for enough favors to bring her inventory position to R units. The favors cost Sue $5 each and are carried on her books with a charge of $I = 0.20$. Each customer denied a favor costs her $25. Lead time is a function of her supplier's production experience. He is required to use job corps workers for production. The number of workers he must employ is best described by the random variable Z distributed as follows:

$$f(Z) = \begin{cases} 0.2 & Z = 1 \\ 0.3 & Z = 2 \\ 0.5 & Z = 3 \end{cases}$$

Each worker, i, adds to the lead time by amount y_i where y_i is estimated to be Poisson distributed with standard deviation of 0.1 years. Daily demands, x_i, for Sue's favors are best described by a binomial distribution with parameters $n = 5$, $p = 0.3$. Assume 50 weeks per year and 7 days per week.

a) Develop the transform of the distribution for demand experienced during a lead time.

b) Set up the equation that must be used to determine the optimum R in terms of the values given. Show the *transform* of the appropriate distribution but do not attempt to invert it.

CHAPTER 12

Waiting-Line Analysis

WITH THE possible exception of inventory theory, there is no subject more often explored in the operations research/management science literature than waiting lines or the theory of queues. There are at least two major reasons for the extensive literature on the topic. First, waiting lines are present in nearly every facet of our industrial and private lives. They range from the queues at the check-out counter in the neighborhood grocery to the stack of unfilled dealer orders at an automotive assembly plant. The second reason for the extensive treatment is the inherent appeal and unlimited challenge queues offer to the mathematicians in the profession. Unfortunately the elegance of the formal mathematical manipulation often exceeds the ability of the practitioner to bring the theoretical results to bear in a real problem context.

The contents of this chapter are limited to the basic model-building techniques which have proven most useful in the analysis of simplified queueing systems.

Components of a Queueing System

No matter how complex the end results may appear, all queueing system analyses begin by making certain assumptions about three basic elements. These are the input population, the service mechanism, and the queue discipline. There have been some attempts to illustrate the mechanics of queueing systems through a deterministic analysis such as that suggested by Saaty.[1] However, most models begin with the premise that one or more of

---

[1] Thomas L. Saaty, *Elements of Queueing Theory with Applications* (New York: McGraw-Hill Book Co., Inc., 1961), pp. 27–30.

the elements of the system can be characterized in a probabilistic sense. The resulting system then is a special type of stochastic process whose description is couched in terms of state probabilities as a function of time. A diagram of the relationship among the basic system elements is contained in Figure 12–1.

Input Population. The input population consists of the set of elements from which customers for the system are drawn. A customer refers to any element requiring service. In the context of an airline ticket counter, a customer is a person who requires certain services such as baggage check-in and reservation confirmation. In the context of an air-traffic control system at a major terminal, a customer is an aircraft which requires service in the form of use of a number of landing aids as well as use of the physical facilities of the airport.

The population may be finite or infinite. The assumption of an infinite population is obviously a mathematical convenience. Even though we know that the population of vehicles requiring gasoline at a service station cannot really be infinite, the assumption that it is simplifies calculations and gives negligible differences when compared with more exact representations. On the other hand, a maintenance operation for a production facility with only 10 turret lathes has a well-defined finite population which must be accounted for in model construction. With numbers this small, removing one element for service has a discernible effect on the number of service calls expected from the remaining population.

Another important characteristic of the input population is the manner in which the elements present themselves for service. In a refrigerator assembly line where cabinet doors are brought to the assembly point by a fixed space conveyor, the time between successive arrivals is constant. On the other hand, arrival of dealer orders for the finished refrigerators may be completely random. If the time between arrivals of successive orders follows the exponential distribution, the input system is said to be Poisson. Between the two extremes of constant arrival spacing and exponential we may have any probability distribution for time between arrivals.

Other characteristics of the input population which we may wish to consider include batching of arrivals and the homogeneity of the population. If we consider the problem of providing ramp space for arriving airliners, arrivals occur singly, i.e., one aircraft at a time. On the other hand if we consider the problem of baggage pick up by the passengers discharged by the airliners, passenger arrivals occur in bulk with the batch size ranging

FIGURE 12–1

A Waiting-Line System

from one to the number of seats on an airliner. These problems require different forms of analyses. From the point of view of homogeneity, an input population may be divided into a number of subgroups. Persons who require lunch in a plant cafeteria may come from a homogeneous population. For purposes of analysis they are indistinguishable from each other. On the other hand persons requiring aid at a plant dispensary may come from a very nonhomogeneous population. Those needing aspirin for a headache are easily distinguished from those bleeding from severe lacerations. The two groups require different types of service and carry different priorities on the nurse's time.

We have outlined only a few of the potential distinguishing characteristics of input populations. The imaginative reader should have no difficulty extending this list from his own personal experience. When the limitless variations on input characteristics are coupled with the vast number of physical systems which can be viewed as queues, one begins to appreciate why the literature is so extensive. It should also be recognized that we have not yet considered queue disciplines and service mechanisms which can be used in combination with all of the potential input configurations.

Service Mechanism.   The service mechanism of a waiting-line system is the part most often subject to control on the part of a designer. Many systems require that service be provided for an input population over which designers and management have no control. The response of the system to the demands placed upon it is determined by the specifications of the service facility and to a lesser extent the queue discipline being followed. On rare occasions service system design may be balanced with control of the input population. An example of this might be the slowing up of ships at sea to prevent congestion at the entrance to a canal.

Many of the same characteristics used to describe an input population may also be used to describe a service mechanism. For instance, service may require a fixed amount of time for every customer or it may be a random variable with any probability distribution. A machining operation in which cylinders are bored by automatic equipment operating with fixed speeds and feeds will require a constant amount of time to bore each cylinder. However, an inspection task for the same cylinders in which inside diameters are checked with a micrometer will require a variable amount of time described by a probability distribution. Both machining and inspection service facilities may be located on the same production line with queues of cylinders existing at each location.

In addition to the stochastic nature of the service operation, the mean rate of service must be considered. In a machining operation the service rate can be altered within certain limits by changing the speeds and feeds used. In a hand assembly task the service rate can be altered by providing incentives for employees. In both cases the system designer must weigh the benefits of increased performance against the cost of providing it. Sometimes the service rate may be a function of the number of customers in the system. For example, it is not uncommon to find the speed of typists increase as the number of waiting letters in the queue goes up.

One of the most commonly exploited characteristics of the service mechanism is the number of identifiable facilities or channels employed. The simplest systems to analyze are those with a single channel. An example of this type is the ticket booth at a small theatre which can process only one customer at a time. Multichannel systems exist whenever more than one customer are having the same service performed simultaneously. The betting windows at a race track provide multichannel service in that a number of customers can place their bets simultaneously. In some extreme cases it may be reasonable to consider an infinite number of service channels in the service facility. In this case each arriving customer is immediately admitted to the service operation and queueing time is nonexistent. An order processing system in which a very large number of clerks are available to service incoming orders might be approximated by an infinite channel model. The term multichannel in this context refers to a number of parallel service operations. It is also possible to consider networks of queues in which service facilities may be located in series with each other. A computer facility in which jobs must be read on to tape, processed by the central processing unit, then printed out exhibits such a series of facilities. The output from the card to tape conversion serves as input to the central processing unit which in turn provides input for the printing facility. Queues exist at each operation.

Bulk service occurs whenever the service facility can admit a group of customers at once and discharge them simultaneously. Bus service in which waiting customers are served in batch sizes up to the capacity of the vehicle represents a bulk service system. Obviously bulk service can be combined with other characteristics of the service mechanism.

Queue Discipline. Queue discipline refers to the order in which arriving units are serviced, their willingness to remain in the system, and constraints on time and space in the queue. The simplest queue discipline is one in which all customers are served in order of their arrival, an unlimited amount of queueing space is available, and all customers remain in the system until they receive service. Such a discipline is followed by truck weighing stations often found along major highways near state borders. Since this is the easiest discipline to handle mathematically, it is often used as an approximation for systems which do not literally follow it. For example, the waiting lines at a bank are limited in size by the physical characteristics of the building, do not follow a first-in first-out (FIFO) discipline by virtue of multiple lines and line switching, and may be diminished by impatient customers who elect to return another day. Yet it is possible to obtain useful design information by treating this system as though the much simpler discipline held.

Truncation of queues occurs whenever the physical facilities are of limited size. Once the waiting room is filled to capacity, arriving units are denied entry and are lost to the system. Truncation must be considered for systems such as automobile service stations which have limited parking space for vehicles awaiting service. Obviously the amount of storage space to be made available is an important system design parameter which can be evaluated by means of queueing models.

Priority disciplines exist whenever arriving units can be classified and served in order of importance. The priority can be either preemptive or nonpreemptive. Preemptive priority exists in systems such as plant maintenance when the breakdown of a critical machine immediately stops all other maintenance work until it is repaired. Nonpreemptive priority exists in systems such as a hospital operating room in which an emergency patient is placed at the head of the queue but cannot preempt a patient who may already be in surgery. The number of priority classes, the means of assigning units to classes, and the effect of preemption on interrupted service are topics to be considered in the design of such systems.

Other variations of queue discipline including customers bargaining for position, customers with limited tolerance for delay, and service in patterns other than FIFO have been considered in the literature. Examples of these and other variations are reported in Saaty.[2]

Let us now turn our attention to the mathematical models which represent a few of the combinations of input, discipline, and service subsystems discussed.

Descriptive versus Prescriptive Models

Mathematical models of systems can be thought of in terms of the function they perform. Models are considered descriptive if their function is to describe the behavior of some physical system without attempting to determine optimum performance. Prescriptive models, on the other hand, are designed to prescribe a solution for system problems. They must be couched in terms of some measure of effectiveness such as profit or cost.

Waiting-line models developed in this chapter are descriptive in nature. They describe the behavior of a system which is well defined in terms of input, queue discipline, and service mechanism without attempting to prescribe an optimum configuration. The decision of which combination of parameters will lead to the most desirable system configuration is left to the subjective evaluation of the designer. The models only provide a vehicle for evaluating the potential performance of a given configuration in terms of waiting time distributions, line length distributions, service facility utilization, and appro-

---

[2] *Ibid.*, chaps. xi and xiii.

priate moments. No value system is imposed upon the designer. Obviously these descriptive models could be used as the basis for prescriptive modeling, but consistent with the usual queueing presentation we will not attempt to do so.

Simple Queues

The Markovian Assumption. The simplest waiting-line systems are Markovian. Although many other waiting-line systems are not inherently Markovian, it is sometimes mathematically convenient to structure the problem such that the states of the system can be treated as Markovian. Such structures are referred to as imbedded Markov chains.

Conceptually, Markov processes are a class of stochastic processes where the future development of the system is completely determined by the present state and is independent of the way in which the present state has been achieved. Such stochastic processes can have either discrete or continuous time parameters. The simplest type of Markov process is the Markov chain in which transition probabilities among states are the same for every trial. The probability of moving from state i to state j on the nth trial is identical to the probability of moving from state i to j on the $n + k$th trial. In this case the transition probabilities are said to be stationary or constant. If the states of the system can be described in terms of the integers $0, 1, 2, \ldots$, and changes in state occur at fixed intervals of time denoted as trial $1, 2, \ldots$, the process is said to be discrete in time and space. Most of the queueing models we will develop are discrete in space but continuous in time. A thorough discussion of Markov chains and their analysis is contained in Feller.[3] A brief introduction to the topic is contained in Chapter 7.

In the language of our waiting-line problems, the state of the system at time t refers to the number of units in the queue plus the number actively in service. In the case of the simple Poisson processes, transitions occur in the interval h where h becomes arbitrarily small. The only requirements for complete specification of a Markov chain are an initial probability vector specifying state probabilities at some arbitrary time t and a matrix of transition probabilities. The transition matrix is stochastic in that it is square, each of its rows sums to one, and each entry is nonnegative. The entries across any row i exhaust all possible ways of moving from i in the system to any other number j in the system. For truncated queues, the transition matrix is finite. For unlimited queues, the transition matrix has an infinite number of rows and columns but all entries except those on and adjacent to the main diagonal are zero.

When a probability row vector at time t is multiplied on the right by the

---

[3] William Feller, *An Introduction to Probability Theory and Its Applications* (2nd ed.; New York: John Wiley & Sons, Inc., 1957 Vol. I,), chaps. xv, xvi, and xvii.

single-stage transition matrix, the result is a probability row vector for time $(t + h)$. This can be seen by the relationship between joint, marginal, and conditional probabilities. That is,

$Pr[n$ in the system at $(t + h)]$

$$= \sum_j Pr[\text{of the joint event } j \text{ in the system at time } t \text{ and } n \text{ at } (t + h)]$$

$$= \sum_j Pr(j \text{ at } t) \, Pr[n \text{ at } (t + h) \text{ given } j \text{ at } t]$$

which is precisely the result obtained for element n of the probability vector $[P_n(t + h)]$ when the multiplication of the vector at t by the transition matrix of conditional probabilities is performed. In terms of matrices,

$$[Pr(n \text{ at } t + h)] = [Pr(j \text{ at } t)][Pr(n \text{ at } t + h \text{ given } j \text{ at } t)]$$

where the square brackets denote matrices or vectors.

The Poisson Process. The simplest queueing models are those which depend upon the Poisson assumption to preserve their Markovian properties. The basic postulates for the Poisson Process are given by Feller as " whatever the number of changes during $(0, t)$, the probability that during $(t, t + h)$ a change occurs is $\lambda h + o(h)$, and the probability that more than one change occurs is $o(h)$."[4] Here h represents an arbitrarily small interval of time and $o(h)$ denotes a quantity which is of smaller magnitude than h. Loosely speaking, the Poisson process assumes that the probability of a single event occurring in a time interval h is proportional to that time interval and the probability of more than one event in that interval is negligible. We have called the proportionality constant λ.

Consider a system which begins operating at time zero with no customers present and accepts arrivals but serves none. Further suppose that the input population operates according to a Poisson process as described by the above postulates. Let

$p_n(t) =$ probability of n customers present at time t

$$\lim_{h \to 0} \frac{\lambda h}{h} = \lambda \tag{12–1}$$

$$\lim_{h \to 0} \frac{o(h)}{h} = 0 \tag{12–2}$$

The probability of finding the system in state n at time $(t + h)$ depends only upon the probability vector for states at time t and a transition matrix covering the interval $(t, t + h)$.

The probability of moving from state n to state $n - 1$ in the interval $(t, t + h)$ is zero since we are assuming that units never leave the system.

---

[4] *Ibid.*, p. 401.

The probability of staying in state n is the probability that no arrivals occur in $(t, t + h)$ or

$$p_{nn} = 1 - \lambda h - o(h) \qquad (12\text{--}3)$$

The probability of moving from state n to state $(n + 1)$ is the probability that a single arrival occurs in $(t, t + h)$.

$$p_{n, n+1} = \lambda h \qquad (12\text{--}4)$$

The probability of moving from state n to any state $(n + k)$ in the interval $(t, t + h)$ where $k > 1$ is negligible by virtue of the Poisson postulates.

The single-stage transition matrix, representing the conditional probabilities of moving into state j at time $(t + h)$ given that the system occupied state i at time t, is then

$$[p_{ij}] = \begin{array}{c|ccccc} & 0 & 1 & 2 & 3 & \cdots \\ \hline 0 & 1 - \lambda h - o(h) & \lambda h & 0 & 0 & \cdots \\ 1 & 0 & 1 - \lambda h - o(h) & \lambda h & 0 & \cdots \\ 2 & 0 & 0 & 1 - \lambda h - o(h) & \lambda h & \cdots \\ 3 & 0 & 0 & 0 & 1 - \lambda h - o(h) & \cdots \end{array} \qquad (12\text{--}5)$$

Note that the row sums will be one if we permit $o(h) \to 0$. Using the usual row into column multiplication for Markov chains, the components of the state probability vector at time t multiplied by the transition matrix yield the components of the state probability vector at time $t + h$. That is,

$$[p_n(t + h)] = [p_n(t)][p_{ij}]$$

or

$$[p_0(t + h), p_1(t + h), \ldots] = [p_0(t), p_1(t), p_2(t) \cdots][p_{ij}] \qquad (12\text{--}6)$$

from which

$$p_0(t + h) = p_0(t)[1 - \lambda h - o(h)]$$

$$p_1(t + h) = p_0(t)(\lambda h) + p_1(t)[1 - \lambda h - o(h)]$$

$$\vdots$$

$$p_n(t + h) = p_{n-1}(t)(\lambda h) + p_n(t)[1 - \lambda h - o(h)] \qquad (12\text{--}7)$$

Transposing terms and dividing by h,

$$\frac{p_n(t + h) - p_n(t)}{h} = \lambda p_{n-1}(t) - \lambda p_n(t) - \frac{p_n(t)o(h)}{h} \qquad (12\text{--}8)$$

In the limit as $h \to 0$ the left-hand side of Equation 12–8 becomes the first derivative of $p_n(t)$.

$$\frac{dp_n(t)}{dt} = \lambda p_{n-1}(t) - \lambda p_n(t) \qquad (12\text{--}9)$$

Equation 12–9 is a differential-difference equation of the variety commonly found in queueing models. It is a differential equation in time, a continuous variable, and a difference equation in n, an integer valued variable representing the number of units in the system. The method most often used to solve this equation is recursion. Beginning with

$$\frac{dp_0(t)}{dt} = -\lambda p_0(t)$$

and using the fact that $p_0(0) = 1$, this differential equation yields

$$p_0(t) = e^{-\lambda t} \tag{12–10}$$

Moving on to the derivative of $p_1(t)$ we have a differential equation of the form

$$\frac{dp_1(t)}{dt} = \lambda p_0(t) - \lambda p_1(t)$$

$$= \lambda e^{-\lambda t} - \lambda p_1(t) \tag{12–11}$$

from which

$$p_1(t) = \lambda t e^{-\lambda t} \tag{12–12}$$

Continuing in this fashion it is possible to solve for $p_n(t)$ since $p_{n-1}(t)$ is always explicitly known from the preceding step. In general

$$p_n(t) = \frac{(\lambda t)^n e^{-\lambda t}}{n!} \tag{12–13}$$

λ - mean arrival rate

which is the well-known Poisson distribution with mean λt. This implies that the simple proportionality constant λ used in our original statement has an important physical interpretation. Lambda represents the mean arrival rate of customers being generated by a Poisson process. The expression $p_n(t)$ is a time varying probability distribution which represents the state of the system at time t.

Solution by Transforms. It is instructive to solve Equation 12–9 by transform techniques. This general approach is employed in more complex situations when the simple recursion used above may break down.

The basic relationship is a differential equation in time, so let us begin by taking Laplace transforms of both sides of Equation 12–9. From Chapter 5 we know that the transform of a derivative of a function is

$$\mathscr{L}\left(\frac{df(t)}{dt}\right) = s\mathscr{L}[f(t)] - f(0)$$

Furthermore, from the conditions of this problem we know that the probability of zero in the system at time zero is one and the probability of more than zero is zero. That is,

$$p_0(0) = 1$$
$$p_n(0) = 0 \qquad \text{for } n \geq 1$$

Using this information for the special case of $p_0(t)$

$$\frac{dp_0(t)}{dt} = -\lambda p_0(t)$$

becomes after transformation

$$s\mathscr{L}[p_0(t)] - p_0(0) = -\lambda\mathscr{L}[p_0(t)]$$

from which

$$(s + \lambda)\mathscr{L}[p_0(t)] = 1 \qquad (12\text{--}14)$$

The general equation

$$\frac{dp_n(t)}{dt} = \lambda p_{n-1}(t) - \lambda p_n(t)$$

is transformed to

$$s\mathscr{L}[p_n(t)] - p_n(0) = \lambda\mathscr{L}[p_{n-1}(t)] - \lambda\mathscr{L}[p_n(t)]$$

from which

$$(s + \lambda)\mathscr{L}[p_n(t)] = \lambda\mathscr{L}[p_{n-1}(t)] \qquad (12\text{--}15)$$

This expression can now be treated as a difference equation in n with the variable being $\mathscr{L}[p_n(t)]$. To emphasize this let us temporarily suppress the function $p_n(t)$ and define

$$\mathscr{L}_n = \mathscr{L}[p_n(t)] \qquad (12\text{--}16)$$

The next step is to multiply each equation in $\mathscr{L}_n$ by z^n and add. That is,

$$(s + \lambda)z^0\mathscr{L}_0 = 1z^0$$
$$(s + \lambda)z^1\mathscr{L}_1 = \lambda z^1\mathscr{L}_0$$
$$(s + \lambda)z^2\mathscr{L}_2 = \lambda z^2\mathscr{L}_1$$
$$\vdots$$

from which, after addition

$$(s + \lambda) \sum_{i=0}^{\infty} z^i\mathscr{L}_i = 1 + \lambda \sum_{i=0}^{\infty} z^{1+i}\mathscr{L}_i \qquad (12\text{--}17)$$

From Chapter 5 we know that the definition of the geometric transform of a function $\mathscr{L}_n$ is

$$G(\mathscr{L}_n) = \sum_{i=0}^{\infty} z^i\mathscr{L}_i$$

Equation 12–17 can then be rewritten in terms of the geometric transform of $\mathscr{L}_n$ as

$$(s + \lambda)G(\mathscr{L}_n) = 1 + \lambda z G(\mathscr{L}_n) \tag{12–18}$$

from which

$$G(\mathscr{L}_n) = \frac{1}{s + \lambda - \lambda z} = \frac{1/(s + \lambda)}{1 - [\lambda/(s + \lambda)]z} \tag{12–19}$$

This transform is of the form

$$G(\mathscr{L}_n) = k\left[\frac{1}{(1 - cz)}\right]$$

where

$$k = \frac{1}{(s + \lambda)}$$

and

$$c = \frac{\lambda}{(s + \lambda)}$$

Reference to the table of transform pairs in Chapter 5 reveals that the inverse is

$$\mathscr{L}[p_n(t)] = kc^n = \frac{\lambda^n}{(s + \lambda)^{n+1}} \tag{12–20}$$

Note that we have inverted a geometric transform of a Laplace transform. Now we must invert the Laplace transform $\mathscr{L}[p_n(t)]$ a function of the complex variable s. From the table of Laplace transform pairs

$$\mathscr{L}^{-1}\left(\frac{\lambda^n}{s^{n+1}}\right) = \frac{(\lambda t)^n}{n!} \tag{12–21}$$

and from the first shifting theorem

$$\mathscr{L}[e^{at}f(t)] = F(s - a)$$

therefore

$$p_n(t) = \mathscr{L}^{-1}\left[\frac{\lambda^n}{(s + \lambda)^{n+1}}\right] = \frac{(\lambda t)^n e^{-\lambda t}}{n!} \tag{12–22}$$

as was previously shown by recursion.

The transform methods illustrated in the development of the Poisson distribution are powerful ones to use in more general queueing phenomena. As we move ahead it will be noted that differential-difference equations of a similar type occur in many models. The basic strategy is

1. Eliminate derivatives by Laplace transforming the equations.
2. Treat the resulting equations as difference equations in n defined on the Laplace transform $\mathscr{L}[p_n(t)]$.

3. Multiply the difference equations by appropriate powers of z and add to obtain an equation in the geometric transform of $\mathscr{L}[p_n(t)]$.
4. Invert the geometric transform to obtain $\mathscr{L}[p_n(t)]$.
5. Invert the resulting Laplace transform to obtain $p_n(t)$.

In some cases we will be interested only in steady-state solutions in which time is no longer a variable. Geometric transforms can then be used directly as suggested by steps 3 and 4 above to obtain the steady-state probabilities p_n.

Time between Events. In the Poisson process the number of events or arrivals in the interval $(0, t)$ is distributed by

$$p_n(t) = \frac{(\lambda t)^n e^{-\lambda t}}{n!}$$

Following the argument of Saaty we note that if an arrival has just occurred, the time to the next arrival will be less than t from this point if and only if one or more arrivals occur in the interval $(0, t)$.[5] The probability of one or more arrivals in $(0, t)$ is equal to one minus the probability of zero arrivals. The probability that time between arrivals will be less than t is then

$$F(t) = 1 - e^{-\lambda t} \tag{12–23}$$

Taking the derivative of this cumulative distribution yields the well-known exponential density.

$$f(t) = \lambda e^{-\lambda t} \tag{12–24}$$

What we have just shown is that an exponential distribution for time between events is equivalent to the number of events in a time interval being Poisson distributed. This is especially convenient when collecting data for a system study. It is often easier to record the time lapse between successive arrivals than it is to tabulate number of arrivals over many different time intervals. If the empirical distribution for time between arrivals can be approximated by an exponential distribution with mean $1/\lambda$, the process is indeed Poisson with mean λt.

Although up to this point we have examined only Poisson arrivals, we will have occasion to consider service times which have exponential distributions. From the arrival distribution development it is obvious that in like fashion exponential service times imply that customers are being serviced by a Poisson process. The exponential distribution exhibits an interesting property which Saaty calls "forgetfulness."[6] It can be shown that if it is applied to service times, for example, the distribution for time to complete service at any time is the same as it is at the start of service. The time a unit has been in service has no influence on the probability of completing service in the next time interval. Similar remarks apply to elapsed time since the last arrival in a Poisson arrival process.

---

[5] Saaty, *op. cit.*, p. 37.
[6] *Ibid.*, p. 38.

Pure Birth Processes. The Poisson process for generating arrival probabilities illustrated in the previous sections can be viewed as a special case of the more general pure birth process. In the pure birth process the probability of a single new arrival in the small interval h is taken to be a function of the number currently in the system. The dependence of arrival rate on current state of the system is noted by subscripting our proportionality constant λ. The postulates of the pure birth process are according to Feller: "If at time t the system is in state E_n $(n = 0, 1, 2, \ldots)$, then the probability that during $(t, t + h)$ a transition to E_{n+1} occurs equals $\lambda_n h + o(h)$; the probability of any other change is $o(h)$."[7]

As before, transitions from state E_n, representing n in the system, are possible only to E_{n+1}. The probability of moving more than one unit in $(t, t + h)$ is negligible. It follows that for any given sequence $\lambda_0, \lambda_1, \lambda_2, \ldots$ characterizing a process, a transition matrix similar to Equation 12–5 could be constructed. From this a set of differential-difference equations similar to Equation 12–7 would evolve. These would be solved in the usual manner to obtain $P_n(t)$.

The Birth and Death Process. In our modeling considerations so far we have satisfactorily described the growth of a queue of potential customers for systems which have not yet begun service on those customers. This suggests that the next step in generalizing the model is to permit the queue of customers to be decreased by a death or service process which operates in similar fashion to the birth or arrival process.

Now transitions will be permitted from state n to $(n - 1)$ by virtue of a single service occurring in $(t, t + h)$ as well as from state n to $(n + 1)$ by virtue of a single arrival occurring in $(t, t + h)$. The probability of a single customer being served in $(t, t + h)$ given that there are n in the system at time t is taken to be $\mu_n h$. The probability of more than one service is $o(h)$ which goes to zero as h becomes small. A formal statement of the postulates for the birth and death process is given by Feller.[8]

As before this process exhibits the Markovian property in that the probability of finding the system in state n at time $(t + h)$ depends only upon the probability vector at time t and the one-stage transition matrix $[p_{ij}]$. The cell entries in the matrix $[p_{ij}]$ are determined by the following arguments:

1. If the system is empty at time t, it will remain empty if one arrival and one service or no arrivals take place in $(t, t + h)$. It will contain one customer if one arrival and no service takes place.
2. If the system contains n customers at time t, it will contain $(n - 1)$ at $(t + h)$ if one service and no arrivals take place. It will contain n at $(t + h)$ if no arrival and no service or one arrival and one service take place. It will contain $(n + 1)$ if one arrival and no service take place.

[7] Feller, *op. cit.*, p. 402.
[8] *Ibid.*, p. 407.

Ignoring the term $o(h)$, which represents the negligible chance of multiple arrivals or multiple services in $(t, t + h)$, the transition matrix becomes

$$[p_{ij}] = \begin{array}{c|cccc} & 0 & 1 & 2 & \cdots \\ \hline 0 & \begin{array}{l} \lambda_0 \mu_0 h^2 \\ +(1 - \lambda_0 h) \end{array} & \lambda_0 h(1 - \mu_0 h) & 0 & \cdots \\ 1 & \mu_1 h(1 - \lambda_1 h) & \begin{array}{l} \lambda_1 \mu_1 h^2 \\ +(1 - \lambda_1 h) \\ \times (1 - \mu_1 h) \end{array} & \lambda_1 h(1 - \mu_1 h) & \cdots \\ 2 & 0 & \mu_2 h(1 - \lambda_2 h) & \begin{array}{l} \lambda_2 \mu_2 h^2 \\ +(1 - \lambda_2 h) \\ \times (1 - \mu_2 h) \end{array} & \cdots \\ \vdots & & & & \end{array} \qquad (12\text{--}25)$$

The elements of the probability vector for number in the system at time $(t + h)$ as functions of the probability vector at time t are obtained by the usual row into column multiplication.

$$[p_n(t + h)] = [p_n(t)][p_{ij}]$$

where $p_n(t)$ represents the probability of n customers in the system at time t. The resulting vector elements are

$$p_0(t + h) = p_0(t)[\lambda_0 \mu_0 h^2 + (1 - \lambda_0 h)] + p_1(t)[\mu_1 h(1 - \lambda_1 h)] \quad (12\text{--}26)$$

for the special case of zero in the system and

$$\begin{aligned} p_n(t + h) = {} & p_{n-1}(t)[\lambda_{n-1} h(1 - \mu_{n-1} h)] \\ & + p_n(t)[\lambda_n \mu_n h^2 + (1 - \lambda_n h)(1 - \mu_n h)] \\ & + p_{n+1}(t)[\mu_{n+1} h(1 - \lambda_{n+1} h)] \end{aligned} \quad (12\text{--}27)$$

for all $n \geq 1$.

The necessary differential-difference equations are obtained by re-arranging terms and letting h approach zero. For example, Equation 12–26 becomes

$$\frac{p_0(t + h) - p_0(t)}{h} = \frac{-\lambda_0 h p_0(t)}{h} + \frac{\lambda_0 \mu_0 h^2 p_0(t)}{h} + \frac{\mu_1 h p_1(t)}{h} - \frac{\lambda_1 \mu_1 h^2 p_1(t)}{h}$$

which in the limit is

$$\lim_{h \to 0} \frac{p_0(t + h) - p_0(t)}{h} = \frac{dp_0(t)}{dt} = -\lambda_0 p_0(t) + \mu_1 p_1(t) \quad (12\text{--}28)$$

Similar calculations for the general term yield

$$\frac{dp_n(t)}{dt} = -(\lambda_n + \mu_n)p_n(t) + \lambda_{n-1}p_{n-1}(t) + \mu_{n+1}p_{n+1}(t) \quad (12\text{--}29)$$

Equations 12–28 and 12–29 are the basis for enumerable queueing models which have appeared in the literature throughout the years. Essentially all that is necessary is to propose a unique set of values for $\{\lambda_i\}$ and $\{\mu_i\}$ and a new model has been created. As long as the assumption of probabilities proportional to time intervals is valid, these equations can be used to reflect a wide assortment of queue disciplines, arrival mechanisms, and service facilities.

Steady-State Solutions

It is possible to obtain some time dependent solutions for $p_n(t)$ from the basic differential-difference equations of the birth and death process. However, the most successful such solution is limited to the single channel, Poisson arrival, negative exponential service case. Even that solution yields a rather formidable expression involving Bessel functions. In general, we will consider transient solutions to Equations 12–28 and 12–29 as being beyond the scope of this text. The interested reader is urged to consult Saaty[9] or Cox and Smith.[10]

A queueing system is said to have reached steady state when the probability distribution no longer changes with time. The general theory of Markov processes has much to say about the conditions under which a steady-state solution will exist. For our purposes we will take the naive point of view that if our equilibrium equations have a unique solution which is a probability distribution, then that is the steady-state solution. Some systems will obviously never reach equilibrium. Suppose for example that our queue represents eggs being stored under federal farm programs and that the arrival rate of eggs for storage exceeds the rate at which they are released for school lunch programs and the like. Obviously the amount in storage will grow without limit as long as these conditions exist and the probability distribution for number in storage is constantly shifting. There is no equilibrium solution.

A General Expression. One means of characterizing an equilibrium or steady-state solution is to say that the derivative of the probability distribution is zero. This is merely another way of saying that the distribution is no longer changing with time. If a system begins with no customers present, it may take a long time for it to reach equilibrium. On the other hand if the initial probability vector is quite close to the equilibrium condition, steady-state values will be reached for small values of t. Without being very precise, we will simply say that the steady-state solution applies only after the system has been in operation for a lengthy period of time.

Since equilibrium implies that the time rate of change of the probability distribution is zero, let us now return to Equations 12–28 and 12–29 to carry out the calculation. That is,

[9] Saaty, *op. cit.*, p. 93.
[10] D. R. Cox, and Walter L. Smith, *Queues* (London: Metheun & Co., 1961), p. 64.

$$\frac{dp_0(t)}{dt} = 0 = -\lambda_0\, p_0(t) + \mu_1 p_1(t)$$

and

$$\frac{dp_n(t)}{dt} = 0 = -(\lambda_n + \mu_n)p_n(t) + \lambda_{n-1}p_{n-1}(t) + \mu_{n+1}p_{n+1}(t)$$

for all $n \geq 1$. Under equilibrium conditions, time is no longer a factor so we will suppress the functional notation and let p_n represent the steady-state probability of n in the system. With that modification and rearranging terms we have

$$\lambda_0\, p_0 = \mu_1 p_1 \qquad (12\text{–}30)$$

and

$$(\lambda_n + \mu_n)p_n = \lambda_{n-1}p_{n-1} + \mu_{n+1}p_{n+1} \qquad (12\text{–}31)$$

for $n \geq 1$.

The usual method for obtaining a solution for this set of equations is recursion. At each stage, i, a solution for p_n is obtained in terms of the parameter sets $\{\lambda_j\}$ and $\{\mu_j\}$, and p_0. Finally p_0 is obtained by recognizing that the sum of all p_n values must equal one. Beginning with p_1, from Equation 12–30,

$$p_1 = \left(\frac{\lambda_0}{\mu_1}\right)p_0$$

Moving to Equation 12–31 with $n = 1$ we have

$$p_2 = \frac{-\lambda_0\, p_0 + (\lambda_1 + \mu_1)p_1}{\mu_2}$$

$$\frac{-\lambda_0\, p_0 + (\lambda_1 + \mu_1)(\lambda_0/\mu_1)p_0}{\mu_2}$$

$$= \left(\frac{\lambda_0 \lambda_1}{\mu_1 \mu_2}\right)p_0$$

Continuing along in this fashion it can be shown that the general term then becomes

$$p_n = \left[\frac{\lambda_0 \lambda_1 \lambda_2 \ldots \lambda_{n-1}}{\mu_1 \mu_2 \ldots \mu_n}\right]p_0 = \frac{\prod_{i=0}^{n-1} \lambda_i}{\prod_{i=1}^{n} \mu_i}\, p_0 \qquad (12\text{–}32)$$

Assuming that conditions are such that a legitimate probability distribution does exist, p_0 is obtained from

$$\sum_{n=0}^{\infty} p_n = 1$$

so that

$$p_0 = \frac{1}{1 + \sum_{n=1}^{\infty} [\prod_{i=0}^{n-1} \lambda_i / \prod_{i=1}^{n} \mu_i]} \qquad (12\text{--}33)$$

Given a proper specification for the sets $\{\lambda_i\}$ and $\{\mu_i\}$, Equations 12–32 and 12–33 will permit the calculation of the steady-state probability distribution for number of customers in the system. From this distribution, desired measures of performance such as mean line length and facility idle time are readily obtainable.

Single-Server Poisson Systems. The simplest possible waiting-line model is that with a single server, Poisson arrivals, exponential service times, and unlimited queue capacity. In terms of the parameters of the general model, this means that the arrival rate is λ regardless of the number of customers in the system and the service rate is μ as long as anyone is in the system. That is,

$$\lambda_n = \lambda \qquad \text{for all } n$$

and

$$\mu_n = \mu \qquad \text{for all } n > 0$$

Applying the results of the last section,

$$p_0 = \frac{1}{1 + \sum_{n=1}^{\infty} (\lambda^n / \mu^n)} \qquad (12\text{--}34)$$

If λ is less than μ, the terms in the denominator form a geometric series whose ratio (λ/μ) is less than one. If λ is greater than μ, the queue will grow without bound and there is no steady-state solution. The closed form for such a series with $(\lambda/\mu) < 1$ is

$$\sum_{n=0}^{\infty} \left(\frac{\lambda}{\mu}\right)^n = \frac{1}{1 - \lambda/\mu} \qquad (12\text{--}35)$$

The complete closed form expressions are then

$$p_0 = \left(1 - \frac{\lambda}{\mu}\right)$$

and

$$p_n = \left(\frac{\lambda}{\mu}\right)^n \left(1 - \frac{\lambda}{\mu}\right) \qquad (12\text{--}36)$$

The quantity λ/μ is often called the utilization factor and given the symbol ρ. The probability distribution for number in the system can be rewritten as

$$p_n = (1 - \rho)\rho^n \qquad (12\text{--}37)$$

This is the well-known geometric distribution.

The geometric transform for p_n is

$$G(p_n) = (1 - \rho) \sum_{n=0}^{\infty} \rho^n z^n$$

which from Chapter 5 is

$$G(p_n) = \frac{1 - \rho}{1 - \rho z} \tag{12–38}$$

The first two factorial moments of the distribution $[p_n]$ are from the transform

$$E(n) = G'(p_n) \bigg|_{z=1} = \frac{\rho(1 - \rho)}{(1 - \rho z)^2} \bigg|_{z=1}$$

$$= \frac{\rho}{1 - \rho} = \frac{\lambda}{\mu - \lambda} \tag{12–39}$$

and

$$E(n^{(2)}) = G''(p_n) \bigg|_{z=1} = \frac{2(1 - \rho z)\rho^2(1 - \rho)}{(1 - \rho z)^4} \bigg|_{z=1}$$

$$= \frac{2\rho^2}{(1 - \rho)^2} \tag{12–40}$$

The variance for number in the system is

$$\mathrm{Var}(n) = E(n^{(2)}) + E(n) - [E(n)]^2$$

$$= \frac{2\rho^2}{(1 - \rho)^2} + \frac{\rho}{1 - \rho} - \frac{\rho^2}{(1 - \rho)^2}$$

$$= \frac{\rho}{(1 - \rho)^2} \tag{12–41}$$

When using this model to design a system, it is well to note that the random variable n includes the unit actively engaged in service. Since the service facility is either busy or empty, the expected number being served is

$$E(s) = 1 \ [Pr \ (\text{one or more are in the system})]$$

$$= 1(1 - p_0)$$

$$= \rho$$

The net number waiting for service is then

$$E(q) = E(n) - E(s)$$

$$= \frac{\rho}{1 - \rho} - \rho = \frac{\rho^2}{1 - \rho} \tag{12–42}$$

Very few physical systems can afford the luxury of unlimited waiting space. For that reason a designer will often work with the cumulative distribution for number in the system. This gives answers to such questions as how large must my lobby be such that the probability of accommodating my customers at any time is at least 0.90? The probability of finding N or less customers in the system is

$$P_N = \sum_{n=0}^{N} p_n = (1 - \rho) + \rho(1 - \rho) + \cdots + \rho^{N-1}(1 - \rho) + \rho^N(1 - \rho)$$

$$= 1 - \rho^{N+1} \tag{12-43}$$

Waiting Time. In addition to being concerned with the number of customers present in a queueing system, it is often desirable to know how long a customer will require to pass through the system. Let us take the position of a newly arrived customer c who comes to the system after equilibrium has been reached. With probability p_n there will be n customers ahead of him.

If there are no customers present, c is immediately admitted to service and his total processing time will be distributed by

$$w(t) = \mu e^{-\mu t}$$

the service time distribution. The Laplace transform of this distribution is

$$\mathcal{L}[w(t)] = \int_0^\infty e^{-st} \mu e^{-\mu t}\, dt = \frac{\mu}{\mu + s} \tag{12-44}$$

If there is one customer already present when c arrives, he must wait for service to be completed on that customer before he can be served. The service time distribution for the first customer is identical to that for c. The total elapsed time for c to clear the system is then the sum of two independent exponentially distributed random variables. The transform of the processing time distribution for c given one customer already present is

$$\mathcal{L}[w(t)\,|\,1 \text{ present}] = \left(\frac{\mu}{\mu + s}\right)^2 \tag{12-45}$$

For the general case the conditional transform given that there are n customers already in the system when c arrives is

$$\mathcal{L}[w(t)\,|\,n \text{ present}] = \left(\frac{\mu}{\mu + s}\right)^{n+1} \tag{12-46}$$

The number present (n) is a random variable with a known probability distribution. The unconditional transform of the total process time distribution is then

$$\mathcal{L}[w(t)] = \sum_{n=0}^{\infty} \mathcal{L}[w(t)\,|\,n]p_n$$

$$= \sum_{n=0}^{\infty} \left(\frac{\mu}{\mu + s}\right)^{n+1} \rho^n(1 - \rho) \tag{12-47}$$

By using the facts that $\rho < 1$ and $\mu/(\mu + s) < 1$, together with our knowledge of the geometric series, this reduces to the form

$$\mathscr{L}[w(t)] = \left[\frac{\mu(1 - \rho)}{\mu + s}\right] \sum_{n=0}^{\infty} \left(\frac{\mu\rho}{\mu + s}\right)^{n}$$

$$= \left[\frac{\mu(1 - \lambda/\mu)}{\mu + s}\right]\left[\frac{1}{1 - \lambda/(\mu + s)}\right]$$

$$= \frac{\mu - \lambda}{\mu - \lambda + s} \tag{12-48}$$

This transform is easily recognized as the transform of another exponential distribution with parameter $(\mu - \lambda)$. The total processing time distribution is then

$$w(t) = (\mu - \lambda)e^{-(\mu - \lambda)t} \tag{12-49}$$

From this distribution we can now obtain any desired measure of performance relative to processing time. The expected time through the system is

$$E(t) = \frac{1}{\mu - \lambda} \tag{12-50}$$

and the variance is

$$\text{Var}(t) = \frac{1}{(\mu - \lambda)^2} \tag{12-51}$$

by virtue of the properties of the exponential distribution. The actual queueing time during which a unit is idle has a mean of

$$E(I) = E(t) - E(\text{service time})$$

$$= \frac{1}{\mu - \lambda} - \frac{1}{\mu}$$

$$= \frac{\lambda}{\mu(\mu - \lambda)} \tag{12-52}$$

It is of interest to note that the expected number of customers in the system can be related to the expected processing time for a customer by

$$E(n) = \lambda E(t) \tag{12-53}$$

This relationship holds for much more general queueing systems and is often used to obtain the expected processing time when calculation of the entire distribution is unduly complicated.

Busy Period. A final measure of system performance is the length of time the service mechanism can expect to be busy with no idle periods. The calculation of busy period distribution in its entirety is not easy to accomplish.

Some of the problems arising from this calculation are dealt with by Cox and Smith.[11] However, following an earlier discussion by Cox and Smith it is possible to obtain some simple results for busy periods by elementary arguments.[12]

A server is alternately busy and idle. When he is idle there is a constant chance $\lambda \Delta t$ of the idle period being ended by the arrival of a customer. This implies that the distribution of the length of idle periods is exponential with mean $1/\lambda$. Under equilibrium conditions the server is idle with probability $(1 - \rho)$. In a very long period of time T we would therefore expect the server to be idle for a time $T(1 - \rho)$. Since each idle period has an expected duration of $1/\lambda$, the expected number of distinct idle periods during T is

$$E(\text{I.P.}) = \frac{T(1 - \rho)}{1/\lambda}$$

$$= T\lambda(1 - \rho) \tag{12-54}$$

Since idle periods are separated by busy periods, this is also the expected number of busy periods in T. The total time occupied by these busy periods is $T\rho$. The mean length of a busy period must then be

$$\frac{T\rho}{T\lambda(1 - \rho)} = \frac{1}{\mu(1 - \rho)} \tag{12-55}$$

where μ represents the mean service rate.

Example.   An aircraft maintenance shop serves a wide variety of general aviation aircraft on a first-come first-served basis. It is a small shop and can handle only one aircraft at a time. The average shop time per aircraft has been estimated to be four hours. The number of aircraft requiring service averages four per day. The shop operates on a 24-hour-per-day basis. Management wants to evaluate the performance of the present system and to consider the effects of system changes.

Making the bold assumption that arrivals are generated by a Poisson process and service follows an exponential distribution, the parameters of the system are

$$\lambda = \tfrac{1}{6} \quad \text{aircraft per hour}$$

$$\mu = \tfrac{1}{4} \quad \text{aircraft per hour}$$

$$\rho = \lambda/\mu = \tfrac{2}{3}$$

From this information we know that the shop will be empty one third of the time. In a 24-hour period the expected idle time is then

$$\text{Idle time} = 24(1 - \rho) = 8 \text{ hours}$$

---

[11] *Ibid.*, pp. 144–59.
[12] *Ibid.*, pp. 58–59.

The average number of aircraft present at the service facility is from Equation 12–39

$$E(n) = \frac{\rho}{1 - \rho} = \frac{\frac{2}{3}}{\frac{1}{3}} = 2 \text{ aircraft}$$

The average downtime for an aircraft needing maintenance is from Equation 12–50.

$$E(t) = \frac{1}{\mu - \lambda} = \frac{1}{\frac{1}{4}-\frac{1}{6}} = 12 \text{ hours}$$

Currently the shop can hangar two aircraft in addition to the one in service. Any others must be tied down until they can be served. The probability that a customers' plane must be tied down is from Equation 12–43

$$Pr(\text{tiedown}) = 1 - P_3 = \rho^4 = (\tfrac{2}{3})^4 = 0.197$$

On the basis of the average shop idle time report, the shop superintendent is considering releasing one mechanic. The net effect is expected to increase the average maintenance time per aircraft from four to five hours. The airport manager on the other hand feels that by cutting his rates and keeping the present crew he can increase his average number of customers to five per day. The merits of each of these proposals can be compared with current operations in the following table:

	Current Operations	Reduced Crew	Increased Business
Expected idle time	8 hrs. per day	4 hrs. per day	4 hrs. per day
Average number in the system	2 aircraft	5 aircraft	5 aircraft
Expected downtime	12 hours	30 hours	24 hours
Probability of tiedown	0.197	0.483	0.483

Note that the effect on all measures of performance except downtime is identical for both proposals. Profit and service considerations must be balanced by management in selecting one of the three proposed alternatives. Since the effect on downtime is rather severe for a marginal reduction on crew idle time, they may want to consider other proposals, especially if part of the maintenance load is for their own flight school aircraft.

Special Cases

The preceding sections have shown in some detail how the general birth and death equations can be used to develop a model for the classical single channel, exponential service, Poisson arrival type waiting-line system. Let us now examine how these same equations can be used to reflect modifications in queue discipline and service operation.

Multichannel Systems.   One of the most obvious changes that can be made in a queueing system is to alter the number of individual service facilities available to serve customers. Such a strategy is reflected by the grocer who installs a new check-out counter, the manufacturer who installs a second milling machine at a bottleneck operation, and the service station operator who installs an additional gasoline island; the effect is to alter the service rate as a function of the number of customers in the system.

Let us assume that each facility operates independently from all others and that there are a total of S identical facilities. When there is one customer in the system, the effective service rate is μ. When a second customer appears, the effective service rate goes to 2μ since each customer is actively being served by separate but equal facilities. The service rate continues to increase linearly until there are S customers present. At that point and for any number greater than S, the service rate is $S\mu$. The sets of $\{\lambda_i\}$ and $\{\mu_i\}$ values are then

n	μ_i	λ_i
0	0	λ
1	μ	λ
2	2μ	λ
$\vdots$	$\vdots$	$\vdots$
S	$S\mu$	λ
$S+1$	$S\mu$	λ
$S+2$	$S\mu$	λ

Applying the general Equations 14–33 and 14–32 we obtain

$$p_0 = \frac{1}{1 + \sum_{n=1}^{\infty} \left(\prod_{i=0}^{n-1} \lambda_i / \prod_{i=1}^{n} \mu_i \right)}$$

$$= \left[\sum_{n=0}^{S-1} \frac{(\lambda/\mu)^n}{n!} + \frac{(\lambda/\mu)^S}{S!(1 - \lambda/s\mu)} \right]^{-1} \qquad (12\text{–}56)$$

and

$$p_n = \begin{cases} \dfrac{(\lambda/\mu)^n}{n!} p_0 & n \leq S \\[2ex] \dfrac{(\lambda/\mu)^n}{S!S^{n-S}} p_0 & n > S \end{cases} \qquad (12\text{–}57)$$

under the assumption that $\lambda < S\mu$.

This model is relatively awkward to handle for large values of S but not unreasonable for S of the order of five or less. By performing the same type calculations illustrated for the single channel case, appropriate measures of performance may be developed. Defining the utilization factor as $\rho = \lambda/S\mu$,

$$E(n) = \frac{(\rho S)^{S+1}}{(S-1)! \sum_{n=0}^{S} [(\rho S)^n/n!][(S-n)^2 - n]} \qquad (12\text{-}58)$$

$$E(\text{queue length}) = \sum_{n=S}^{\infty} (n-S)p_n$$

$$= \frac{(\lambda/\mu)^S \rho p_0}{S!(1-\rho)^2} \qquad (12\text{-}59)$$

$$E(\text{idle wait}) = \frac{E(\text{queue length})}{\lambda} \qquad (12\text{-}60)$$

$$E(t) = E(\text{idle wait}) + \frac{1}{\mu} \qquad (12\text{-}61)$$

$$Pr(\text{idle wait} > t) = \frac{p_0(\rho S)^S e^{-S\mu t(1-\rho)}}{S!(1-\rho)} \qquad (12\text{-}62)$$

Detailed developments for these and other measures are contained in texts such as Saaty[13] and Hillier and Lieberman.[14]

Truncated Queues. Truncation occurs whenever a system has limited facilities for waiting customers. If the maximum number of customers which can be accommodated at one time is M, any who arrive when the system is in that state will be denied admission. In terms of the arrival rate function

$$\lambda_n = \begin{cases} \lambda & n \leq M-1 \\ 0 & n \geq M \end{cases}$$

If the system has a single service facility, $\mu_n = \mu$ for all $n \geq 1$. Obviously the set $\{\mu_i\}$ could be modified in the same manner as used in the last section if the system has multiple channels.

Referring to our basic steady-state results we have

$$p_0 = \frac{1}{\sum_{n=0}^{M} (\lambda/\mu)^n}$$

$$= \frac{1-\rho}{1-\rho^{M+1}} \qquad (12\text{-}63)$$

and

$$p_n = \left(\frac{\lambda}{\mu}\right)^n p_0$$

$$= \frac{\rho^n(1-\rho)}{1-\rho^{M+1}} \quad \text{for } n \leq M \qquad (12\text{-}64)$$

[13] Saaty, *op. cit.*, pp. 116–17.
[14] Frederick S. Hillier and Gerald L. Lieberman, *Introduction to Operations Research* (San Francisco: Holden Day, 1967), pp. 307–10.

Again, appropriate measures of performance can be developed from the basic probability statements.

Limited Source. When considering a system such as a machine maintenance facility within one plant, it is obvious that the number of potential customers is limited. A customer in this instance is a machine which requires maintenance. The queue is formed when a number of machines are down waiting for service. In many cases it is reasonable to expect that time between failures for a given piece of equipment will be exponentially distributed. If there are N such identical machines to be served by a single maintenance crew, the effective arrival rate changes as a function of the number of machines down. When all are running, the probability of a single breakdown (an arrival for the maintenance department) in time Δt is $N\lambda\Delta t$. Simultaneous breakdowns are considered a rare event and can be ignored. When one machine is down, $(N-1)$ remain to provide potential additions to the queue. The effective arrival rate is then $(N-1)\lambda$. When n machines are down the arrival rate is reduced to $(N-n)\lambda$. In terms of our general model

$$\lambda_n = \begin{cases} (N-n)\lambda & 0 \le n \le N \\ 0 & n > N \end{cases}$$

$$\mu_n = \mu \qquad 1 \le n \le N$$

The steady-state solution from our general model becomes

$$p_0 = \frac{1}{1 + \sum_{n=1}^{N} \left(\prod_{i=0}^{n-1} (N-i)\,\lambda \,/\, \prod_{i=1}^{n} \mu \right)}$$

$$= \frac{1}{\sum_{n=0}^{N} \left[(N!/(N-n)!)(\lambda/\mu)^n \right]} \tag{12-65}$$

$$p_n = \frac{\prod_{i=0}^{n-1} (N-i)\lambda}{\prod_{i=1}^{n} \mu} p_0$$

$$= \frac{N!}{(N-n)!} \left(\frac{\lambda}{\mu}\right)^n p_0 \tag{12-66}$$

Further Developments. The previous paragraphs have indicated how one can employ the basic steady-state equations resulting from the birth and death process to reflect multichannel systems, limited waiting space, and finite populations. Each of these models reflects a change in one of the three basic elements of a queueing system, i.e., service mechanism, queue discipline, and input population. It should be obvious to the reader that many different combinations of specification on the three basic elements can be modeled in similar fashion. Some of these are reflected in the problems at the end of the chapter. The reader is urged to work a number of these problems to develop facility in constructing the basic model as well as manipulating the probability distributions to obtain desired performance measures.

Advanced Topics

Every waiting-line model introduced so far has depended upon the postulates of the birth and death process. There are obviously many systems for which the assumptions are not valid. Among such systems are those with arrival and service time distributions which are not exponential. For example, a system with a constant service time for every unit can be modeled, but not with our general steady-state results of Equations 12–32 and 12–33. In addition, bulk service systems, general arrival distributions, priority systems, etc., all pose different modeling problems. It is the purpose of this section to outline some of the general techniques for solving such problems. Because of limited space in a text this broad, no attempt will be made to provide detailed solutions.

Imbedding Procedures. As soon as either the arrival or service times are permitted to follow any distribution other than exponential, the basic queueing process is no longer Markovian. This is true since it is no longer sufficient to know only the number in the system now to predict how many will be present after the next instant of time. The transition also depends upon how long it has been since the last arrival or since service was begun on the unit now at the service facility.

The benefits of Markov analysis can be preserved if either the service or the arrival time distribution remains exponential. Suppose for instance that arrivals are still generated by a Poisson process but we have a single channel facility with a general service time distribution. An imbedded Markov chain is created by examining the system at isolated points in time such as the moment at which service on a customer has just terminated. Changes in the number of customers in the system between that point and the next point at which a service is completed are controlled by a Poisson process, the arrival pattern. This process, with transitions defined over a random length of time covering successive occasions of service, is Markovian. It is well to note, however, that results obtained in this fashion represent an approximation in that one has only snapshots of the system at isolated points rather than a continuous representation of its behavior.

Cox and Smith have used this approach together with a number of transform techniques to develop performance measures for the single-channel queue with an arbitrary distribution of service times.[15] Their results include a general expression for expected number in the system as a function of the mean and variance of the service time distribution and the mean arrival rate.

$$E(n) = \rho + \frac{\rho^2(1 + C^2)}{2(1 - \rho)} \qquad (12\text{--}67)$$

---

[15] Cox and Smith, *op. cit.*, pp. 50–58.

where

$$\rho = \frac{\text{mean service time}}{\text{mean time between arrivals}} = \frac{1/\mu}{1/\lambda} = \frac{\lambda}{\mu}$$

$C = $ coefficient of variation of service time

$$= \frac{\sigma}{1/\mu}$$

Expected processing time is obtained from

$$E(t) = \frac{E(n)}{\lambda} \qquad (12\text{--}68)$$

Similar techniques can be employed for a general input distribution and exponential service times as well as for multichannel variations of the model. It is important to note, however, that most models with reasonably easy-to-calculate results preserve the Markovian property by assuming that either the arrival or the service distribution is exponential. General input and general service distributions in combination can lead to very awkward expressions which are beyond the scope of this text.

Erlang Distributions.   A very important type of probability distribution used in queueing models is the Erlang. It is a special form of the Gamma distribution with density.

$$f(t) = \frac{(\mu k)^k}{(k-1)!} t^{k-1} e^{-k\mu t} \qquad t \geq 0 \qquad (12\text{--}69)$$

It is particularly useful because of the wide variety of shapes it can assume as a function of changes in the parameter k. For example, the exponential distribution is an Erlang with $k = 1$ while a constant service time can be viewed as an Erlang with $k = \infty$. Values of k between these extremes offer a wide selection of potential shapes to fit to empirical data. These distributions will have mean $= 1/\mu$ and variance $= 1/k\mu^2$. Once an appropriate Erlang distribution for service has been selected, Equations 12–67 and 12–68 may be used for evaluating system performance.

Recall from our earlier work in Chapter 6 that the sum of exponentially distributed random variables is gamma distributed. This offers another benefit for the Erlang distribution. It is possible to view service as taking place by passing a customer through a series of k independent exponential channels before being discharged. The net effect is to simulate an Erlang service operation with a series of exponential channels which we can analyze by the basic birth and death equations. This is called the method of stages, used to construct analogs for coefficients of variation between zero and one. Similar techniques for stages in parallel can be used to construct analogs for coefficients of variation greater than one. Similar analysis can be performed on the arrival side by assuming that each arrival must pass through a series of timing channels before being admitted to the system.

In this type of analysis the state of the system is now defined in terms of an additional variable. We must know both the total number in the system and the status of the unit now in service relative to its progress through the series of channels. The calculations based upon equations similar to 12–30 and 12–31 are tedious but straightforward for small values of k. For example, consider an Erlang service distribution with $k = 2$ and a Poisson arrival pattern. The system functions as indicated in Figure 12–2. No unit is admitted to service until the one currently occupying the facility has cleared all channels. Let

p_{ni} = probability that there are n customers in the system and that the lead customer has i channels to pass through

Then

$$2\mu p_{11} - \lambda p_{00} = 0 \qquad\qquad (12\text{--}70)$$

$$2\mu p_{12} - (2\mu + \lambda)p_{11} = 0$$

$$2\mu p_{n2} - (2\mu + \lambda)p_{n1} + \lambda p_{n-1, 1} = 0, \qquad n > 1 \text{ and one channel to go}$$

$$2\mu p_{n+1, 1} - (2\mu + \lambda)p_{n2} + \lambda p_{n-1, 2} = 0 \qquad n > 1 \text{ and two channels to go}$$

State probabilities can be developed from these balance equations. A general model of this variety is developed in Cox and Smith.[16]

Networks of Queues. As long as the input process to a single channel queueing system with exponential service is Poisson and the service rate exceeds the arrival rate, the output stream from that channel will also be Poisson with the same mean rate as the input. Furthermore, if several Poisson streams are combined to serve as input to a service facility, the total input will be Poisson with a mean rate equal to the sum of the mean rates of the component streams. Finally, if a Poisson stream with rate λ is split in random fashion with a portion (a_i) of the total flow going to each of several new streams, each of the new streams will be Poisson with rate $a_i\lambda$. Proofs for these assertions are contained in problems at the end of the chapter.

FIGURE 12–2
Simulating an Erlang Service Distribution

INPUT → XXXX / QUEUE → [2μ] → [2μ] → OUTPUT

ERLANG SERVICE
WITH MEAN RATE μ

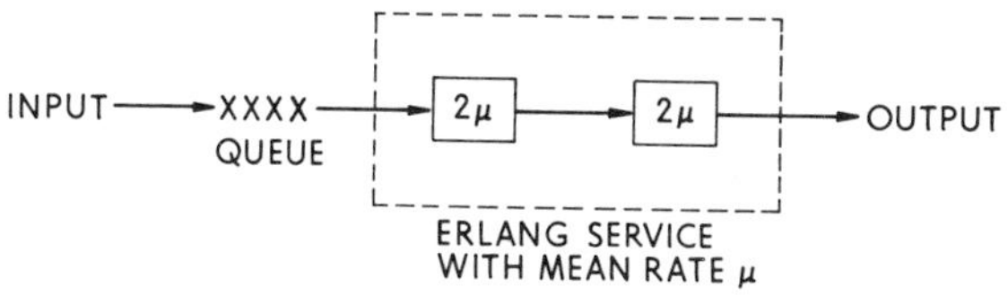

[16] *Ibid.*, pp. 110–17.

This information permits one to easily analyze networks of waiting lines as long as the nodes in the network represent exponential service facilities with unlimited waiting space. When general service times are encountered, the arrival mechanism is not Poisson, and complex nets of parallel and series channels with limited storage space are to be modeled, simulation techniques may be required. In fact, the majority of real world systems consisting of many interesting queues will require simulation if high resolution is desired.

SELECTED BIBLIOGRAPHY

Cox, D. R., and Smith, Walter L. *Queues*. London: Methuen & Co., 1961.

Feller, William. *An Introduction to Probability Theory and Its Applications*, Vol I. 2d ed. New York: John Wiley & Sons, Inc., 1957.

Hillier, Frederick S., and Lieberman, Gerald L. *Introduction to Operations Research*. San Francisco: Holden-Day,1967.

Lee, A. M. *Applied Queueing Theory*. London: Macmillan, 1966.

Saaty, Thomas L. *Elements of Queueing Theory*. New York: McGraw-Hill Book Co., Inc., 1961.

PROBLEMS

12-1 A queueing model which frequently appears in the literature is

$$p_n = \frac{\prod_{i=0}^{n-1} \lambda_i}{\prod_{i=1}^{n} \mu_i} p_0 \qquad \text{for } n = 1, 2, \ldots$$

a) Define each of the terms in this model.
b) List the assumptions necessary to use this model to analyze a real system.
c) Illustrate the use of this model in analyzing a finite population, multiple server queueing system. Calculate the probability of at least one idle server using numbers of your own choice.
d) Are queueing systems inherently Markovian? Explain.
e) How does the Erlang distribution arise in queueing theory?
f) What is meant by an imbedded Markov chain? What does this have to do with queues?

12-2 In the text we developed queueing equations to describe a single channel system with infinite capacity under the assumption of Poisson arrivals at a rate λ and negative exponential services at a rate μ. Extend this to a three-channel system with a total capacity of four units.
a) Develop an expression for the steady-state probability p_n as a function of p_0.
b) Calculate the proportion of time the system will be idle if $\lambda = 3$ per minute and $\mu = 5$ per minute.

12-3 The processing capability of a certain clerk has been found during very busy eight-hour days to have a mean of 16 invoices and a standard deviation of four. It is desirable to keep the delay time on an invoice to less than three working hours. Determine the mean rate at which invoices can be delivered to this clerk such that 90 percent of them meet the delay time criterion. List all assumptions.

12-4 Consider a service station which has three gas pumps and a capacity of six cars including those at the pumps. The usual procedure is for the attendants to serve one car at a time with one attendant per car. The cumulative service time distribution is $1 - e^{-5t}$ for each attendant. Time between vehicle arrivals is distributed by $(10)(2.718)^{-10t}$. (Time is measured in hours.)

a) Determine the steady-state distribution for vehicles at the station.

b) Calculate the expected number of vehicles at the station. Compare this with the expected number given that there are no restrictions on the number that can enter. (Assume a single attendant working at three times his usual rate.) How do you explain the difference?

12-5 The local Smell Station has two gas pumps, two attendants, and a total parking capacity of three vehicles including those at the pumps. The service time distribution for each attendant has been estimated as

$$f(t) = 5e^{-5t}$$

where t is measured in hours. The probability that time between arrivals for vehicles will exceed t hours is given by

$$G(t) = e^{-6t}$$

a) What is the mean time between arrivals for vehicles?

b) What is the mean service rate for a single attendant?

c) Suppose that only one attendant is on duty and that there is no limit to the number of vehicles in the queue. What will be the mean line length?

d) For the conditions originally stated in this problem, determine the probability distribution for the number of vehicles in the system. (It is sufficient to express each term as a function of p_0.)

e) What proportion of time will both attendants be idle simultaneously?

12-6 Consider a machining operation in which storage facilities for incoming products are limited to a capacity of three pieces, including the one currently in service. The machine operates with a negative exponential service time distribution at a mean processing rate μ. Units present themselves for service in Poisson fashion at the rate λ. Any units arriving when the system is full are lost.

a) Develop an expression for $dp_n(t)/dt$ where $p_n(t)$ represents the probability of n persons in line at time t.

b) Derive a steady-state expression for p_n, the probability of n in the system, as a function of λ and μ.

12-7 Professor Backwards has a queueing problem with students desiring to pump him for exam information. He has observed that with one student or less in the office the effective student arrival rate is 15 per hour. When more than one student is present, the arrival rate drops to 10 per hour. Professor Backwards can dispose of students at the rate of 15 per hour as long as no more than one is in his office. When more than one are present, his disposal rate goes to 20 per hour. Unfortunately his office facilities are limited to a maximum of four students at one time. All who arrive when four are present are denied service.

a) Develop a set of steady-state equations describing p_n, the probability of n in the system, as a function of p_0. Note: You may begin with the steady-state balance equations shown in class. Do not go through the development of the differential equations.

b) Calculate numerical values for the probability function p_n for all n.

c) What portion of the time will Professor Backwards be occupied with students?

d) What is the probability that a student arriving at random will be denied service?

12–8   The mean distance between trees along a road has been estimated to be 15 yards. The variance is 225 yards. An infantryman has orders to advance to a position 150 yards up the road.

a) Determine the probability that he will have 12 or more trees for cover in advancing to his objective.

b) Enemy positions along the road are randomly spaced. From his present position the nearest enemy contact along his path is believed to follow a geometric distribution of the form $(0.4)(0.6)^x$ where x represents the number of trees passed before contact is made. What is the probability of reaching his objective with no enemy contact?

c) If he is moving along the road at a constant speed of five yards per minute what is the expected time until the first enemy contact?

12–9   Consider a delay device in a production line designed to batch units for subsequent operations. Units are received in Poisson fashion at a rate of 15 per hour. The delay device is set to release batches of five units.

a) Determine the p.d.f. for time between batches.

b) Because of a poor sensing device this unit has recently been releasing batches of 4, 5, and 6 with frequencies 0.2, 0.5, and 0.3, respectively. Find the mean and variance for time between batches under these conditions.

12–10   Consider a telephone receiver which can occupy only two states. Either it is busy or it is empty. Calls arrive in Poisson fashion with rate λ. Service time is exponentially distributed with mean $1/\mu$.

a) Formulate the state probability problem as a simple Markov chain.

b) Determine the probability that the system will be busy at time t given that it is busy at time zero.

c) Find the steady-state probability distribution.

12–11   Consider a customer ordering system in which customers arrive at a rate "A" to place orders for a custom-built product. Production time for each order is a random variable, negative exponentially distributed with mean time of five days. Production time for any customer in the system is independent of the number in the system and orders are permitted to cross.

a) Model this as a queueing system with an unlimited number of servers.

b) Determine the critical rate "A" for which an order processing system with capacity 50 will remain adequate 90 percent of the time.

12–12   An airline terminal is provided with a group of six loading docks on the main concourse. Any planes which cannot obtain service here are assigned to less desirable docks on the back concourse. Recent data taken during the peak traffic hour indicate that 54 percent of the arriving flights are routed to the back concourse. How many docks should be added to the main concourse so that it can handle at least 80 percent of the arriving flights?

12–13 Consider a modification to the simple Poisson queue in which each arrival is actually the arrival of two customers.
a) Modify the equilibrium equations to reflect these bulk arrivals.
b) If we define $\rho = 2\lambda/\mu$, prove that the probability generating function of $\{p_n\}$ is

$$P(z) = \frac{2(1 - \rho)(1 - z)}{\rho z^3 - (2 + \rho)z + 2}$$

c) Find the mean and variance for number in the system.
d) Repeat parts (a) and (b) for the general case of m customers with each arrival.

12–14 Service time per customer by a local mixologist is believed to be uniformly distributed in the interval $(0, 5)$ minutes. Furthermore, the ratio of mean interarrival time to mean service time has been established as $5 : 1$.
a) Find the mean number of lushes at the bar.
b) Find the expected waiting time per customer.

12–15 Matchmakers at a local social club have noted that bucks and does arrive independently at random rates B and D. They measure the state of their system by the unmated bucks or does present. If the state variable S_t at time t is negative, a line of bucks is present if S_t is positive, does are queued. Each evening begins with $S_0 = 0$.
a) Develop the geometric transform for the distribution of S_t.
b) For the special case of $B = D = 36$, develop an approximation for the 90 percent confidence interval for crowd size as t becomes large.
c) Suppose that $B = 25$ and $D = 16$ per hour. At the end of the first hour, what is the approximate probability of finding an unattached doe?

12–16 The queue for football tickets has been observed to be 20 students at 9:00. The mean arrival rate (random) is estimated to be 60 per hour in the A.M. and 15 per hour in the P.M. Service time is normally distributed with mean three minutes and $\sigma^2 = 0.9$.
a) Estimate the mean line length at 10:30.
b) What is the expected wait for a customer who arrives then?
c) If the queue at 1:00 is 90, how long will it take to reach equilibrium?

12–17 Passengers for check-in at Levitation Airways ticket counter arrive by automobile. The autos appear in Poisson fashion at a rate of five per hour. However, each auto contains a random number of passengers x distributed by

$$g(x) = \begin{cases} 0.4 & x = 1 \\ 0.2 & x = 2 \\ 0.1 & x = 3 \\ 0.3 & x = 4 \end{cases}$$

Customer service time measured in minutes is uniformly distributed in (1, 5).

a) Develop a closed form expression for the probability generating function of number of customers arriving in time *t*.

b) Express the probability generating function for the number of arrivals during the service of a customer as a function of the Laplace transform of the service distribution.

c) Calculate the expected line length.

d) Show how to develop the generating function for the waiting time distribution.

12–18   A local flight school employs two mechanics full time to maintain their fleet of six aircraft. Records show that the mean time between failures for an individual aircraft is 3.0 days. Furthermore, when an aircraft fails, it requires an average of 0.8 days for a single mechanic to repair it. When only one aircraft is down, both mechanics work on it but at an estimated efficiency of 75 percent. When more than one is down, each works alone at 100 percent efficiency. The supervisor will help out whenever more than four aircraft are down.

a) Develop a general statement for p_n under the usual Poisson assumptions.

b) What is the probability that the entire fleet is operational?

c) What portion of the time must the supervisor work as a mechanic?

12–19   Develop the following quantities for the special case of a multichannel system with Poisson arrivals and negative exponential service:

a) The probability that an arriving unit must join a queue as opposed to obtaining immediate service.

b) The probability that an arriving unit will remain in the queue longer than *t*, given that it must queue.

c) The probability that the total process time including both queue and service time will exceed *t*.

12–20   Consider a service facility which receives an input stream which is Poisson with an arrival rate less than the facility's exponential service rate. If this facility is connected in series with a second similar facility, prove that the arrival pattern at the second facility will be the same as at the first facility.

12–21   Consider a system in which several Poisson streams, each with a unique arrival rate, are combined to serve as total input to a service facility. Prove that the total input will be Poisson with a mean rate equal to the sum of the mean rates of the component streams.

12–22   Consider a system in which a single Poisson stream with rate λ is split in random fashion with a portion a_i of the total flow going to each of several new streams. Prove that the new streams will be Poisson with rates $a_i \lambda$.

12–23   Use the results of Problems 12–20, 12–21, and 12–22 to solve the following network problem. A repair facility receives electric motors for service which arrive in Poisson fashion at a rate of 15 per hour. The first operation is an inspection which functions in exponential fashion at a rate of 20 per hour. Coming out of inspection, units are routed to brush replacement with probability 0.4, bearing replacement with probability 0.2 and rewind with probability 0.4. Each of these facilities functions in negative exponential fashion with rates of 30, 20, and 10 per hour, respectively. All units coming from rewind go to bearing then brush repair. All bearing repair units also receive new brushes. After leaving brush repair all units go to the paint shop where service time is uniformly distributed in the interval two to three minutes.

a) Draw a schematic model for flows in this network.

b) Calculate the expected number of units at each point in the repair facility.

c) Calculate the expected time for a randomly arriving unit to pass completely through the service facility.

CHAPTER 13

Mathematical Programming

THE PURPOSE of this chapter is to introduce some of the basic concepts of mathematical programming. We will use the term mathematical programming to denote any technique in which scarce resources are allocated among competing demands in such a way that a mathematical expression representing a measure of performance is optimized. The best known of these techniques is linear programming in which both the criterion function and constraining equations are linear functions of the decision variables. We will discuss linear programming in some detail. In addition we will briefly discuss Lagrange multiplier techniques to indicate possible means of solving the more general, nonlinear problems.

Constrained Optimization

In many of the models developed so far in this text we have been faced with the problem of determining the value of the decision variable, or variables, for which profit is maximized or cost minimized. Generally, the only constraints on our solutions were boundary conditions such as the order quantity must be nonnegative. Now we will consider problems in which more general constraints on solutions must be satisfied.

Equality Constraints. Consider a very simple inventory system in which two items are stocked. By management decree it has been established that the total average amount of stock on hand will be U units. Suppose for the moment that this is a deterministic system with constant demand rates and instantaneous production. Consistent with the notation of Chapter 10, the order quantity for item i is Q_i, purchase price is C_i, order cost is A_i, carrying charge is I, and annual demand is λ_i. The problem may then be stated as minimize

$$K = \sum_{i=1}^{2} \left(\frac{\lambda_i A_i}{Q_i} + \frac{IC_i Q_i}{2} \right) \tag{13-1}$$

subject to

$$\sum_{i=1}^{2} \left(\frac{Q_i}{2} \right) = U \tag{13-2}$$

Obviously a similar expression would be obtained for n items being stocked.

Since the equality constraint Equation 13–2 must be satisfied exactly, a straightforward solution procedure is to use direct elimination. In this technique one of the decision variables Q_i is solved in terms of the remaining variables, using the constraint equation. This expression is then substituted into the criterion function resulting in the elimination of one decision variable. The final expression can be optimized by the usual methods of calculus. Applying this technique to our sample problem, let us eliminate Q_2. From Equation 13–2

$$\frac{Q_1}{2} + \frac{Q_2}{2} = U$$

or

$$Q_2 = 2U - Q_1 \tag{13-3}$$

By substitution into Equation 13–1 we have

$$K = \frac{\lambda_1 A_1}{Q_1} + \frac{IC_1 Q_1}{2} + \frac{\lambda_2 A_2}{Q_2} + \frac{IC_2 Q_2}{2}$$

$$= \frac{\lambda_1 A_1}{Q_1} + \frac{IC_1 Q_1}{2} + \frac{\lambda_2 A_2}{(2U - Q_1)} + \frac{IC_2(2U - Q_1)}{2} \tag{13-4}$$

Taking the derivative with respect to Q_1 gives

$$\frac{dK}{dQ_1} = -\frac{\lambda_1 A_1}{Q_1^2} + \frac{IC_1}{2} + \frac{\lambda_2 A_2}{(2U - Q_1)^2} - \frac{IC_2}{2} = 0 \tag{13-5}$$

Finding the roots of this equation in general terms can be a formidable task. However, given particular values for the parameters of the problem, numerical techniques such as Newton's method can be employed.

Newton's Method. If it can be established that the function $f(Q) = 0$ has a real root in the neighborhood of $Q = a_1$ such that $f(a_1)$ and $f'(a_1)$ have the same sign and if $f''(a_1)$ does not change sign in the interval $a_1 \le Q \le r$, then a_1 can be used to calculate a point $Q = a_2$ which is a closer approximation to the root r under study. As discussed by Saaty, the basic recursion formula is[1]

$$a_n = a_{n-1} - \frac{f(a_{n-1})}{f'(a_{n-1})} \qquad n = 2, 3, 4, \ldots \qquad (13\text{--}6)$$

The solution procedure then is to make an educated guess concerning the value of Q satisfying the equation $f(Q) = 0$, use this guess to establish a new value of Q from Equation 13–6, use the second value obtained to establish a third, etc. The process stops when the difference between two successive estimates of the root are negligible. In the event that the conditions on the second derivative are not satisfied, successive estimates will oscillate back and forth without identifying the desired root.

Example. Suppose that the parameters of our inventory system are as follows:

Item	1	2
λ_i	1,000 per year	450 per year
C_i	\$10	\$50
A_i	\$25	\$10
U	60 units limit on average inventory	
I	0.20	

From Equation 13–5

$$f(Q_1) = \frac{-25{,}000}{Q_1^2} + 1 + \frac{4{,}500}{(120 - Q_1)^2} - 5 = 0 \qquad (13\text{--}7)$$

Taking derivatives we have

$$f'(Q_1) = \frac{50{,}000}{Q_1^3} + \frac{9{,}000}{(120 - Q_1)^3} \qquad (13\text{--}8)$$

If there was no constraint on the problem, the optimum solution would be to order each item in an amount equal to the economic order quantity

$$Q = \sqrt{\frac{2\lambda A}{IC}} \qquad (13\text{--}9)$$

That is,

$$Q_1 = \sqrt{\frac{2(1{,}000)(25)}{(0.2)(10)}} = 158$$

---

[1] Thomas L. Saaty, *Mathematical Methods of Operations Research* (New York: McGraw-Hill Book Co., Inc., 1959), p. 102.

and

$$Q_2 = \sqrt{\frac{2(450)(10)}{(0.2)(50)}} = 30$$

which gives an average inventory of

$$\frac{Q_1}{2} + \frac{Q_2}{2} = 94$$

in violation of the constraint of 60 units. Let us use $a_1 = Q_1 = 100$ as our first approximation to a root of Equation 13–7.

From Equations 13–7 and 13–8,

$$f(100) = 4.75$$

and

$$f'(100) = 1.175$$

Applying the recursion Equation 13–6 we obtain

$$a_2 = 100 - \frac{4.75}{1.175} = 95.96$$

Reevaluating the function and its derivative gives approximately

$$f(95.96) = 0.08$$
$$f'(95.96) = 0.13$$

from which

$$a_3 = 95.96 - \frac{0.08}{0.13} = 95.34$$

Since there has been a relatively small change between our second and third estimates, let us round off the answer and say that $Q_1 = 95$ is a near optimal solution. In order to satisfy the constraint, Q_2 must then be

$$Q_2 = 120 - 95 = 25$$

The second derivative of our cost function at the point ($Q_1 = 95$, $Q_2 = 25$) is positive which verifies that we do have a local minimum.

Lagrange Multipliers. Direct elimination can become a very arduous exercise, particularly if a number of constraints are involved. For that reason, we will normally employ Lagrange multipliers to develop solutions under constraint. Consider a function in n variables $f(x_1, x_2, \ldots, x_n)$ for which we must find an extremum subject to a constraint of the form $g(x_1, x_2, \ldots, x_n) = k$. Lagrange's method states that the necessary conditions for this constrained extremum are obtained by defining a Lagrangian function $h(x_1, x_2, \ldots, x_n, \theta)$ in the $(n + 1)$ variables x_i and the Lagrange multiplier θ:

$$h(x_1, x_2, \ldots, x_n, \theta) = f(x_1, x_2, \ldots, x_n) + \theta[g(x_1, x_2, \ldots, x_n) - k] \quad (13\text{–}10)$$

and setting the partial derivatives with respect to the x_i's and θ equal to zero

$$\frac{\partial h}{\partial x_1} = 0$$

$$\vdots$$

$$\frac{\partial h}{\partial x_n} = 0$$

$$\frac{\partial h}{\partial \theta} = 0$$

In the event that a number of constraints m less than n must be satisfied, the method can be generalized by adding m terms to the criterion function. That is, let

$$h(x_1,\ldots,x_n,\theta_1,\ldots,\theta_m) = f(x_1,\ldots,x_n) + \sum_{i=1}^{m} \theta_i[g_i(x_1,\ldots,x_n) - k_i] \quad (13\text{--}11)$$

and set the $(n + m)$ partials with respect to the unknown x_i's and θ_i's equal to zero. Note that the Lagrangian function h is essentially the original criterion with a zero added. Details concerning why this technique works are contained in Taylor[2] and Teichroew.[3]

As Teichroew points out, one disadvantage of Lagrange multipliers is that the number of variables and equations which must be solved has been increased. A major advantage, however, is that this method provides a value of θ which has significance as a sensitivity indicator. The multiplier θ indicates the effect of small changes in the constraining equation. If θ is positive it indicates the rate by which h will decrease if the parameter k is increased. If θ is negative it indicates the rate by which h will increase if k is increased.

Example. Let us now apply the method of Lagrange multipliers to our previous example of a constrained inventory system. Using the cost expression Equation 13–1 and the constraint Equation 13–2 we obtain the Lagrangian function

$$h(Q_1, Q_2, \theta) = \sum_{i=1}^{2} \left(\frac{\lambda_i A_i}{Q_i} + \frac{IC_iQ_i}{2}\right) + \theta\left(\sum_{i=1}^{2} \frac{Q_i}{2} - U\right) \quad (13\text{--}12)$$

The partial derivatives are

$$\frac{\partial h}{\partial Q_1} = \frac{-\lambda_1 A_1}{Q_1^2} + \frac{IC_1}{2} + \frac{\theta}{2} = 0 \quad (13\text{--}13)$$

$$\frac{\partial h}{\partial Q_2} = \frac{-\lambda_2 A_2}{Q_2^2} + \frac{IC_2}{2} + \frac{\theta}{2} = 0 \quad (13\text{--}14)$$

$$\frac{\partial h}{\partial \theta} = \sum_{i=1}^{2} \frac{Q_i}{2} - U = 0 \quad (13\text{--}15)$$

---

[2] Angus Taylor, *Advanced Calculus* (Boston, Mass.: Ginn & Co., 1955), pp. 198–201.
[3] Daniel Teichroew, *An Introduction to Management Science* (New York: John Wiley & Sons, Inc., 1964), pp. 296–301.

from which

$$Q_i = \left[\frac{2\lambda_i A_i}{(IC_i + \theta)}\right]^{1/2} \tag{13-16}$$

Using the values of the parameters previously given, the equation for Q_i shown in Equation 13–16, and the constraining Equation 13–15 we obtain

$$\frac{1}{2}\left[\left(\frac{2(1,000)(25)}{0.2(10) + \theta}\right)^{1/2} + \left(\frac{2(450)(10)}{0.2(50) + \theta}\right)^{1/2}\right] - 60 = 0$$

from which

$$\frac{224}{(2 + \theta)^{1/2}} + \frac{94.8}{(10 + \theta)^{1/2}} - 120 = 0$$

and θ is approximately 3.65. Substituting this value of θ into Equation 13–16 gives an approximate solution of

$$Q_1 = \left[\frac{2(1,000)(25)}{2 + 3.65}\right]^{1/2} = 95$$

and

$$Q_2 = \left[\frac{2(450)(10)}{10 + 3.65}\right]^{1/2} = 25$$

in agreement with our previous calculations. The value of θ indicates that we could decrease our average annual cost by approximately \$3.65 if we permitted one more unit of average stock to be held.

Inequality Constraints. So far our discussion has considered only those problems in which a precise value is placed on the constraining factor. A more common problem is one in which an upper or lower limit is placed on the constraining factor. In the inventory problem for instance, a more usual form of constraint is that the average inventory must not be greater than U. The revised problem statement would then be

minimize $K = \sum_{i=1}^{2} \frac{\lambda_i A_i}{Q_i} + \frac{IC_i Q_i}{2}$

subject to $\sum_{i=1}^{2} \frac{Q_i}{2} \le U$

The Lagrange multiplier technique can be used to solve problems with inequality constraints if we examine carefully what such a constraint implies. Consider a trivial constrained optimization in one decision variable. For example, suppose we have a deterministic single item inventory system in which maximum storage capacity is limited to S units. A graph of the average annual variable cost as a function of Q for such a system with $\lambda = 450$, $A = \$10$, $I = 0.20$, $C = \$50$ is shown in Figure 13–1. From our previous

FIGURE 13–1

Inventory Operating Costs

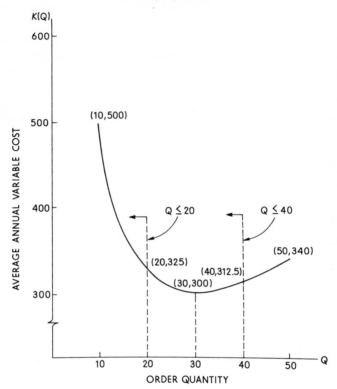

work with this model we know that the cost curve reaches a minimum at

$$Q = \sqrt{\frac{2\lambda A}{IC}} = 30 \text{ units}$$

If the order quantity Q, and hence maximum inventory level, is restricted to an S value of 40, the constraint has no effect on our optimal solution. This is obvious from Figure 13–1. The minimum point on our cost curve occurs at $Q = 30$ which satisfies the constraint that Q must be less than or equal to 40. In such a case we will say that the constraint is inactive. If on the other hand our storage capacity is such that Q must be less than or equal to 20, our original minimum cost solution is not valid since our analytic optimum of 30 exceeds that limit. In this case we say that the constraint is active.

When the constraint is binding or active it no longer behaves as an inequality but rather acts as an equality constraint. In our trivial example the cost curve is monotonically decreasing for all Q values less than the minimum point. Obviously then, the optimum solution under the constraint that Q must be less than or equal to 20 is to let $Q = 20$. When the constraint requires that Q be less than or equal to 40, our solution obtained by ignoring the constraint satisfies it and the optimum occurs at $Q = 30$.

For n-dimensional problems the solutions under inequality constraints are not so obvious as the previous graphical example, but they can be solved using a similar reasoning process. This is the technique suggested by Hadley and Whitin.[4] Consider first a single inequality constraint. Either the constraint is active or it is inactive. If it is inactive, an optimal solution can be obtained by the usual methods of calculus, ignoring the constraint. If it is active, it holds as a strict equality and we can obtain a solution using the Lagrange multiplier technique. The steps in solving problems under an inequality constraint are then

1. Solve the problem ignoring the constraint. Here the usual caveats for determining global versus local optima apply.
2. Check the answer obtained in step 1. If this answer satisfies the constraint it is the optimal solution. If this answer violates the constraint, proceed to step 3.
3. Form a Lagrangian function treating the constraint as a strict equality and optimize.

Example.   Refer to the two-item inventory example on page 492. Suppose that the constraint on average inventory was

$$\sum_{i=1}^{2} \frac{Q_i}{2} \le 100$$

From Equation 13–9 we determined that the order quantities with no constraints should be $Q_1 = 158$ and $Q_2 = 30$. Checking these against the constraint of $U \le 100$ shows that

$$\frac{Q_1}{2} + \frac{Q_2}{2} = 79 + 15 = 94 < 100$$

and the constraint is inactive. In this case $Q_1 = 158$ and $Q_2 = 30$ is the optimum solution. If on the other hand we invoke the original constraint that $U \le 60$, our average inventory of 94 exceeds the upper limit. We must then carry out the solution treating this as an equality constraint. This was done in the original problem where we determined that the minimum of

$$K = \sum_{i=1}^{2} \left(\frac{\lambda_i A_i}{Q_i} + \frac{I C_i Q_i}{2} \right)$$

[4] G. Hadley, and T. M. Whitin, *Analysis of Inventory Systems* (Englewood Cliffs, N.J.: Prentice-Hall, Inc., 1963), pp. 54–59.

subject to

$$\sum_{i=1}^{2} \frac{Q_i}{2} = 60$$

was $Q_1 = 95$ and $Q_2 = 25$.

Multiple Inequality Constraints. When more than one inequality constraint is present we are faced with an additional computational difficulty. Now we must check for different combinations of potentially active constraints. If we have two constraints, for example, it is possible that both are inactive, one active with the other inactive, or both active. The implied solution procedure is then

1. Solve the problem ignoring both constraints.
2. Check the answer obtained in step 1. If this answer satisfies *both* constraints the solution is optimal. If this answer violates either constraint proceed to step 3.
3. Introduce the first constraint as an equality, ignore the second, and solve. If this answer satisfies the second constraint the solution is optimal; if not proceed to step 4.
4. Introduce the second constraint as an equality, ignore the first, and solve. If this answer satisfies the first constraint the solution is optimal; if not proceed to step 5.
5. Introduce both constraints as equalities and solve by the usual methods of Lagrange multipliers.

The values of the Lagrange multipliers obtained by this technique are referred to by some economists as shadow prices. They reflect the marginal price of one unit of the constraining variable. This gives a measure of the worth of attempting to relieve the constraining factor by a small amount.

Obviously when there are three or more inequality constraints this technique becomes prohibitive in terms of computation time. All constraints must be checked in all possible groups of one, then two, then three, etc., up to achievement of a feasible solution. With multiple constraints, alternative solution procedures must be sought.

Kuhn-Tucker Conditions. In the previously discussed solution procedure for inequality constraints, we began with the assumption that no constraints were active, then introduced them one at a time until we achieved a feasible solution. An alternative approach is to begin with the full-blown Lagrangian function under the assumption that all constraints are active. If this gives a nonoptimal solution, constraints are then relieved one at a time until optimization occurs. The Lagrange multipliers are used to determine whether or not optimization has occurred. The conditions that must be satisfied at an extremum are known as the "Kuhn-Tucker" conditions. For a single constraint, the necessary conditions for a constrained optimum involve the sign on the Lagrange multiplier.[5] Sufficiency depends upon the concavity

---

[5] Teichroew, *op. cit.*, p. 307.

of the function and convexity of the constraint. Teichroew also offers a discussion of these conditions for more than one inequality constraint.[6] The interested reader should consult that source for an alternative to the multiple constraint optimization problem of the last section.

Linear Programming

Whenever an optimization problem consists of a linear criterion function subject to linear constraints, we can draw upon a variety of algorithms from the field of linear programming. Although special subproblems such as the diet problem and the transportation problem were posed earlier, the general problem of linear programming was developed and applied in 1947 by George B. Dantzig and his associates for the Department of the Air Force. Dantzig has authored an excellent text describing in detail the development of his simplex procedure as well as many other techniques and special subproblems which have arisen since his original work in the area.[7]

In the discussion which follows we will outline the major features of linear programming problems without being mathematically rigorous. Our intent is to provide a basic understanding of the structure of such problems so that the reader will not blindly apply one of the many computer packages available in the area to problems for which the model is a poor fit. Fortunately, however, this simple structure has found application in a wide variety of real world problems. Examples reported in the literature include production planning, product blending, market research, machine loading, distribution among warehouses, and many others.

Assumptions. Before proceeding with a linear programming model for a physical system, the analyst must be cognizant of the major assumptions which limit its applicability. Dantzig emphasizes the general assumptions of proportionality, nonnegativity, additivity, and a linear objective function.[8] To these, Hillier and Lieberman add the limitations of divisibility and determinacy when considering the basic linear programming model.[9] The latter two assumptions can be relaxed when considering the special extensions of integer and stochastic programming.

Proportionality means that the quantities of flow of various items into and out of an activity are always proportional to the activity level. For instance, suppose that the activity of shipping freight requires inputs of men and trucks. If we wish to double the number of units shipped in a given period we would have to double both the number of men and trucks in use. Proportionality reflects the primary requirement of linear programming, that

---

[6] *Ibid.*, pp. 309–13.
[7] George B. Dantzig, *Linear Programming and Extensions* (Princeton, N.J.: The Rand Corporation, Princeton University Press, 1963).
[8] *Ibid.*, pp. 32–33.
[9] Frederick S. Hillier and Gerald J. Lieberman, *Introduction to Operations Research* (San Francisco: Holden-Day, 1967), pp. 135–38.

is, that the objective function and all constraints must be linear. This assumption eliminates many industrial processes, such as high labor content assembly, where unit output will change as a function of activity level. However, it may be reasonable to assume linearity as an approximation over limited ranges of output values if the analyst is aware of the implications. It is interesting to note that some simple functions termed linear in basic algebra, such as those encountered in processes involving a setup charge, do not satisfy the proportionality assumption. The function

$$f = A + cx$$

cannot be used as a restriction or criterion function in the simple linear programming algorithms.

Nonnegativity means that negative quantities of an activity are not possible. It is not possible to manufacture a negative number of TV sets, for example. For most problems this makes obvious physical sense. However, one should keep this assumption in mind when considering problems such as those involving returned inventory items when the temptation might be to treat returns as negative demand rather than introduce a new variable.

Additivity means that for given activity levels, the total amounts of each input and the associated output are the sums of the inputs and output for each individual process. This implies that each item present in the system being modeled must satisfy a material balance equation. Processes such as those with by-products produced from scrap from the primary product are eliminated. Here joint interactions regarding total usage of a resource have occurred. The total output is not a simple sum of quantities which would result from each activity occurring individually.

The presence of an objective function means that one of the items in the system is regarded as "precious" in the sense that the output of that item measures the payoff. The model is prescriptive in that there is a criterion function to be optimized. This can be contrasted with purely descriptive models such as queueing models which do not identify any precious item by which performance can be measured. The objective function as well as the constraints must satisfy the proportionality assumption and hence be linear.

Divisibility means that fractional values of the decision variables must be permitted, i.e., each activity is capable of continuous proportional expansion or reduction. This causes no problems in production of liquids such as gasoline where input and output quantities can be measured on a continuous scale. It is at best an approximation when the model must account for the number of workers to be hired and lathes to be purchased in a machining context. However, the procedure is still used in applications requiring integer solutions. If the answer is an integer, it is optimal; if not, it is often rounded to the nearest integer. The dangers here are that with rounding the solution may no longer be feasible and even if feasible may not be close to the true optimum.

Determinacy means that all of the coefficients in the linear programming model are known constants. In the real system the coefficients available may be merely estimates based on predictions of future conditions rather imprecisely determined. In addition they may really be random variables based upon some underlying probability distribution. Assuming that they are constants may indeed be a bold assumption.

Problem Statement.   The basic linear programming problem involves an optimizing process in which nonnegative values for a set of decision variables $X_1, X_2, \ldots, X_n$ are selected so as to

maximize $\qquad C_1 X_1 + C_2 X_2 + \cdots + C_n X_n$

subject to $\qquad A_{11} X_1 + A_{12} X_2 + \cdots + A_{1n} X_n \leq b_1$

$\qquad\qquad A_{21} X_1 + A_{22} X_2 + \cdots + A_{2n} X_n \leq b_2$

$\qquad\qquad \vdots$

$\qquad\qquad A_{m1} X_1 + A_{m2} X_2 + \cdots + A_{mn} X_n \leq b_m \qquad (13\text{-}17)$

The symbols C_i, A_{ij}, and b_i represent constants. This form of the problem is general. We could equally well write it as a minimization problem and have some or all of the inequalities reversed.

Graphical Solution.   When only two decision variables are involved, it is possible to illustrate the solution of a linear programming problem graphically.

Consider the problem faced in expanding the shop facility of an aircraft repair station. The expanded facility will perform airframe and engine overhauls. The accounting department estimates that each engine overhaul will yield a marginal profit to the company of $500. Each airframe overhaul will yield $700. To overhaul an engine requires one man for two weeks. An airframe requires two men for two weeks. Ten mechanics qualified to work on either airframes or engines are available for hire. During overhaul an engine with its work space takes up 80 square feet of floor space. Each airframe requires 900 square feet. The hangar facility to be converted to shop has 5,000 square feet of floor space. This facility will be devoted to contract maintenance for a large flight school. Management can get any portion of the flight school's estimated 200 engine and 80 airframe overhauls per year. The problem is to select the combination of engines and airframes to be contracted such that annual profit is maximized.

Let us begin by structuring this problem in the standard linear programming format. The decision variables are the number of engines (X_1) and number of airframes (X_2) to be overhauled annually. The criterion function is annual marginal profit

$$P = 500X_1 + 700X_2$$

We are constrained by available mechanics, floor space, and work load. Converting the mechanic constraint to man-weeks per year, we have

$$2X_1 + 4X_2 \leq 520$$

The floor-space constraint can be expressed in terms of the number of square-feet weeks available each year. Five thousand square feet for 52 weeks gives 260,000 square-feet weeks. To overhaul an engine requires 160 square-feet weeks, and an airframe requires 1,800 square-feet weeks. The constraint is then

$$160X_1 + 1,800X_2 \leq 260,000$$

The available work load constraints for engines and airframes respectively are

$$X_1 \leq 200$$

and

$$X_2 \leq 80$$

The complete problem statement is then

maximize $\qquad\qquad 500X_1 + 700X_2$

subject to $\qquad\qquad 2X_1 + 4X_2 \leq 520$ $\qquad\qquad$ (13–18)

$$160X_1 + 1,800X_2 \leq 260,000$$

$$X_1 \leq 200$$

$$X_2 \leq 80$$

$$X_1 \geq 0,\ X_2 \geq 0$$

Any combination of the variables X_1 and X_2 which satisfy the constraints can be used as a "feasible" solution. Figure 13–2 shows the bounds on feasible solutions for this problem. The nonnegativity requirements limit all such solutions to the first quadrant. The restrictions on available work load further restrict the feasible solution space to the rectangle $(OAFH)$ defined by the axes and the lines $X_1 = 200$ and $X_2 = 80$. If these were the only restrictions, profit would obviously be maximized by contracting to the limit of $X_1 = 200$ and $X_2 = 80$. However, the solution space is further limited by the manpower constraint which eliminates the point (200, 80) from consideration. The floor space constraint is dominated by the other restrictions. It falls completely outside the final solution space and does not enter the calculations. This may be a fortunate condition since scheduling overhauls would inevitably lead to underutilization of the shop space. The divisibility assumption is not valid. All feasible solutions to this problem fall in the area $(OAEGH)$. The set of points defined by this polygon is called a *convex set* meaning that if any two arbitrary points in the set are joined by a straight line, that line will contain only points of the polygon or set.

If we were to select any particular profit figure, possible combinations of X_1 and X_2 leading to that profit would appear along a straight line. For example, Figure 13–2 illustrates iso-profit lines for profits of $35,000, $70,000,

FIGURE 13–2

Graphical Solution

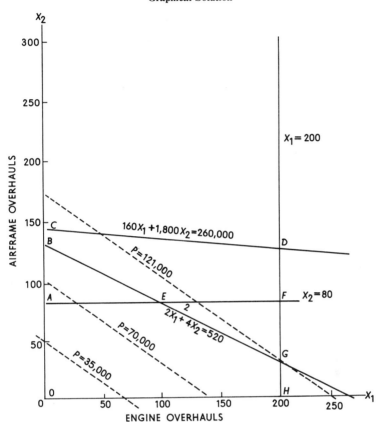

and \$121,000. As the profit increases its representation as an iso-profit line moves farther from the origin. All profit lines are parallel to each other. With no constraints, the optimum solution would be to move the iso-profit line infinitely far from the origin. In the constrained problem we want to move the line as far from the origin as possible such that at least one point on that line falls within our feasible solution space. The line

$$500X_1 + 700X_2 = 121,000$$

satisfies the requirement. The optimal solution occurs at vertex G of our feasible solution space; that is a maximum profit of \$121,000 for

$$X_1 = 200$$
$$X_2 = 30$$

From Figure 13–2 it is easy to see that the optimum solution will always occur at a vertex or extreme point of the set of feasible solutions. This is the key to all linear programming problems. In two dimensions, the extreme points of our solution space are determined by the intersection of lines defining the constraints. In problems involving n decision variables (n space) the extreme points are determined by the intersection of hyperplanes defining the constraints. Referring to our example problem, one means of determining the optimum solution would be to determine the coordinates of the extreme points of our solution space polygon, evaluate the profit for each of these sets of coordinates, and pick the largest profit from among those so evaluated. In this fashion, at most a finite number of points will be evaluated as opposed to the infinite number of potential candidates contained in the total solution space. This is basically how most of the popular linear programming algorithms work. They proceed from extreme point to extreme point in the feasible solution space comparing profits at each step, suggesting which extreme point to examine next, and giving a test for determining when further profit improvement is impossible. In that sense the simplex procedure which we will discuss offers an efficient search routine among extreme point solutions. Extreme point solutions are called basic solutions.

In our sample problem the candidates for an optimum solution are (0, 0), (200, 0), (200, 30), (100, 80), and (0, 80). The profit associated with each of these sets is given below:

X_1	X_2	$Profit = 500X_1 + 700X_2$
0	0	0
200	0	$100,000
200	30	121,000
100	80	106,000
0	80	56,000

The coordinates used were obtained by solving the constraining equations as equalities in groups of two. For example the point (200, 30) comes from the simultaneous solution of

$$2X_1 + 4X_2 = 520$$

$$X_1 = 200$$

We will refer to this extreme point solution as a basic feasible solution. The intersection of $2X_1 + 4X_2 = 520$ with $X_2 = 0$ is a basic solution but is not a basic feasible solution since the point $X_1 = 260$ falls outside our feasible solution space.

Mathematical Preliminaries.   The success of linear programming algorithms at providing efficient search procedures depends upon several theorems from linear algebra. The interested reader is urged to consult the text by Carr and Howe for a brief but rigorous discussion of these theorems.[10] We will mention only a few of the major implications of these theorems.

All of the restrictions in our standard linear programming format are in the form of weak linear inequalities. Each such inequality specifies a closed half-space. In two dimensions for example, the weak inequality

$$3X_1 + 4X_2 \leq 12$$

divides the X_1X_2 plane into two sets of points. The points in this two-space falling on and to the left of the line

$$3X_1 + 4X_2 = 12$$

constitute a closed half-space. It is closed because the set includes those points on the boundary. If we add two nonnegativity restraints we further divide the X_1X_2 plane into identifiable regions. The intersection of the three closed half-spaces defined by

$$3X_1 + 4X_2 \leq 12$$

$$X_1 \geq 0$$

$$X_2 \geq 0$$

is represented by the cross-hatched area in Figure 13–3. This could be taken as the area of feasible solutions for a linear programming problem with the given constraints.

When we have n variables in our weak linear inequalities, we are defining closed half-spaces in n space by means of hyperplanes rather than straight lines. In linear programming problems it is the intersection of these closed half-spaces which constitutes the set of feasible solutions. A theorem of primary importance to linear programming tells us that a closed half-space is a convex set. Convexity in n space means that the line segment joining any two points in the convex set will lie wholly within the set. Symbolically, if the points p and q have coordinates $(p_1, p_2, \ldots, p_n)$ and $(q_1, q_2, \ldots, q_n)$, the coordinates of points x on the line segment are given by the set

$$x_1 = ap_1 + (1 - a)q_1$$

$$x_2 = ap_2 + (1 - a)q_2$$

$$\vdots$$

$$x_n = ap_n + (1 - a)q_n$$

where "a" is a parameter such that $0 \leq a \leq 1$. Here, for example, if $a = 0$, x is the point q. If $a = 1$, x is the point p. If $0 < a < 1$, x is a linear combination of p and q.

---

[10] Charles R. Carr and Charles W. Howe, *Quantitative Decision Procedures in Management and Economics* (New York: McGraw-Hill Book Co., Inc., 1964), pp. 183–211.

FIGURE 13–3

The Intersection of Closed Half-Spaces

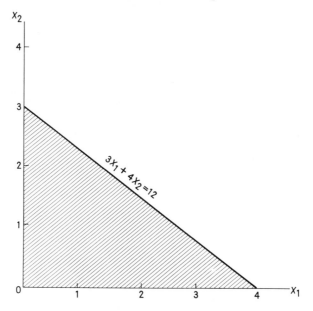

$3X_1 + 4X_2 = 12$

A second theorem of major importance tells us that the intersection of a finite number of closed half-spaces is a closed convex set having a finite number of extreme points. Any point in n space which satisfies all of the restriction inequalities will be called a feasible solution. The extreme points of the feasible solution space constitute basic feasible solutions. These are the ones to be evaluated in establishing the optimum since due to the closed convex shape of the space, the optimum will always occur at an extreme point. The simplex procedure starts at some basic feasible solution and moves only to other basic feasible solutions, or extreme points, while guiding us to solutions which are better in the sense of increasing the value of our criterion function.

Solution of Simultaneous Equations.   In the process of performing the simplex calculations we will do the same type of matrix reduction used in Gauss-Jordan elimination. This is the procedure often used to solve sets of simultaneous linear equations. For example consider the solution to the following set of equations:

$$3X_1 + 4X_2 + X_3 = 12$$

$$2X_1 + 3X_2 + X_3 = 6$$

$$X_1 + X_2 + X_3 = 6$$

The coefficients of the X_i values and the constants can be listed in an array called the augmented coefficient matrix as

$$
\begin{array}{ccc|c}
3 & 4 & 1 & 12 \\
2 & 3 & 1 & 6 \\
1 & 1 & 1 & 6
\end{array}
$$

Since the first line represents an equation, the system will not be affected by dividing that line through by a constant. We want a one in the upper left-hand corner and hence will divide the first row by three. The following array is equivalent to the first:

$$
\begin{array}{ccc|c}
1 & \frac{4}{3} & \frac{1}{3} & 4 \\
2 & 3 & 1 & 6 \\
1 & 1 & 1 & 6
\end{array}
$$

By subtracting the first from the third row and by multiplying the first row by two then subtracting from the second, we can eliminate X_1 from the second and third equations. That is,

$$
\begin{array}{ccc|c}
1 & \frac{4}{3} & \frac{1}{3} & 4 \\
0 & \frac{1}{3} & \frac{1}{3} & -2 \\
0 & -\frac{1}{3} & \frac{2}{3} & 2
\end{array}
$$

Next we can add row two to row three, multiply the second row by 3, and subtract four thirds times that result from the first row to get

$$
\begin{array}{ccc|c}
1 & 0 & -1 & 12 \\
0 & 1 & 1 & -6 \\
0 & 0 & 1 & 0
\end{array}
$$

Finally, by subtracting row three from row two and adding it to row one, we obtain

$$
\begin{array}{ccc|c}
1 & 0 & 0 & 12 \\
0 & 1 & 0 & -6 \\
0 & 0 & 1 & 0
\end{array}
$$

This matrix, with ones on the main diagonal and zeroes elsewhere in the coefficient portion, is said to be in canonical form. Converting to our original equation format from this reduced matrix shows that the solution is

$$
X_1 = 12 \\
X_2 = -6 \\
X_3 = 0
$$

Although this method is reasonably efficient for hand calculation, authors such as Gass use matrix inversion to accomplish the same ends.[11] Matrix

[11] Saul I. Gass, *Linear Programming* (2d ed.; New York: McGraw-Hill Book Co., Inc., 1964).

inversion is particularly useful when seeking computer solutions since this is an operation easily programmed for the digital computer.

Gauss-Jordan elimination has been introduced in the context of a system of linear equations to be solved simultaneously. The linear programming problem on the other hand involves the solution of a system of inequalities representing the constraining factors. In order to facilitate the calculation it is desirable to convert the system of inequalities to equalities. This is accomplished by means of "slack" variables.

In the general linear programming problem statement, Equation 13–17, the set of constraints to be satisfied were

$$A_{11}X_1 + A_{12}X_2 + \cdots + A_{1n}X_n \leq b_1$$

$$A_{21}X_2 + A_{22}X_2 + \cdots + A_{2n}X_n \leq b_2$$

$$\vdots$$

$$A_{m1}X_1 + A_{m2}X_2 + \cdots + A_{mn}X_n \leq b_m$$

The parameter b_i represents the total amount of resource i available for use. The coefficient A_{ij} represents the amount of resource i consumed by one unit of item j. The decision variable X_j represents the number of units of item j to be generated. Row i of this set of inequalities can be converted to an equality by adding a new nonnegative decision variable X_{n+i}. That is,

$$A_{i1}X_1 + A_{i2}X_2 + \cdots + A_{in}X_n \leq b_i$$

is converted to

$$A_{i1}X_1 + A_{i2}X_2 + \cdots + A_{in}X_n + X_{n+1} = b_i$$

The physical interpretation of the variable X_{n+i} is that it represents the amount of resource i which is unused when particular values are assigned to the variables $\{X_j\}$. The revised problem statement is to select nonnegative values for the decision variables $(X_1, X_2, \ldots, X_n, X_{n+1}, \ldots, X_{n+m})$ so as to

maximize $\qquad C_1X_1 + C_2X_2 + \cdots + C_nX_n$ $\qquad\qquad$ (13–19)

subject to $\qquad A_{11}X_1 + A_{12}X_2 + \cdots + A_{1n}X_n + X_{n+1} = b_1$

$$A_{21}X_1 + A_{22}X_2 + \cdots + A_{2n}X_n + X_{n+2} = b_2$$

$$A_{m1}X_1 + A_{m2}X_2 + \cdots + A_{mn}X_n + X_{n+m} = b_m$$

We will refer to this as the augmented form. The contribution of a slack variable is generally assumed to be zero and hence does not appear in the criterion function.

The augmented form of the aircraft maintenance problem, Equation 13–18, is

maximize $\qquad\qquad\qquad 500X_1 + 700X_2$

subject to $\qquad 2X_1 + 4X_2 + X_3 = 520 \qquad\qquad\qquad$ (13–20)

$$160X_1 + 1{,}800X_2 + X_4 = 260{,}000$$

$$X_1 + X_5 = 200$$

$$X_2 + X_6 = 80$$

where the variables (X_3, X_4, X_5, X_6) are slack variables. Recall that the optimum solution to this problem is $(X_1 = 200, X_2 = 30)$. From the restraining equations above it follows that the optimum values of the slack variables must be

$$X_3 = 0$$

$$X_4 = 174{,}000$$

$$X_5 = 0$$

$$X_6 = 50$$

The fact that $X_3 = 0$ tells us that all of the 520 man-weeks of mechanic time in the system have been used in the optimum solution. Similarly $X_5 = 0$ tells us that the 200 available engines will all be overhauled if we behave optimally. On the other hand $X_6 = 50$ implies that 50 of the potential 80 airframe overhauls will not be performed under an optimal policy. There are 50 units of "slack" in the potential overhaul resource. Likewise $X_4 = 174{,}000$ implies that the area-week resource is underutilized by that amount with an optimal policy.

Note the character of the set of Equations 13–20. We have four equations containing six variables to be solved simultaneously. From basic algebra we know that it takes n independent equations to uniquely determine values for n variables. Here we are faced with the prospect of determining $n + m$ variables from a set of m equations. Whenever the number of decision variables exceeds the number of independent equations involved, we will refer to it as an underdetermined set of linear equations.

Such a set of underdetermined linear equations does not possess a unique solution. However, we can obtain a particular solution by arbitrarily assigning n of the variables the value zero and solving the resulting set of m equations in m unknowns by the usual techniques of linear algebra. Such a solution which yields no more than m nonzero X_i's is called a basic solution. When we impose the additional restriction that the X_i's obtained be nonnegative, we have a basic feasible solution. The m nonzero variables in the solution are called basic variables. Recall from our earlier discussion that the maximum value of our criterion function will appear at an extreme point of solution space or equivalently at a basic feasible solution. To optimize we must examine the value of the criterion function for a series of basic feasible solutions and choose the maximum.

The Simplex Procedure

Let us introduce the simplex procedure by considering the simple aircraft maintenance problem shown in augmented form in Equation 13–20. The matrix of coefficients and constants in the restriction equations appears as

X_1	X_2	X_3	X_4	X_5	X_6	b_i	
2	4	1	0	0	0	520	
160	1,800	0	1	0	0	260,000	(13–21)
1	0	0	0	1	0	200	
0	1	0	0	0	1	80	

An initial basic feasible solution to this set of equations is readily apparent from the last five columns of the array. Since we have four equations in six unknowns we will arbitrarily assign the variables X_1 and X_2 the value zero. The last five columns then represent four equations in four unknowns which are already in canonical form. Our initial basic feasible solution is then $X_1 = 0$, $X_2 = 0$, $X_3 = 520$, $X_4 = 260,000$, $X_5 = 200$, $X_6 = 80$. The variables with nonzero values are called basic variables. The physical interpretation of this solution is that no engines or airframes are to be overhauled and that all of our resources will be idle. Graphically, this solution appears at the origin of Figure 13–2. Since our criterion function contains only X_1 and X_2, the value of this solution is obviously zero.

The next step is to develop a second basic feasible solution which will give us a larger value for the criterion function. For a solution to qualify as a nondegenerate basic feasible solution, it must contain exactly m, or in this case four, positive X_i.[12] We can select a new set of four basic variables by assigning a positive value to one of the variables currently set at zero and removing from the basis one of the current basic variables. The selection of the variable to be brought into the basis and the variable to leave the basis is the heart of the simplex procedure.

To facilitate these calculations, let us add several rows and columns to our restriction equation array 13–21. The top row of the revised array represents the criterion function. Its entries are the coefficients of the X_i in our profit expression. The row identified as z_j represents the cost part of the criterion for each variable. The row identified as $C_j - z_j$ represents the values of the simplex criterion for each variable. The two columns on the right are for bookkeeping convenience. The column headed " Basis " identifies which of the variables are currently assigned nonzero values, and the C_j column gives the contribution of each unit of the basic variables to the

---

[12] Degeneracy occurs when we have a basic feasible solution with less than m positive X_i. This case requires additional computation.

criterion function. The element at the intersection of the b_i column and z_j row is the current value of the criterion function. The total array is referred to as a simplex tableau:

X_1 500	X_2 700	X_3 0	X_4 0	X_5 0	X_6 0	b_i	Basis	C_j
2	4	1	0	0	0	520	X_3	0
160	1,800	0	1	0	0	260,000	X_4	0
1	0	0	0	1	0	200	X_5	0
0	1	0	0	0	1	80	X_6	0
0	0	0	0	0	0	(0)		z_j
500	700	0	0	0	0			$C_j - z_j$

$$(13\text{--}22)$$

Now consider each column in the main body of the simplex tableau to be a vector in n space. For example, the vertical array in column two of our sample problem

$$P_2 = \begin{pmatrix} 4 \\ 1,800 \\ 0 \\ 1 \end{pmatrix}$$

can be viewed as a vector in four-space. Columns 3, 4, 5, and 6 are independent vectors in four-space in that none of them can be expressed as a linear combination of other members of the set. Four such independent vectors in four-space are said to form a basis and span that space. This means that any four-dimensional vector not in the basis can be represented as a linear combination of the basis vectors in the spanning set. We can construct vector P_2, for example, by the following linear combination of vectors P_3, P_4, P_5, and P_6

$$4P_3 + 1,800P_4 + 0P_5 + 1P_6 = P_2 \qquad (13\text{--}23)$$

or

$$4\begin{pmatrix} 1 \\ 0 \\ 0 \\ 0 \end{pmatrix} + 1,800\begin{pmatrix} 0 \\ 1 \\ 0 \\ 0 \end{pmatrix} + 0\begin{pmatrix} 0 \\ 0 \\ 1 \\ 0 \end{pmatrix} + 1\begin{pmatrix} 0 \\ 0 \\ 0 \\ 1 \end{pmatrix} = \begin{pmatrix} 4 \\ 1,800 \\ 0 \\ 1 \end{pmatrix}$$

Suppose that we wish to obtain a new solution to our problem which contains the variable X_2 as well as the present basic variables X_3, X_4, X_5, and X_6. The existing solution can be written in terms of the basic vectors and the constant vector P_0 as

$$P_3X_3 + P_4X_4 + P_5X_5 + P_6X_6 = P_0 \qquad (13\text{-}24)$$

or

$$\begin{pmatrix} 1 \\ 0 \\ 0 \\ 0 \end{pmatrix} 520 + \begin{pmatrix} 0 \\ 1 \\ 0 \\ 0 \end{pmatrix} 260,00 + \begin{pmatrix} 1 \\ 0 \\ 1 \\ 1 \end{pmatrix} 200 + \begin{pmatrix} 1 \\ 0 \\ 0 \\ 1 \end{pmatrix} 80 = \begin{pmatrix} 520 \\ 260,000 \\ 200 \\ 80 \end{pmatrix}$$

This solution has exhausted all of our available resources. If the variable X_2 is to be admitted, the quantities of X_3, X_4, X_5, and X_6 must be reduced to stay within the total resource constraints. Let us refer to the reduced quantity of variable j as X'_j. In order to be feasible the revised solution containing X_2 in addition to the original basic variables must satisfy

$$P_2X_2 + P_3X'_3 + P_4X'_4 + P_5X'_5 + P_6X'_6 = P_0 \qquad (13\text{-}25)$$

From Equation 13–23 we know that the vector P_2 can be represented as a linear combination of the vectors P_3, P_4, P_5, P_6. Multiplying Equation 13–23 by X_2 on both sides yields

$$4X_2P_3 + 1,800X_2P_4 + X_2P_6 = X_2P_2 \qquad (13\text{-}26)$$

By subtracting Equation 13–26 from our original basic feasible solution represented by Equation 13–24, we can obtain explicit expressions for the revised quantities X'_j. That is,

$$P_2X_2 + P_3(520 - 4X_2) + P_4(260,000 - 1,800X_2)$$
$$+ P_5(200 - 0) + P_6(80 - X_2) = P_0 \qquad (13\text{-}27)$$

The solution represented by Equation 13–27 is not basic since it contains nonzero quantities for five variables $(X_2, X_3, X_4, X_5, X_6)$. It will not even be feasible unless all of the variables remain nonnegative. To develop a new basic feasible solution, a value for X_2 must be selected such that one of the current basic variables is driven to zero while none are forced to be negative. For example, if we elect to drive the current value of $X_3 = 520$ to zero, the number of airframes (X_2) which can be admitted is obtained from the coefficient of P_3 in Equation 13–27. That is,

$$X'_3 = 520 - 4X_2 = 0$$

or

$$X_2 = 130$$

However, this is not a feasible solution since an X_2 value of 130 would violate the availability constraint of $X_2 \le 80$. Equivalently this could be viewed as forcing X_6 to take on a negative value to maintain the resource constraints. That is,

$$X'_6 = 80 - X_2 = 80 - 130 = -50$$

which is not a feasible solution for X_6. In selecting the maximum number of airframes (X_2) which we can admit into our solution, we must examine the revised amounts of all basic variables and select that value which forces one current basic variable to zero without violating feasibility requirements. From X_4' we have

$$X_4' = 260,000 - 1,800X_2 = 0$$

or

$$X_2 = 144$$

From X_6' we have

$$X_6' = 80 - X_2 = 0$$

or

$$X_2 = 80$$

The X_5' expression does not contain X_2 and from that point of view X_2 could be infinite. Obviously the binding variable is X_6'. The maximum amount of X_2 which can be admitted is $X_2 = 80$. Our new basic feasible solution contains positive values for the variables X_2, X_3, X_4, and X_5. That is,

$$X_1 = 0$$
$$X_2 = 80$$
$$X_3 = 520 - 4 \times 80 = 200$$
$$X_4 = 260,000 - 1800 \times 80 = 116,000 \tag{13-28}$$
$$X_5 = 200$$
$$X_6 = 0$$

In terms of our graphical solution to this problem we have moved from the origin to the point A in Figure 13–2. If we avoid using solutions already generated, it is possible to generate all possible basic feasible solutions and thus to locate all of the extreme points in the solution space of Figure 13–2 by this same technique.

Let us now examine in general terms what happens to our criterion function by virtue of bringing X_2 into the solution. Let the original value of the criterion function be K_0 and the revised value be K_1. Further suppose that each variable X_j carries a general contribution to profit of C_j per unit. Combining the general form of the profit statement

$$K = C_1X_1 + C_2X_2 + C_3X_3 + C_4X_4 + C_5X_5 + C_6X_6$$

with the X_j' values of our revised solution yields

$$K_1 = C_1(0) + C_2X_2 + C_3(520 - 4X_2) + C_4(260,000 - 1,800X_2)$$
$$\quad + C_5(200) + C_6(80 - X_2)$$
$$\quad = [C_1(0) + C_2(0) + C_3(520) + C_4(260,000) + C_5(200) + C_6(80)]$$
$$\quad + X_2[C_2 - C_3(4) - C_4(1,800) - C_5(0) - C_6(80)]$$
$$\quad = K_0 + X_2[C_2 - z_2] \tag{13-29}$$

When written in this form, the quantity $(C_2 - z_2)$ represents the marginal increase in profit achieved by bringing one unit of X_2 into the solution and making appropriate adjustments in the values of the basic variables to maintain feasibility. Since we want to maximize profit, it is intuitively appealing to bring in as many units as possible of that variable with the largest marginal contribution to profit at each stage. Furthermore we want to stop whenever bringing in any variable would lead to a decrease in our current value of the profit function. This is the simplex criterion.

The calculations of the preceding paragraphs can be summarized in terms of the entries of our initial simplex tableau, Equation 13–22. The z_j entries were obtained by taking the inner products of the C_j and X_j columns. That is,

$$z_j = C_{b1}A_{1j} + C_{b2}A_{2j} + C_{b3}A_{3j} + C_{b4}A_{4j} \qquad (13\text{--}30)$$

Where A_{ij} represents the ith entry in the jth column and C_{bi} represents the contribution of the ith basic variable to the criterion function. For the initial tableau the C_j values and hence the C_{bi} values of all basic variables are zero. Thus the z_j row contains all zeros. The $(C_j - z_j)$ entries were obtained by subtracting z_j values from the contribution to the criterion function of one unit of the variable j. In a sense C_j can be viewed as the gross income from one unit of X_j and z_j can be viewed as the cost of bringing one unit of X_j into the solution at this stage of the calculation.

Since the simplex criterion $(C_j - z_j)$ for X_2 in our sample problem is 700 compared with 500 for X_1 and zero for all other variables, X_2 is the most desirable variable to bring into the solution. This is indicated by circling the X_2 column which is now our key column. The variable leaving the basis is identified by the restriction equation which is most binding on X_2. As previously noted, X_2 is limited to a maximum of 80 by the bottom line in the body of our tableau representing the restriction on airframe overhauls. This means that X_2 replaces X_6 as a basic variable.

The revised values for X_2 and the remaining basic variables are acquired automatically if we employ Gauss-Jordan elimination to obtain a one at the intersection of the key row and column (called the pivot element) and zeros elsewhere in the key column. At this stage in our example we already have the pivot element $A_{42} = 1$ and the element $A_{32} = 0$. To force the element A_{22} to zero we can multiply row 4 by 1,800, subtract the product from row 2, and enter the results in place of the original row 2. This is equivalent to replacing our second restriction equation with a linear combination of the original second and fourth restrictions. The revised equation represented by row 2 appears thus,

$$160X_1 + 0X_2 + 0X_3 + X_4 + 0X_5 - 1,800X_6 = 116,000$$

Since X_4 is now the only basic variable in this equation with a nonzero coefficient, the new line two demonstrates that $X_4 = 116,000$ consistent with Equations 13–28. The element A_{12} is forced to zero by subtracting four times row 4 from row 1. The results of these calculations lead to our second simplex tableau:

X_1	X_2	X_3	X_4	X_5	X_6	b_i	Basis	C_j
500	700	0	0	0	0			
2	0	1	0	0	-4	200	X_3	0
160	0	0	1	0	-1800	116,000	X_4	0
1	0	0	0	1	0	200	X_5	0
0	1	0	0	0	1	80	X_2	700
0	700	0	0	0	700	(56,000)		z_j
500	0	0	0	0	-700			$C_j - z_j$

$$(13\text{–}31)$$

The z_j row is again obtained by successive multiplication and addition of the entries in column j with the entries of the C_j column. For example,

$$z_2 = C_{b1}A_{12} + C_{b2}A_{22} + C_{b3}A_{32} + C_{b4}A_{42}$$
$$= C_3 A_{12} + C_4 A_{22} + C_5 A_{32} + C_2 A_{42}$$
$$= (0)(0) + (0)(0) + (0)(0) + (700)(1) = 700$$

The value of the current solution is obtained by multiplying the number of units for each of the basic variables by the contribution of each to profit and summing. (Recall that any variables not in the basis are currently zero.) That is,

$$\text{Profit} = C_1 X_1 + C_2 X_2 + C_3 X_3 + C_4 X_4 + C_5 X_5 + C_6 X_6$$
$$= (500)(0) + 700(80) + 0(200) + 0(116,000) + 0(200) + 0(0)$$
$$= 56,000$$

In terms of our simplex tableau this is equivalent to taking the inner product of the current b_i and C_j columns. The value of the solution appears at the intersection of column b_i and row z_j.

From the $(C_j - z_j)$ row see that each additional engine overhaul (X_1) which we admit to the solution will provide a net gain of \$500. Each additional unit of the slack variable X_6 will provide a negative gain or a loss of \$700. The variables X_2, X_3, X_4, and X_5 provide neither gain nor loss if admitted. We obviously want to increase the number of engines (X_1) in order to proceed toward the maximum profit solution. The number we can admit is limited by the present reduced restriction equations whose coefficients are given in the rows of the tableau. If row one was the only restriction, we could bring in a maximum of

$$X_1 = 200 \div 2 = 100$$

From row two

$$X_1 = 116,000 \div 160 = 725$$

From row three

$$X_1 = 200$$

From row four, X_1 could be infinite. Row one is therefore the most restrictive. Our new solution is to let $X_1 = 100$. This requires that we remove X_3 from the basis and adjust the value of all other basic variables to maintain feasibility. Following the usual Gauss-Jordan elimination we obtain our third tableau:

X_1 500	X_2 700	X_3 0	X_4 0	X_5 0	X_6 0	b_i	Basis	C_j
1	0	$\frac{1}{2}$	0	0	-2	100	X_1	500
0	0	-80	1	0	$-1,480$	100,000	X_4	0
0	0	$-\frac{1}{2}$	0	1	2	100	X_5	0
0	1	0	0	0	1	80	X_2	700
500	700	250	0	0	-300	(116,000)		z_j
0	0	-250	0	0	300			$C_j - z_j$

$$(13\text{--}32)$$

Note the character of this solution. We have admitted 100 engine overhauls at a net gain of $500 each. This has increased our profit from the previous solution of $56,000 to $56,000 + $500(100) or $116,000 as noted in the tableau. From Figure 13–2 this indicates that we have progressed from vertex A to vertex E of our solution space polygon. Note also that the simplex criterion $(C_j - z_j)$ for the variable X_6 is now positive. Even though on the previous iteration we eliminated X_6 from the basis, at this point our criterion indicates that we could gain $300 for every unit of this slack variable we can admit.

Recall that in order to maintain feasibility, X_6 must be nonnegative. Therefore, the only restrictions to be considered at this point are those shown in lines 3 and 4 of the last tableau. From those restrictions, the maximum amount of X_6 which can be admitted is 50 units controlled by line 3. The variable X_6 now enters the basis and X_5 leaves. Performing the usual elimination calculations around the pivot element A_{36} leads to our final tableau:

X_1 500	X_2 700	X_3 0	X_4 0	X_5 0	X_6 0	b_i	Basis	C_j
1	0	0	0	1	0	200	X_1	500
0	0	-450	1	740	0	174,000	X_4	0
0	0	$-\frac{1}{4}$	0	$\frac{1}{2}$	1	50	X_6	0
0	1	$\frac{1}{4}$	0	$-\frac{1}{2}$	0	30	X_2	700
500	700	175	0	150	0	(121,000)		z_j
0	0	-175	0	-150	0			$C_j - z_j$

$$(13\text{–}33)$$

At this point our simplex criterion tells us that any additional variables brought in will reduce our annual profit. Since $(C_j - z_j) \leq 0$ for all j we have reached the optimum solution. From the b_i and Basis columns we see that

$$X_1 = 200$$
$$X_4 = 174,000$$
$$X_6 = 50$$
$$X_2 = 30$$

for an annual profit of $121,000. This is consistent with our graphical solution of Figure 13–2. We have now progressed to vertex G of our solution polygon.

Step-by-Step Procedure. In the preceding paragraphs we have discussed the solution to a particular linear programming problem. Let us now summarize the techniques employed by listing a step-by-step procedure for carrying out the simplex calculation.

1. Formulate the problem and the objective function in the standard format.[13] That is, find nonnegative values for the X_j's so as to

   maximize $$\sum_{j=1}^{n} C_j X_j$$

   subject to $$\sum_{j=1}^{n} A_{1j} X_j \leq b_1$$
   $$\vdots$$
   $$\sum_{j=1}^{n} A_{mj} X_j \leq b_m$$

2. Develop an initial simplex tableau in the form of Equation 13–22 as the first basic feasible solution. Enter in column C_j the contribution of each slack variable to the criterion function.

---

[13] Techniques for fitting other forms of problem statements into this standard format will be discussed in the next section.

3. Calculate the z_j values by the inner product of columns C_j and j. That is,

$$z_j = \sum_{i=1}^{m} A_{ij} C_{bi}$$

where C_{bi} is the C_j value of the basic variable in row i.

4. Calculate the entries for the simplex criterion row from $(C_j - z_j)$ where C_j is the contribution of the jth variable to the criterion function.

5. Select the column with the largest positive value of $(C_j - z_j)$ as the critical column, say column X_k. In case of ties, pick the column with the lowest index k. If no column has a positive value, the present solution, depicted by column b_i and the associated basic variables, is optimal.

6. Variable X_k is to become a basic variable. Consider only positive A_{ik}. The maximum number of units of X_k which can be admitted to the basis is determined from max $X_k = \min_i(b_i/A_{ik})$ where A_{ik} is the current tableau entry at the intersection of row i and column k and b_i is the current entry for row i under the b_i column. The row in which max X_k occurs is called the critical row, say row c. The basic variable currently associated with that row is the variable to be replaced by X_k in the basis.

7. The intersection of the critical row and critical column is called the pivot element. Reduce the pivot element to one by dividing all elements in row c, including element b_c, by A_{ck}. Enter this row as the new row c in a new tableau. Identify X_k as the basic variable associated with this row.

8. Reduce all other elements in column K to zero by Gauss-Jordan elimination. Enter the results in the new tableau.

9. Repeat steps 3 through 8 for the new tableau.

10. When no further improvement is possible, identify the optimal solution from the final values of the basic variables given in column b_i. The value of this solution is shown by the element at the intersection of column b_i and row z_j.

Special Considerations

Minimization Problems.   Our solution procedure has been phrased in terms of maximizing the criterion function. Often we may be faced with problems in which the measure of performance is cost. In such cases we must adapt our procedure so as to minimize

$$\sum_{j=1}^{n} C_j X_j$$

Recall that $(C_j - z_j)$ represents the marginal contribution of one unit of variable j to the criterion function. If that criterion function is to be minimized rather than maximized, we then want to bring into the basis the variable with the most negative value for $(C_j - z_j)$. This will give us the most rapid decrease in the criterion function. For minimization problems step 5 in our solution procedure should read:

5. Select the column with the most negative value of $(C_j - z_j)$ as the critical column, say column X_k. If no column has a negative value the present solution is optimal.

All other steps in the procedure for minimization problems are identical to those for maximization.

An equivalent means of obtaining the same results is to define a cost expression as negative profit. That is,

minimize

$$\sum_{j=1}^{n} C_j X_j$$

is equivalent to

maximize

$$\sum_{j=1}^{n} -C_j X_j$$

If the criterion function is redefined in this manner, the original solution procedure can be used without alteration.

Reversed Inequalities.   Our standard format for the linear programming problem began with the premise that all restriction inequalities could be written in the form

$$\sum_{j=1}^{n} A_{ij} X_j \leq b_i \tag{13-34}$$

This form of the restriction equation arises whenever we have upper bounds on the resources available to us. For example, in charging a cupola to melt gray iron, the weight of the charge is limited on the upper end by the capacity of the cupola. The sum of weights for the pig iron, scrap, coke, and limestone to be included in the charge cannot exceed that capacity. At the same time it may be desirable to control the physical properties of the resulting melt by insuring a certain minimum level of silicon content. If say three grades of pig iron with varying percentages of silicon content are to be melted with 100 pounds of pure iron and scrap containing 5 percent silicon and we want a product with a minimum of 10 percent silicon content, the restriction would be written as

$$P_1 X_1 + P_2 X_2 + P_3 X_3 + 0.05 X_4 \geq 0.10(X_1 + X_2 + X_3 + X_4 + 100)$$

which reduces to

$$(P_1 - 0.10)X_1 + (P_2 - 0.10)X_2 + (P_3 - 0.10)X_3 - 0.05 X_4 \geq 10 \tag{13-35}$$

The general inequality form for such lower bound restrictions is

$$\sum_{j=1}^{n} A_{ij} X_j \geq b_i \tag{13-36}$$

To make this an equality consistent with our augmented form, it is necessary to subtract a slack variable X_{n+1}. That is,

$$A_{i1}X_1 + A_{i2}X_2 + \cdots + A_{in}X_n - X_{n+1} = b_i \qquad (13\text{-}37)$$

This equation is difficult to use in our simplex procedure since an initial solution involving the slack variable X_{n+1} would not be feasible. For X_{n+1} to be a member of the initial basis, its value must be $(-b_i)$. However, recall that feasibility in the sense of the programming algorithm requires that all variables be nonnegative. For that reason whenever inequalities of the form of Equation 13-36 appear in a problem statement, we will normally add yet another variable X_{n+2} called an artificial variable. The complete restriction equation is then

$$A_{i1}X_1 + A_{i2}X_2 + \cdots + A_{in}X_n - X_{n+1} + X_{n+2} = b_i \qquad (13\text{-}38)$$

The artificial variable X_{n+2} is strictly a computational convenience designed to establish an initial basic feasible solution of $X_{n+2} = b_i$. Although X_{n+2} is a member of the initial basis, it has no physical significance. To guarantee that it will not appear in the optimum solution, X_{n+2} is given an infinite cost in the criterion function. This insures that X_{n+2} will be one of the first variables to leave the basis as we proceed through the simplex algorithm. Once removed from the basis, all artificial variables and their associated tableau columns can be eliminated from future iterations.

Degeneracy. Degeneracy is said to occur whenever we have a basic feasible solution with less than m positive X_j, m being the number of restriction equations in the problem. For example, if an equation of the form ≥ 0 were to appear in a problem statement, the initial basic feasible solution would be degenerate since the artificial variable used in the basis would take the value zero. If this were the case, then the value of a new variable to be admitted to the basis could also be zero, in which case the value of the objective function for both new and old solutions would be the same. For this situation it is conceivable that the simplex procedure we have outlined could repeat a basis and hence keep returning to that basis. The procedure is then said to have cycled, and our computational routine breaks down. During routine calculations under the simplex procedure, degeneracy is reflected by basic solutions with less than m positive decision variables or by more than one row yielding

$$\max X_k = \min_i \left(\frac{b_i}{A_{ik}} \right)$$

If the i is not unique one of the basic variables in the new solution will equal zero.

There are special computational procedures available to resolve the problems of degeneracy. One such technique is described by Dantzig.[14] However,

---

[14] Dantzig, *op. cit.*, pp. 231–36.

Gass notes that only three linear programming problems have been known to cycle and these were artificially constructed to demonstrate the phenomenon.[15] For that reason, the usual procedure is to treat degenerate solutions within the normal framework of the simplex algorithm without incorporating special degeneracy techniques. When degeneracy occurs, that basic variable with zero value is treated as nothing unusual. When ties occur among the restriction rows as the variable to be dropped from the basis is selected, the rule we will follow is to drop the variable with the smallest index i.

Duality. Every linear programming problem has associated with it another linear programming problem called the dual. The original problem in its relation to the dual is called the primal problem. It can be shown that the optimum basic feasible solutions to these problems are such that one can easily be used to obtain solutions to the other. It is often convenient to use the dual to solve a linear programming problem since the dimensions of the original problem may be considerably reduced over the primal formulation. Since duality is a very rich theory with many implications beyond those we are able to discuss in this text, the interested reader is urged to consult one of the advanced programming references listed at the end of this chapter.

In addition to its computational convenience, the solution to the dual problem provides an interesting economic interpretation. The standard linear programming problem as originally posed seeks to allocate scarce resources among competing activities such that a profit function is maximized. In the same manner in which we imputed costs for marginal units of scarce resources by means of Lagrange multipliers, we can determine how much profit is being foregone for lack of additional units of the scarce inputs in our linear programming framework. Duality implies that a solution which maximizes our original criterion function will have associated with it a set of prices for the scarce resources. When these prices are used to value the total supplies of resources, they will give a minimum aggregate value. We will refer to the original problem formulation as the primal problem and to the formulation which seeks to minimize the cost of resources as the dual problem.

Referring to the sample problem posed in Equations 13–18, the primal problem is to

maximize $\qquad\qquad 500X_1 + 700X_2$

subject to $\qquad\qquad 2X_1 + 4X_2 \leq 520$

$$160X_1 + 1{,}800X_2 \leq 260{,}000$$

$$X_1 \leq 200$$

$$X_2 \leq 80$$

$$X_1 \geq 0,\, X_2 \geq 0$$

---

[15] Gass, *op. cit.* p. 63.

The corresponding dual problem is to

minimize $520y_1 + 260{,}000y_2 + 200y_3 + 80y_4$

subject to $2y_1 + 160y_2 + y_3 \geq 500$

$$4y_1 + 1{,}800y_2 + y_4 \geq 700$$

$$y_1, y_2, y_3, y_4 \geq 0$$

Note that the dual has as many variables as the primal has restraints and as many restraints as the primal has variables. This means that it may be possible to reduce the size of the solution effort by judicious choice of the problem to be solved. Fewer restrictions imply fewer potential extreme points to be examined.

Mechanically, the dual problem is formulated as follows:

1. If the primal is a maximization problem, the dual is a minimization problem and vice versa.
2. The coefficients of the primal objective function become the constraint constants of the dual.
3. The constraint constants of the primal become the coefficients of the dual variables in the dual objective function.
4. Coefficients for the dual variables in their restraining equations are obtained from the transpose of the matrix of coefficients for the primal.
5. The inequalities are reversed.

The values of the dual variables can be determined from the last m entries of row z_j in our standard simplex tableau for the special case of the symetric dual. This holds when the last m variables form the initial primal basis and $C_j = 0$ for each of those basic variables. The optimum values of the dual variables for our sample problem are, from tableau 13–13:

$$y_1 = 175, \; y_2 = 0, \; y_3 = 150, \; y_4 = 0$$

In this manner if we elect to solve the dual rather than the primal problem, the conversion back to the original primal variables is automatically taken care of by row z_j in our final solution. Note that this technique only works when our initial simplex tableau has the identity matrix associated with a slack solution appearing on the right side of the tableau. For a detailed discussion of duality the reader is urged to consult Dantzig[16] or Gass.[17]

There is a great deal to know about the simplex method which is not shown here. We have discussed only the essential procedures which will enable us to solve simple problems, although not always in the most efficient manner. The hope is that the reader now possesses a sufficient understanding of the problem structure to permit intelligent use of existing computer packages and to provide a start in comprehending more advanced literature in the area.

---

[16] Dantzig, *op. cit.*, pp. 123–40.
[17] Gass, *op. cit.*, chap. v.

Example. Consider the problem faced by a manufacturer of bronze castings who must determine the mix of raw materials to include in each charge he places in the furnace. Three classes of ingots are available. Class one costs $0.60 per pound and contains 90 percent copper and 10 percent tin. Class two costs $0.55 per pound and contains 80 percent copper, 10 percent tin, and 10 percent lead. Class three costs $0.45 per pound and contains 75 percent copper, 5 percent tin, 15 percent lead, and 5 percent zinc. Casting specifications call for an alloy with a minimum of 78 percent copper, a minimum of 6.7 percent tin, and a maximum of 10 percent lead. The object is to determine the proper melt such that specifications are met at minimum cost.

Note that the quantities of copper, lead, and tin in the final alloy have not been specified but rather their percentages are given. However, the criterion function requires that we minimize cost per pound of alloy. In order to develop specific measures for our restriction equations, let us assume that a fixed amount of alloy, say one pound, is to be produced. If we can minimize the cost of producing one pound, it is a simple matter to scale all decision variables by the factor n if we are required to produce a melt of n pounds. Expressing the copper restriction in terms of the pounds of ingots (X_1, X_2, X_3) necessary to produce one pound of alloy which contains at least 0.78 pounds of copper, we have

$$0.90X_1 + 0.80X_2 + 0.75X_3 \geq 0.78$$

To meet the tin restriction we have

$$0.10X_1 + 0.10X_2 + 0.05X_3 \geq 0.067$$

To meet the lead restriction we have

$$0.10X_2 + 0.15X_3 \leq 0.10$$

A fourth restriction implied by the one pound production quantity is

$$X_1 + X_2 + X_3 = 1.0$$

The complete problem statement is to select nonnegative values for X_1, X_2, and X_3 so as to

minimize $0.60X_1 + 0.55X_2 + 0.45X_3$

subject to $0.90X_1 + 0.80X_2 + 0.75X_3 \geq 0.78$

$$0.10X_1 + 0.10X_2 + 0.05X_3 \geq 0.067$$

$$0.10X_2 + 0.15X_3 \leq 0.10$$

$$X_1 + X_2 + X_3 = 1.0$$

Note that this problem statement involves a minimization and contains inequalities running both directions as well as an equality among the constraints. Several of the techniques of this chapter must be employed to carry out the solution. The equality constraint can be handled by introducing another artificial variable. The optimum blend which produces an alloy costing $0.50 per pound is

$$X_1 = \tfrac{1}{3} \text{ pound}$$

$$X_2 = 0$$

$$X_3 = \tfrac{2}{3} \text{ pound}$$

The reader is urged to verify this result by performing the necessary simplex calculations.

The Transportation Problem

We have previously noted that a very large class of problems can be formulated as linear programming problems. Further we have noted that the simplex method is powerful enough to handle all of these problems. Since the simplex method is a very general approach, it follows that it may not be the most efficient computation method for certain special types of linear programming problems. One such "special" problem for which more efficient algorithms exist is the so-called transportation problem.

Distribution or transportation problems appeared in the literature much earlier than the simplex method. One of the earliest published accounts of a mathematical solution for the transportation problem appeared in 1941.[18] During and after World War II many advances were made in the solution of distribution problems. Authors such as Dantzig, Koopmans, Kuhn, Charnes, and Cooper all contributed to further improvements in computation techniques.

The transportation problem takes its name from the problem faced by the traffic manager of a decentralized company who must determine the most economical means of transporting goods from a number of diverse origins to a number of destinations. However, the form of this problem occurs in a variety of contexts not directly related to transportation. For example, the allocation of goods to be manufactured on a number of different production facilities has the same mathematical structure as the allocation of goods to be shipped from factories to warehouses.

Problem Structure. In the general linear programming problem we were concerned with the allocation of a number of scarce resources among competing demands to optimize a criterion function. It was not unusual to find constraints on money, men, equipment, and materials all present in the same problem. In the transportation problem we have a special subcase in which there is only one commodity we are attempting to control. We have a fixed amount of that single resource, being generated at a variety of sources,

---

[18] Frank L. Hitchcock, "The Distribution of a Product from Several Sources to Numerous Locations," *Journal of Mathematics and Physics*, Vol. XX, 1941, pp. 224–30.

available to us. The problem is to distribute that resource among a number of competing users in the most economical fashion. System balance is assumed in that the total available supply must equal total demand. This restriction is necessary in order to employ the algorithms but causes no difficulty in an inherently unbalanced problem context. If, for example, supply exceeds demand we can create a dummy warehouse with demand sufficient to force system balance. If demand exceeds supply we can create a dummy source to achieve balance.

Mathematically the transportation problem is to find X_{ij} ($i = 1, 2, \ldots, m$; $j = 1, 2, \ldots, n$) in order to

minimize

$$\sum_{i=1}^{m} \sum_{j=1}^{n} C_{ij} X_{ij}$$

subject to

$$\sum_{j=1}^{n} X_{ij} = a_i \qquad \text{for } i = 1, 2, \ldots, m$$

$$\sum_{i=1}^{m} X_{ij} = b_j \qquad \text{for } j = 1, 2, \ldots, n$$

$$X_{ij} \geq 0 \qquad \text{for all } i \text{ and } j \qquad\qquad (13\text{-}39)$$

Suppose that m factories supply n warehouses with a certain product. In this context a_i is the production capacity of factory i, b_j is the demand for the product at warehouse j, C_{ij} is the shipping cost of one unit from i to j, and X_{ij} is the number of units shipped from i to j. This model has feasible solutions only if total supply equals total demand. That is,

$$\sum_{i=1}^{m} a_i = \sum_{j=1}^{n} b_j \qquad\qquad (13\text{-}40)$$

Furthermore, if all a_i and b_j are integers it can be shown that there must exist an optimal solution involving only integers. This avoids the difficulties of the general linear programming problem in which divisibility of resources was assumed. We are in no danger of being asked to ship one half an auto in this framework.

An examination of the constraint equations implied by Equations 13–39 and 13–40 reveals that one of them is redundant. That is,

$$\sum_{i=1}^{m} a_i = \sum_{i=1}^{m} \sum_{j=1}^{n} X_{ij} = \sum_{j=1}^{n} b_j$$

therefore any one of the equations can be derived from the rest of them. The problem statement contains $(m + n)$ linear restriction equations, m for production capacity, and n for demand. However, only $(m + n - 1)$ are linearly independent equations so that a nondegenerate basic feasible solution must have exactly $(m + n - 1)$ nonzero X_{ij} values.

For computational convenience the information contained in the problem statement is usually arranged in a transportation array as follows

Destination

From \ To	1	2	....	n	Supply	
1	C_{11} X_{11}	C_{12} X_{12}		C_{1n} X_{1n}	a_1	
2	C_{21} X_{21}	C_{22} X_{22}		C_{2n} X_{2n}	a_2	(13–41)
Source :					:	
m	C_{n1} X_{n1}	C_{n2} X_{n2}		C_{mn} X_{mn}	a_m	
					Total	
Demand	b_1	b_2	....	b_n	Total	

At any stage of the algorithm, cell (i, j), located at the intersection of row i and column j, contains the cost of shipping from i to j in the upper right-hand corner and the current numerical value assigned to X_{ij} in the main block. Any nonbasic X_{ij} lacks an entry and hence assumes the value zero. As with the simplex method, when degeneracy occurs zero-valued basic variables are indicated by a zero entry with computation carried out in a normal fashion. Each row and each column of the array represents a restriction equation. That is,

row equations: $\sum_{j=1}^{n} X_{ij} = a_i$ $(i = 1, 2, \ldots, m)$

column equations: $\sum_{i=1}^{m} X_{ij} = b_j$ $(j = 1, 2, \ldots, n)$

The criterion function is contained in the sum of all block entry products. That is,

$$\text{Cost} = \sum_{i=1}^{m} \sum_{j=1}^{n} C_{ij} X_{ij}$$

Computational Procedures

Dantzig notes that even though typical linear programs require hand-operated calculators, or for larger problems, high-speed computers, the transportation problem is often best solved by paper and pencil techniques.[19] Simple additions and subtractions are the only calculations required. For a discussion of the theory behind the computation techniques to be discussed the reader is urged to consult more advanced texts such as Dantzig.[20] For the mechanics of carrying out the calculations more elementary texts, such as the one by Metzger, are suggested.[21]

---

[19] Dantzig, *op. cit.*, p. 308.
[20] *Ibid.*, pp. 299–315.
[21] Robert W. Metzger, *Elementary Mathematical Programming* (New York: John Wiley & Sons, Inc., 1958).

The first step in the transportation algorithm is to select an initial set of basic variables. Recall that there are $(m + n - 1)$ independent equations and hence $(m + n - 1)$ nonzero X_{ij} values in a nondegenerate basic feasible solution. There are many ways of making the choice for an initial basis. Among the more popular are the "northwest-corner rule" and "Vogel's approximation method" (VAM).

The Northwest-Corner Rule.   The northwest-corner rule begins at the upper left-hand corner of the array. The maximum number of units possible are assigned to X_{11} consistent with the row and column restrictions. That is,

$$X_{11} = \min(a_1, b_1)$$

The row or column whose capacity has been exhausted is eliminated from further calculation. The available capacity of the remaining row or column involved in determining X_{11} is reduced by that amount. One then moves either horizontally or vertically one square to determine the value of the second basic variable. The direction of the move is governed by whether the row or column at the last assignment was eliminated. If a row restriction was satisfied, the next basic variable occurs in the same column as the previous one. If a column restriction was satisfied, the next basic variable occurs in the same row as the previous one. In the event that a row and column are simultaneously satisfied, the next basic variable with a value zero can come from either the adjacent row or column entry. In that case we have an initial degenerate basic feasible solution.

To illustrate this technique consider the following array:

From \ To	1	2	3	4	a_i
1	[3] 15	[5] 10	[2] 5	[7]	30
2	[4]	[4]	[6] 15	[2]	15
3	[5]	[3]	[4] 5	[5] 5	10
b_j	15	10	25	5	

(13–42)

The maximum number of units which can be assigned to X_{11} is 15 as determined by the demand b_1 at destination one. This reduces the available supply (a_1) at source one from 30 to 15 units. Moving horizontally, the second basic element is X_{12} with an assignment of 10 units. Only 10 can be assigned since demand at destination two $(b_2 = 10)$ is still less than the remaining supply at source one $(a_1^1 = 15)$. The supply at source one is now further reduced to five units. This restricts the third basic variable X_{13} to five units and so forth throughout the matrix as indicated in 13–42. Note that this technique has provided us with the required $(m + n - 1)$ basic variables, six in this case.

Vogel's Approximation Method (VAM). Although the northwest-corner rule always yields a basic feasible solution, it does not utilize any of the available cost information. VAM is a technique designed to give a better initial basic feasible solution in the sense of having a lower value for the criterion function than would normally be expected from the northwest-corner solution. By selecting a lower cost initial solution, the number of iterations of the transportation algorithms necessary to reach an optimal solution can be materially reduced. In fact, VAM will directly yield the optimum solution in many distribution problems.

Vogel's approximation method is based on the use of the arithmetic difference between the two lowest cost elements in each row and column of the transportation array. The detailed steps involved in VAM are summarized below.

1. Calculate for each row and column the difference between the two lowest cost elements in that row or column.
2. Select the row or column with the largest difference. If ties occur select any of the tied vectors.
3. Allocate the maximum number of units possible to the lowest cost cell in that row or column.
4. Eliminate any row or column where the supply or demand is exhausted.
5. Redetermine the differences as necessary, omitting the rows and columns eliminated in step 4.
6. Repeat steps 2 through 5 until all assignments are made.

To illustrate the technique let us apply VAM to the array 13–42 which is reproduced below for convenience:

From \ To	1	2	3	4	a_i	Row Difference
1	5 [3]	[5]	25 [2]	[7]	30	1
2	10 [4]	0 [4]	[6]	5 [2]	15	2
3	[5]	10 [3]	[4]	[5]	10	1
b_j	15	10	25	5		
Column Difference	1	1	2	3		

$$(13\text{–}43)$$

The two lowest cost elements in row one are $C_{11} = 3$, $C_{13} = 2$. The difference $(C_{11} - C_{13} = 1)$ is noted to the right of row one. The two lowest cost elements in column 4 are $C_{34} = 5$ and $C_{24} = 2$. The difference $(C_{34} - C_{24} = 3)$ is entered below column four. Similar calculations are performed for all rows and columns with the results noted in the array above.

The largest difference in the array is 3 associated with column four. The lowest cost element in column four is $C_{24} = 2$. We therefore assign five units to X_{24}, consistent with our restrictions on row two and column four. Column four is now eliminated and the entire cycle is repeated. After recalculating the differences for the reduced array obtained by eliminating column four, the second assignment occurs in column three. Twenty-five units are assigned to element X_{13}. Repeated iterations lead to the total initial basic feasible solution noted in the array. Note that there are only five positive elements in this VAM solution. The solution satisfies all of the constraints but is degenerate. The sixth basic variable has been selected as $X_{22} = 0$ and will be carried in future calculations as though it was positive. Here we are employing the same philosophy used in the simplex method for degeneracy, namely that cycling is unlikely to occur even though we treat X_{22} as a member of the basis.

The Modified Distribution Method (MODI).   Once we have achieved an initial basic feasible solution, by whatever method, we must then determine whether or not improvement is possible by bringing new variables into the basis. One method of identifying potential improvement is the so-called MODI method. MODI is a primal-dual approach, sometimes called the $u - v$ method.

Recall that in carrying out the simplex procedure, z_j values were calculated for each column of the simplex tableau. The variables z_j were shown to be the marginal profit (or cost) of bringing one more unit of item j into the basis. The quantity $C_j - z_j$ then measured the amount by which our criterion function would increase or decrease if one unit of item j was admitted to the basis. The MODI method works essentially the same way. In the context of a transportation problem we seek to establish relative cost figures for each row and column such that the simplex criterion coefficients of the basic variables vanish. The technique is analogous to the use of simplex multipliers employed in the revised simplex method.[22]

Computationally the procedure begins by assigning an arbitrary value, zero in this case, to the index number for one row or column in the transportation array. Relative values for all remaining rows and columns are computed such that the marginal change in the criterion function for all basic variables is zero. Each cell (i, j) in the array can then be evaluated by subtracting the sum of its row and column indices from the cost of shipping one unit from i to j. Cells yielding positive values from this calculation should not be admitted to the basis since that indicates a net increase in operating cost. Cells with negative values are candidates for becoming members of the

---

[22] Dantzig, *op. cit.*, chap. ix.

basis since a negative quantity indicates a decrease in the criterion function. In a minimization problem the cell with the most negative value should be admitted to the basis at each iteration since that is the path yielding the most improvement in the criterion function. When all cells have positive or zero values, no more improvement is possible and an optimal solution has been achieved.

As with the simplex tableau, when a new variable X_{ij} is to be admitted to the basis, a current basic variable must leave to guarantee that we are examining only extreme point solutions. The number of units which can be assigned to an entering basic variable is limited by total supply and demand requirements within its row and column. If we add units to X_{ij} we must subtract a like number from some other current basic variable within the same row and column. When we do, the balance in the row or column of the revised basic variables must be maintained by further additions to another basic variable in the same row or column. The easiest method of bookkeeping to assure that balance is maintained is to establish a path from the cell of a variable about to enter the basis through cells of current basic variables and ultimately back to the new basic variable cell. This closed path moves either horizontally or vertically (never diagonally) making right angle turns only at those cells currently in the basis. Units are alternately added and subtracted at the corners of this path to keep the supply and demand restrictions in balance. The number of units moving around the path is limited by the smallest value of any of the basic variables in the path. Recall that to maintain feasibility no variable can be assigned a negative value.

As an example of this procedure, consider the assignment portion of the array 13–42 reproduced below:

From \ To	1	2	3	4	a_i
1	− 15	10	+ 5		30
2			15		15
3	+ X		− 5	5	10
b_j	15	10	25	5	

Suppose that X_{31} is to be brought into the basis. If we add units to X_{31} then we must reduce the current value of $X_{11} = 15$ to maintain the requirement that $b_1 = 15$ since

$$X_{11} + X_{21} + X_{31} = 15$$

Similarly, having subtracted units from X_{11} we must add the same number to X_{23} or X_{33} to maintain the row balance

$$X_{11} + X_{12} + X_{13} + X_{14} = 30$$

We cannot add them to X_{22} since column two contains only one basic variable. There is no other variable to subtract from in order to maintain column two balance. If we add to X_{13} then we must subtract from X_{23} or X_{33}. Again only one of these variables is a candidate in order to maintain feasibility. Subtracting from X_{33} will achieve the required balance. Examination of the vertices of our closed path indicates that a maximum of five units can be moved without driving any existing basic variable negative. The limit is established by X_{33} which is the variable to leave the basis. The new basic feasible solution is then

From \ To	1	2	3	4	a_i
1	10	10	10		30
2			15		15
3	5			5	10
b_j	15	10	25	5	

The steps in the solution procedure can be summarized as follows:

1. Construct a transportation array with unit shipping costs for shipment from i to j in the upper right-hand corner of cell (i, j). List the supply restriction for source i to the right of row i and the demand restriction for destination j below column j.
2. If total supply is not equal to total demand, add dummy sources or destinations as necessary to achieve balance. Unless conditions of the problem dictate otherwise, shipping costs associated with the dummy are zero.
3. Establish an initial basic feasible solution using the northwest-corner rule or VAM.
4. Select the row (or column) with the largest number of basic variables. Assign that row (or column) an implicit price $u_i = 0$ (or $v_j = 0$). Compute all other row and column prices by applying the following relationship to the basic cells:

$$C_{ij} - u_i - v_j = 0$$

5. Calculate for all nonbasic cells the relative cost factors

$$K_{ij} = C_{ij} - (u_i + v_j)$$

6. If $K_{ij} \geq 0$ for every cell in the array the current solution is optimal. If any $K_{ij} < 0$, select X_{st} to enter the basis where

$$K_{st} = \min_{(ij)} (K_{ij} < 0)$$

7. Assign a number B to X_{st}. Establish a closed path among other basic variables symbolically adjusting those variables alternately by $(-B)$ and $(+B)$. The numerical value of B is the largest numerical value which does not require any basic variables to be negative. Adjust the X_{ij} values at the corners of the closed path by that amount.

8. If two basic variables go to zero during step 7, arbitrarily assign one of them a value ε to indicate that even though degenerate, it is still a member of the basis. The only restriction on the zero basis element is that it must not form a cycle with other basic variables. Carry the value ε through future iterations as though it were a positive number.

9. Return to step 4.

Sample Calculation. To illustrate the above computational procedure, let us consider the array 13–43 which contains an initial degenerate basic feasible solution as determined by VAM. The array is reproduced below complete with an ε assignment for the variable X_{22} to complete the basis.

From \ To	1	2	3	4	a_i	u_i
1	5 $\;^3$	$\;^5$	25 $\;^2$	$\;^7$	30	-1
2	10 $\;^4$	$\varepsilon \;^4$	$\;^6$	5 $\;^2$	15	0
3	$\;^5$	10 $\;^3$	$\;^4$	$\;^5$	10	-1
b_j	15	10	25	5		
v_j	4	4	1	2		

(13-44)

Beginning with step 4, row 2 contains three basic variables (X_{21}, X_{22}, X_{24}) and is selected to receive the implicit price $u_2 = 0$. From the basic variable X_{21}, the price of column one is established as

$$v_1 = C_{21} - u_2 = 4 - 0 = 4$$

In similar fashion, X_{22} and X_{24} yield

$$v_2 = C_{22} - u_2 = 4$$

and

$$v_4 = C_{24} - u_2 = 2$$

Since we have established a price for column one, the implicit price for row one can now be calculated from the basic variable X_{11} as

$$u_1 = C_{11} - v_1 = 3 - 4 = -1$$

Similarly from X_{32} and X_{13} we obtain

$$u_3 = C_{32} - v_2 = 3 - 4 = -1$$

and

$$v_3 = C_{13} - u_1 = 2 - 1 = 1$$

The results of these calculations are summarized on the rim of the array 13–44.

Following step 5 we next calculate the relative cost factors for all nonbasic cells. That is,

$$K_{ij} = C_{ij} - (u_i + v_j)$$

or

$$K_{12} = 5 - (-1 + 4) = 2$$

$$K_{14} = 7 - (-1 + 2) = 6$$

$$K_{23} = 6 - (0 + 1) = 5$$

$$K_{31} = 5 - (-1 + 4) = 2$$

$$K_{33} = 4 - (-1 + 1) = 4$$

$$K_{34} = 5 - (-1 + 2) = 4$$

Since $K_{ij} \geq 0$ for all (i, j) the current solution is optimal and no further calculations are necessary.

Shipping Example. A chain outlet for dryers with stores in Atlanta, Boston, Chicago, and Dallas is supplied from appliance manufacturers in Miami and Los Angeles. Purchase price at the factory is the same for both manufacturers. Shipping charges per dryer between locations are given as follows:

From	To	Charge	From	To	Charge
Miami	Atlanta	$10	Los Angeles	Atlanta	$25
	Boston	15		Boston	40
	Chicago	20		Chicago	16
	Dallas	18		Dallas	12

The Miami plant can furnish a maximum of 3,000 dryers per month. The Los

Angeles plant can furnish up to 4,000 per month. Monthly sales at the outlets are estimated to be

Atlanta . . . .   500 per month
Boston. . . . .1,500 per month
Chicago. . . .2,500 per month
Dallas . . . . .1,000 per month

A quick glance at supply and demand reveals that the factories can produce 7,000 per month but that the outlets can absorb only 5,500 per month. In order to utilize the transportation format, we therefore introduce a "dummy" outlet with a monthly demand for 1,500 units to force a balance between supply and demand. The dummy demand of 1,500 units really represents unused production capacity. The associated shipping costs are therefore zero. The complete array is:

To From	Atlanta	Boston	Chicago	Dallas	Dummy	Supply
Miami	10	15	20	18	0	3,000
Los Angeles	25	40	16	12	0	4,000
Demand	500	1,500	2,500	1,000	1,500	

Following the northwest-corner rule, a basic feasible monthly shipping schedule is

Miami to Atlanta	500	Los Angeles to Chicago	1,500
Miami to Boston	1,500	Los Angeles to Dallas	1,000
Miami to Chicago	1,000	Unused Los Angeles	1,500

The cost of this solution is

$$C = \sum_{i,j} C_{ij} X_{ij} = \$83,500$$

To test for optimality u_i and v_j values are computed from $C_{ij} - (u_i + v_j) = 0$ for basic variables. That is,

$$u_1 = 0 \qquad v_1 = 10$$

$$u_2 = -4 \qquad v_2 = 15$$

$$v_3 = 20$$

$$v_4 = 16$$

$$v_5 = 4$$

The resulting relative cost factor for nonbasic variables are

$$K_{14} = C_{14} - (u_1 + v_4) = 18 - (0 + 16) = 2$$
$$K_{15} = C_{15} - (u_1 + v_5) = 0 - (0 + 4) = -4$$
$$K_{21} = C_{21} - (u_2 + v_1) = 25 - (-4 + 10) = 19$$
$$K_{22} = C_{22} - (u_2 + v_2) = 40 - (-4 + 15) = 29$$

Since K_{15} is less than zero, monthly shipping costs can be reduced by providing idle capacity at Miami. The change in basic variables is noted in the following array by the bracketed quantities:

	Atlanta	Boston	Chicago	Dallas	Dummy	Supply
Miami	500	1,500	(0) 1,000		(1,000)	3,000
Los Angeles			(2,500) 1,500	1,000	(500) 1,500	4,000
Demand	500	1,500	2,500	1,000	1,500	

The value of this solution is

$$C = \sum_{i,j} C_{ij} X_{ij} = \$79,500$$

Note that our cost has been reduced by

$$\$83,500 - \$79,500 = \$4,000$$

in moving from the first to the second solution. This is precisely the amount indicated by our relative cost factor ($K_{15} = -4$) since we added 1,000 units to X_{15} at a relative decrease of $4 each for $4,000 total cost advantage.

Repeating the calculation of relative cost factors based on our last array reveals that all factors are nonnegative. This indicates that the solution shown is optimal. That is,

Ship   500 from Miami   to Atlanta
Ship 1,500 from Miami   to Boston
Ship 2,500 from Los Angeles to Chicago
Ship 1,000 from Los Angeles to Dallas

with Miami and Los Angeles having excess capacity of 1,000 and 500 units per month, respectively.

Special Techniques. Some of the special computational techniques which can be used to force a problem to conform to the transportation format have already been discussed. For example, whenever supply and demand are not in balance we have suggested the addition of a dummy source or user as required to achieve balance. Also whenever degeneracy occurs we have suggested that a basic variable with zero assignment be generated and carried forth throughout future calculations.

In addition to these cases, two other commonly encountered problems should be mentioned. How does one handle a profit maximization problem and how can we prevent assignment of source-destination pairs which are physically impossible? The algorithms we have discussed are based upon the concept of cost minimization. If we have a criterion to be maximized we can either alter our decision criterion concerning which variable to admit to the basis or we can treat the problem as one of minimizing a negative cost. If we alter the decision criterion then we must admit to the basis those variables with the largest *positive* values of $(C_{ij} - u_i - v_j)$. Profit will be maximized when no variable X_{ij} has a positive criterion value. If we elect to treat profit as a measure of negative cost, all cost entries in our array will be prefixed by a minus sign. The calculation then proceeds exactly as outlined for the original transportation problem which seeks to minimize cost.

It is possible that some combinations of source and destination are physically impossible. This might occur when distributing a product if there were no direct connections between cities A and B. It might occur when distributing work loads among personnel if worker W did not have the necessary skills to perform job J. If the measure of performance is cost, the undesirable combination can be eliminated from consideration by assigning an infinitely large cost, say M, to that cell. If profit is the criterion the cell value would be $(-M)$. In either event the number M is treated as an integer and carried throughout the execution as are all other costs or profits. Its very large value insures that it will never appear in the optimal solution.

Other Techniques.   Many other solution techniques in the general area of mathematical programming are available for special problems. For example, we have said nothing about the assignment problem, integer programming techniques, or quadratic programming. That is not to say that they are unimportant but rather that space limitations preclude their discussion in this text. The hope is that with the brief introduction offered by this chapter, the reader may be able to solve simple problems and have sufficient understanding to provide an entree into more advanced literature as the need arises.

SELECTED BIBLIOGRAPHY

CARR, CHARLES R., AND HOWE, CHARLES W. *Quantitative Decision Procedures in Management and Economics.* New York: McGraw-Hill Book Co., Inc. 1964.

DANTZIG, GEORGE B. *Linear Programming and Extensions.* Princeton, N. J.: The Rand Corporation, Princeton University Press, 1963.

GASS, SAUL I. *Linear Programming Methods and Applications*, 2d ed. New York: McGraw-Hill Book Co., Inc., 1964.

GRAVES, ROBERT L., AND WOLFE, PHILIP (eds.). *Recent Advances in Mathematical Programming.* New York McGraw-Hill Book Co., Inc., 1963.

GUE, RONALD L., AND THOMAS, MICHAEL E. *Mathematical Methods in Operations Research.* New York: The Macmillan Co., 1968.

HILLIER, FREDERICK S., AND LIEBERMAN, GERALD J. *Introduction to Operations Research.* San Francisco: Holden-Day, 1967.

METZGER, ROBERT W. *Elementary Mathematical Programming.* New York: John Wiley & Sons, Inc., 1958.

SAATY, THOMAS L. *Mathematical Methods of Operations Research.* New York: McGraw-Hill Book Co., Inc., 1959.

TAYLOR, ANGUS. *Advanced Calculus.* Boston, Mass.: Ginn & Co., 1955.

TEICHROEW, DANIEL. *An Introduction to Management Science.* New York: John Wiley & Sons, Inc., 1964.

PROBLEMS

13–1 Find all of the stationary points for the following function and identify each as a local maximum, local minimum, or neither:

$$f(z_1, z_2, z_3) = 4z_1 z_3 + 5z_1 - 3z_3^2 - 2z_2 - 50e^{-z_2} + 10z_3 - 0.5z_1^3$$

13–2 Consider the expression in Problem 13–1 to be a profit function in which

$z_1 =$ thousands of dollars average inventory

$z_2 =$ units of 10,000 square feet of floor space

$z_3 =$ hours of operation per day

It costs the company $8,000 working capital to maintain a one hour per day production schedule. To impress the public, management requires that space be utilized so that the average value of stock held is at least $8 per square foot. The pool of funds available for production and inventory investment is $30,000.

a) What constraints are implied by this problem?

b) Use Lagrangian techniques to determine an optimum operating policy.

13–3 A perfume manufacturer wants to produce deodorant for both men and women. The sales price per gallon for Eau de Man is $3. Eau de Woman is $5 per gallon. Both use a discontinued mouthwash as the prime ingredient. One hundred gallons of the mouthwash have been provided free by a bankrupt competitor. Each gallon of Man uses 0.9 gallons of mouthwash while Woman uses 0.5 gallons. It costs $0.05Q_w^2$ to produce Q_W gallons of Eau de Woman and $0.20(Q_M)^{3/2}$ to produce Q_M gallons of Eau de Man. The company wants to maximize their profit for disposing of the 100 gallons of mouthwash.

a) Formulate this problem in the standard mathematical programming framework.

b) Determine the optimum production mix.

c) Establish an imputed cost per gallon for mouthwash.

13–4 Fran Tick is considering a number of investment alternatives. Each dollar invested in alternative j will provide a gain of g_j at the end of Fran's planning horizon. The gains (g_j) are random variables. Fran has in his possession estimates for the means (μ_j), variances (σ_j^2), and correlation coefficients (r_{ij}) related to these variables. The *proportion* of available funds to be allocated to alternative j is x_j. Fran has established an aspiration level (a) as the lowest acceptable expected gain per dollar invested in the entire program. Since Fran is quite risk conscious, he has decided to choose the x_j so as to minimize the variance of his actual total gain subject to the limitations of his aspiration level and available funds.

a) Formulate the general criterion function and constraints for this problem as functions of x_j, μ_j, σ_j, r_{ij}, a.

b) By using your knowledge of Lagrangian techniques, determine the optimum policy when

$$\mu_1 = 4.0 \qquad \sigma_1^2 = 16 \qquad r_{12} = 0.4$$

$$\mu_2 = 6.0 \qquad \sigma_2^2 = 25 \qquad a = 5$$

13–5 The Loose Screw Company manufactures a mixture of wood and sheet metal screws. The same automatic screw machine produces both items from bar stock costing $1 per linear foot. Because storage space is very limited, they require that bar stock suppliers replenish their supply every day such that they start the single daily shift with 1,000 feet of stock available. Cost accounting estimates the hourly operating expense on this equipment at $12. Marketing will accept only 12,000 wood screws per day but will take all of the sheet metal screws they can get. One foot of stock will provide 20 wood screws or 10 metal screws. The machine can produce wood screws at a rate of 2,400 per hour and metal screws at a rate of 1,500 per hour. A wood screw sells for $0.25 and a metal screw for $0.30.

a) Construct a model of this system to maximize profit.

b) Represent the solution space graphically.

c) Establish the optimum daily production for each item.

13–6 The Caviar Dog Food Company makes two grades of food. *Profits* on these two grades are:

Nikita $3 per pound
Boris $2 per pound

Average production and sales rates are

Type	Production Rate	Sales Rate
Nikita	100 lbs. per hr.	200 lbs. per hr.
Boris	300 lbs. per hr.	100 lbs. per hr.

A contract with the Bolshevik Trade Union limits production to eight hours per day. Under the latest five-month plan, maximum daily quantities of raw material available limit the maximum amount of food that can be produced in a day to 700 pounds of Nikita and 900 pounds of Boris.

a) Assume that it is desired to maximize total daily profit. Set up the equations which represent the above situation.

b) Represent the solution space graphically. Identify which restrictions are effective.

c) Using graphic techniques, establish the optimum daily production for each type. (Explain how you did it and why it works.)

d) What is the maximum profit?

13–7 The XYZ Corporation has agreed to supply at least 600 pounds of Angelfood (*A*) and 300 pounds of Batfood (*B*) to a local grocery chain. Each pound of *A* requires 0.002 horses, 0.10 chickens, and 0.15 rabbits. Each pound of *B* requires 0.005 horses and 0.40 rabbits. XYZ has 4 horses, 75 chickens, and 400 rabbits in stock. The marginal contribution of each pound of *A* is $0.46 and each pound of *B* is $1.15.

a) Formulate this problem in standard linear programming format.

b) Indicate the solution space graphically.

c) Determine the optimum number of pounds of *A* and *B* to produce.

13–8 Joe College has two final exams to prepare for. Each hour of study he devotes to course "*A*" is expected to return $600 in terms of long-range job benefits. Each hour devoted to course "*B*" is expected to return $300 in terms of long-range benefits. The stores are all closed, and Joe only has 15 cigarettes remaining. He feels the he needs one cigarette every 20 minutes while studying for "*B*" and one every 12 minutes while studying for "*A*." Time is running short, and only four hours remain to prepare for the exams. With the draft board breathing down his neck he figures that he must devote at least two hours to studying. Obviously Joe would like to maximize his returns for effort expended.

a) Formulate this problem in the standard linear programming format.

b) Illustrate the feasible solution space graphically. (Show by crosshatching.)

c) Determine an optimal policy for Joe.

13–9 Consider a moonshiner who manufacturers both white and black lightning. White sells for $5 per gallon, and black sells for $3 per gallon. Each gallon of white lightning contains 0.5 gallons of refined turpentine while black contains 0.9 gallons. The shiner has 100 gallons of turpentine in stock. His operation can produce white lightning at a rate of 10 gallons per hour or black at a rate of 20 gallons per hour. Production costs are $2.50 per gallon for white and $2 per gallon for black. The budget for this run is $300. The shiner can only work eight hours at this task before he must cease operation. He wants to maximize profit by choosing an optimum mix of white and black lightning.

a) Formulate this problem in the standard programming framework.

b) Show the solution space graphically.

c) Find the optimum production mix.

13–10 A lumber company owns two different tracts of woodland from which they log raw material for three grades of pulp. They have a contract with A. W. Fulodor Paper Mills to provide 24 truckloads of Grade *A*, 16 of Grade *B*, and 48 of Grade *C* each week. In an average day's logging in tract No. 1 the lumber company can produce 12 truckloads of *A*, 4 of *B*, and 8 of *C* while in tract No. 2 they can produce 4 of *A*, 4 of *B*, and 24 of *C*. Daily logging costs are $200 in tract No. 1 and $160 in tract No. 2.

a) Write the equations defining this problem.

b) Determine the optimum logging policy.

13–11   A machine shop has capability of turning, drilling, milling, and welding. The machine capacity is 16 hours per day in turning, 16 hours per day in milling, and 16 hours per day for welding and drilling. (The same operator performs both welding and drilling.) The following amounts of machine time are required for pipe tampers and nut crackers:

	Tampers	Crackers
Turning	10 min.	5 min.
Milling	12	8
Drilling	2	4
Welding	8	6

Tampers yield a profit of $2.50 per unit, and crackers yield $3 per unit.

a) Formulate this as a general linear program problem.

b) Determine the optimum quantity of each by both graphic and simplex procedures.

13–12   The following information is known about four products and three raw materials:

Material	Requirements per Unit of Products (Pounds)			
	Product 1	Product 2	Product 3	Product 4
1	3	2	3	0
2	2	2	4	0
3	0	1	3	4

Material Available	Cost of Manufacture
Material 1.... 66 lbs.	Product 1.....$3.00
Material 2.... 33 lbs.	Product 2..... 2.25
Material 3.... 44 lbs.	Product 3..... 3.75
	Product 4..... 3.25

a) Formulate a mathematical statement for this problem.

b) Determine the optimum production quantities.

13–13   A local black-market operator is engaged in bootlegging copies of the Autumn Quarter 842 exam. He operates from a briefcase that can hold 300 exams. Each month he can sell any number he chooses up to his stock available at the beginning of the month. Each month he can bribe a student assistant for copies to be delivered at the end of the month. For the next four months, after which he goes to Fort Lauderdale, he has the following error-free forecast of costs and sales prices:

Month	i	1	2	3	4
Cost per exam	c_i	10	12	8	9
Sales price per exam	p_i	18	13	7	12

In addition to the purchase price, our merchant must pay protection money of $0.10 per copy for the average of the stock at the first of the month and the stock immediately before delivery at the end of the month. He currently (at the beginning of month 1) has 100 exams in stock.

a) Formulate this as a linear programming problem for determining his optimal policy. (Let x_i be the quantity purchased and y_i the quantity sold in month i.)

b) Formulate the *dual* for this problem.

13–14 A local hippie can sell all of the sunflower seeds, bananas, and cornsilk he can grow. He can obtain 19 cents a flower for sunflowers, 10 cents a peel for bananas, and 25 cents a husk for cornsilk. The average yield per acre is 2,000 sunflowers, 3,000 banana peels, or 1,000 husks. Fertilizer is available at 10 cents per word, and the amount of fertilizer required per acre is 100 words for sunflowers and bananas and 50 words for cornsilk. Labor required for chanting, marching, and harvesting per acre is five flower-people-days for sunflowers and cornsilk and six flower-people-days for bananas. The hippie farm consists of 100 acres. A total of 80 flower-people are available for 5 days at $20 each per day to perform the necessary labor.

a) Formulate this as an LP model.

b) Use the simplex method to determine what action the hippie should take. (Neglect other costs such as cost of seeds, protection, etc.)

c) Additional labor can be obtained at a 25 percent premium. Should he use this premium cost labor? If yes, how much and for what?

13–15 Consider the following table of transportation costs and requirements:

Warehouses / Factories	A	B	C	D	E	Capacity
X	0.37	0.27	0.28	0.34	0.31	100
Y	0.29	0.31	0.32	0.27	0.29	125
Z	0.33	0.26	0.35	0.30	0.30	150
Demand	50	60	70	80	90	

a) Set up a *simplex tableau* for this problem and identify your initial basic feasible solution. Properly identify all vectors in the format used in class, i.e., $C_j - z_j$ form.

b) The following shipping schedule has been identified as a candidate for the optimum solution:

$$XB = 5 \qquad YA = 50 \qquad ZB = 55$$
$$XC = 70 \qquad YD = 75 \qquad ZD = 5$$
$$ZE = 90$$

Prove whether or not this solution is in fact optimal. Show all calculations.

13–16   Inverted Airlines, the carrier for upset passengers, has been chartered to transport 700 fans to the Super Bowl game. Inverted employs 60 persons, who double as pilots and stewardesses, to man their fleet of Screaming Jets and Wobbley Props. The jets can make the trip with 65 passengers and a crew of 5 at a cost of $9,000. The props carry 30 passengers and a crew of 3 at a cost of $5,000 for the trip. The question to be answered is how many of each aicraft should be allocated for the trip.

a) Structure the problem in the standard LP format.
b) Solve the problem graphically and by the simplex procedure.
c) If your solution is not integer valued, determine the optimum integer solution.

13–17   Harry's Hash Houses provide exclusive lunch service for two local industries. Harry has four locations, *N*, *S*, *E*, and *W*. *N* can cater four, *S* can cater six, *E* can cater five, and *W* can cater eight luncheons per day. Industry *A* has 8 departmental luncheons, and *B* has 12 departmental luncheons each day. After all expenses are paid, Harry estimates his clear daily profit for various combinations of locations serving industries as follows:

$$AN = \$9 \qquad AS = \$21 \qquad AE = \$9 \qquad AW = \$10$$
$$BN = \$15 \qquad BS = \$20 \qquad BE = \$12 \qquad BW = \$8$$

a) Formulate this problem in a standard LP format.
b) Develop the matrix necessary to present this as a transportation problem.
c) Determine an initial solution to part (*b*) by the "northwest-corner rule."
d) Use Modi to achieve an optimum solution.

13–18   Companies X, Y, and Z are interviewing on campus for arts majors, business organization majors, and engineers to fill positions in a government training program. Company X refuses to hire arts majors as a matter of principle. The costs associated with training each student in each company are shown below (in thousands of dollars):

	X	Y	Z
Arts	—	10	9
B.O.	8	7	9
Engineers	5	6	8

Company X must have 15 trainees, Y must have 6 trainees, and Z must have 4 trainees. Ten students from each college are on the interview schedule. The goal is to properly place students with companies such that the total training cost is minimized.

a) Place this problem in a linear programming format suitable for solution by the simplex procedure, i.e., write the mathematical statements necessary.

b) Place this problem in the proper format for solution as a "transportation" problem, i.e., set up the complete matrix with proper entries.

c) Determine an initial feasible solution for your transportation formulation using Vogel's approximation method.

d) Prove whether or not your VAM solution is optimal.

13–19 A contractor has agreed to supply an arsenel with nerveless wardheads to be delivered in April and May. He must supply 120 warheads in April and 180 in May. Using an eight-hour shift the contractor can produce only 140 assemblies each month. However, by hiring protest pickets from in front of the plant at regular pay scale for two hours overtime each day, an additional 20 warheads per month can be made. The increase in cost for the additional units is $18 per warhead. Since large groups of warheads get too much nerve, DOA policy limits their storage by the contractor to a maximum of 30 units. Storage costs the contractor $4 per head per month. Each month has 21 workdays.

a) Set up a standard L.P. model to find a construction program which minimizes contractor costs.

b) Set up the dual to this problem. Explain the meaning of each variable.

c) Structure this problem as a transportation problem (assume no storage restriction) and check a solution, which requires manufacturing 150 warheads each month, for optimality.

13–20 The Illicit Drug Company manufactures aspirin, barbituates, and codeine. Demand for each of these products over a three-week period is as follows:

	a	b	c
Week 1	70 boxes	50 bottles	40 bags
Week 2	90	80	60
Week 3	100	120	110

It requires 48 man-minutes to manufacture a box of aspirin, 1 man-hour for a bottle of barbituates, and 30 man-minutes for a bag of codeine. Each product may be manufactured on regular or overtime. Available man-hours during the next three weeks are:

	Regular Time	Overtime
Week 1	160	160
Week 2	80	80
Week 3	120	80

Storing one box, bottle, or bag from one week to the next requires that lockers be rented at the following rates:

    i) $0.10 per box   *ii*) $0.50 per bottle   *iii*) $0.40 per bag

The overtime penalty, expressed in *dollars per hour*, for all products is $0.80. The company wants an optimum production schedule.

    a) Formulate this as a transportation problem.

    b) Find an initial feasible solution using Vogel's approximation method.

    c) Establish the optimum schedule.

13–21   The XYZ Corporation is faced with the problem of moving go-carts from factories in Atlanta (A), Baltimore (B), and Chicago (C) to retail outlets in Detroit (D) and Elyria (E). Mileages between cities are estimated to be

$$A \text{ to } D = 900 \text{ miles}$$
$$A \text{ to } E = 800 \text{ miles}$$
$$B \text{ to } D = 650 \text{ miles}$$
$$B \text{ to } E = 500 \text{ miles}$$
$$C \text{ to } D = 320 \text{ miles}$$
$$C \text{ to } E = 450 \text{ miles}$$

Since the trip is hard on go-cart drivers, XYZ wants to hold mileage traveled to a minimum. The number of carts per month available from Atlanta $= 20$, Baltimore $= 24$, and Chicago $= 16$. Retail demands in Detroit are estimated to be 30 carts and in Elyria 20 carts per month. Because of some nonunion labor used in Atlanta, the Elyria outlet refuses to handle carts from that source.

    a) Set up the equations describing this situation as a linear programming problem.

    b) Set up an appropriate matrix identifying all elements as a transportation problem.

    c) Determine an initial feasible solution using the northwest-corner rule. Find an optimum solution by Modi.

CHAPTER 14

Scheduling Techniques

Introduction

COORDINATION of activities is an important function of management at all levels. Decisions must be made concerning the synchronization of complex sets of events, the sequence in which events should be ordered, and the assignment of resources to tasks. A number of quantitative tools designed to promote rational and sometimes optimal decisions in these areas have appeared in recent years. They appear under a variety of titles, including job shop scheduling, sequencing, and critical path methods. For our purposes, the single term "scheduling" will be used to denote this very broad class of coordination problems.

The pervasive nature of scheduling problems can be illustrated by considering some examples. The production foreman in a job shop must decide which of several waiting jobs should be processed first on each of several pieces of equipment. The jobs may have a well-defined order which they must follow from machine to machine. The foreman would like to schedule the jobs such that due dates are met, costs are minimized, or machine utilization maximized. A general superintendent on a large construction project must coordinate the arrival of men and materials at the proper points in time to insure that construction proceeds on schedule with a minimum of idle time. Care must be exercised to see that pipes and wiring are installed before interior walls, that finish carpentry work is done before painting, etc. The tower operator at a large airport must establish a proper sequence for landing aircraft such that delays are minimized, safety standards are met, and reasonable runway utilization is achieved. Each of these diverse activities has the same basic problem of efficient ordering of resources and events in time. This we take to be the essence of the scheduling problem.

545

The scheduling-type problems of concern to us in this chapter are routinely resolved in the daily operations of existing systems. The parts do get machined, the buildings do get constructed, and the aircraft do land without benefit of elegant mathematical analysis. However, this does not mean that the tasks are always performed in an efficient manner. It is the purpose of this chapter to introduce some useful techniques to improve upon system efficiency.

Although there have been many years of effort devoted to the development of scheduling aids, the reader will soon become painfully aware that the state-of-the-art still leaves something to be desired. Sophistication of the models ranges from the visual aid of Gantt charts through the complex equations of priority queueing models. Since scheduling problems are inherently difficult, even the complicated models for optimization can capture only simplified versions of most systems. However, by attempting to structure a model of a scheduling system even if optimization cannot be achieved, the operations engineer and management are better able to understand interrelationships among activities and be more orderly in their decision making. The value of activity structuring is recognized by the federal government who now requires that most potential research and development contractors submit PERT charts depicting the manner in which proposed projects will be executed.

Classical Methods.

The Gantt Chart.   One of the earliest attempts to offer modeling assistance for complex planning and scheduling problems was made by Henry L. Gantt during World War I. Gantt was concerned with mass production and large-scale training and procurement programs. The techniques he developed are still widely used by production scheduling departments, procurement offices, development project leaders, and many others. In each of these areas, management must allocate limited available resources to competing activities in order to achieve desired output. In addition to planning for the best use of facilities, management must control the system to see that plans are properly executed. The Gantt chart is a device used to assist in these functions.

Gantt charts are extremely simple graphic models. They display load and work progress for activities, equipment, or orders as a function of time. The usual form consists of a series of bars displayed horizontally on a time axis. Two lines are commonly reserved for each activity scheduled. One shows the work planned and the other shows the work completed. The addition of a vertical line or identifier which is moved with the elapse of calendar time provides at a glance the status of activities. Some may be ahead of schedule, and others behind. By bringing this to the attention of management, resources may be shifted or added to bring the project nearer to the planned schedule. In this way they strengthen the control function.

In the planning stage, allocation of available time is accomplished by trial and error. The times for the tasks to be performed are juggled among available capacities until a feasible solution is found. Traditionally, this is accomplished by manual manipulation, although in some instances computers have been used to search for feasible solutions.

Example.   Figure 14–1 illustrates a Gantt chart for order processing in a job shop producing bronze bushings and bearings. This particular chart is based upon a one-month scheduling period. The open bars represent scheduled time for each order. The solid bars represent work completed. The numbers in each bar identify the department in which the work is being performed. The *V* symbol identifies the current calendar date. From the chart it is readily apparent that order 7137 is behind schedule by three days in the machine shop. Order 7138 has been completed ahead of schedule. Order 7139 currently in clean-up is one day ahead of schedule. Order 7140 should begin in the pattern shop in two days.

FIGURE 14–1

A Gantt Chart

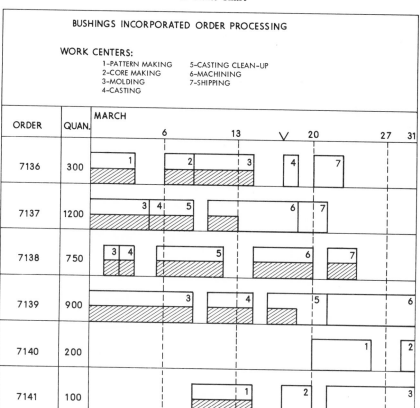

For such a chart to be useful, someone must be assigned the task of updating the status of all orders every day. Information which is several days old is obviously useless for day-to-day control. The fact that someone must maintain constant surveillance on order progress has both good and bad features. It is an overhead expense which can only be justified by improved system performance. However, improved performance may be achieved just by the simple act of requiring a daily report on order status. The planned schedule often becomes self-fulfilling simply because no order can be lost in the shuffle if constant inquiries are being made.

If production schedules are released on a weekly or monthly basis, the maintenance of charts like Figure 14–1 is relatively simple. However, when Gantt chart techniques are used in systems in which plans and schedules are frequently changed after production starts, they become unwieldy. For that reason they are being replaced in many of the larger industries with computer aided scheduling techniques.

Variations. The previous example illustrated only one use of the Gantt chart technique. Similar charts can be developed for the layout of tasks on individual pieces of equipment. Here each segment of the horizontal bar might represent an individual order to be processed on a particular machine. Other variations represent the projected cumulative load on different work centers over future months as jobs are accepted. These can be used for long-range manpower and machine capacity planning. Still another application is in project planning in which many subassemblies or subtasks must be completed in a specified order before the project can be finished. Here another dimension is often added to the chart by inserting connecting lines between subproject start and completion dates to indicate when tasks cannot start before others are completed. Such charts are called connected Gantt charts and are closely related to the critical path techniques discussed later in this chapter.

Many commercial devices are available to ease the task of preparing and modifying Gantt charts. "Productrol boards," "Schedugraphs," and "Boardmasters" are commercial names of some of the more widely used mechanical aids. Some use strings and pegs or colored tape to construct the equivalent of a bar. Others use cards inserted in pockets to represent the time scale. All are Gantt-type control charts designed to identify prospective trouble in complex scheduling operations.

Network Analysis

In recent years a number of techniques have been developed to improve upon the Gantt-type control methods for the planning, scheduling, and controlling of large projects. The most popular acronyms used to identify these techniques are PERT (Program Evaluation and Review Technique), CPM (Critical Path Method), and CPP (Critical Path Planning). They have in common the network presentation of sequence information and the determination of a critical or bottleneck path through the network. They differ in their emphasis on cost and the uncertainty of job time estimates.

The techniques to be discussed in this section are used for project coordination and control as opposed to the production control devices used in continuous manufacture of consumer goods. These network analysis methods have been employed for such diverse projects as highway and building construction, weapon system development, computer installation, and automotive die production. Their pervasive nature can be attributed to the facts that they are easy to understand, they provide a convenient method to record complex interactions, and the computations involved are readily programmed for the digital computer.

Historical Development. Both PERT and CPM were announced at about the same time, even though they were essentially independent developments. CPM was developed for E.I. DuPont de Nemours and Company in 1957. The work was performed by Morgan R. Walker representing DuPont and James E. Kelley representing Remington Rand.[1] They first applied the technique to the construction of a chemical plant and later to the shutdown of chemical plants for overhaul and maintenance. The abstract model selected to portray such engineering projects was the arrow diagram. This diagram gives a graphical representation of the interrelationships among jobs for any project. The duration of jobs was assumed to be deterministic and under some control by management. Time could be reduced by increasing the expenditures for a job. Although the notation differs from PERT, CPM uses the same basic network diagram and method of calculating the longest path through it.

In 1958 a parallel effort was initiated in concert with Booz, Allen, and Hamilton, consultants for the Polaris Fleet Ballistic Missile Program, Special Projects Office, Bureau of Ordnance, U.S. Navy. This effort first reported by D. G. Malcolm, J. H. Roseboom, C. E. Clark, and W. Fazar was designated Project PERT or Program Evaluation Research Task.[2] It was later renamed Program Evaluation and Review Technique. The main thrust of the original PERT effort was to account for the uncertainty in the time estimates for each of the distinct activities in large research and development projects. Ideally they expressed a desire to have a probability distribution for all time estimates. Practically they had to settle for a range of three estimates for each time from which they hypothesized a probability distribution. The statistical questions surrounding the use of these three estimates proved to be the most controversial aspects of the original PERT. Cost considerations were not a part of the model.

---

[1] James E. Kelley, and Morgan R. Walker, *Critical Path Planning and Scheduling*, 1959 Proceedings of the Eastern Joint Computer Conference.

[2] D. G. Malcom, J. H. Roseboom, C. F. Clark, and W. Fazar, "Application of a Technique for Research and Development Program Evaluation," *Operations Research*, Vol. VII, No. 5 (September–October, 1959), pp. 646–70.

Since the introduction of PERT and CPM, many variations which combine features of both systems have appeared. At the same time the distinguishing features of the original models have become blurred to the point that "PERT" is now often taken to mean any network scheduling technique which features the calculation of a critical or longest time path. When cost control is also considered, the title PERT/COST is employed. A degree of standardization has evolved since the establishment by the federal government in 1962 of a uniform Guide on PERT/COST.

As noted by Levy, Thompson, and Wiest, the characteristics of projects which can profitably employ critical path analysis are[3]

1. The project consists of a well-defined collection of activities which must be completed to end the project.
2. The activities within a given sequence may be started and stopped independently of each other.
3. The activities must be performed in a given sequence.

These qualifications define the limits of PERT-type models.

The Critical Path Method

For our purposes, we will reserve the term critical path method for the basic technique of constructing a network diagram and determining the most limiting path through it. This means that we will limit the immediate discussion to an ordered set of activities with single estimates of their time requirements. This is sometimes referred to as simplified PERT. Probability and cost considerations will be discussed in later sections.

Constructing the Network Diagram. The usual presentation of critical path concepts begins with a project network or an arrow diagram. An example of such a diagram is shown in Figure 14–2. The convention adopted

FIGURE 14–2

An Arrow Diagram

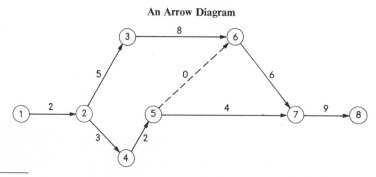

---

[3] F. K. Levy, G. L. Thompson, and J. D. Wiest, "Introduction to the Critical Path Method" in J. F. Muth and G. L. Thompson (eds.), *Industrial Scheduling* (Englewood Cliffs, N.J.: Prentice-Hall, Inc., 1963).

in this text is that the arrows represent activities or jobs and the nodes represent events. An event is simply a point of transition marking the end of one or more activities and the start of a new group of activities. The expected duration of each activity is noted by the small number along the activity arrow.

It should be noted that the arrow diagram is merely a graphic model of the sequence structure of a project. The same information could be captured by means of a set of ordered pairs or a precedence matrix. The matrix model form is the one which is used internally by the computer to perform the necessary calculations. Figure 14–3 shows the equivalence of the three model forms.

FIGURE 14–3

The Equivalence of Model Forms

a) Arrow Diagram

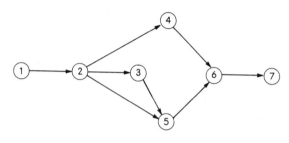

b) Set of Ordered Pairs

$$\begin{bmatrix} 1,2 \\ 2,3 \\ 2,4 \\ 2,5 \\ 3,5 \\ 4,6 \\ 5,6 \\ 6,7 \end{bmatrix}$$

c) Precedence Matrix—Nonzero Entry (i, j) Denotes That i Is Preceded by j

	1	2	3	4	5	6	7
1	0	0	0	0	0	0	0
2	1	0	0	0	0	0	0
3	0	1	0	0	0	0	0
4	0	1	0	0	0	0	0
5	0	1	1	0	0	0	0
6	0	0	0	1	1	0	0
7	0	0	0	0	0	1	0

Constructing the network diagram is a pure planning function. It involves identifying explicitly all the activities or jobs which must occur in a project. Furthermore one must clarify the sequence, i.e., exactly which jobs cannot start before others are finished and which jobs must be finished before any given job can start. Although this sounds easy, it can involve some very detailed thought, analysis, and coordination for large projects. The clarity of planning required to generate the initial network for a project may in fact be the major benefit of CPM in many applications.

In addition to the activities which obviously consume resources in a project it may be necessary to introduce dummy activities of zero duration. Activity (5, 6) in Figure 14–2, shown by a dotted line is a dummy activity. Such dummies may be necessary to clarify the dependency of one activity upon another or to distinguish between two parallel activities.

For example, suppose that an initial analysis of a project shows that activity C must be preceded by activities A and B as diagrammed below:

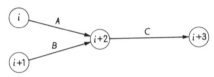

However, closer examination reveals that activity C is only partially dependent upon A. Work can really begin on C when A is partially completed. To capture that dependence, A may be broken into two portions, one which must be completed before C can begin and a second which has no effect on C. The new activity $(j, i + 2)$ is a dummy with zero performance time.

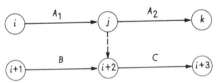

In other cases there may be resource constraints which require the insertion of a zero-time activity. If, for example, both A and B require the same piece of equipment but are otherwise sequence independent, we may need a dummy to guarantee that both jobs will not be competing for that equipment at the same time. The zero-time dummy activity (2, 3) guarantees that B will not begin until A has relinquished the critical resource.

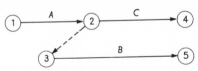

Still another use for the dummy occurs when the network must be coded for computer use. The computer requires that any two events be directly connected by no more than one activity. Duplicate activities *A* and *B*, which might be diagrammed as

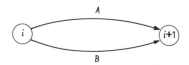

are distinguishable when only event numbers are used for identification. By inserting another node *j* and defining the dummy activity *C* by the pair (i, j), the computer can distinguish between *A* and *B* by their event codes.

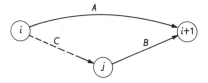

We can summarize this discussion by paraphrasing the basic rules of network logic proposed by Moder and Philips:[4]

1. No activity can begin until all activities preceding it are completed.
2. The length and direction of arrows are irrelevant. They imply logical precedence only.
3. Two events can be directly connected by no more than one activity.
4. Each event number must be unique.
5. Networks may have only one initial event and one terminal event.

These are the rules to be observed in constructing the CPM networks for the problems of this text.

Project Scheduling. One of the benefits of the CPM approach is that it separates the planning and scheduling functions. The production of the network diagram constitutes the planning cycle. Scheduling, here defined as the act of producing project timetables, follows planning. Scheduling considers the plan, as represented by the network, activity duration times, and in more advanced models, costs. For the time being, we will assume that each activity has associated with it a fixed duration. When we discuss the original PERT, different methods for estimating those durations will be introduced. All activity durations are assumed to be measured in the same units, such as weeks.

---

[4] Joseph J. Moder and Cecil R. Philips, *Project Management with CPM and PERT*, (New York: Reinhold Publishing Corp., 1964), p. 17.

The following nomenclature will be used in the various scheduling computations:

$t_{i,j}$ = estimated duration time for activity (i, j)
E_i = expected occurrence time for event i
L_i = latest occurrence time for event i
ES = earliest start time for an activity
EF = earliest finish time for an activity
LS = latest allowable activity start time
LF = latest allowable activity finish time
S = total activity slack or float
S_F = free slack or float for an activity

On the network diagrams selected ones of these quantities will appear as follows:

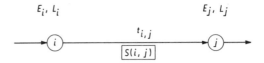

Expected Event Times.   The first stage in the scheduling process is to calculate the earliest or expected event times. This calculation is performed by

1. Taking the initial event time of the network as zero.
2. Starting each activity as soon as its predecessor event occurs.
3. Determining event times by the largest of the earliest finish times of activities leading into an event.

The network is analyzed from beginning to end in that fashion. Symbolically, steps 2 and 3 imply

$$ES(i, j) = E_i \qquad (14\text{--}1)$$

$$EF(i, j) = E_i + t_{i,j} \qquad (14\text{--}2)$$

and

$$E_j = \max(E_{i1} + t_{i1, j}, E_{i2} + t_{i2, j}, E_{i3} + t_{i3, j}, \dots) \qquad (14\text{--}3)$$

where $i1$, $i2$, $i3$, etc., are all preceding events of activities which terminate at event j.

This forward calculation is illustrated in Figure 14–4. Event 1 starts at $t = 0$. Event 2 is preceded only by event 1; therefore its expected occurrence time is

$$E_2 = E_1 + t_{1, 2} = 0 + 3 = 3$$

Similarly

$$E_3 = E_1 + t_{1, 3} = 0 + 4 = 4$$

FIGURE 14–4

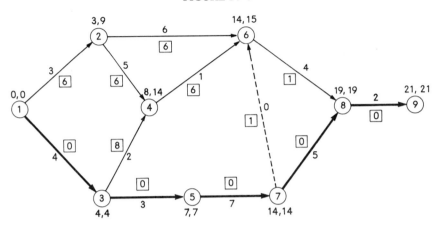

Event 4 signals the completion of both activities (2, 4) and (3, 4). The expected occurrence time for event 4 is then

$$E_4 = \max(E_2 + t_{2,4}, E_3 + t_{3,4})$$

$$= \max(3 + 5, 4 + 2) = 8$$

Calculation for the remaining events in the network proceeds in a similar fashion.

From the network diagram it is obvious that the earliest possible completion time for the project is 21 weeks. This is the expected time of event 9 and represents an initial scheduling benchmark.

Latest Event Times. The second stage of the scheduling process is to calculate the latest event times. This is accomplished in similar fashion to the earliest event time calculation by working through the network backwards. In this case we start with the final event and calculate latest event times such that the project can be completed on schedule. For purposes of computation it is common to set the latest event time for the terminal event equal to the earliest event time for that event. This is not necessary, however, since any desired project limit could be used to initialize the backward computation. For our purposes the latest-event-time calculation is performed by

1. Setting the latest time for the terminal event equal to its earliest time as computed in the forward computation.
2. Starting each activity at the latest time of its successor event less the duration time of the activity.
3. Determining event times by the smallest of the latest allowable start times of all activities emanating from an event.

Symbolically these rules imply that

$$LF(i, j) = L_j \tag{14-4}$$

$$LS(i, j) = LF(i, j) - t_{i, j} = L_j - t_{i, j} \tag{14-5}$$

and

$$L_i = \min(L_{j1} - t_{i, j1}, L_{j2} - t_{i, j2}, \ldots) \tag{14-6}$$

where $j1, j2, j3$, etc., are all successor events of activities which start at event i.

Again referring to Figure 14-4, event 9 must occur at $t = 21$. Event 8 is succeeded only by event 9. Its latest time is

$$L_8 = L_9 - t_{8,9} = 21 - 2 = 19$$

Event 6 is succeeded only by event 8 which leads to

$$L_6 = L_8 - t_{6,8} = 19 - 4 = 15$$

Event 7, however, is succeeded by both events 6 and 8. The latest event time in this case is

$$L_7 = \text{Min}(L_6 - t_{7,6}, L_8 - t_{7,8})$$
$$= \text{Min}(15 - 0, 19 - 5) = 14$$

The remaining events are treated in similar fashion.

As a result of this calculation, it is obvious that the earliest and latest times for event 1 are identically zero. If, on the other hand, we had elected to establish a lenient project deadline of say 30 weeks, we could find at least one path of that length between nodes 1 and 9. In so doing, the latest time for event 1 would have been nine weeks. All other late event times would be adjusted accordingly. Such a result would imply that the project start time could be slipped by as much as 9 weeks without jeopardizing the desired 30-week schedule.

Determining the Slack Times.   The third stage of the scheduling process is to determine the slack times for activities in the project. The two types of slack of interest to us are the total slack and the free slack. Slack time is synonymous with spare time.

The amount of total slack for an activity measures the time by which that activity could be extended without affecting the total project completion date. In terms of events, the total slack for an event is simply the difference between its earliest and latest dates.

$$S_i = L_i - E_i \tag{14-7}$$

In terms of activities, the total slack for activity (i, j) is the difference between the latest allowable time for event j and the earliest finish time for (i, j)

$$S(i, j) = L_j - EF(i, j)$$

$$= L_j - (E_i + t_{i, j}) \qquad (14\text{-}8)$$

Applying this calculation to the network of Figure 14–4, the total slack for activity (8, 9) is

$$S(8, 9) = L_9 - E_8 - t_{8,9} = 21 - 19 - 2 = 0$$

The total slack for activity (6, 8) is

$$S(6, 8) = L_8 - E_6 - t_{6,8} = 19 - 14 - 4 = 1$$

Results of similar calculations performed for the remaining activities are shown in the square boxes on the network.

Free slack for an activity measures the amount of time that the activity completion time can be delayed without affecting the earliest start time for any other activity in the network. Symbolically,

$$S_F(i, j) = E_j - EF(i, j)$$

$$= E_j - (E_i + t_{i, j}) \qquad (14\text{-}9)$$

Free slack for activity (4, 6), for example, is

$$S_F(4, 6) = E_6 - E_4 - t_{4, 6}$$

$$= 14 - 8 - 1 = 5 \text{ weeks}$$

This indicates that activity (4, 6) could be started anywhere in the interval from 8 to 13 weeks without affecting the start time of any other activity on the project. It is apparent that

$$S_F(i, j) \leq S(i, j) \qquad (14\text{-}10)$$

at all times.

The Critical Path and the Schedule. At this point we have all of the necessary numbers to determine the critical activities and to establish a schedule. The critical activities are those with zero slack. This means that any delay on a critical activity will delay the total project completion time. A critical path is simply that path through the network defined by the arrows associated with critical activities. We will denote the critical path by a double line.

When an activity has zero total slack, its scheduled start time is predetermined. These activities must be scheduled to start at their calculated earliest start time or the project will be delayed. Those activities with some positive slack can be used by the scheduler to help smooth work loads. Their start times can be moved within the bounds of the slack time without affecting the project completion date. Finally, those jobs with free slack can be used for flexibility at the operating level. Here, for instance, the foreman might be given discretion on exactly when to start a job within the bounds set by the scheduled start and free slack.

Referring again to the network of Figure 14–4, the final schedule for this project might appear as shown on Figure 14–5. Obviously, in a final schedule

FIGURE 14–5

Project Schedule

Activity Description	Duration	Expected Start	Expected Finish	Latest Start	Latest Finish	Total Slack
1, 2	3 weeks	0	3	6	9	6
1, 3	4	0	4	0	4	0
2, 4	5	3	8	9	14	6
2, 6	6	3	9	9	15	6
3, 4	2	4	6	12	14	8
3, 5	3	4	7	4	7	0
4, 6	1	8	9	14	15	6
5, 7	7	7	14	7	14	0
6, 8	4	14	18	15	19	1
7, 6	0	14	14	15	15	1
7, 8	5	14	19	14	19	0
8, 9	2	19	21	19	21	0

for a real project the activity code would be replaced by verbal descriptions of those activities or jobs.

Gantt Chart Comparison.   It is interesting to note that all of the information contained on the network diagram of Figure 14–4 could be captured by a connected Gantt chart. The equivalent Gantt chart is shown in Figure 14–6. Here each activity or job is represented by a horizontal bar, the length of which defines job duration. The vertical lines denote event times. This approach is reasonable only for relatively small projects. When the number of activities becomes much larger than 10, it is extremely difficult to portray all of the interactions. At that point a network presentation is mandatory.

The Gantt chart does give an explicit picture of the dependency among jobs and the amount of slack available. For example, from Figure 14–6 it is obvious that job (3, 4) can be shifted to any 2-week block in the interval of 4 to 14 weeks. Its total slack of eight weeks is then easily verified graphically. Note also that even though jobs (1, 2) and (2, 4) both have a total slack of six weeks, they are not independent. If, for example, we were to use three weeks of the available slack for job (1, 2), job (2, 4) would then have available only three weeks rather than six weeks of total slack. If we were to delay job (1, 2) by its total available slack of six weeks, job (2, 4) would have zero slack, and job (2, 4) would then become a critical activity.

FIGURE 14-6

Scheduling with a Connected Gantt Chart

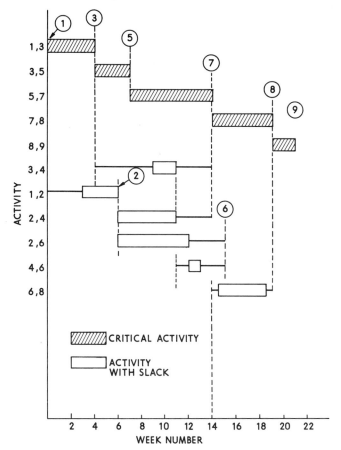

Updating and Control. The dynamic nature of project work leads to the final stage of the CPM analysis, updating, and control. All of the analysis discussed so far is carried out at the beginning of a project. However, as work is started on various activities, there are bound to be variations between planned and actual performance. If, for example, a noncritical activity is delayed for any reason, the slack calculations for all tasks in the project may change. Jobs which were formerly noncritical may suddenly become critical as noted by our last example. In addition, added resources may become available permitting work on critical activities to be accelerated. Other activities may take longer than planned because of erroneous estimates, strikes, floods, fires, etc.

All of these potential changes in project configuration require that the network be periodically revised to enable management to exercise continuous control. For a project of the duration of our example, weekly revisions might suffice. For other projects with longer activity times, a monthly revision cycle could be adequate. The length of the revision cycle is also a function of the anticipated variance in task performance time. Projects in which there is little a priori reason to suspect that activity duration will not be reasonably constant can tolerate lengthy revision cycles. Projects, such as some research and development programs in which each activity time may be highly variable, may warrant much shorter revision cycles. The question of how often to update the analysis as usual revolves around the economic tradeoff between cost of revision versus potential benefits.

PERT

We noted earlier that the term PERT has gradually evolved into a general expression for critical path techniques. However, for purposes of discussion in this section we will use the term PERT to denote the original probability-based analysis developed for the U.S. Navy.

Estimating Activity Duration.   According to Malcolm, Roseboom, Clark, and Fazar, the PERT team felt that the most important requirement for project evaluation was the provision for detailed estimates of time constraints on future activities.[5] Furthermore, since they were concerned with research and development activities which tend to be highly uncertain, they felt that ideally they should have a probability distribution of times for each activity. They recognized that project status is really a function of dollars and technical performance of subsystems as well as time. However, since no criterion function integrating time, performance, and resources was readily available and since the PERT project time was limited, they elected to pursue an approach which considered only the time variable.

The structure of the basic network for a project proceeds exactly as it did with the CPM method of the last section. However, the estimates of activity duration are different. The method of obtaining the estimates and their use in probability statements are the distinguishing characteristics of PERT.

If historical data are available for the activities of a project, it may be possible to develop empirical distributions for activity times. In such instances the empirical distributions or their best-fit analytical approximations should be used in the probability calculations. However, statistical information of this type is not normally available for the large-scale, one-shot projects of the type considered by the PERT team. For that reason one must rely on estimates by persons responsible for each activity to establish some feel for expected activity duration and its variability.

---

[5] Malcolm *et al., op. cit.*, p. 648.

The original PERT team suggested that a more realistic evaluation of activity duration could be made if three estimates for each activity were made. This is a decided departure from the CPM approach of requiring a single estimate of activity duration. The three estimates that each activity manager must provide under PERT are

a = optimistic time
b = pessimistic time
m = most likely time

The most likely estimate, m, is intended to be the most realistic estimate for activity time. The optimistic estimate, a, is intended to be the smallest reasonable completion time if everything goes exceptionally well. The pessimistic estimate, b, is an estimate the longest time for the activity under the worst possible conditions.

Once the three time estimates for each activity are obtained, they are assumed to be connected by a unimodal probability distribution with m being the modal value. The difference between a and b is assumed to represent the range of reasonable time requirements and a simple approximation is used to convert range to variance. Since with many probability distributions the tails of the curve are considered to lie within about 3σ units of the mean, there should be a spread of about six standard deviations between the tails. Therefore, a reasonable approximation for the range seems to be

$$6\sigma = (b - a)$$

Solving for variance, we have

$$\sigma^2 = [\tfrac{1}{6}(b - a)]^2 \qquad (14\text{--}11)$$

The beta distribution is used as the model of the distribution of activity time. The equation for the beta distribution can be written as

$$f(t) = K(t - a)^c(b - t)^d \qquad (14\text{--}12)$$

where K, c, and d are functions of the three time estimates. By assuming this form of the distribution and its variance, as expressed by Equation 14–11, an empirical approximation to the expected value of the distribution has been developed as

$$t_e = \tfrac{1}{6}(a + 4m + b) \qquad (14\text{--}13)$$

The notation t_e is standard in the PERT literature, although we will use $\bar{t}$ notation later. This is the value to be used in the network for purposes of calculating expected start times, late start, slack, etc. The calculation of these numbers and the determination of a critical path follow exactly the same procedures discussed for CPM.

The choice of the beta distribution as a model has several apparent advantages. It is a unimodal distribution defined only for nonnegative arguments with finite limits. It can be skewed right or left depending upon the location of m relative to a and b. This permits the estimator to have considerable leeway in his estimates and relates the mean time to them in what seems to be a reasonable way. Finally, the calculations of mean and variance are simple to perform. However, the choice of the beta distribution is arbitrary and should not deter the analyst from using some other distribution when he has data to develop better approximations for the errors in activity time estimates.

Estimating Project Duration. Once the distributions of activity times in the network have been obtained by whatever means, their expected values and variances can be calculated. Let

$\bar{t}_{i,j}$ = expected duration time for activity (i, j)
$\sigma^2_{i,j}$ = variance of duration time for activity (i, j)

The critical path calculation proceeds as with CPM using $\bar{t}_{i,j}$ in the role of $t_{i,j}$. However, a new dimension is added by carrying along an estimate of the variance for the early and late occurrence times of each event.

If a network has only n events in series, the project duration is given by

$$E_n = t_{1,2} + t_{2,3} + \cdots + t_{n-1,n} \qquad (14\text{-}14)$$

Furthermore, if the activity durations are independent,

$$\bar{E}_n = \bar{t}_{1,2} + \bar{t}_{2,3} + \cdots + \bar{t}_{n-1,n} \qquad (14\text{-}15)$$

and

$$\sigma^2_{(E_n)} = \sigma^2_{1,2} + \sigma^2_{2,3} + \cdots + \sigma^2_{n-1,n} \qquad (14\text{-}16)$$

However, if we have a network of parallel activities the project duration is given by

$$E_n = \max(t_{1,2}, t_{1,3}, \ldots, t_{1,n}) \qquad (14\text{-}17)$$

If the cumulative density of $t_{i,j}$ is $F_{i,j}(t)$, the distribution for project duration is

$$F_n(t) = F_{1,2}(t)F_{1,3}(t)\cdots F_{1,n}(t) \qquad (14\text{-}18)$$

Although there are no simple analytical expressions for $\bar{E}_n$ and $\sigma^2_{(E_n)}$ in this case, we could in theory calculate them from

$$\bar{E}_n = \int_0^\infty [1 - F_n(t)]\, dt \qquad (14\text{-}19)$$

and

$$\sigma^2_{(E_n)} = \int_0^\infty (t - \bar{E}_n)^2 \left(\frac{dF_n(t)}{dt} \right) dt \qquad (14\text{-}20)$$

Normally such integrals can be conveniently evaluated only numerically.

After making the point of the difficulty of calculating exact expressions for the mean and variance of a simple parallel network, Carruthers notes that most realistic networks include not only series and parallel sets of activities but also crosslinking activities.[7] The expressions for distributions in these networks become truly unwieldy. He suggests that the only way to derive the correct distribution for project completion time is then by Monte Carlo methods.

However, the PERT technique ignores these difficult considerations. PERT simply takes the mean and variance of project duration time to be the sum of the means and variances of the durations of activities on the critical path. This assumption is rigorously correct only for projects with a single chain of activities. As the number of parallel activities and cross-linkages increases, the mean and in many cases the variance of project duration are progressively underestimated. The possibility that another path will actually have the largest total elapsed time is ignored.

The final simplification in the PERT analysis is to invoke the central limit theorem. The earliest time to complete a project is assumed to be made up of a sum of n times along the critical path, each with a known mean and variance. The central limit theorem implies that such a sum is approximately normal with mean equal to the sum of the component means and variance equal to the sum of the variances. By assuming that the distribution of the earliest time to complete the project is normal, one can calculate the probability that the project will be completed by any specified date.

For example, suppose that the critical path in a project consists of five activities with the following time estimates:

Activity	a	m	b
1, 3	4	6	10
3, 6	2	3	5
6, 7	1	2	4
7, 8	3	4	5
8, 9	4	5	7

The expected time for activity (1, 3) is

$$\bar{t}_{1,3} = \tfrac{1}{6}(a + 4m + b) = \tfrac{1}{6}(38) = 6.33$$

The variance for activity (1, 3) is

$$\sigma_{1,3}^2 = [\tfrac{1}{6}(b - a)]^2 = [\tfrac{1}{6}(10 - 4)]^2 = 1.00$$

---

[7] J. A. Carruthers, " Probabilistic Times," in Gail Thornley (ed.), *Critical Path Analysis in Practice* (London: Tavistock Publications, 1968).

Similar calculations for the remaining activities yield:

Activity	$\bar{t}_{i,j}$	$\sigma^2_{i,j}$
1, 3	6.33	1.00
3, 6	3.17	0.25
6, 7	2.17	0.25
7, 8	4.00	0.11
8, 9	5.17	0.25
	20.84	1.86

Now if the project schedule calls for a target completion date of 22 weeks,

$$P(E_9 \leq 22) = P\left(z \leq \frac{22 - 20.84}{\sqrt{1.86}}\right)$$

$$= P(z \leq 0.853) \approx 0.80$$

from the normal tables. This says that we have about an 80 percent chance of meeting the assigned schedule.

The same approach can be used to evaluate the probability of positive slack at any given event in the network. The expected late time for an event is calculated by the usual backward path through the network, using expected values instead of the deterministic times of CPM. The variance for late time of each event is taken to be the sum of the variances of all activities along the backward path leading to that event. Since $\bar{E}_i$ and $\bar{L}_i$ are only mean values, it is possible for the actual E_i to be greater than L_i. When this occurs, the actual slack at an event is negative even though the expected slack is positive. The probability of positive slack at node i is then

$$P(S_i > 0) = P(L_i - E_i > 0) \tag{14-21}$$

Again using the normality assumption, the quantity $(L_i - E_i)$ will be normally distributed with mean $(\bar{L}_i - \bar{E}_i)$ and variance $[\sigma^2_{(L_i)} + \sigma^2_{(E_i)}]$.

For example, suppose that the network calculation yields

$$\bar{L}_i = 10 \text{ weeks} \qquad \sigma^2_{(L_i)} = 0.60$$

$$\bar{E}_i = 8 \text{ weeks} \qquad \sigma^2_{(E_i)} = 0.40$$

The probability of positive slack at this node is then

$$P(L_i - E_i > 0) = P\left(z > \frac{-2}{1}\right) \approx 0.98$$

Under these conditions, this is unlikely to become a critical event. This concept permits the ranking of paths in terms of their probability of positive slack. In this way management attention can be focused on those subcritical paths which may develop into critical ones as the project continues.

In spite of the obvious shortcomings of the many simplifying assumptions in the probability calculations of PERT, this approach can be useful for management of projects with highly uncertain activity times. It does offer ballpark estimates for quoting probabilities for completion dates.

Optimization in Critical Path Planning

One of the earlier developments in network techniques was that of total dollar optimization. This was an integral part of the critical path planning (CPP) discussion first presented by Kelley and Walker. However, because of the difficulties involved in using the technique, it has not been used as extensively as the simpler methods we discussed under CPM to plan and control projects from beginning to end. Its most successful applications have been with planning projects in which the network is used primarily to assist in the general development of ideas.

There have been later developments of a theoretical nature which relieve some of the more restrictive assumptions of CPP. However, the original computational procedure does produce results in an efficient manner which are in a restricted sense optimal. Since the later developments are orders of magnitude more difficult and since CPP has been successfully applied to many projects, we will limit our discussion to the original approach.

Time-Cost Tradeoffs. The network analysis techniques introduced so far have emphasized the time elements of a project structure. For any given project structure, the time to perform an activity has been treated as though it was beyond the control of management. The effect on project completion time of changes in performance level can be evaluated by those techniques, but how such changes came about is beyond the scope of the models. The CPP technique, on the other hand, attempts to reflect the possibility of management control of activity times by relating the time required to the cost incurred. These data are then used to produce a minimum cost schedule for any desired completion date.

The computational procedure requires that the tradeoff curves between time and cost for all activities be continuous linear or piecewise linear decreasing curves of the type shown in Figures 14–7 and 14–8. The actual cost curve for an activity is assumed to be convex. If its shape does not depart too significantly from a straight line, a single line between the "normal" and "crash" points is used as an approximation. This is shown in Figure 14–7. If the actual cost curve is severely curved, it may be approximated by a series of straight-line segments. Each segment is treated as the time-cost curve for a distinct psuedo-activity. In Figure 14–8, for example, the real activity J has been replaced by three pseudo-activities $J_1, J_2,$ and J_3. Each has its own unique time-cost curve. The equation for J_2, for example, is

$$K_2 = (C_d - \Delta C_1) - \left(\frac{\Delta C_2}{\Delta t_2}\right)(t - d_{ij} - \Delta t_1)$$

FIGURE 14–7

Activity Cost Curve

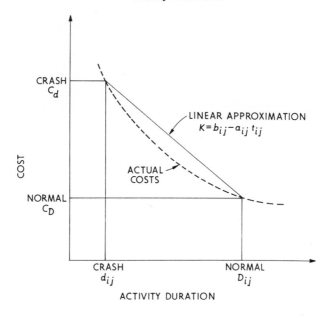

ACTIVITY DURATION

for

$$d_{ij} + \Delta t_1 < t < d_{ij} + \Delta t_1 + \Delta t_2$$

The linear cost curves are defined by normal cost–normal time and crash cost–crash time points. The idea is that the duration of jobs may be allowed to vary within certain limits. The so-called "normal" time is the upper limit denoted by D_{ij}. Cost of operating at this level is minimum. The "crash" time, d_{ij}, is the least time in which an activity can be accomplished. To expedite the job costs money. The crash cost then is the amount which must be expended to keep activity time to a minimum. Any schedule between the normal and crash schedules is assumed to be feasible with an associated expense which is a linear function of the time required. The costs considered are direct costs and do not include administration, overhead, etc.

To formalize these concepts, let

$$t_i = \text{time that event } i \text{ occurs}$$
$$t_{ij} = \text{duration of activity } (i, j)$$
$$D_{ij} = \text{normal duration of activity } (i, j)$$
$$d_{ij} = \text{crash duration of activity } (i, j)$$
$$C_D(i, j) = \text{normal cost of activity } (i, j)$$
$$C_d(i, j) = \text{crash cost of activity } (i, j)$$

FIGURE 14–8

A Piecewise Linear Approximation to a Convex Time-Cost Curve

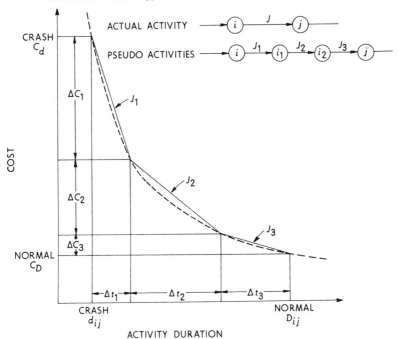

ACTIVITY DURATION

For the simple linear approximation we must select a value for t_{ij} such that

$$d_{ij} \le t_{ij} \le D_{ij}$$

The time-cost curve can be calculated from

$$K_{ij} = C_d(i, j) + \left(\frac{C_d(i, j) - C_D(i, j)}{D_{ij} - d_{ij}}\right)d_{ij} - \left(\frac{C_d(i, j) - C_D(i, j)}{D_{ij} - d_{ij}}\right)t_{ij} \quad (14\text{–}22)$$

which we will write as

$$K_{ij} = b_{ij} - a_{ij}t_{ij} \quad (14\text{–}23)$$

in order to conserve space.

Establishing a Schedule. Establishing a schedule now means that durations t_{ij} must be assigned to activities and occurrence times t_i to events for the total project. Project cost for any particular feasible schedule is given by

$$K = \sum_i \sum_j (b_{ij} - a_{ij}t_{ij}) \quad (14\text{–}24)$$

The duration of a schedule is defined by the occurrence time of the terminal event, t_n.

Let us assume that the initial event occurs at $t_1 = 0$ and the terminal event at some time T. It is reasonable to suppose that among all feasible schedules with a given duration, there is at least one which will minimize the project cost K. Schedule feasibility requires that

$$t_{ij} + t_i - t_j \leq 0 \qquad (14\text{--}25)$$

in addition to the earlier stated restrictions on t_{ij}. Since the b_{ij} values are all fixed constants, total project costs are minimized when the term $\sum_i \sum_j a_{ij} t_{ij}$ is maximized. The complete scheduling problem can now be stated as, select (t_{ij}, t_i, t_j) to

maximize $\qquad\qquad K^1 = \sum_i \sum_j a_{ij} t_{ij} \qquad\qquad (14\text{--}26a)$

subject to $\qquad\qquad t_{ij} + t_i - t_j \leq 0 \qquad$ all $i, j \qquad (14\text{--}26b)$

$$t_{ij} \leq D_{ij} \qquad \text{all } i, j \qquad (14\text{--}26c)$$

$$t_{ij} \geq d_{ij} \qquad \text{all } i, j \qquad (14\text{--}26d)$$

$$t_n \leq T \qquad\qquad\qquad (14\text{--}26e)$$

$$t_1 = 0 \qquad\qquad\qquad (14\text{--}26f)$$

The variables t_i and t_j carry zero cost and do not appear in the criterion function.

The above statement is easily recognized as a linear programming problem. It can be solved using the simplex method discussed earlier in this text. However there are more efficient ways of performing the calculation. The interested reader should refer to the articles by Kelley[8] and Fulkerson.[9] Basically, one seeks to generate optimum schedules for various values of the parameter T using a modified network-flow algorithm. The results provide a whole set of critical paths and schedules with their associated minimum costs.

Intuitively, the method works as follows. First the network is analyzed in the usual CPM manner with every activity taking its normal duration, i.e., $t_{ij} = D_{ij}$. A critical path and schedule are produced with the earliest project completion time being $T = E_n = t_n$. Since D_{ij} is the minimum cost duration for activity (i, j), the resulting schedule is a minimum cost schedule for project duration T. A reduction in project completion time is then forced by expediting the least marginal cost activities on the critical paths. As the project completion time is reduced, new jobs become critical. The analysis is then repeated with the activities which had their time reduced costing more

---

[8] J. E. Kelley, Jr., "Critical Path Planning and Scheduling: Mathematical Basis," *Operations Research*, Vol. 9, No. 3 (1961), pp. 296–320.

[9] D. R. Fulkerson, "A Network Flow Computation for Project Cost Curves," *Management Science*, Vol. VII, No. 2 (January, 1961), pp. 167–79.

than before. This process is repeated until the project duration can be reduced no further.

Each schedule produced by this process is a minimum cost schedule for the particular value of T in effect at that instant. The costs of these schedules plotted versus their respective durations is called the project cost curve. As shown in Figure 14–9 this function is nonincreasing, piece-wise linear and convex. With the information from the project cost curve, management can select any desired duration from normal to full crash and have some feel for the costs they will be incurring.

The analysis can be extended one more step if indirect costs are added as a separate line on the graph as in Figure 14–10. These costs are not attached directly to the network activities and increase with time. Equipment rental is an example of the type of cost included here. The total cost curve for the project then has a minimum point. This final result gives the minimum cost duration for the project.

Resource Allocation.   In addition to allocating dollars in project scheduling, one must also consider the allocation of available equipment and manpower. Such problems are of two basic types. One considers the leveling of resource demands by shifting slack activities and altering their durations. The second concerns the minimization of project duration time with constraints on the total availability of some resources. Most techniques suggested to solve these problems are heuristic in nature and are still undergoing

FIGURE 14–9

Representative Project Cost Curve

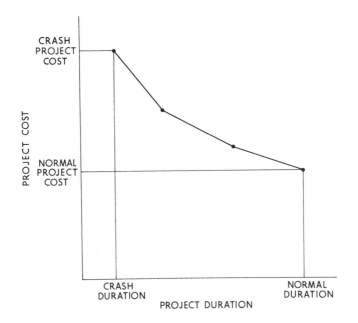

FIGURE 14–10

Total Project Cost Curve

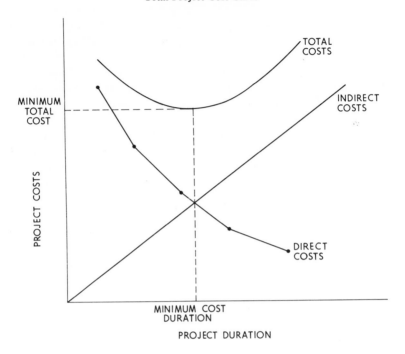

PROJECT DURATION

extensive research. The interested reader is urged to consult the references listed at the end of this chapter.

Network Cost Control

In addition to planning a project to optimize its total expected cost, one needs a means of controlling expenditures as the project progresses in time and achievement. This is accomplished by a status report system which seeks to compare actual with planned accomplishments and project costs. In addition, such a system should project future expenditures to indicate anticipated overrun or underrun at each reporting date. Several computer programs have been developed by individual CPM and PERT users to accomplish these cost control objectives. However, formal interest in the area has been most affected by a manual jointly issued by The Department of Defense and The National Aeronautics and Space Administration in 1962.[10] The

---

[10] Office of the Secretary of Defense and the National Aeronautics and Space Administration, *DOD and NASA Guide, PERT Cost Systems Design* (Washington, D.C.: U.S. Government Printing Office, June, 1962).

manual, *DOD and NASA Guide, PERT Cost Systems Design*, introduced the basic PERT cost procedures which have become requirements on many government sponsored research and development contracts.

PERT Cost Characteristics.   PERT cost procedures are simple in concept but sometimes difficult to implement. Essentially, they require an activity cost accounting system in which actual expenditure data can be identified with the specific activities in the project network. The output from the system consists of project summary reports organized by time period, areas of responsibility, and technical subdivisions of the project.

The major difficulty in installing a PERT cost system is that its accounting requirements are different from traditional cost accounting procedures used by most companies. The emphasis in traditional accounting procedures has been on the organizational unit. Budgets are planned by department, and even when project summaries are available, this is often the lowest level of reporting available to operating management. The object of the PERT cost system, however, is to provide detailed information and control within projects. This requires a more elaborate data system than the traditional approach. The level of detail required and provided by this system is both a strength and a weakness. Greater detail permits tighter management control, but if carried to extremes may require an unreasonable burden on project personnel who must provide the input data.

As a practical compromise to detailed activity accounting, the *DOD–NASA Guide* suggests that cost accounts be developed for groups of activities, or "work packages." Work packages are groups of activities that define a particular unit of work for some organizational unit. For example, the major end items to be produced by a project might be identified. They would then be divided into component parts, the component parts further subdivided and so forth, down to a level where the subdivisions become manageable units for planning and control purposes. The end item subdivisions at this last level are then divided into major work packages such as engineering, manufacturing, testing, etc. At this point the work packages are also assigned to corresponding operating units in the organization. The work packages formed at the lowest level constitute the basic units by which actual costs are collected and compared with estimates for purposes of cost control.

Developing a Budget.   PERT cost begins with the same network computations discussed earlier. For our purposes we will assume that each activity represents a unique work package. The network then has added to it the estimated cost data for each activity. The first cost computation involves summing all estimated costs by time period. For most activities we will assume that expenses occur linearly throughout the duration of the activity. For budgeting purposes we might construct one cumulative cost curve assuming that all jobs will begin at their earliest start times and a second based upon the late start times. The final budget might then be a compromise curve falling between these two limits.

To illustrate the technique, suppose that costs are estimated for each of the activities of the project summarized in Figure 14–5. The essential data are shown in Table 14–1. Using the *ES* times, expenditures for the first three

TABLE 14–1

Activity	Estimated Cost	ES	LS	Duration
1, 2	$ 3,000	0	6	3
1, 3	6,000	0	0	4
2, 4	4,000	3	9	5
2, 6	3,000	3	9	6
3, 4	3,000	4	12	2
3, 5	3,600	4	4	3
4, 6	1,400	8	14	1
5, 7	3,500	7	7	7
6, 8	4,000	14	15	4
7, 6	0	14	15	0
7, 8	3,500	14	14	5
8, 9	2,000	19	19	2
Total cost	$37,000			

weeks will be for activities (1, 2) and (1, 3). The total expended at the end of three weeks will be

$$\$3,000 \text{ [from (1, 2)]} + \$4,500 \text{ [from (1, 3)]} = \$7,500$$

During the fourth week activities (1, 3), (2, 4), and (2, 6) will be operating. The cumulative expense through $t = 4$ is then

$$\$7,500 + \$1,500 \text{ [from (1, 3)]} + \$800 \text{ [from (2, 4)]} + \$500 \text{ [from (2, 6)]} =$$

$$\$10,300$$

The calculation continues in this manner throughout the 21-week life of the project. Similar calculations are performed under *LS* conditions. The results are shown in Figure 14–11.

Status Reports.   At periodic intervals throughout the duration of the project, status reports are issued. These reports summarize the activities completed and in progress as of the reporting date. The report includes both cost and time expenditures for each activity. In addition, a summary is prepared to compare overall planned to actual expenditures and estimate future expenditures. This information may also be plotted on the cumulative cost curve.

For example, using the data of the previous section, suppose that a status report is being prepared at the end of the sixth week. An analysis of the accounting records shows the following:

Completed Activities	Started	Finished	Actual Duration	Actual Cost
1, 2	1	5	4	$3,600
1, 3	0	4	4	6,000
Activities in Progress	Started	Duration to Date	Estimated Time to Complete	Cost to Date
2, 4	4	2	3	$1,600
2, 6	5	1	5	800
3, 5	4	2	1	2,000

FIGURE 14–11

Cumulative Cost Curves

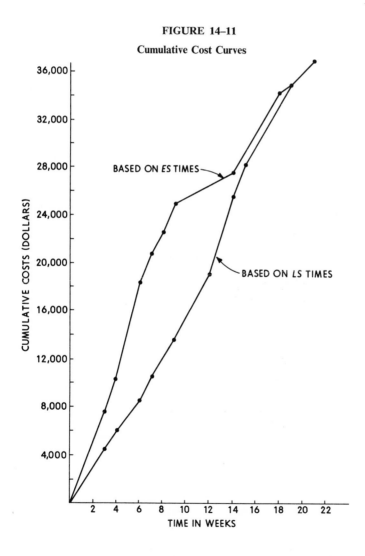

Comparing these data with the plan of Figures 14–5 and 14–11, we see that activity (1, 2) went $600 over budget and took one week longer than planned. The starting dates on activities (1, 2), (2, 4), and (2, 6) have all been postponed beyond their early start times but are within their allowable slack range. The critical path has not yet changed, and all critical activities are on schedule. Activity (3, 5) is currently $400 under budget. An executive summary shown in Figure 14–12 has been prepared from these data and the *ES* budget curve. The new prediction for total project cost was based upon an extrapolation of the $500 overrun for the first six weeks. Obviously other methods of prediction may also be used.

FIGURE 14–12

Project Cost Report

Reporting Date	6
Planned Cost to Date	$18,300
Actual Cost to Date	14,000
Planned Cost of Work Completed	13,500
Amount Over Budget for Work Completed	500
Predicted Total Project Cost	38,750

Job Sequencing at a Single Facility

In the various network scheduling models of the previous sections, the sequence of activities was specified on the basis of technological considerations. There are many problems, however, in which a number of jobs must be processed by a common facility performing similar operations on all jobs. The jobs should be ordered so that some measure of performance such as total processing time or mean flow time is optimized. Determining the order of work on a job shop milling machine and determining the landing sequence of aircraft at an airport are examples of quite different physical problems which share the characteristics of the single facility sequencing problem.

Deterministic Single Facility Sequencing. The simplest of all sequencing problems is that in which a finite number of jobs, each consisting of a single operation with a known processing time, are to be scheduled for a single facility. Since the job population is known in advance and since all processing times are predetermined, the total elapsed time to complete the schedule is constant for all sequences. However, the mean flow time (time from the beginning of the schedule period to the completion of a particular job) is sequence dependent. This will be our first measure of performance.

Let

p_i = processing time for job i

$p_{(i)}$ = processing time for the ith position in a sequence

$F_{(i)}$ = flow time for the ith job in a sequence

$\bar{F}$ = mean flow time

The flow time for a job in the kth position of an arbitrary sequence is simply the total elapsed time necessary to process all jobs up through the kth position.

$$F_{(k)} = \sum_{i=1}^{k} p_{(i)} \tag{14-27}$$

The mean flow time for an n job sequence is then

$$\bar{F} = \sum_{k=1}^{n} \frac{F_{(k)}}{n}$$

$$= \sum_{i=1}^{n} \frac{(n - i + 1)p_{(i)}}{n} \tag{14-28}$$

In order to minimize $\bar{F}$, it can be shown that the jobs should be sequenced such that

$$p_{(1)} \leq p_{(2)} \leq \cdots \leq p_{(n)} \tag{14-29}$$

This result says that the jobs should be processed in order of nondecreasing processing time. This is sometimes called SPT (shortest-processing-time) sequencing. To maximize mean flow time the jobs should be processed in the reverse order, i.e.,

$$p_{(1)} \geq p_{(2)} \geq \cdots \geq p_{(n)} \tag{14-30}$$

A complete discussion of these and other results is given by Conway, Maxwell, and Miller.[11]

The shortest-processing-time principle of sequencing occurs with many variations throughout the literature. Even when such a rule does not lead to an optimal solution, it often is better than most rules of thumb. One common variation of this rule occurs when the flow times for different jobs carry different weights. The weights, u_i, which might be dollar costs per unit time, describe the relative importance of jobs. Mean weighted flow time is given by

$$\bar{F}_u = \frac{1}{n} \sum_{i=1}^{n} u_i F_i \tag{14-31}$$

Both total and mean weighted flow time are minimized by selecting a sequence such that

$$\frac{p_{(1)}}{u_{(1)}} \leq \frac{p_{(2)}}{u_{(2)}} \leq \cdots \leq \frac{p_{(n)}}{u_{(n)}} \tag{14-32}$$

The usual method of proof for such rules is to compare performance measures of two sequences which differ only in one position. An interchange of positions k and $k + 1$ is indicated when total weighted flow time is decreased. Such

---

[11] Richard W. Conway, William L. Maxwell, and Louis W. Miller, *Theory of Scheduling* (Reading, Mass.: Addison-Wesley Publishing Co., 1967), pp. 26–27.

two-by-two comparisons throughout the sequence leads to the optimal rule of Equation 14–32.[12]

Sequence Dependent Setup Times. An interesting variation in the single facility sequencing problem occurs when processing times are sequence dependent. Such is the case for some processing operations in which each job requires a setup. In an injection molding operation, for example, it would take less setup time to follow a white plastic molded product with a black one than vice versa, due to potential color contamination. Similarly, the total approach times in an instrument landing system for a slow aircraft following a fast would be less than for a fast following slow, due to separation requirements.

Here we will let s_{ij} be the time to change over from job i to job j. The term $s_{(0)(1)}$ represents the time necessary to bring the system from an initial idle configuration to a state ready to process the first job. Flow times are now given by

$$F_{(1)} = s_{(0)(1)} + p_{(1)}$$

$$F_{(2)} = F_{(1)} + s_{(1)(2)} + p_{(2)}$$

$$F_{(i)} = F_{(i-1)} + s_{(i-1)(i)} + p_{(i)} \qquad (14\text{–}33)$$

The easiest measure of performance to evaluate here is the maximum flow time given by

$$F_{\max} = F_{(n)} = \sum_{i=1}^{n} s_{(i-1)(i)} + \sum_{i=1}^{n} p_{(i)} \qquad (14\text{–}34)$$

Since $\sum_{i=1}^{n} p_{(i)}$ is constant regardless of sequence, the maximum flow time is minimized by minimizing the sum of the n setup times.

As noted by Conway[13], *et al.*, this problem corresponds to the so-called traveling salesman problem. In the traveling salesman problem, a salesman must visit each of n cities once and only once then return to his home base in a manner which will minimize the total distance, cost, or time expended. Since we have n jobs and an idle state, the flow-time problem corresponds to an $(n + 1)$-city problem. The problem can be characterized by an $(n + 1) \times (n + 1)$ matrix whose elements are the setup times s_{ij}. The problem is to find an $(n + 1) \times (n + 1)$ matrix X with

$$x_{ik} = 0 \text{ or } 1 \qquad i = 0, 1, 2, \ldots, n, \qquad k = 0, 1, 2, \ldots, n$$

$$\sum_{i=1}^{n} x_{ik} = 1 \qquad k = 0, 1, 2, \ldots, n$$

$$\sum_{k=1}^{n} x_{ik} = 1 \qquad i = 0, 1, 2, \ldots, n$$

---

[12] *Ibid.*, p. 44.
[13] *Ibid.*, p. 55.

such that

$$\sum_{i=0}^{n} \sum_{k=0}^{n} x_{ik} s_{ik}$$

is minimized. In addition, no tour can return to its starting point until all cities (or setups) have been visited.

There are solutions to this problem for small values of n, but most require a large-scale computer and considerable time to execute. An approximation algorithm involving "visiting the next closest unvisited city" or in sequencing terminology selecting the job with the next smallest setup time might be used. This procedure does not guarantee an optimal solution but does perform reasonably well for many cases.

Intermittent Arrivals. In contrast to the cases discussed so far, many sequencing problems must be solved in a dynamic environment. Rather than having the total population of n jobs available at once, intermittent arrivals may occur. In this situation, the possibility of preemption must be considered. The extreme cases of preemption are preempt-resume and preempt-repeat disciplines. Preempt resume means that an interrupted job has the same total processing time in spite of the interruption. This might occur in a time sharing computer environment in which interruptions do not affect total machine running time on a particular job. With preempt repeat, any processing already completed at the time of preemption is lost. This might occur in a computer processing system in which a preempted job is thrown off the machine and must be resubmitted. The preempted job must begin anew when it returns to the facility. Between these extremes are the cases where only a portion of the prior processing time is forfeited. Lost setup time is a common instance of the intermediate case.

Under a preempt-resume discipline, one can follow essentially the same rules developed for simultaneous arrivals.[14] At the time of an arrival of a job, the sequencing decision is reviewed considering only the remaining processing time on the job currently in progress. At each such point the best selection is made from the jobs currently available. The shortest-processing-time rule is now modified to the shortest-remaining-processing-time rule. This minimizes the mean flow time without requiring any advanced information about job arrivals.

There are no equally general results to date for the preempt-repeat case. Under these conditions advance information about impending arrivals has a definite effect on the schedule. Idle time may be profitably inserted if we know that the next job will arrive before any jobs currently waiting can be processed.

Probabilistic Systems. The single facility sequencing rules discussed so far have been based upon deterministic systems in which arrivals occur at

---

[14] *Ibid.,* p. 69.

known instants and all processing times are known in advance. Frequently, it may be more realistic to treat service times and time between job arrivals as random variables drawn from known probability distributions. Models for such probabilistic systems appear in the queueing literature. The particular case of interest in this section is the nonpreemptive priority queueing model.

Priority Classes. In a nonpreemptive priority queueing system, jobs are identified by priority class. In an n-class system, class 1 jobs have highest priority and class n jobs have lowest priority. Randomly arriving jobs are placed in a queue to await service. If a class 1 job arrives when there are no other class 1 jobs present, it immediately advances to the head of the queue. Under nonpreemptive rules it cannot dislodge a job already in service but will be the one processed at the next occasion of service. If other class 1 jobs are present, the latest class 1 arrival is placed in the rear of the class 1 queue. Within priority class, all jobs are handled on a first-come first-served basis. No class 2 job can be processed while there are class 1 jobs in the queue. However, class 2 jobs have nonpreemptive priority over classes 3 through n. Other priority classes are treated in similar fashion.

The sequencing rule developed for this type of system is based upon the characteristics of the different priority classes. As with the deterministic models, one seeks to minimize mean flow time or some weighted average of expected flow times. The number and mix of jobs awaiting service is constantly changing.

As with most queueing models, this one requires that one side of the system be Poisson. The number of arrivals of each class is assumed to be Poisson distributed. The processing time for a member of each class is a random variable drawn from a general service time distribution. Let

λ_i = arrival rate for class i customers

$b_i(t)$ = probability density function for service time of class i customers

$E(t_i^n)$ = nth moment of service time for i class customers

ρ_i = $\lambda_i E(t_i)$ = utilization factor for i class

λ = $\sum_{i=1}^n \lambda_i$ = total job arrival rate

Since the actual processing time for a job is beyond the control of the decision maker, let the first measure of performance be the mean waiting time, exclusive of service time, for a k-class job. It can be shown that the expected waiting time for a k-class job is[15]

$$W_k = \frac{\sum_{i=1}^n \lambda_i E(t_i^2)}{2(1 - \sum_{i=1}^{k-1} \rho_i)(1 - \sum_{i=1}^k \rho_i)} \tag{14-35}$$

as long as $\sum_{i=1}^n \rho_i < 1$.

Let us further suppose that it costs c_k dollars per unit time to delay a k-class job. The average delay cost for a k-class job is then

---

[15] See, for example, Thomas L. Saaty, *Elements of Queueing Theory* (New York: McGraw-Hill Book Co., Inc., 1961), pp. 232–34.

$$K_k = c_k W_k \tag{14-36}$$

Since the portion of total jobs which will be k-class jobs is given by λ_k/λ, it follows that the overall average cost per job is

$$K = \sum_{k=1}^{n} \frac{\lambda_k}{\lambda} c_k W_k = \sum_{k=1}^{n} \frac{\lambda_k c_k \sum_{i=1}^{n} \lambda_i E(t_i^2)}{2\lambda(1 - \sum_{i=1}^{k-1} \rho_i)(1 - \sum_{i=1}^{k} \rho_i)} \tag{14-37}$$

This is the performance measure to be minimized.

By the same interchange argument used for deterministic models, the optimal priority assignment is seen to be

$$\frac{E(t_1)}{c_1} \le \frac{E(t_2)}{c_2} \le \cdots \le \frac{E(t_n)}{c_n} \tag{14-38}$$

This says that jobs with the smallest ratio of expected processing time to delay cost per unit time should be processed first. The sequence decision is made after each occasion of service. These results are comparable to the deterministic rule given by Equation 14–32 except that expected values for job classes rather than known service times for individual jobs are employed.

Shortest-Processing-Time Discipline. If the delay cost is the same for all priority classes, the rule of Equation 14–38 reduces to one which says give top priority to the job class with the shortest expected processing time. This presupposes that the classes have been previously specified.

Now let us suppose that processing times for all arriving jobs are random variables drawn from a single distribution. Further suppose that once a job enters the queue, its processing time can be accurately predicted. Such a system might be viewed as one with an infinite number of priority classes. A processing time p falling in the interval

$$t < p < t + dt$$

defines a priority class.

If jobs are selected for processing on the basis of highest priority for the lowest service times of jobs waiting in the queue and the delay cost for all jobs is c, Equation 14–37 becomes in the limit

$$K = \frac{c\lambda E(t^2)}{2} \int_0^{\infty} \frac{f(t)}{[1 - \lambda \int_0^t sf(s)\,ds]^2}\,dt \tag{14-39}$$

Here, $f(t)$ is the probability density function for processing time of all jobs.[16] Under conditions of no preemption, the shortest-processing-time discipline is again optimal if we have no advance information about impending arrivals other than the p.d.f. for service time. However, if processing time can be predicted in advance of a unit's arrival at the queue, it is possible to do better than this. The problem of how best to utilize such advance information, possibly by inserting idle time, has not been satisfactorily resolved.

---

[16] *Ibid.*, p. 237.

Queueing models which consider varying degrees of preemption and due date disciplines have also been developed. Readers interested in these extensions are urged to consult Conway, Maxwell, and Miller[17] or one of the many advanced queueing texts available.

The General Job Shop Problem

The last section treated both deterministic and probabilistic problems associated with sequencing jobs for a single facility. Now let us turn to a broader class of scheduling problems in which multiple facilities must be considered. The general job shop scheduling problem involves scheduling n jobs on m different machines where each job may require processing on any number of the machines and may be constrained by a required technological sequence. This is an intrinsically difficult problem which looks deceptively simple on the surface. The difficulty stems from the large number of theoretically possible sequences, given by $(n!)^m$. If, for example, we wanted to enumerate all possible cases for a simple 5-job, 5-machine problem, there are approximately 25 billion schedules to be evaluated. Obviously complete enumeration, even for problems of modest dimensions, is impossible.

Conway, Maxwell, and Miller note that the only job shop problem for which an optimal solution is really known is the n-job, two-machine problem in which the objective is to minimize the total time necessary to process all jobs.[18] This problem is a generalization of the two-machine flow-shop problem solved by Johnson.[19]

Johnson's Algorithm. The problem considered by Johnson involves sequencing n jobs on two machines, A and B, where all jobs must be processed in the order AB. Furthermore, each machine can work on only one job at a time and each job can be in process on only one machine at a time. The processing times are

A_i = time for job i on machine A

B_i = time for job i on machine B

Johnson shows that total elapsed time for the entire operation could be minimized by using the following rule:

1. Select the smallest processing time from among the sets $\{A_i\}$ and $\{B_i\}$.
2. If the minimum time is A_r, do the rth job first. If it is B_s, do the sth job last. In case of ties select either smallest processing time.
3. Eliminate the job now scheduled and repeat steps 1 and 2 on the reduced set of processing times.
4. Continue until all jobs have been ordered.

---

[17] Conway, *et al., op. cit.,* pp. 169–89.

[18] Conway *et al., op. cit.,* p. 105.

[19] S. M. Johnson, "Optimal Two- and Three-Stage Production Schedules with Setup Times Included," *Naval Research Logistics Quarterly,* Vol. I, No. 1 (March, 1954).

The order specified by this technique holds for the flow through both machines. To illustrate the rule suppose that we have the following set of jobs and their associated processing times:

Job	A_i	B_i
1	3 hrs.	6 hrs.
2	4	2
3	1	3
4	5	7
5	9	4

The smallest value is $A_3 = 1$. This says that job 3 should be processed first. Of the remaining time $B_2 = 2$ is the smallest. Job 2 should come last. Continuing in this manner, the optimal ordering is (3, 1, 4, 5, 2). A Gantt chart for this ordering is shown in Figure 14–13. From the chart, the minimum total elapsed time is 24 hours, as determined by the time at which job 2 leaves machine B.

Johnson also solved the n-job, three-machine problem under a very restrictive set of conditions. The general three-machine problem does not appear to have been solved.

Extension of the Two-Machine Problem. Jackson provided a direct generalization of Johnson's two-machine flow problem to account for the

FIGURE 14–13

Optimal Loading for a Two-Machine Flow Problem

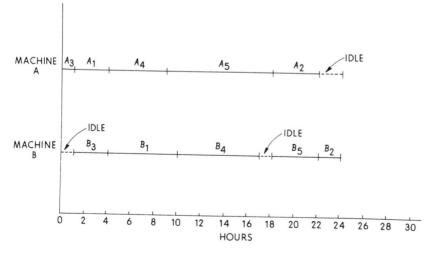

possibility of different technological restrictions among jobs.[20] His solution requires that each job can have, at most, two operations.

As described by Conway et al., Jackson's general rule proceeds as follows:[21]

1. Partition the n jobs into four sets.
    $\{A\}$ = set of jobs which have only one operation which is to be performed on machine A.
    $\{B\}$ = set of jobs which have only one operation which is to be performed on machine B.
    $\{AB\}$ = set of jobs which have two operations to be performed in the order AB.
    $\{BA\}$ = set of jobs which have two operations to be performed in the order BA.
2. Sequence the jobs of $\{AB\}$ by Johnson's algorithm independent of all others.
3. Sequence the jobs of $\{BA\}$ by Johnson's algorithm independent of all others.
4. Select any arbitrary order for the jobs of $\{A\}$ and $\{B\}$.
5. On machine A, order jobs in $\{AB\}$ before jobs in $\{A\}$ before jobs in $\{BA\}$ without changing the order within each set.
6. On machine B, order jobs in $\{BA\}$ before jobs in $\{B\}$ before jobs in $\{AB\}$.

Although various simulation techniques may be employed, extensions to the general m machine case are not yet generally available. However, research is being conducted in the area with some algorithms being developed which are theoretically sound but as yet computationally infeasible for use by the average operations engineer.[22]

SELECTED BIBLIOGRAPHY

BARNETSON, PAUL. *Critical Path Planning*. London: Newnes Books, 1968.

CONWAY, RICHARD W.; MAXWELL, WILLIAM L.; and MILLER, LOUIS W. *Theory of Scheduling*. Reading, Mass.: Addison-Wesley Publishing Co., 1967.

JACKSON, J. R. "An Extension of Johnson's Result on Job Lot Scheduling," *Naval Research Logistics Quarterly*, Vol. III, No. 3 (September, 1956).

JOHNSON, S. M. "Optimal Two- and Three-Stage Production Schedules with Setup Times Included," *Naval Research Logistics Quarterly*, Vol. III, No 1 (March, 1954).

KELLY, J. E., JR. "Critical Path Planning and Scheduling: Mathematical Basis," *Operations Research*, Vol. IX, No. 3 (May, 1961).

---

[20] J. R. Jackson, "An Extension of Johnson's Result on Job-Lot Scheduling," *Naval Research Logistics Quarterly*, Vol. 3, No. 3 (September, 1956).

[21] Conway et al., *op. cit.*, p. 105.

[22] See for example, *Naval Research Logistics Quarterly*, Vol. 15, No. 2 (June, 1968). This is a special issue devoted to papers presented at the Symposium on Industrial Sequencing held at Stevens Institute of Technology, December 11–13, 1967.

MALCOLM, D. G.; ROSEBOOM, J. H.; CLARK C. E.; AND FAZAR, W. "Application of a Technique for Research and Development Program Evaluation," *Operations Research*, Vol. VII, No. 5 (September, 1959)

MILLER, ROBERT W. *Schedule, Cost, and Profit Control with PERT.* New York: McGraw-Hill Book Co., Inc., 1963.

MODER, JOSEPH J., AND PHILIPS, CECIL R. *Project Management with CPM and PERT.* New York: Reinhold Publishing Corp., 1964.

MUTH, JOHN F., AND THOMPSON, GERALD L. (eds.). *Industrial Scheduling.* Englewood Cliffs, N.J.: Prentice-Hall, Inc., 1963.

THORNLEY, GAIL (ed.). *Critical Path Analysis in Practice.* London: Tavistock Publications, 1968.

PROBLEMS

14–1 PERT and critical path planning were discussed in the text. Compare these two techniques with respect to
a) Input information required.
b) Output information provided.

14–2 Consider the following precedence matrix in which each entry represents both precedence and time information:

	1	2	3	4	5	6	7
1	0	0	0	0	0	0	0
2	4	0	0	0	0	0	0
3	2	5	0	0	0	0	0
4	1	0	3	0	0	0	0
5	0	0	0	8	0	0	0
6	0	0	0	0	2	0	0
7	0	0	0	0	1	4	0

a) Construct an arrow diagram from this information.
b) Find the critical path.
c) Draw a connected Gantt chart to depict slack relationships among the activities.

14–3 A project has been analyzed in which 10 major events or benchmarks have been identified. The activities connecting these benchmarks and their associated deterministic time estimates are given below:

(1, 2).....3 wks.	(5, 8).....5 wks.
(1, 3).....4	(5, 10).....9
(1, 4).....2	(6, 8).....8
(2, 3).....2	(6, 7).....1
(2, 5).....2	(7, 8).....2
(3, 5).....6	(7, 9).....6
(3, 6).....7	(8, 10).....1
(4, 7).....3	(9, 10).....4

In addition to these requirements, it has been established that activity (4, 7) cannot begin before benchmark 3 has been reached. Similarly, activities (5, 10) and (5, 8) must wait until activity (3, 6) is completed.

    a) Construct a network diagram for this project.
    b) Establish the critical path.
    c) Calculate the total slack and free slack for every activity in the network.

    14–4 Consider the data of Problem 14–3 which are now expanded to include the following cost estimates for each activity:

(1, 2)......$4,800		(5, 8)......$2,500	
(1, 3)...... 6,000		(5, 10)...... 5,400	
(1, 4)...... 3,000		(6, 8)...... 6,400	
(2, 3)...... 4,000		(6, 7)...... 1,400	
(2, 5)...... 1,600		(7, 8)...... 800	
(3, 5)...... 6,000		(7, 9)...... 6,600	
(3, 6)...... 9,100		(8, 10)...... 700	
(4, 7)...... 2,400		(9, 10)...... 3,200	

    a) Construct cumulative cost curves based upon both early and late start times.

    b) Assume that the final budget is established from early start time estimates and that the project has been underway for six weeks. Activities (1, 2) and (1, 3) are complete. Activity (1, 4) is three-fourths completed and (2, 3) and (2, 5) are one-half complete. No other activities have been started. $18,000 has been spent to date. Prepare a project status report for management.

    14–5 An enterprising student has agreed to undertake the design and fabrication of a Dating Response Analysis Gage (DRAG). He has identified the following activities with their associated time estimates and precedence relationships:

Activity	Time (Days)	Immediate Predecessors
1. Establish design specs	5, 6, 8	–
2. Electrical design	7, 9, 10	1
3. Mechanical design	6, 7, 8	2
4. Breadboard fabrication and test	2, 3, 3	2
5. Prepare materials order	1, 1, 2	1
6. Fabricate and test prototype	4, 10, 12	3, 4
7. Prepare blueprints	1, 1, 1	3, 6
8. Prepare final report	3, 4, 5	6, 7

For personal reasons the project cannot be started until final exams are over (16 days from now). Fabrication and test of the prototype must await the arrival of his wife for obvious reasons. She will not be on campus until two weeks after final exams. Materials for the prototype require three weeks' delivery.

    a) Establish a PERT network for this project designating appropriate activities with arrows and events with nodes. Comment on any difficulties encountered and how they may be solved.

    b) Estimate the earliest expected time and the variance for starting the mechanical design activity.

14-6 In a certain small research project the following activities have been identified together with their three classical PERT type time estimates:

Activity	a	m	b
(1, 2)	–	–	–
(1, 3)	3	6	9
(2, 3)	1	2	9
(2, 4)	3	3	9
(3, 4)	1	2	3
(3, 5)	2	8	8
(4, 5)	1	2	9
(4, 6)	4	5	12
(5, 6)	1	3	5

The critical path on the PERT chart has been identified as the one passing through the events (or benchmarks) 1, 2, 3, 5, 6. The time estimates for activity (1, 2) have been misplaced, but the project manager feels that a good guess is that they came from a symmetric distribution. It is known that the variance for time to complete the project has been calculated to be 30/9. It is also known that the probability of being able to meet a 20-day deadline is 0.8643. Calculate the missing estimates of time for activity (1, 2).

14-7 A certain small research project has been identified by the following activities and time estimates:

Activity	a	m	b
(1, 2)	4	5	6
(1, 3)	3	6	9
(2, 3)	1	2	9
(2, 4)	3	3	9
(3, 4)	1	2	3
(3, 5)	2	8	8
(4, 5)	1	2	9
(4, 6)	4	5	12
(5, 6)	–	–	–

The critical path has been identified as the one passing through the events 1, 2, 3, 5, 6. The time estimates for activity (5, 6) have been misplaced, but the project manager feels that they come from a symmetric distribution. It is known that variance for time to complete the project is 30/9. It is also known that the probability of being able to meet a 20-day deadline is 0.8643.

a) Calculate the missing estimates for activity (5, 6).

b) Calculate the probability that event 3 will have positive slack greater than 1.

14-8   O. R. Student is busily planning his trip to the Poppy Bowl. He has identified seven major benchmarks that he must achieve before the project is completed. Being a polished practitioner of probability theory, he has better estimates than most people concerning the probability distributions associated with each of his activities. He has assembled the following data for the project:

Activity (i,j)	Immediate Predecessors	Time Estimate (t_{ij})
(1, 2)	—	$f(t_{12}) = (0.2)(0.8)^{t_{12}-1}$
(1, 3)	—	$f(t_{13}) = \dfrac{6^{t_{13}}e^{-6}}{t_{13}!}$
(1, 4)	—	$f(t_{14}) = \dfrac{24(0.5)^4}{(t_{14})!(4 - t_{14})!}$
(2, 5)	(1, 2), (3, 2)	$f(t_{25}) = 0.2$ for $t_{25} = 1, 2, 3, 4, 5$
(3, 2)	(1, 3)	$f(t_{32}) =$ chi-square distributed with mean 4
(3, 5)	(1, 3)	$a = 2, m = 5, b = 5$
(3, 7)	(1, 3)	$a = 7, m = 7, b = 7$
(4, 6)	(1, 4)	$a = 2, m = 3, b = 4$
(5, 7)	(2, 5), (3, 5), (6, 5)	$f(t_{57}) =$ normal with mean $= 3$, variance $= 1$
(6, 5)	(4, 6)	$f(t_{65}) =$ Poisson with standard deviation $= 2$

a) Construct an arrow diagram, with activities as arrows, for this project.

b) Construct a table for mean and variance for each activity.

c) Identify the critical path and expected completion time.

d) Calculate the probability that he can finish the project in 15 days.

e) Suppose that event i has mean and standard deviation for early time of 15 and 4 and a mean and variance for late time of 20 and 9. Find the probability that event i will become critical.

f) O. R. Student is conservative and does not want to make any assumptions about the form of the distribution for project completion time. However, he believes that the mean and variance will be 20 and 16. Establish for him a probability interval on completion time such that the probability of falling within that interval is at least 0.84.

14-9   Many of you are now engaged or will soon become engaged in thesis research. As with any research project there are certain well-defined events and activities which must occur. As an exercise of personal interest and usefulness as well as an exercise to satisfy this problem requirement, prepare a PERT analysis of your thesis activities.

a) Make a complete list of activities together with all predecessor and successor events.

b) Make the required three estimates of time to perform each activity. (Use days as the unit of time.)

c) Construct the PERT network.

d) Calculate the critical path.

e) Assume that you are now 120 days (2 quarters) from proposed graduation.

On the basis of your PERT analysis, what is the probability of graduating on time?
(For Ph.D., assume 240 days.)

f) How many days before proposed graduation should your thesis research
begin in order to be 90 percent confident of graduating on time?

14-10 General Foulup is planning his next offensive. He has identified five
separate intermediate objectives which must be achieved before the campaign is
completed. Major Mindsore has established the following estimates for the time
necessary to move from objective to objective:

Activity	Immediate Predecessors	Time Estimates (t_{ij}) in Days
(1, 2)	—	$t_{12} = 20$
(1, 3)	—	$f(t_{13}) = N(\mu = 18, \sigma = 4)$
(2, 4)	(1, 2)	$f(t_{24}) = $ exponential, $\sigma^2 = 225$
(3, 4)	(1, 3)	$t_{34} = 10$ or 14 equally likely
(3, 5)	(1, 3)	$t_{35} = \dfrac{6^{t_{35}}e^{-6}}{t_{35}!}$
(4, 6)	(2, 4), (3, 4)	$f(t_{46}) = \dfrac{1}{3}$, $t_{46} = 8, 10, 12$
(5, 6)	(3, 5)	$a = 2, m = 3, b = 10$

a) Construct an arrow diagram for the campaign.
b) Determine the critical path.
c) What is the probability of completing the campaign within 50 days? (State
all assumptions.)
d) What is the probability that the path 1, 3, 4, 6 will in fact be critical? (State
all assumptions.)

14-11 Using *Johnson's algorithm* for sequencing *N* jobs on two machines,
determine the sequence for the five following jobs which will minimize elapsed
time *T*. (All jobs must be processed in the order *AB*, and no passing is permitted.)
What is the minimum elapsed time? What is the idle time on each machine? Draw
a Gantt chart for each machine.

Job	Processing Time (Hours) Machine A	Machine B
1	5	2
2	1	6
3	9	7
4	3	8
5	10	4

14–12   The Swing Time Skirt Company has orders for five types of hula skirts. The technology of hula skirt manufacturing is such that every skirt must begin at the bamboo shredder. Most skirts then to on to the hip threader for completion. An entire lot of each type of skirt is processed at the first machine before any work on that lot can be performed by the next machine. Swing Time has only one shredder and one threader. Processing times for each lot at each machine are given below. What is the sequence of lots which will minimize total elapsed time? What is the idle time on each machine? Draw a Gantt chart for each machine.

Skirt Type	Lot Threader Time (Hrs.)	Lot Shredder Time (Hrs.)
1	5	2
2	0	3
3	6	9
4	8	3
5	4	10

14–13   The Indian Maid Jewelry Company manufactures tie-clips for department stores. They have received an order for 50 Type 1, 20 Type 2, 30 Type 3, 10 Type 4, and 5 Type 5 clips from Gumball's Department Store. All clips except Type 2 are first blanked from copper sheet. Type 2 is imported from Japan and does not require blanking. All types are then hand stamped "Indian Maid." Since these are Gumball's own designs, they are to be batch processed, i.e., all units of Type 1 are blanked before any are stamped. Processing times for each clip are given below:

Clip	Blank	Stamp
1	2 min. per clip	3 min. per clip
2	4	2
3	3	5
4	1	2
5	8	6

a) Determine the optimal sequence for processing these orders assuming that one wishes to minimize total through-put time.

b) Construct a Gantt chart for each machine.

c) What will be the minimum time necessary to fill the order?

d) What is the idle time on each machine under optimal conditions?

14–14   Joe College has a stack of "I" assignments which are already overdue. Joe estimates that the time required to finish assignment i is a_i. The shortest assignment in the lot requires more than one hour to complete. Professor Hardnose has established a rule whereby the grade received on each assignment is inversely proportional to the product of times devoted to all assignments accomplished to date. Let S be the schedule which does assignment 1 first, assignment 2 second, etc.

Develop a scheduling rule which will maximize Joe's potential score. Give a brief proof that your rule leads to an optimal schedule.

14–15 Suppose that "*I*" jobs must be scheduled on an electronic computer. Job *i* requires a_i minutes to process. All times are known with certainty, and all jobs are available for processing at time zero. The completion time for job *i* is the sum of its own processing time and the processing times for all jobs which precede it. If S represents the schedule which does job 1 first, 2 second, etc., the completion time for job *i* may be written as

$$\sum_{j=1}^{i} a_j.$$

a) Develop a scheduling rule which will minimize the sum of completion times as an overall measure of customer service.

b) Give a brief proof that your rule leads to an optimal schedule.

14–16 Consider a simplified version of the problem faced by a controller who is attempting to sequence a group of aircraft for landing. All aircraft must hold at the outer marker until released by the controller. No aircraft can depart the marker until the preceding aircraft is clear of the runway. Three classes of aircraft are to be served, each with its own approach and landing time and each with a different average number of passengers on board. When the controller takes over his position he is faced with the following population of aircraft in the holding pattern:

Type	Approach and Landing Time	Average Passengers	Number of Aircraft Holding
1	3 min.	1	2
2	4	180	3
3	5	3	5

a) If no other aircraft arrive, determine the optimal landing sequence for minimizing the mean time to land an aircraft.

b) Determine the optimal sequence if the criterion is average passenger-minutes delay.

14–17 Consider again the data of Problem 14–16. Suppose that the controller begins processing the given population at $t = 0$. However, a sequence of new aircraft arrive with no prior warning as follows:

Time	Arriving Aircraft/Type	Time	Arriving Aircraft/Type
5 min.	2	11	2
7	3	13	1
10	2	17	3

a) Determine the optimal sequence for landing all of these aircraft under a nonpreemptive discipline and assuming that the measure of performance is mean aircraft delay time.

b) Comment on the weaknesses of your solutions for aiding a real controller.

14–18   Consider a maintenance facility which assigns nonpreemptive priorities to arriving customers as follows:

Customer	Priority	Arrival Rate	Service Distribution (Minutes)
Corporation	1	3 per hour	$b_1(t) = 0.25, 8 \le t \le 12$
Individual	2	5	$b_2(t) = 0.50, 3 \le t \le 5$
Nonprofit organization	3	2	$b_3(t) = 0.5e^{-0.5t}, t \ge 0$

a) Determine the expected waiting time for each class of customer.

b) Establish an optimum sequencing rule for this system and compare the delay times with part (*a*).

c) Suppose that each corporate customer represents $10 profit, each individual represents $15, and each nonprofit organization represents $8. Determine the optimum sequence and estimate the overall average cost per job.

14–19   Consider the standard single-channel, Poisson arrival, negative exponential service system with an arrival rate of 20 per hour and service rate of 25 per hour. Compare the expected processing time for a first-come, first-served discipline with expected processing time of a priority system in which highest priorities are given to the lowest service time jobs.

14–20   A group of 10 jobs is to be sequenced for processing on a milling machine and lathe. The jobs with their technological restrictions and processing times are listed below.

Job	Time on Mill	Time on Lathe	Order
1	15 min.	12 min.	M-L
2	—	10 min.	L
3	20 min.	22 min.	L-M
4	18 min.	30 min.	L-M
5	6 min.	10 min.	M-L
6	15 min.	—	M
7	—	10 min.	L
8	20 min.	—	M
9	16 min.	12 min.	M-L
10	—	8 min.	L

a) Determine the optimum sequence for jobs to minimize total elapsed time.

b) Construct a Gantt chart for the loading on each machine.

CHAPTER 15

Simulation

SIMULATION is a modeling technique which retains a high degree of isomorphism with the real world phenomena it represents. The term encompasses activities as diverse as instrument training for pilots in Link trainers and analysis of job shop production scheduling. The Link trainer is a physical model of an aircraft. It responds to changes in control movement by indicating on both cockpit and external instruments what effects such movements would have on aircraft direction, speed, altitude, etc. Only those aspects of the real aircraft necessary to control and record instrument flight are retained. For instance, the trainer does not have an operating airfoil attached or tires to be checked for proper inflation prior to takeoff.

A job shop simulation is not generally a physical model but rather is a collection of mathematical statements and logical connections which record the state of the system in a bookkeeping sense. Time histories of in-process inventory, release and delivery dates, machine utilization, etc., together with computed measures of performance such as operating cost, are recorded. In the same manner as with physical models, only those aspects of the system essential to understanding the problem being analyzed are retained. The simulation is not generally concerned with safety practices, lighting, power requirements, and the like. It is concerned with machining times, reliability, scheduling, and dispatching. Simulation for the balance of this chapter will refer to special models of management control systems similar to the job shop scheduling model.

Perspective

Simulation refers to the dynamic operation of a model of a system. The essential ingredients of a simulation study as suggested by Gregory and Van Horn are

1. Data concerning the behavior of variables.
2. A statement of the rules which gives the outcome of various combinations of decisions and circumstances.
3. A statement of management policies relevant to the problem.[1]

Note that these are the same basic requirements placed on the actual control system. Simulation merely reproduces the operation of the real system under selected conditions of environmental and management policies.

Relationship to Other Modeling Techniques. Simulation models are constructed for the same reasons that all other models discussed in this text were constructed. Namely,

1. To highlight problems of interest.
2. To provide economical experimentation.
3. To force precision of thought.
4. To solve operational problems.

The type of model most frequently referred to up to this point has been the mathematical model. Mathematical models use symbols to represent the characteristics of the phenomena from which they abstract. Simulation models are special cases of the general class of mathematical models. As such they may be classified according to the number of variables involved, predictability of events in the system, and the intent of the model.

Simulation can obviously be used as an alternative to analytical methods such as inventory and queueing theory. For that reason any attempt to clearly define unique applications for the tool leads to ambiguities. However, it can be said that simulation is strongest in the analysis of large and complex systems involving stochastic elements for which dynamic solutions are desirable. Simulation usually involves only the larger more complex systems for two reasons: cost and precision. If the system is simple enough we can often get analytic solutions on paper much more cheaply than we can write, debug, and make repeated runs of the computer programs usually required for simulation. At the same time, where analytic solutions are possible we can be more precise and hence sure of our results.

Simulation models are often very realistic, falling just short of actual experimentation with the real system. Analytic models, on the other hand, often are very abstract in terms of the operations performed to obtain solutions and in terms of performance measures offered to management. Placing the three major study techniques on a scale of realism would find analytical models at the bottom and real world experimentation at the top with simulation falling nearer to real experimentation. However, increased realism implies increased expense, decreased ease of manipulation, and more

---

[1] R. H. Gregory, and R. L. Van Horn, *Automatic Data Processing Systems* (San Francisco: Wadsworth Co., 1960).

difficulty in discerning cause and effect. There is generally a very large jump in expense between simulation and real system experiments and a somewhat smaller but often quite significant jump between the most sophisticated analytic models and simulation.

Why Simulate. We have alluded to many of the reasons for having simulation models. At this point let us enumerate these reasons more specifically:

1. *Complexity.* Many problems are too complex to be solved by more classical means. This is especially true if one seeks a time varying solution for a stochastic system.
2. *Reality.* Simulation models are often the closest representation to the real system short of physical reproduction of the system. They can handle many variables, and they are comparatively easy to understand. The form of the input and output is the same as that which is witnessed in the real system.
3. *Data Fit.* Simulation models are not necessarily concerned with the mathematical fit of input data. They can operate on the data as they exist with few simplifying assumptions.
4. *Performance Criteria.* The decision maker is not limited to a single measure of performance but has available to him a wide range of measures with which to evaluate tradeoffs.
5. *High Speed.* Months of operating experience in the real system can be compressed into minutes in many computer simulation models.
6. *Validation.* Because of its high degree of realism the actual time history of an operating system can be checked against parallel simulations run under similar operating conditions.

It is well to inject a note of caution at this point. Simulation is a powerful tool and is often the only means of analyzing very complex systems. It is also fairly straightforward to develop; and given enough perseverance, it will yield results. However, it is an experimental tool which is essentially descriptive in nature and as such can never guarantee an optimum solution. It may be possible to get better solutions by more formal mathematical methods of analysis. Such solutions are often overlooked because of the complexity of the symbolism of the analytical models as opposed to the relative ease of simulation. Availability of computers and funding may lead to lazy analysis. This can be an expensive oversight both in terms of the expense of achieving results and the quality of those results. That is not to say that a system as complex as a job shop scheduling system will yield to more formal mathematics. It is only a caution to the reader so that the benefits of the many available operations research models for studying limited portions of the larger system will not be overlooked. Some other pitfalls of simulation are discussed later in this chapter.

Role of Computers

There is no inherent relationship between simulation and digital computers. To simulate means to set up a model of a system and then perform experiments on that model. If the size of the system is limited and the sample size is small, perfectly good simulations can be run with paper and pencil. However, for large systems requiring a vast amount of sampling, the computer is a necessity. Simulation gains its power as an experimental tool only when large amounts of data with many different policies can be analyzed in a short time span. The electronic computer makes this possible.

Relationship to the Operating System. The use of electronic data processing has provided important opportunities for changes in management thinking. Many of the current generation of high-speed, digital computers are capable of simultaneously performing a large portion of a corporation's routine clerical tasks, providing programmed decision making for repetitive operations and serving as experimental tools for testing new policies.

Using the computer as an experimental device to simulate the effects of new management policies on system performance represents an enlightened viewpoint on the part of management. In areas such as inventory control, for example, initial use of computers was limited to bookkeeping functions which merely totaled daily sales and purchases to give management reports of current inventory position. Later, users began to program for the computer routine policy decisions such as when and how much to order. The computer could then maintain records, issue shipping notices, and flag exceptional cases for management attention. Now some inventory programs such as IBM's IMPACT include routine decision making, complete with demand forecasting and a continuously operating simulation program.[2] The simulator permits management to test the effects of changing forecasting schemes and reorder levels by processing real data and without disturbing current operations. The fully mature computer system is then capable of functioning simultaneously as a routine data processor, a control device, and an experimental tool.

Simulation Experiments

Simulation is an experimental technique. As such it can benefit from the same technology of experimental design and statistical analyses applied to real world experiments with physical systems. This means that one must take care to establish proper controls, make efficient use of experiment runs, and couch results in statistical terms. However, simulation does have a number of advantages over real world experimentation in terms of efficient experimental design. Among such advantages are the elimination of nonessential

---

[2] *Retail IMPACT*, IBM Application Program, White Plains, New York, 1965.

system detail and the ability to exactly reproduce a time series of data under a variety of operating rules.

Realism. The high degree of realism it is possible to capture with simulation can be a mixed blessing. On the positive side, a detailed simulation can capture a much larger number of interacting variables than can be captured with analytical models. At the same time, experiments can be performed on the simulated system much more cheaply than on its real world counterpart. The high isomorphism with the real world also provides a ready sales device to impress skeptical managers. The simulation performs the same calculations and expresses results in the same terms as experienced in daily operations. The belief that the analyst really understands the system is particularly strengthened when he can show model validation by producing simulated results which closely parallel the real system operating under the same rules over a test period.

On the negative side, some simulation models may err in being overly realistic. It is not always necessary to have an exact replica of an operating system to experiment with major policy changes. Too much trivia may obscure cause and effect relationships. In addition unnecessary detail multiplies the time necessary to create the model, may make it difficult to fit the program into available machine storage, and incurs large amounts of avoidable expense.

Experimental Control. One important advantage of simulation over real world experiment is the ability to provide the same set of economic conditions over and over. This permits conclusions to be drawn relative to alternative proposals without worrying about the influence of varying market conditions, employee performance, and the like. In inventory systems, for example, the effects of changing the reorder point may be extremely difficult to evaluate if one can only compare new system performance with performance evidenced over past time periods. There is no guarantee that observed changes are solely the result of the new ordering policy. With simulation studies utilizing pseudo-random numbers it is possible to measure system performance under both sets of ordering rules while all other aspects of the system, including demand patterns, are held constant.

Variance reducing techniques such as stratified sampling can be used to reduce the number of samples necessary to achieve the desired precision in sample estimates. Essentially such techniques guarantee that different portions of probability distributions will be sampled with different frequencies to guarantee that relatively rare events located on the tail of the curve will be represented. Hillier and Lieberman have a brief outline of how such techniques work.[3] For purposes of this text we will adopt a straightforward Monte Carlo technique but recognize that more efficient methods are available for advanced students of simulation.

---

[3] Frederick S. Hillier and Gerald J. Lieberman, *Introduction to Operations Research* (San Francisco: Holden-Day Co., 1967), pp. 452–62.

Simulation Details

After questions concerning the number of variables and the general experimental design have been answered, the mechanics of operating the simulator must be considered. This means that we must answer questions such as the following: Should we use real time series data or sample from probability distributions? If probability distributions are used should they be empirical or reasonably fit theoretical approximations to empirical data? What will be the initial conditions for the simulation study? Should we use random numbers (or pseudo-random numbers) to carry out our sampling? Should we use a time clock with which simulation time is advanced at fixed intervals, or an event clock with which simulation time is keyed to critical events? These questions will be discussed below.

Live Data Simulation. When studying a real system already in existence, it is often possible to develop a time series of critical events with that system. For example, in analyzing an inventory control system, demand data may be represented by a sales tape which lists in sequence the exact time history of demand experienced by that system. The analyst then has the alternatives of using this sequence as presented, developing an empirical probability distribution from these data or fitting a theoretical distribution to the data. We will refer to the use of the actual time sequence as live data simulation.

A live data simulation literally reproduces the bookkeeping transactions experienced by the real system. For example if the transactions tape for sales of automobile windshields from a parts supply warehouse shows 5 sales on Monday, 3 on Tuesday, and 10 on Wednesday, those are exactly the numbers used in the simulation study for those days. Simulated inventory would be reduced by 5, 3, then 10 units on the first 3 days of the week as was the real inventory system. This technique can be contrasted with Monte Carlo methods in which histograms for daily sales frequency must be constructed by examining a long history of sales. Random samples are then drawn from these distributions to determine the particular sales figure to be used by the simulated system each day. Depending upon the statistical characteristics of the data, a single distribution or separate ones for each day of the week may be required.

Live data simulation has at least three major advantages. First, it permits simulation model validation by comparing real with simulated performance while employing exactly the same input for each system. Second, it permits the real system to operate as an experimental control when the simulation is run under revised policies in parallel with the real system operating under existing policies. Finally, the importance of live data in establishing management confidence in results cannot be overemphasized.

Consider the analysis of an inventory control system. When real and simulated systems are run with exactly the same input data and exactly the same policy statements, validation takes the form of reproduction of results. Other than the fact that some unnecessary detail may have been omitted from the simulation, it may function exactly as the real inventory system. In a sense many such studies are not simulations at all but rather experiments in running a reproduction of the real system. This form of analysis can be used to advantage when the simulation is run in parallel with the operating system, absorbing the same input data as they are generated. Once validated, one can provide controls by running the simulation under revised policies and comparing with the time series of performance measures generated by the real system. In addition, if management elects to alter the policies in the real system, the simulation can be run under the old rules to provide a dynamic benchmark with which to compare system performance. In this instance the simulation serves as a control for the real world experiment. The live data simulation permits management to answer the question of what would have happened last month if . . . .

Most simulation studies are easier to sell to nontechnically trained managers than are the often more powerful techniques of formal mathematical analysis. This is true simply because the simulation absorbs data and produces results in a manner familiar to management people. In a sense it looks like the system being modeled. Such a statement may not be possible for a system of integral or differential equations. A point by point comparison of time series output is much more easily interpreted. That is not to say that the results are as meaningful as the aggregate of many runs of a well-designed Monte Carlo simulation experiment or careful mathematical analysis. The strength of live data simulations for nonmathematically trained management personnel is their intuitive appeal.

Before investing heavily in live data simulations, one must carefully weigh their disadvantages. First, it may be impossible to collect the desired time series data from existing system records. This limitation is most obvious for new system design with no operating history. Second, even if such data are available they may not be the ones needed. For example, a simulation of an inventory system which uses a shipping tape to provide demand data can be very misleading. Units shipped today may reflect sales several days past, the availability of stock, possible freight connections, etc. To use such data as exact representations of demand under revised inventory policies could be disastrous. Third, the particular time sequence of data observed represents only a sample of one. There is no guarantee that future time periods will in any way resemble the test period used. In addition, one must state results in terms of a single observation rather than being able to make confidence interval statements about the precision of the observed output.

In the eyes of management science purists such limitations far outweigh the several advantages of live data simulation. On the other hand this technique has been employed on at least two very large inventory systems within the author's experience with resulting system changes which management felt saved many thousands of dollars.

Monte Carlo Simulation. The term Monte Carlo has been used to describe numerical techniques for solving equations, variance reducing techniques, and simulation in general. We will adopt the point of view that Monte Carlo techniques refer to all sampling procedures used in simulation studies which involve using random numbers to obtain particular values of random variables in the model.

For a sequence of digits to qualify as random numbers, each successive number must have an equal probability of taking on any one of the possible values and be statistically independent of other numbers in the sequence. There are a number of techniques available for generating such a sequence ranging from physical devices to recurrence relations started from a seed number and proceeding through a series of multiplications and modulo divisions. When a digital computer is being used for the simulation, commercial packages for generating simple random numbers as well as random numbers from well-known probability distributions are usually available. When simulations are run by hand, the most popular source for random numbers is a Rand Corporation publication.[4] A brief table of random numbers is reproduced in the Appendix.

In the strictest sense of the word, most numbers generated by the computer are not random numbers. They are predictable and a given sequence can be reproduced by starting with the same parameters each time. Such numbers are sometimes called pseudo-random numbers. The fact that a given sequence can be reproduced can be used to advantage. Since it is possible to generate the same set of input data points for each of a number of successive runs of the simulation, policies can be tested by the same techniques suggested for live data simulations. The effects of pseudo-random numbers can be obtained in manual simulations by always starting at the same point and proceeding in the same direction in the table of random numbers.

The particular probability distribution from which samples are drawn in simulation studies may be a relative frequency diagram of empirical data, a known probability function which approximates empirical data, or a hypothesized probability distribution for elements with no historical data. Basic Monte Carlo techniques can be used in each of these cases.

One of the major advantages of simulation over most analytical techniques is the ability to utilize empirical distributions without regard to the particular mathematical equation which may describe the shape of the observed curve. Again there are two sides to the issue. One camp argues that empirical curves offer more realism in that no approximations are used to guarantee a fit. Another camp argues that fitting a known probability function to the observed data rather than sampling from the theoretical curve is better for several reasons. First, an empirical distribution represents a brief sample of past history. There is no guarantee that the exact conditions leading to those

---

[4] The Rand Corporation, *A Million Random Digits with* 100,000 *Normal Deviates* (Glencoe, Ill.: The Free Press, 1955).

data will ever be present again. They argue that well-known probability distributions which reasonably fit such data may in fact give a better picture of future events than the empirical curve itself. In a sense the empirical curve can be viewed as a sample drawn from a more basic underlying distribution. A second argument in favor of theoretical curves over empirical ones is the limited sample sizes often used to develop the data. For example, lead-time data collected in an inventory system over a one-year period might show no occasions of lead time exceeding four weeks. However, lead times as high as eight weeks may be possible even though they are relatively infrequent. If no such times are observed, samples taken from the empirical distribution will treat them as impossible events even though those rare events may be the ones most critical for successful inventory control system design. A final advantage of theoretical distributions over empirical curves is the ease of manipulating data within the computer. If an equation for the distribution exists, it is a simple matter to obtain the value of the random variable associated with a particular random number. Empirical distributions on the other hand may require storage of large amounts of data and considerable computer time to perform table look-up operations.

The basic Monte Carlo technique consists of generating a random number in the range zero to one, associating that number with a corresponding point on the cumulative probability distribution, then determining the value of the random variable from the distribution. To illustrate the method of calculation, consider a random variable x with the following distribution:

$$f(x) = \begin{cases} 0.2 & x = 0 \\ 0.5 & x = 1 \\ 0.3 & x = 2 \end{cases}$$

The relative frequency with which x takes the value zero is two tenths. This means that if we were to generate many samples of 100 random numbers each, on the average we want 20 of those numbers to be associated with an x value of zero. If we look at the cumulative distribution for x shown in Figure 15–1, we note that the fraction of the vertical axis covered by the zero bar is 0.2, that covered by the one bar is 0.5, and that covered by the two bar is 0.3. We could generate random numbers in the interval 00 to 99 and say that any number from 00 to 19 represents $x = 0$, from 20 to 69 represents $x = 1$, and 70 to 99 represents $x = 2$. Since all the digits from 00 to 99 are equally likely, the proper relative frequency of x values would be obtained in the long run.

The sampling procedure can be illustrated graphically. First, place the value of the random number on the vertical axis of the cumulative distribution diagram shown in Figure 15–1. Next, draw a horizontal line from that point until it meets the cumulative curve. Finally move vertically down to read the x value associated with the sample random number. The example shown starts with the two-digit random number 79 which converted to a

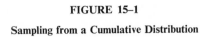

FIGURE 15–1

Sampling from a Cumulative Distribution

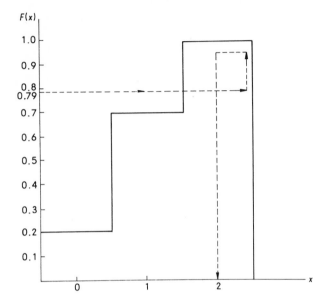

zero-one scale is 0.79. The associated value of the random variable is $x = 2$. For continuous distributions the technique works exactly the same except that each random number and hence horizontal line, is associated with a unique value of the random variable. This can be contrasted with our discrete example in which any random number between 70 and 99 gives the same random variable value of $x = 2$.

Initial Conditions. The choice of initial conditions for a simulation study is a function of the intent of the study. Sometimes the purpose of the study is to develop steady-state estimates of system performance measures, such as the average waiting time and average queue length in queueing problems. In that case one wishes to start the simulation with the system as near to steady-state configuration as possible. In a queueing problem that may mean starting with n units in the system spread in judicious fashion among the various service centers. As a time sequence of simulated results accumulate, we would hope that they would evidence a "settling down" to statistical equilibrium more quickly than results generated for a system which is initially at rest. To avoid biasing steady-state estimates with unwanted initial transients, simulations may also be started with the system at rest and run for some time before performance statistics are collected. In this fashion it is hoped that results will be representative of a mature system.

For many studies, however, simulation is the chosen tool simply because it does reflect transient conditions. For example, in a given queueing configuration we may want to know how long the lines will be at some specified time in the future after the service facility has opened. Opening may occur with no units in the system, as might be the case at a teller's window in a bank at 9:00 A.M. Alternatively opening may occur with a number of units present as might occur at the ticket window for a popular play. In the first case we might want to know how the queue builds up as the day progresses. In the second we might want to know how the queue dissipates over time. We could complicate the system even further by sampling from different arrival and service distributions as the simulated day progresses. Such transient conditions are easily simulated but often nearly impossible to capture by analytical models.

Simulation Timing.   The internal bookkeeping functions of a simulation can be carried out in several ways. In fixed interval timing the simulation clock is advanced as are real life timing devices, say five minutes at a time. In each fixed interval all potential events are sampled and their effects tabulated before the clock moves to the next interval. Although time can be compressed, in the sense of representing hours by minutes on the computer, these simulations essentially follow a one for one time count with the real system.

An alternative to this approach might be called an event clock. In this case time between major events determines when bookkeeping takes place. Nothing about the state of the system is recorded during the intervening interval. In a queueing problem, for example, we might sample from the distribution of time between arrivals. At arrival n the state of the system would be noted then the simulation clock would be advanced by the sample value of elapsed time t to the next arrival. At that point a second random variable representing possible number of services during t would be selected and the arithmetic leading to the current number in the system would be performed. The simulation clock leaps from point to point on the time scale with the length of each advance controlled by the time between significant events. A fixed interval counterpart of the queueing example would be to sample from the probability distribution for arrivals and services in an interval of length L, update all records, advance to the next interval, repeat the sampling, etc. The advantage of significant event timing is that it conserves computer time by leaping over periods of inactivity. Its disadvantage is that the state of the system at every instant of time is no longer available.

Synopsis.   Either fixed-interval or significant event simulations can employ deterministic or probabilistic events and both can provide the same steady-state measures of performance. A probabilistic representation of service times may be more realistic especially where human operators are involved. One always runs the risk, however, that particular results from a probabilistic model may be mere freaks of sampling rather than resulting from conscious changes of rules by the experimenter. For that reason, Monte Carlo simulations must be repeated many times or run long enough to gain confidence in the results. The distinction of significant-event versus fixed-interval simulations is one of different methods of interval control by the computer. All simulations are in reality mathematical models which are run rather than solved in the sense of more formal techniques.

Example. A computer installation at a research laboratory currently handles all of its jobs on a first-come, first-served basis. A proposed priority policy is to process all jobs with estimated processing times less than or equal to 15 minutes on a first-come, first-served basis. Any job whose estimated running time exceeds 15 minutes is to be postponed and will not be processed until after the 6:00 P.M. quitting time for most research personnel. The computer will be run as long as necessary to complete the day's backlog of work. In the event that the work load is so great that the 15-minute jobs carry-over into the next processing day, they are handled before the new shorter jobs. Since much of the work load consists of scientific problems which require many attempts at compiling and relatively short tests, management hopes to decrease the turnaround time and hence increase the efficiency of their research personnel by postponing the more lengthy production runs until the second shift. They want easy access to the computer for their scientific programmers.

Data have been collected from job cards submitted with each request for computer service. These cards record the time that the job was submitted and the estimated processing time. As a first approximation we will assume that estimated processing time is the same as actual processing time. The number of jobs submitted varies by hour of the day. This information is presented in relative frequency form by Table 15–1. The required processing time for each job is a random variable ranging from 5 to 60 minutes. The empirical distribution for these times, to the nearest five minutes, is given in Table 15–2.

For purposes of illustration we will make the simplifying assumptions that (1) all jobs arrive on the hour; (2) all jobs have exactly the processing time indicated; (3) even if the computer is idle, no jobs requiring more than 15 minutes will be processed before 6:00 P.M.; and (4) the total number of jobs submitted in one day, k, can be fixed by the experimenter. The measure of performance is turnaround time defined as elapsed time from submission of a job until processing on that job is complete. The flow chart for one feasible

TABLE 15–1

Job Arrival Frequencies

Hour of the Day	Proportion of Jobs Submitted	Hour of the Day	Proportion of Jobs Submitted
7:00 A.M.	0.016	1:00 P.M.	0.110
8:00	0.100	2:00	0.092
9:00	0.111	3:00	0.078
10:00	0.105	4:00	0.139
11:00	0.086	5:00	0.058
12:00 P.M.	0.052	6:00	0.053

TABLE 15–2
Processing Time Distribution

Processing Time	Proportion of Jobs	Processing Time	Proportion of Jobs
5 min.	0.30	35 min.	0.01
10	0.32	40	0.01
15	0.18	45	0.01
20	0.10	50	0.01
25	0.03	55	0.01
30	0.01	60	0.01

method for carrying out this simulation is given in Figure 15–2. This chart illustrates an efficient method for hand computation, although it could undoubtedly be improved upon for machine calculations.

The first step in the simulation study is to convert the arrival and service distributions into cumulative terms. The cumulative distribution for arrivals is then

Hours (a)	Probability that Arrival Occurs at or Before (a)
7:00	0.016
8:00	0.116
9:00	0.227
10:00	0.332
11:00	0.418
12:00	0.470
1:00	0.580
2:00	0.672
3:00	0.750
4:00	0.889
5:00	0.947
6:00	1.000

The cumulative distribution for service becomes:

Process Time (P)	Probability that Processing Time is Less than or Equal to (P)
5 min.	0.30
10	0.62
15	0.80
20	0.90
25	0.93
30	0.94
35	0.95
40	0.96
45	0.97
50	0.98
55	0.99
60	1.00

FIGURE 15–2

Simulation Flow Chart

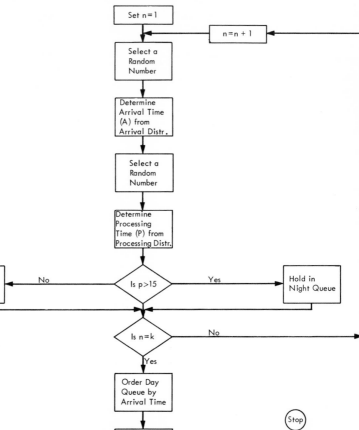
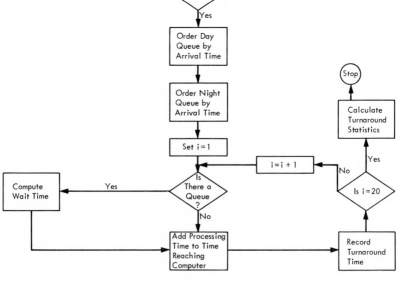

To sample from the arrival distribution we will use three-digit random numbers. If the random number falls between 001 and 016 we will say that an arrival occurred at 7:00. If it falls between 017 and 116 we will say that an arrival occurred at 8:00 and so forth. In similar fashion we can use two-digit random numbers to sample from the process time distribution. If the random number selected falls between 01 and 30 we will say that processing time for the job in question was five minutes. Proceeding up the scale, if the random number is 00 we will say that the processing time was 60 minutes. This procedure is equivalent to the graphical technique outlined in Figure 15–1.

Suppose that we wish to determine average turnaround time for a day in which 20 jobs are processed. Following our flow-chart procedure in Figure 15–2, a random number, say 784, is selected. This number falls between 751 and 889, which, from our cumulative arrival distribution, means that an arrival occurs at 4:00 P.M. A two-digit random number, say 45, is then selected to determine the processing time for this job. From our process time distribution this means that the job will require 10 minutes of machine time. Twenty such pairs of numbers have been generated in like fashion with the following results:

Job n	First Random Number	Arrival Time	Second Random Number	Process Time
1	784	4 : 00	45	10 min.
2	787	4 : 00	97	45
3	064	8 : 00	97	45
4	047	8 : 00	62	10
5	971	6 : 00	80	15
6	719	3 : 00	84	20
7	788	4 : 00	58	10
8	612	2 : 00	15	5
9	050	8 : 00	59	10
10	959	6 : 00	43	10
11	199	9 : 00	25	5
12	035	8 : 00	98	50
13	568	1 : 00	52	10
14	876	4 : 00	26	5
15	951	6 : 00	24	5
16	056	8 : 00	38	10
17	659	2 : 00	18	5
18	590	2 : 00	51	10
19	066	8 : 00	88	20
20	113	8 : 00	10	5

Recall that our policy statement requires that all jobs with processing times greater than 15 minutes must be delayed until after 6:00 P.M. and after all short jobs are finished. The 20 jobs must now be split into day and night operations and placed in order of arrival times so that turnaround times can be calculated. From our initial list we have four 8:00 A.M. arrivals with process times less than 15 minutes. We have three 8:00 A.M. arrivals with process times exceeding 15 minutes. The first four lead the daytime queue and the last three lead the nighttime queue. Since the first daytime job arriving at 8:00 has a process time of 10 minutes and no waiting time, its turnaround is 10 minutes. The second daytime job arriving at 8:00 must wait for the computer to complete processing the first job before its process time of ten minutes can begin. Turnaround time for the second job is then 10 minutes of wait plus 10 minutes of processing for 20 minutes total. All daytime jobs are analyzed in similar fashion, the last one being completed at 6:30 P.M. The first night-time job then begins its 45-minute processing at 6:30 P.M., although it has been in the queue since 8:00 A.M. Total turnaround time for this job is then 11 hours and 15 minutes. These calculations are summarized in Table 15–3.

TABLE 15–3

Simulated Twenty-Job Day

Arrival Number	Arrival Time	Process Time	Time at the Computer	Time Out	Turnaround
1	8 : 00	10 min.	8 : 00 A.M.	8 : 10	10
2	8 : 00	10	8 : 10	8 : 20	20
3	8 : 00	10	8 : 20	8 : 30	30
4	8 : 00	5	8 : 30	8 : 35	35
5	9 : 00	5	9 : 00	9 : 05	05
6	1 : 00	10	1 : 00 P.M.	1 : 10	10
7	2 : 00	5	2 : 00	2 : 05	05
8	2 : 00	5	2 : 05	2 : 10	10
9	2 : 00	10	2 : 10	2 : 20	20
10	4 : 00	10	4 : 00	4 : 10	10
11	4 : 00	10	4 : 10	4 : 20	20
12	4 : 00	5	4 : 20	4 : 25	25
13	6 : 00	15	6 : 00	6 : 15	15
14	6 : 00	10	6 : 15	6 : 25	25
15	6 : 00	5	6 : 25	6 : 30	30
Night Queue					
1	8 : 00	45	6 : 30	7 : 15	11 : 15
2	8 : 00	50	7 : 15	8 : 05	12 : 05
3	8 : 00	20	8 : 05	8 : 25	12 : 25
4	3 : 00	20	8 : 25	8 : 45	5 : 45
5	4 : 00	45	8 : 45	9 : 30	5 : 30
				Total Job Time	51 : 30
				Average Turnaround	2.57 hours

From Table 15–3 it can be noted that average turnaround time for this single 20-job day is 2.57 hours. To effectively test the policy, many such runs should be made. Furthermore, it might be feasible to develop a probability distribution for number of jobs per day so that a long series of simulated days could be run to more closely fit the actual system. If these results indicate further refinement is in order, more exact data concerning arrival times, service times at several intermediate steps, such as card to tape conversion, central processing unit (cpu) time, and printout time, etc., must be developed. The reader is asked to pursue some of these extensions in the problems at the end of the chapter.

Simulation Languages

Most simulation studies require many iterations of the basic model before meaningful results can be obtained. This, coupled with the large number of variables involved, makes use of the digital computer mandatory. Simulation has become a viable tool for analysis only because we have high-speed digital computers with large storage capabilities available to us.

Unfortunately, users of simulation often find that programming is more time consuming than basic problem formulation. Communicating with the computer requires that the analyst be familiar with computer codes or he must transfer the logic of the problem formulation to a professional programmer who can communicate directly with the computer. Unless he routinely works in a programming capacity, an analyst who writes his own machine code programs is apt to find many subtle bugs creeping into his simulation which may require days of detailed search to uncover. On the other hand if an analyst depends upon professional programmers to translate the logic of his model into workable machine code, he may find that the subtleties of the structure are misinterpreted by the programmer. In either case the effect is to promote inefficient use of the model builder's time in translating problem formulation to machine execution.

The solution to the analyst's dilemma is to provide a computer language which is easily learned and used by engineering personnel. A number of such languages are now available. The choice of which to use requires trade-offs among familiarity on the part of the analyst, programming time required, and efficiency of running the end program.

General-Purpose Languages. The highest level of program abstraction normally achieved by analysts who use simulation is that of one of the well-known general-purpose languages such as FORTRAN, ALGOL, or COBOL. The use of more basic assembly languages, such as FAP, SAP, and MAP, is limited to professional programmers and occasional debugging exercises.

When a general-purpose language such as FORTRAN is used, a maximum of flexibility is possible. Each system being simulated has its own custom designed program. The format of input and output, the kinds of experiments to be performed, and the mathematical statements admissible are completely at the command of the analyst.

The major advantages of using a general-purpose language are the freedom in model format offered to the analyst and the efficient running of the finished product. If a very large number of runs are to be made with a given program, this can offer considerable savings in computation expense over more specialized simulation languages. The major penalty paid is in terms of added programming time. This includes the difficulty of writing and debugging simulation programs in a general-purpose language as well as repeating similar sets of logic many times in each program and among parallel studies.

Simulation Languages. Much of the time spent in logical formulation and programming of simulation models is common from one program to the next. It was the recognition of this fact, together with the desire to provide languages easily learned and used by nonprofessional programmers, which led to the development of a number of special-purpose simulation languages. Among these languages are GPSS, SIMSCRIPT, GASP, SIMPAC, DYNA-MO, and SIMULATE.

Each of these languages has different characteristics and each has special problem types for which it is best suited. Naylor *et al.*, presents an excellent comparison among these and other languages.[5] If networks of queues are to be analyzed, the analyst might prefer GPSS. If large-scale economic systems involving extensive information feedback mechanisms are being modeled, DYNAMO might be the preferred language. SIMSCRIPT and GASP are somewhat more general simulation languages which could be profitably used in a variety of contexts. With the exception of GASP, which is basically a FORTRAN main program and attached subroutines, most of the special-purpose languages require their own particular symbols and instructions.

The main advantages for most of the simulation languages are the speed with which programs can be written and the ease of learning the language. A relatively few instructions are involved. The penalties for programming ease are that flexibility and running time are sacrificed. Systems to be modeled must be made to conform to the basic logical structure of the language. Model subtleties may be either unattainable or require extensive programming to circumvent the relatively rigid structure of the language. Special-purpose simulation languages are most helpful in answering questions relative to fairly standard industrial engineering problems, such as queues and inventories.

Simulation Games

All of the discussion in this chapter has concerned the use of simulation as an experimental arm of the usual form of engineering analysis. Another popular form of simulation is the so-called business game or its military counterpart the war game. In these studies a model of the business or military

---

[5] Thomas H. Naylor, Joseph L. Balintfy, Donald S. Burdick, and Kong Chu, *Computer Simulation Techniques* (New York: John Wiley & Sons, Inc., 1966), Chap. vii.

operation is provided with continuous inputs from human participants. The participants make sequential decisions about the policies of the system and in this way assume the role of managing the simulated operation. Texts such as that by Greenlaw *et al.*, describe how such games are conducted.[6] Simulations of this variety are excellent management education devices and can be used for research on the human decision maker. Since they are not routinely employed in engineering analysis, nothing more will be said of them here.

SELECTED BIBLIOGRAPHY

GORDON, G. "A General Purpose Systems Simulator," *IBM Systems Journal*, Vol. I, (1962).

GREENLAW, PAUL S.; HERRON, LOWELL W.; AND RAWDON, RICHARD H. *Business Simulation*. Englewood Cliffs, N.J.: Prentice-Hall, Inc., 1962.

GREGORY, R. H., AND VAN HORN, R. L. *Automatic Data Processing Systems*. San Francisco: Wadsworth Co., 1960.

HILLIER, FREDERICK S., AND LIEBERMAN, GERALD J. *Introduction to Operations Research*. San Francisco: Holden-Day Co., 1967.

MARKOWITZ, HARRY M.; HAUSNER, BERNARD; AND KARR, HERBERT W. *SIMSCRIPT*, The Rand Corporation. Englewood Cliffs, N.J.: Prentice-Hall, Inc., 1963.

A Million Random Digits with 100,000 Normal Deviates, The Rand Corporation. Glencoe Ill.: The Free Press, 1955.

NAYLOR, THOMAS H.; BALINTFY, JOSEPH L.; BURDICK, DONALD S.; AND CHU, KONG. *Computer Simulation Techniques*. New York: John Wiley & Sons, Inc., 1966.

Retail Impact. IBM Applications Program, White Plains, New York, 1965.

PROBLEMS

15–1 Consider the computer system described by Table 15–1 and Figure 15–2. Suppose that this example is extended to a 30-job day. Simulate the results of this increased load. Calculate the time the last job will leave the computer and the average turnaround time. Compare these results with the 20-job example in the text.

15–2 Suppose that the computer processing example is changed to investigate a priority rule which states that only those jobs with processing times longer than 10 minutes will be delayed until 6:00 P.M. Simulate a 20-job day under this rule. Compare these results to 15-minute and 20-minute cutoff policies.

15–3 Suppose that the computer processing example is changed to accept all jobs on a first-come, first-served basis. Simulate the results of a 20-job day under this policy. Compare the simulated results with a steady-state approximation developed from the standard queueing formulations of Chapter 12.

---

[6] Paul S. Greenlaw, Lowell W. Herron, and Richard H. Rawdon, *Business Simulation* (Englewood Cliffs, N.J.: Prentice Hall, Inc., 1962).

15–4   In the computer processing example, suppose that a distribution for the number of units arriving each day is available. Alter the design of the simulation to take advantage of this information and explain how you would conduct experiments to test management proposals about job segregation.

15–5   Design a simulation to investigate the operation of a computer system in which arriving jobs are first processed on one of two card to tape conversion units. Tapes are not made available to the CPU until some fixed number of jobs n_1 are on the tape. If the CPU is busy when the number of jobs on either tape reaches n_1, that tape can continue to accept jobs until it reaches n_2 or until it can gain access to the CPU. Once a tape has access to the CPU, all jobs on that tape are processed before a new tape is admitted. From the CPU, a_1 portion of the jobs go to the printer, a_2 go to the card punch, and a_3 go to a new tape. Probability distributions for arrival times and service times at each of the service facilities are available.

a) Draw a flow chart for your simulation program.

b) Explain the measures of performance you would like to provide to management from this simulation which would assist in a decision concerning the possible purchase of new equipment.

15–6   Use the table of random numbers to select four observations from each of the following probability distributions:

a) Normal with mean 5 and variance 2.

b) Exponential with mean 10.

c) Poisson with mean 8.

d) Uniform in the interval $6 \leq x \leq 10$ where x is discrete.

e) Uniform in the interval $6 \leq x \leq 10$ where x is continuous.

15–7   Simulate the operation of a two-man barbershop over an eight-hour day. Customers are taken on a first-come, first-served basis. Barber A cuts hair at an average rate of 12 minutes per head. Barber B takes an average of 15 minutes per head. The variation around these numbers is assumed to be normal with zero mean and variance 6.25 for A and uniform with zero mean and range 5 for B. The measures of performance are expected waiting time, expected total processing time, and average number of customers present. Customers arrive in Poisson fashion at a rate of six per hour.

a) Simulate this system assuming zero in line at the start of the day.

b) Simulate this system assuming that the arrival rate for the first 4 hours is 12 per hour and for the last 4 hours, 4 per hour.

15–8   Simulate the operation of a traffic light at an intersection. The arrival rates for vehicles coming from north, south, east, and west are 120, 480, 300, and 60 per hour respectively. The time between vehicles is exponentially distributed. The time required by a vehicle to clear the intersection is uniformly distributed between three and five seconds. The light is timed so that the north-south flow has a green light for three minutes followed by a two-minute red light. Begin the simulation with a red light for north-south traffic and 5, 12, 6, and 2 cars in the north, south, east, and west queues respectively. Simulate two hours of traffic flow recording the line lengths at each signal change. Calculate the average line length and the expected delay from each direction. Compare these results with a simple analytical solution which ignores the batching properties of the signal.

15–9 Consider the operation of landing a group of 12 aircraft. All aircraft are in a holding pattern awaiting service. Each must go through a 15-mile final approach before reaching the runway. There are 6 aircraft with mean approach speeds of 90 m.p.h., 3 with 120 m.p.h., and 3 with 180 m.p.h. Because of variation in pilot skills, actual speeds may vary ±10 m.p.h. around these figures. Time to clear the runway after touchdown is 1.0, 1.2, and 1.5 minutes respectively for the three classes of aircraft. No aircraft is permitted to pass another on final and only one can occupy the runway at any point in time. When conflicts occur, the overtaking aircraft must return to the holding pattern at the same speed with which he was coming down the final approach. Simulate the landing of these aircraft under each of the sets of conditions listed below. Record system performance in terms of total aircraft delay time and total time to land all aircraft.

a) Initial separation of three miles required, service in random order.

b) Initial separation of six miles required, service in random order.

c) Initial separation of three miles required, aircraft served in order of expected approach speed with the fastest first.

15–10 Data from the Office of the Registrar indicate that the frequency distribution for time between arrivals of students during a sample period was

Time between Arrivals	Number of Observations
1 min.	328
2	312
3	110
4	103
5	97
6	50

A study of clerk efficiency reveals that the time a clerk requires to serve a student is distributed by

t (Minutes)	$f(t)$
1	0.05
2	0.34
3	0.11
4	0.20
5	0.13
6	0.07
7	0
8	0
9	0
10	0.10

Simulate the operation of the Registrar's Office for serving the first 10 students of the day under each of the following conditions.

i) A single clerk is available.

ii) Two clerks are available, a single line forms, and the next man up steps to the first open window.

iii) Human clerks are replaced by a computer which serves all students at a rate of two minutes per student.

In each of the above cases, calculate service facility idle time, maximum line length, and average through time per student.

15–11   Monte Carlo has a battlefield simulation ready to operate on site near the island of Nirvana. To operate the simulation he needs to sample from a normal distribution with mean 20 and variance 16. He has no way to directly generate the required normal observations. However, he can send out 10-man patrols to check the enemy stables. From old Prussian Army data he believes that the number of kicks inflicted on a man assigned to such a patrol will be distributed by a nonnormal distribution with a mean of 3.0 and variance 2.5.

a) Develop and justify a method for obtaining the necessary normal observations from patrol missions.

b) Illustrate your method for the particular set of $(1, 0, 3, 5, 6, 4, 2, 2, 0, 3)$ kicks suffered by the members of a patrol.

Appendix

TABLE A

Cumulative Normal Distribution*

$$F(x) = \int_{-\infty}^{x} \frac{1}{\sqrt{2\pi}} e^{-t^2/2}\, dt$$

z	.00	.01	.02	.03	.04	.05	.06	.07	.08	.09
.0	.5000	.5040	.5080	.5120	.5160	.5199	.5239	.5279	.5319	.5359
.1	.5398	.5438	.5478	.5517	.5557	.5596	.5636	.5675	.5714	.5753
.2	.5793	.5832	.5871	.5910	.5948	.5987	.6026	.6064	.6103	.6141
.3	.6179	.6217	.6255	.6293	.6331	.6368	.6406	.6443	.6480	.6517
.4	.6554	.6591	.6628	.6664	.6700	.6736	.6772	.6808	.6844	.6879
.5	.6915	.6950	.6985	.7019	.7054	.7088	.7123	.7157	.7190	.7224
.6	.7257	.7291	.7324	.7357	.7389	.7422	.7454	.7486	.7517	.7549
.7	.7580	.7611	.7642	.7673	.7704	.7734	.7764	.7794	.7823	.7852
.8	.7881	.7910	.7939	.7967	.7995	.8023	.8051	.8078	.8106	.8133
.9	.8159	.8186	.8212	.8238	.8264	.8289	.8315	.8340	.8365	.8389
1.0	.8413	.8438	.8461	.8485	.8508	.8531	.8554	.8577	.8599	.8621
1.1	.8643	.8665	.8686	.8708	.8729	.8749	.8770	.8790	.8810	.8830
1.2	.8849	.8869	.8888	.8907	.8925	.8944	.8962	.8980	.8997	.9015
1.3	.9032	.9049	.9066	.9082	.9099	.9115	.9131	.9147	.9162	.9177
1.4	.9192	.9207	.9222	.9236	.9251	.9265	.9279	.9292	.9306	.9319
1.5	.9332	.9345	.9357	.9370	.9382	.9394	.9406	.9418	.9429	.9441
1.6	.9452	.9463	.9474	.9484	.9495	.9505	.9515	.9525	.9535	.9545
1.7	.9554	.9564	.9573	.9582	.9591	.9599	.9608	.9616	.9625	.9633
1.8	.9641	.9649	.9656	.9664	.9671	.9678	.9686	.9693	.9699	.9706
1.9	.9713	.9719	.9726	.9732	.9738	.9744	.9750	.9756	.9761	.9767
2.0	.9772	.9778	.9783	.9788	.9793	.9798	.9803	.9808	.9812	.9817
2.1	.9821	.9826	.9830	.9834	.9838	.9842	.9846	.9850	.9854	.9857
2.2	.9861	.9864	.9868	.9871	.9875	.9878	.9881	.9884	.9887	.9890
2.3	.9893	.9896	.9898	.9901	.9904	.9906	.9909	.9911	.9913	.9916
2.4	.9918	.9920	.9922	.9925	.9927	.9929	.9931	.9932	.9934	.9936
2.5	.9938	.9940	.9941	.9943	.9945	.9946	.9948	.9949	.9951	.9952
2.6	.9953	.9955	.9956	.9957	.9959	.9960	.9961	.9962	.9963	.9964
2.7	.9965	.9966	.9967	.9968	.9969	.9970	.9971	.9972	.9973	.9974
2.8	.9974	.9975	.9976	.9977	.9977	.9978	.9979	.9979	.9980	.9981
2.9	.9981	.9982	.9982	.9983	.9984	.9984	.9985	.9985	.9986	.9986
3.0	.9987	.9987	.9987	.9988	.9988	.9989	.9989	.9989	.9990	.9990
3.1	.9990	.9991	.9991	.9991	.9992	.9992	.9992	.9992	.9993	.9993
3.2	.9993	.9993	.9994	.9994	.9994	.9994	.9994	.9995	.9995	.9995
3.3	.9995	.9995	.9995	.9996	.9996	.9996	.9996	.9996	.9996	.9997
3.4	.9997	.9997	.9997	.9997	.9997	.9997	.9997	.9997	.9997	.9998

z	1.282	1.645	1.960	2.326	2.576	3.090	3.291	3.891	4.417
F (z)	.90	.95	.975	.99	.995	.999	.9995	.99995	.999995
2[1 - F(z)]	.20	.10	.05	.02	.01	.002	.001	.0001	.00001

* Reprinted with permission of the publisher from Alexander M. Mood, *Introduction to the Theory of Statistics* (New York: McGraw-Hill Book Co., Inc., 1950), p. 423.

TABLE B

Cumulative Poisson Probabilities × 1,000*

μ \ x	0	1	2	3	4	5	6	7	8	9	10	11	12	13	14
0.1	905	995	1,000												
0.2	819	982	999	1,000											
0.3	741	963	996	1,000											
0.4	670	938	992	999	1,000										
0.5	607	910	986	998	1,000										
0.6	549	878	977	997	1,000										
0.7	497	844	966	994	999	1,000									
0.8	449	809	953	991	999	1,000									
0.9	407	772	937	987	998	1,000									
1.0	368	736	920	981	996	999	1,000								
1.1	333	699	900	974	995	999	1,000								
1.2	301	663	879	966	992	998	1,000								
1.3	273	627	857	957	989	998	1,000								
1.4	247	592	833	946	986	997	999	1,000							
1.5	223	558	809	934	981	996	999	1,000							
1.6	202	525	783	921	976	994	999	1,000							
1.7	183	493	757	907	970	992	998	1,000							
1.8	165	463	731	891	964	990	997	999	1,000						
1.9	150	434	704	875	956	987	997	999	1,000						
2.0	135	406	677	857	947	983	995	999	1,000						
2.2	111	355	623	819	928	975	993	998	1,000						
2.4	091	308	570	779	904	964	988	997	999	1,000					
2.6	074	267	518	736	877	951	983	995	999	1,000					

TABLE B (Continued)
Cumulative Poisson Probabilities × 1,000

μ \ x	0	1	2	3	4	5	6	7	8	9	10	11	12	13	14
2.8	061	231	469	692	848	935	976	992	998	999	1,000				
3.0	050	199	423	647	815	916	966	988	996	999	1,000				
3.2	041	171	380	603	781	895	955	983	994	998	1,000				
3.4	033	147	340	558	744	871	942	977	992	997	999	1,000			
3.6	027	126	303	515	706	844	927	969	988	996	999	1,000			
3.8	022	107	269	473	668	816	909	960	984	994	998	999	1,000		
4.0	018	092	238	433	629	785	889	949	979	992	997	999	1,000		
4.2	015	078	210	395	590	753	867	936	972	989	996	999	1,000		
4.4	012	066	185	359	551	720	844	921	964	985	994	998	999	1,000	
4.6	010	056	163	326	513	686	818	905	955	980	992	997	999	1,000	
4.8	008	048	143	294	476	651	791	887	944	975	990	996	999	1,000	
5	007	040	125	265	440	616	762	867	932	968	986	995	998	999	1,000
6	002	017	062	151	285	446	606	744	847	916	957	980	991	996	999
7	001	007	030	082	173	301	450	599	729	830	901	947	973	987	994
8	000	003	014	042	100	191	313	453	593	717	816	888	936	966	983
9	000	001	006	021	055	116	207	324	456	587	706	803	876	926	959
10	000	000	003	010	029	067	130	220	333	458	583	697	792	864	917
11		000	001	005	015	038	079	143	232	341	460	579	689	781	854
12		000	001	002	008	020	046	090	155	242	347	462	576	682	772
13			000	001	004	011	026	054	100	166	252	353	463	573	675
14				000	002	006	014	032	062	109	176	260	358	464	570
15				000	001	003	008	018	037	070	118	185	268	363	466

Cumulative Poisson Probabilities × 1,000

x \ μ	15	16	17	18	19	20	21	22	23	24	25	26	27	28	29
7	998	999	1,000												
8	992	996	998	999	1,000										
9	978	989	995	998	999	1,000									
10	951	973	986	993	997	998	999	1,000							
11	907	944	968	982	991	995	998	999	1,000						
12	844	899	937	963	979	988	994	997	999	999	1,000				
13	764	835	890	930	957	975	986	992	996	998	999	1,000			
14	669	756	827	883	923	952	971	983	991	995	997	999	999	1,000	
15	568	664	749	819	875	917	947	967	981	989	994	997	998	999	1,000

x \ μ	0	1	2	3	4	5	6	7	8	9	10	11	12	13	14
16					000	001	004	010	022	043	077	127	193	275	368
17					000	001	002	005	013	026	049	085	135	201	281
18						000	001	003	008	015	030	055	092	143	208
19						000	001	002	004	009	018	035	061	098	150
20							000	001	002	005	011	021	039	066	105
21								000	001	003	006	013	025	043	072
22								000	001	002	004	008	015	028	048
23									000	001	002	004	009	017	031
24										000	001	003	005	011	020

TABLE B (*Concluded*)

Cumulative Poisson Probabilities × 1,000

x \ μ	15	16	17	18	19	20	21	22	23	24	25	26	27	28	29
16	467	566	659	742	812	868	911	942	963	978	987	993	996	998	999
17	371	468	564	655	736	805	861	905	937	959	975	985	991	995	997
18	287	375	469	562	651	731	799	855	899	932	955	972	983	990	994
19	215	292	378	469	561	647	725	793	849	893	927	951	969	980	988
20	157	221	297	381	470	559	644	721	787	843	888	922	948	966	978
21	111	163	227	302	384	471	558	640	716	782	838	883	917	944	963
22	077	117	169	232	306	387	472	556	637	712	777	832	877	913	940
23	052	082	123	175	238	310	389	472	555	635	708	772	827	873	908
24	034	056	087	128	180	243	314	392	473	554	632	704	768	823	868

x \ μ	30	31	32	33	34	35	36	37	38	39	40	41	42	43	44
16	999	1,000													
17	999	999	1,000												
18	997	998	999	1,000											
19	993	996	998	999	999	1,000									
20	987	992	995	997	998	999	1,000								
21	976	985	991	994	997	998	999	999	1,000						
22	959	973	983	989	994	996	998	999	999	1,000					
23	936	956	971	981	988	993	996	997	999	999	1,000				
24	904	932	953	969	979	987	992	995	997	998	999	999	1,000		

* W. J. Fabrycky and Paul E. Torgersen, *Operations Economy: Industrial Applications of Operations Research*, © 1966. Reprinted by permission of Prentice-Hall, Inc., Englewood Cliffs, N.J.

TABLE C

Table of Random Digits

54941	72711	39406	94620	27963	96478	21559	19246	88097	44026
02349	71389	45608	60947	60775	73181	43264	56895	04232	59604
98210	44546	27174	27499	53523	63110	57106	20865	91683	80688
11826	91326	29664	01603	23156	89223	43429	95353	44662	59433
96810	17100	35066	00815	01552	06392	31437	70385	45863	75971
81060	33449	68055	83844	90942	74857	52419	68723	47830	63010
56135	80647	51404	06626	10042	93629	37609	57215	08409	81906
57361	65304	93258	56760	63348	24949	11839	29793	37457	59377
24548	56415	61927	64416	29934	00755	09418	14230	62887	92683
66504	02036	02922	63569	17906	38076	32135	19096	96970	75917
45068	05520	56321	22693	35089	07694	04252	23791	60249	83010
99717	01542	72990	43413	59744	44595	71326	91382	45114	20245
05394	61840	83089	09224	78530	33996	49965	04851	18280	14039
38155	42661	02363	67625	34683	95372	74733	63558	09665	22610
74319	04318	99387	86874	12549	38369	54952	91579	26023	81076
18134	90062	10761	54548	49505	52685	63903	13193	33905	66936
92012	42710	34650	73236	66167	21788	03581	40699	10396	81827
78101	44392	53767	15220	66319	72953	14071	59148	95154	72852
23469	42846	94810	16151	08029	50554	03891	38313	34016	18671
35342	56119	97190	43635	84249	61254	80993	55431	90793	62603
55846	18076	12415	30193	42777	85611	57635	51362	79907	77364
22184	33998	87436	37430	45246	11400	20986	43996	73112	88474
83668	66236	79665	88312	93047	12088	86937	70794	01041	74867
50083	70696	13558	98995	58159	04700	90443	13168	31553	67891
97765	27552	49617	51734	20849	70198	67906	00880	82899	66065
49988	13176	94219	88698	41755	56216	66832	17748	04963	54859
78257	86249	46134	51865	09836	73966	65711	41699	11732	17173
30946	22210	79302	40300	08852	27528	84648	79589	95295	72895
19468	76358	69203	02760	28625	70476	76410	32988	10194	94917
30806	80857	84383	78450	26245	91763	73117	33047	03577	62599
42163	69332	98851	50252	56911	62693	73817	98693	18728	94741
39249	51463	95963	07929	66728	47761	81472	44806	15592	71357
88717	29289	77360	09030	39605	87507	85446	51257	89555	75520
16767	57345	42285	56670	88445	85799	76200	21795	38894	58070
77516	98648	51868	48140	13583	94911	13318	64741	64336	95103
87192	66483	55649	36764	86132	12463	28385	94242	32063	45233
74078	64120	04643	14351	71381	28133	68269	65145	28152	39087
94119	20108	78101	81276	00835	63835	87174	42446	08882	27067
62180	27453	18567	55524	86088	00069	59254	24654	77371	26409
56199	05993	71201	78852	65889	32719	13758	23937	90740	16866
04994	09879	70337	11861	69032	51915	23510	32050	52052	24004
21725	43827	78862	67699	01009	07050	73324	06732	27510	33761
24305	37661	18956	50064	39500	17450	18030	63124	48061	59412
14762	69734	89150	93126	17700	94400	76075	08317	27324	72723
28387	99781	52977	01657	92602	41043	05686	15650	29970	95877

Source: Extracted from "Table of 105,000 Random Decimal Digits," Statement No. 4914, File No.261–A–1
(Washington, D.C.: Interstate Commerce Commission, 1949).

TABLE D

Capital-Recovery Factors for Interest Rates from 6% to 50%*

n	$\dfrac{i(1+i)^n}{(1+i)^n-1}$				Given P, To Find R				RP t-n (xxxxx)		n
n	6%	8%	10%	12%	15%	20%	25%	30%	40%	50%	n
1	1.06000	1.08000	1.10000	1.12000	1.15000	1.20000	1.25000	1.30000	1.40000	1.50000	1
2	0.54544	0.56077	0.57619	0.59170	0.61512	0.65455	0.69444	0.73478	0.81667	0.90000	2
3	0.37411	0.38803	0.40211	0.41635	0.43798	0.47473	0.51230	0.55063	0.62936	0.71053	3
4	0.28859	0.30192	0.31547	0.32923	0.35027	0.38629	0.42344	0.46163	0.54077	0.62308	4
5	0.23740	0.25046	0.26380	0.27741	0.29832	0.33438	0.37184	0.41058	0.49136	0.57582	5
6	0.20336	0.21632	0.22961	0.24323	0.26424	0.30071	0.33882	0.37840	0.46126	0.54812	6
7	0.17914	0.19207	0.20541	0.21912	0.24036	0.27742	0.31634	0.35687	9.44192	0.53108	7
8	0.16104	0.17401	0.18744	0.20130	0.22285	0.26061	0.30040	0.34191	0.42804	0.52030	8
9	0.14702	0.16008	0.17364	0.18768	0.20957	0.24808	0.28876	0.33123	0.42034	0.51335	9
10	0.13587	0.14903	0.16275	0.17698	0.19925	0.23852	0.28007	0.32346	0.41432	0.50823	10
11	0.12679	0.14008	0.15396	0.16842	0.19107	0.23110	0.27349	0.31773	0.41013	0.50585	11
12	0.11928	0.13270	0.14676	0.16144	0.18448	0.22526	0.26845	0.31345	0.40718	0.50388	12
13	0.11296	0.12652	0.14078	0.15568	0.17911	0.22062	0.26454	0.31024	0.40510	0.50258	13
14	0.10758	0.12130	0.13575	0.15087	0.17469	0.21689	0.26150	0.30782	0.40363	0.50172	14
15	0.10296	0.11683	0.13147	0.14682	0.17102	0.21388	0.25912	0.30598	0.40259	0.50114	15
16	0.09895	0.11298	0.12782	0.14339	0.16795	0.21144	0.25724	0.30458	0.40185	0.50076	16
17	0.09544	0.10963	0.12466	0.14046	0.16537	0.20944	0.25576	0.30351	0.40132	0.50051	17
18	0.09236	0.10670	0.12193	0.13794	0.16319	0.20781	0.25459	0.30269	0.40094	0.50034	18
19	0.08962	0.10413	0.11955	0.13576	0.16134	0.20646	0.25366	0.30206	0.40067	0.50023	19
20	0.08718	0.10185	0.11746	0.13388	0.15976	0.20536	0.25292	0.30159	0.40048	0.50016	20
25	0.07823	0.09368	0.11017	0.12750	0.15470	0.20212	0.25095	0.30043	0.40009	0.50002	25
30	0.07265	0.08883	0.10608	0.12414	0.15230	0.20085	0.25031	0.30011	0.40002	0.50000	30
40	0.06646	0.08386	0.10226	0.12130	0.15056	0.20014	0.25003	0.30008	0.40001	0.50000	40
50	0.06344	0.08174	0.10086	0.12042	0.15014	0.20002	0.25000	0.30001	0.40000	0.50000	50
100	0.06018	0.08004	0.10001	0.12000	0.15000	0.20000	0.25000	0.30000	0.40000	0.50000	100
∞	0.06000	0.08000	0.10000	0.12000	0.15000	0.20000	0.25000	0.30000	0.40000	0.50000	∞

* H. G. Thuesen, *Engineering Economy*, 2d ed., © 1957. Reprinted by permission of Prentice-Hall, Inc., Englewood Cliffs, N.J.

TABLE E

Present-Worth Factors for Interest Rates from 6% to 50%*

					Given S, To Find P						
	$\dfrac{1}{(1+i)^n}$								PS i-n (xxxxx)		
n											n
	6%	8%	10%	12%	15%	20%	25%	30%	40%	50%	
1	0.9434	0.9259	0.9091	0.8929	0.8696	0.8333	0.8000	0.7692	0.7143	0.6667	1
2	0.8900	0.8573	0.8264	0.7972	0.7561	0.6944	0.6400	0.5917	0.5102	0.4444	2
3	0.8396	0.7938	0.7513	0.7118	0.6575	0.5787	0.5120	0.4551	0.3636	0.2963	3
4	0.7921	0.7350	0.6830	0.6355	0.5718	0.4823	0.4096	0.3501	0.2603	0.1975	4
5	0.7473	0.6806	0.6209	0.5674	0.4972	0.4019	0.3277	0.2693	0.1859	0.1317	5
6	0.7050	0.6302	0.5645	0.5066	0.4323	0.3349	0.2621	0.2071	0.1328	0.0878	6
7	0.6651	0.5835	0.5132	0.4523	0.3759	0.2791	0.2097	0.1594	0.0949	0.0585	7
8	0.6274	0.5403	0.4665	0.4039	0.3269	0.2326	0.1678	0.1226	0.0678	0.0390	8
9	0.5919	0.5002	0.4241	0.3606	0.2843	0.1938	0.1342	0.0943	0.0484	0.0260	9
10	0.5584	0.4632	0.3855	0.3220	0.2472	0.1615	0.1074	0.0725	0.0346	0.0173	10
11	0.5268	0.4289	0.3505	0.2875	0.2149	0.1346	0.0859	0.0558	0.0247	0.0116	11
12	0.4970	0.3971	0.3186	0.2567	0.1869	0.1122	0.0687	0.0429	0.0176	0.0077	12
13	0.4688	0.3677	0.2897	0.2292	0.1625	0.0935	0.0550	0.0330	0.0126	0.0051	13
14	0.4423	0.3405	0.2633	0.2046	0.1413	0.0779	0.0440	0.0254	0.0090	0.0034	14
15	0.4173	0.3152	0.2394	0.1827	0.1229	0.0649	0.0352	0.0195	0.0064	0.0023	15
16	0.3936	0.2919	0.2176	0.1631	0.1069	0.0541	0.0281	0.0151	0.0046	0.0015	16
17	0.3714	0.2703	0.1978	0.1456	0.0929	0.0451	0.0225	0.0115	0.0033	0.0010	17
18	0.3503	0.2502	0.1799	0.1301	0.0808	0.0376	0.0180	0.0089	0.0023	0.0007	18
19	0.3305	0.2317	0.1635	0.1161	0.0703	0.0313	0.0144	0.0068	0.0017	0.0005	19
20	0.3118	0.2145	0.1486	0.1037	0.0611	0.0261	0.0115	0.0053	0.0012	0.0003	20
25	0.2330	0.1460	0.0923	0.0588	0.0304	0.0105	0.0038	0.0014	0.0002	...	25
30	0.1741	0.0994	0.0573	0.0334	0.0151	0.0042	0.0012	0.0004	...	...	30
40	0.0972	0.0460	0.0221	0.0107	0.0037	0.0007	0.0001	...	...	...	40
50	0.0543	0.0213	0.0085	0.0035	0.0009	0.0001	...	...	...	...	50
100	0.0029	0.0005	0.0001	...	...	...	...	...	...	...	100

* H. G. Thuesen, *Engineering Economy*, 2d ed., © 1957. Reprinted by permission of Prentice-Hall, Inc., Englewood Cliffs, N.J.

Index

*This book has been set in 10 and 9 point Times
New Roman, leaded 2 points. Chapter numbers
are in 18 and 48 point Bodoni Bold Condensed
and chapter titles are in 30 point Bodoni Bold
Condensed. The size of the type page is 27 by
45½ picas.*